STRATIGRAPHIC PRINCIPLES
AND PRACTICE

HARPER'S GEOSCIENCE SERIES
Carey Croneis, Editor

STRATIGRAPHIC
PRINCIPLES
AND PRACTICE

J. Marvin Weller

UNIVERSITY OF CHICAGO

HARPER & BROTHERS, PUBLISHERS, NEW YORK

Contents

OF SEDIMENTS; DEPOSITION OF SEDIMENTS—Marine Environment—Terrestrial Environment—Littoral Environment

PART IV. APPENDIX

List of Tables

Editor's Introduction

MARVIN WELLER's *Stratigraphic Principles and Practice* is an important book about an important, and perhaps too little appreciated, subject. Professor Weller himself states that "stratigraphy is the indispensable heart and core of geology." This is not the standard and anticipated hyperbole of the enthusiastic expert who is overly preoccupied with his own subject. It is a literal fact.

Geology—with its core of stratigraphy—is a science with the most extraordinary ramifications. The word itself first appeared—as "geologia"—in 1735 and originally meant the "science of earthy things." Twenty years later "geology" was defined as "the science which treats of the earth in general." To a certain degree this essentially all-inclusive definition of 1755 is still valid. Thus, in the broad sense, chemists, physicists, mathematicians, biologists, archeologists, meteorologists, geographers and oceanographers are all part-time geologists when—as commonly is the case—they are employing their special talents and training in the solution of problems which, strictly speaking, are partly or wholly geological. A stratigrapher, however, is always a geologist. The development of the concepts of geology and stratigraphy, as reflected in their accepted definitions, will substantiate this statement.

In 1865 stratigraphy—literally "the study of strata"—was first defined as "the branch of geology that is concerned with the order and relative position of the strata of the earth's crust." As early as 1795, however, geology itself was described as being "the science which investigates the earth's crust, the strata which compose it, with their mutual relations, and the successive changes to which their present conditions and positions are due." It is apparent, then, that the concept of the science of geology just prior to 1800 differed little from the concept of the subdiscipline of stratigraphy as defined some seventy years later.

The common modern view about stratigraphy may be well comprehended by making a brief analysis of the subjects covered in the present volume. Weller first discusses stratigraphy and time, and he points out the contribution of stratigraphic studies to the understanding of the difficult concept of essentially illimitable time. The author then includes a chapter describing the development of stratigraphic thought and analyses. Chapter 3, which deals with geological classifications, demonstrates how substantially the geological systems are rooted in stratigraphic determinations.

Part II includes six important chapters which, broadly speaking, deal with the "materials" of the subject. Topics considered are classification and composition of sediments and rocks, their textures, structures and colors, their physiography, their paleoecology, their formation as a result of, and their reaction to, tectonic activity. There is also a section on the interpretation of the origin and history of rocks and sediments.

Part III deals with the interpretation of stratigraphic bodies—that is, strata and their units—and their relations within the framework of space and time. Altogether seven chapters are required to treat this very broad topic adequately. The subjects covered include stratification itself and the resulting vertical sequence of beds, as well as the breaks or unconformities which commonly separate such rock sequences. The serious problems of stratigraphic classification and stratigraphic nomenclature are also discussed in some detail.

Both in theoretical studies and in petroleum exploration the subjects of lateral variation and facies control of sediments have been receiving increasing attention. They, and the associated problem of correlation, are fully discussed in Chapters 14 and 15. Chapter 16 is devoted to historical geology, which is so largely dependent on stratigraphy and stratigraphical paleontology.

Part IV is an appendix of two intensely practical chapters concerned with the necessary adjuncts to, and bases for, stratigraphic studies, i.e., careful field work and precise geological mapping as well as the graphical representations required to make the results of such work more significant, not only to the student, but to the original investigator as well.

The foregoing brief review of the major topics considered by the author fails to do justice to the scope and breadth of this significant text and compendium. It will be readily apparent, even on casual examination, however, that Weller's *Stratigraphic Principles and Practice* is a new departure in books on this subject. Stratigraphy here is in no sense a world stratigraphy, for it is not directly concerned with details regarding Cambrian strata or Pleistocene sedimentation, or with the Mesozoic rocks of Germany or the Tertiary sequence of Egypt. Rather it is deeply concerned with the stratigraphic principles which are applicable to the analyses of the stratified rocks of all ages in all areas of the globe.

Professor Weller's background for writing such a valuable book has been particularly fortunate. He is the son of the famous stratigrapher and paleontologist, Stuart Weller, who among many other accomplishments wrote much of the extended stratigraphic, paleontologic, and historical sections of the great three-volume Chamberlin and Salisbury *Geology*. This was literally the "handbook" of several generations of American stratigraphers;

and thus Marvin Weller grew up in a surcharged atmosphere of stratigraphic emphasis and productivity.

The author's field experience has included extended reconnaissance surveys in India, the interior of China, and the Philippines, as well as detailed investigations in various parts of North America, especially in that stratigrapher's "happy hunting grounds"—the broad upper Mississippi Valley and Great Lakes Region. After richly productive years as a member of the staff of the Illinois Geological Survey, Dr. Weller in 1945 succeeded to the professorship at the University of Chicago formerly held by his distinguished father. At this point the editor cannot refrain from revealing a deep personal interest, and a possible favorable bias, by mentioning that for a 16-year period between the death of Stuart Weller and the appointment of Marvin Weller, he himself had the privilege of occupying that same chair at the University of Chicago. Favorable bias aside, however, other and more disinterested observers are very likely to accord Marvin Weller's volume the tacit honor of an easily reached spot on their bookshelves. And because it does deal with principles, the book should find wide usage in libraries and laboratories, as well as in classrooms, both in this country and abroad.

CAREY CRONEIS

The Rice Institute

Preface

This book is based on lectures presented from time to time over a number of years at the University of Chicago. The main idea motivating their preparation is my belief that stratigraphy occupies a position at the heart of the geologic sciences and that its broad consideration involves both scientific and philosophic aspects that should be the common meeting ground of all geologists. To me stratigraphy is a dynamic subject not confined to the definitions of formations, which any student can easily look up in a reasonably good library. It is, instead, a subject based on certain principles and conventions applied to natural phenomena and leads to the recognition and, I hope, to the solution of a variety of broad problems that should be of interest and importance to all geologists regardless of their specialties.

Just as certain aspects of geology merge with physics, chemistry, biology, and astronomy, so also the boundaries of stratigraphy are ill defined. Its connections with some phases of petrology, sedimentology, and paleontology are particularly close and its position as the foundation of historical geology is obvious. There are excellent books devoted to sedimentary petrology and paleontology but, insofar as these deal with stratigraphy at all, stratigraphy is considered from the standpoint of the petrologist or paleontologist. Thus stratigraphy is drawn upon as a supplemental aid in the investigation of problems peculiar to these other fields of study. I have sought to reverse this emphasis because I believe that the applications of sedimentary petrology and paleontology to stratigraphy have not been presented adequately.

The choice and organization of the subject matter in this book have been determined by my interests, and the data are drawn to a very large extent from my own observations and experience, supplemented, of course, from many other sources. The presentation undoubtedly is colored by my own prejudices, but I hope that I have been reasonably attentive to the opinions of other persons. My purpose has not been to prepare a work of reference and I offer no apology for failure to document all statements. Many of these can be followed up in the bibliographies appended to each chapter and the references cited in the listed articles and books. Finally, I am not particularly concerned that solutions are not provided for many of the problems which are raised. Numerous geologic problems will not soon be solved and surely their recognition and the consideration of ideas are more stimulating than the detailing of most bodies of presumed facts.

I gladly admit my debt in the preparation of this book to many friends, both personal and those known to me only by their writings. I am particularly grateful to Dr. Carey Croneis, who read the manuscript at various stages of completion. His interest, helpfulness, and many valuable suggestions are much appreciated. I extend my thanks to the various publishers who have graciously granted permission for the reproduction in more or less modified form of figures selected from their books and journals. I also wish to thank my daughter Harriet for the painstaking care which she devoted to drafting of the illustrations.

Chicago, Illinois   J. MARVIN WELLER
June, 1959

Part I

INTRODUCTION

Geology is a science that had a piecemeal origin. Minerals and fossils attracted attention far back in pre-Christian times, but rocks did not become the subject of serious study until the late seventeenth or early eighteenth century. At first they seem to have been regarded more or less abstractly. By the mid-eighteenth century, however, a few persons began to take note of the mutual relations of rocks as they occur naturally in the field, and geology was born.

Although the term *stratigraphy* was not invented until 1865, it was the pioneer stratigraphic work of the late eighteenth century that served to unite the interests and excite the imaginations of mineralogists, petrographers, and paleontologists. Then and later for about 100 years stratigraphy was so much at the center of most geologic studies that no need was felt for any special designation. During the first half of the nineteenth century stratigraphy far outstripped the older branches of geology in both accomplishments and popular interest. In those days a geologist *was* a stratigrapher.

In later years the ever increasing knowledge and broader understanding of the history of the earth have stimulated geologists in the investigation of many other aspects of geology. The part that stratigraphy has played, however, in the development of geology, and the fact that there could be no unity in this field of science without it, justifies the conclusion that stratigraphy is the indispensable heart and core of geology.

1

Stratigraphy and Time

STRATIGRAPHY

Stratified rocks occur at the surface of about three-quarters of the total land area of the world, and stratigraphy is the branch of geology that deals with their observation and their study. Many geologists are concerned almost exclusively with stratigraphic investigations, and most others, whether they realize it or not, are more or less dependent upon stratigraphy for basic data or a general background without which their specialized studies would have comparatively little meaning.

Definitions of Stratigraphy

It is interesting to review briefly some of the opinions that have been expressed about stratigraphy and to see how geologists of varied interests have considered it with reference to their specialties. Thus a geologist concerned with continental evolution has written: "Stratigraphy is the interpretation of the record of progressive movements evidenced in sedimentation." A paleontologist believed that "stratigraphy is the knowledge of the evolution and succession and of the horizontal and vertical distribution of plants and animals during geologic history." And a paleogeographer stated: "It is the aim of the stratigrapher to relate the events that have occurred during the existence of the earth in the order in which they have taken place. He tries, therefore, to restore the physical geography of each given time in the past and in this way to write a connected history."

These, of course, are not good definitions of stratigraphy, but the quota-

3

tions indicate clearly the fundamental part that stratigraphy plays in connection with some widely varied geologic specialties.

One well-known geologist has expressed the opinion that "the purpose of stratigraphic work is two-fold: first, to describe and classify strata; and second, to correlate them from one area to another and to fit them into a chronology, preferably a world wide chronology." Another has contended that geochronology based on paleontologic and radioactive correlations is not a part of stratigraphy because stratigraphy is concerned with spacial but not temporal relations. A more comprehensive and satisfactory definition was offered by a third: "Stratigraphy is the branch of geological science that has to do with the definition and description of major and minor natural divisions of the rocks, mainly sedimentary, and interpretation of their significance in geologic history." An oil geologist wasted no words when he wrote that stratigraphy is the "study of the character, sequence, relationship, distribution and origin of sedimentary rocks."

Considering its brevity, this last definition cannot be much improved except by stating the same ideas somewhat more fully, thus: *Stratigraphy is the branch of geology that deals with the study and interpretation of stratified and sedimentary rocks and with the identification, description, sequence, both vertical and horizontal, mapping, and correlation of stratigraphic rock units.*

This definition distinguishes between the truly scientific aspects of stratigraphy, which are study and interpretation, and the more practical aspects demanding the attention of stratigraphers. It omits reference to "natural" stratigraphic units because most recognized units are more or less arbitrary and artificial. It also implies that all stratified rocks are not necessarily sedimentary and that all sedimentary rocks are not necessarily stratified. A little thought will show that stratigraphy involves the consideration of some igneous rocks and their derivatives, such as lava flows and pyroclastic material that accumulated on the surface of the earth, but not sills, which occur in stratigraphic sequences but did not form at the surface. Also some sedimentary deposits, such as glacial till and loess, are unstratified except in their grosser aspects. Finally some unusual accumulations, like cave fillings and collapse breccias, must find a place in stratigraphy although they are not to be classified with any ordinary type of rock.

Metamorphic rocks provide a stratigraphic borderland. Their study is rightfully a part of stratigraphy so long as their stratified or sedimentary characters are distinguishable.

Basis of Stratigraphy

All stratigraphy is based on field studies because only in the field can the larger features and mutual relations of stratified rocks be observed adequately. Rock samples and fossils are commonly collected for detailed laboratory investigations. Such studies are very important for stratigraphic progress. Concentration on many of the problems that they introduce, however, leads over to the fields of sedimentary petrology and paleontology, and contact with stratigraphy may become vague. This does not mean that petrology and paleontology should not be emphasized, but many of the studies of specialists in these fields have little relation to stratigraphy until they are applied to definitely stratigraphic problems. A closer integration of sedimentary petrology, paleontology, and field stratigraphy can do much to increase the significance and usefulness of work in all of these fields.

The study of cores, cuttings, and logs of wells has developed greatly in recent years and there are now many specialists in subsurface stratigraphy. Their work has added an extremely important third dimension to stratigraphy. The thousands of wells drilled every year in the United States have provided a wealth of information that is not duplicated in any other large region of the world. It should be realized, however, that information obtained from wells is based on extremely minute samples and there are many features of both rocks and fossils that cannot be fully appreciated or interpreted correctly without supplementary information obtainable only by the study of actual outcrops. It is important, therefore, that subsurface stratigraphers maintain an interest in surface stratigraphy and return to the study of outcrops in the field at every opportunity.

Successive Stratigraphic Steps

Discrimination of Stratigraphic Units

Stratigraphy begins with the discrimination and description of stratigraphic units such as formations or whatever else they may be called. This basic step is necessary in order that the complexities present in every stratigraphic section may be reduced, simplified, and organized. Without the recognition of stratigraphic units a stratigrapher would be lost in a maze of details, and effective communication between stratigraphers would be impossible. It is important to realize at the very start, however, that most recognized stratigraphic units are more or less arbitrary sequences of strata. The nature and limits of these units are likely to have been determined by the practical requirements of geologic work in some particular area at some particular time. In any stratigraphic study, earlier-distinguished units may be accepted and employed, or new or modified units that are more useful may be set up. This selection of preferred stratigraphic units is largely a matter of opinion, and it is not logical to contend that any unit is either right or wrong. Each stratigraphic unit should be judged only on the basis of whether or not it is convenient, reasonable, and meaningful with respect to the study that is in progress.

Determination of Stratigraphic Sequence

Stratified rocks were laid down in an orderly sequence. At any locality where outcrops or other types of information are abundant and structural complications are not great, this sequence should be determinable by any reasonably competent geologist. Elsewhere great skill and good judgment may be required to evaluate all types of available evidence and to interpret them correctly.

Geologic Mapping

The next step generally is geologic mapping. This expression is used in a broad sense to include both the areal mapping of outcropping units and the continuous tracing of subsurface units. In this type of work the stratigrapher is concerned with the spacial distribution of three-dimensional rock units. Such work is largely mechanical, and more an engineering than a scientific occupation. It requires, however, skillful observation and in many areas the interpretation of more or less obscure evidence.

These first three steps may be accomplished in the foregoing order or they may be carried out together. They are, nevertheless, different operations that depend upon each other and involve (1) decision as to what strata should be grouped as units, (2) determination of the relations of these units in one dimension or vertical sequence, and (3) determination of the units' relations to the surface in two dimensions and their subsurface relations in three dimensions.

The gradual growth of a geologic map or the understanding of the distribution and relations of subsurface formations can be the source of much personal satisfaction. When the results of such work are compiled and put down on paper in final form, there is a tangible result to show for months or years of study. Many stratigraphers have considered the satisfactory completion of this task as their main objective.

The discrimination of stratigraphic units, the building of stratigraphic sections, and geologic mapping are based on scientific principles but they do not require scientific reasoning to any very high degree except in regions where geology is complicated or obscure. So far, stratigraphy consists of a succession of rather routine procedures, but it is extremely important that this work be done thoroughly and accurately. These operations furnish the essential basic and factual data which must be relied upon in any further stratigraphic considerations. If the foundation of facts is not well laid, the superstructure of conclusions and interpretations cannot be sound. Stratigraphy at this level, therefore, should be recognized as being predominantly practical, and investigations should be conducted and results expressed as objectively as possible. Reliance upon theoretical considerations in the process of accumulating facts is almost certain to result in later misunderstandings and disagreements.

Stratigraphic Correlation

Most of the commonly recognized problems of stratigraphy that do not result from inadequate local information are concerned with attempts to relate stratigraphic sequences observed at different places. Thus the problems of correlation are introduced. Correlations should be based on all evidence that the rocks afford. This evidence is of two kinds, physical and biologic. The application of petrology and paleontology to the solution of these problems is obvious. Stratigraphers need not be specialists in these allied fields but they should be well enough acquainted with them to appreciate the merits and limitations of their application and to evaluate the findings and opinions of collaborating specialists.

Correlation, or the determination of the time relations and equivalence of rock units, is based on evidence that may be differently interpreted by different persons. Any correlation involves drawing a conclusion that is based upon a set of facts. The conclusion is no more than an opinion, no matter how well founded it may be, and it may or may not be correct. This is the point at which stratigraphic studies leave the realm of facts and it should be recognized that correlations never can be absolutely proved.

Except in tracing strata for comparatively short distances, most modern correlations are based on paleontologic evidence. Many stratigraphers do not possess the requisite specialized knowledge to make detailed paleontologic correlations; generally the services of an expert paleontologist are required. Unfortunately, some paleontologists are not much interested in stratigraphy and in their attempts at correlation they may place entire reliance upon the fossils. Stratigraphers should understand this situation and realize that paleontologists can be mistaken. They should know that under some circumstances physical evidence is equal in significance or possibly even superior to the evidence of fossils. The point here is that all evidence should be equally considered.

Stratigraphic Interpretation

Most modern geologists recognize that the study of stratified rocks can and should be carried beyond correlation to the fullest possible interpretation of the basic stratigraphic data in terms of paleogeography and geologic history. Judging from the great majority of geologic reports, however, this rather clear objective is rarely realized. Most stratigraphic interpretations have been extremely superficial and commonly they have not been extended much beyond the bare outlines of the most obvious conclusions. If stratigraphy is to accomplish no more than this, if it is to remain predominantly descriptive and not extend beyond the preparation of geologic and structural contour maps, cross sections, and correlation tables, it is bound to be regarded as a useful but uninspiring study of little interest to imaginative and dynamically inclined geologists.

There is no reason why stratigraphers should be satisfied to accept such an evaluation of their work. Without question, the further detailed extension of stratigraphic studies directed toward their recognized objectives provides promising opportunities for future geologic research of great significance. More effort, however, will be required to search out information, and more ingenuity and imagination will be demanded in its interpretation. Full advantage must be taken of the many and important contributions that can be derived from sedimentologic, petrologic, and paleontologic studies. Close coöperation of specialists in these allied fields is almost indispensable.

Paleontologic information has been widely used by stratigraphers but a great deal of it has not been based on modern biologic principles or ideas. Much improvement is possible here. Detailed petrologic interpretations are less common but a significant start has been made in several types of sedimentary and stratigraphic analysis. Pertinent data, however they may be acquired, must be coördinated in terms of both space and time by geologists of broad interests and understanding. Undoubtedly great opportunities for progress lie in this direction.

Importance of Stratigraphy

For Basic Information

The importance of stratigraphy as a source of basic information valuable to geologists interested in other fields of investigation and applicable to the deciphering of geologic history cannot be overemphasized. Stratified rocks outcrop throughout larger areas in most parts of the world than do other kinds of rocks, and stratified sediments are present almost everywhere on the sea bottom. Few geologic studies, except those devoted entirely to igneous terrains and mineralogy and those concerned with the more restricted aspects of geophysics and geochemistry, do not require some consideration of stratigraphy. This is reflected clearly by a review of articles published in all unspecialized geologic journals. More than half of these deal directly with stratigraphy or depend on it for controlling data. The great majority of all geologists customarily deal with stratigraphy or stratigraphic problems in the course of their regular activities. In the economic field, petroleum geology in particular is dependent upon a thorough understanding of stratigraphy.

As a Unifying Agent

The importance of stratigraphy can be evaluated in another way that becomes clear when the historical quality of geology as a science is considered. Among all the branches of geology, stratigraphy is the one most closely con-

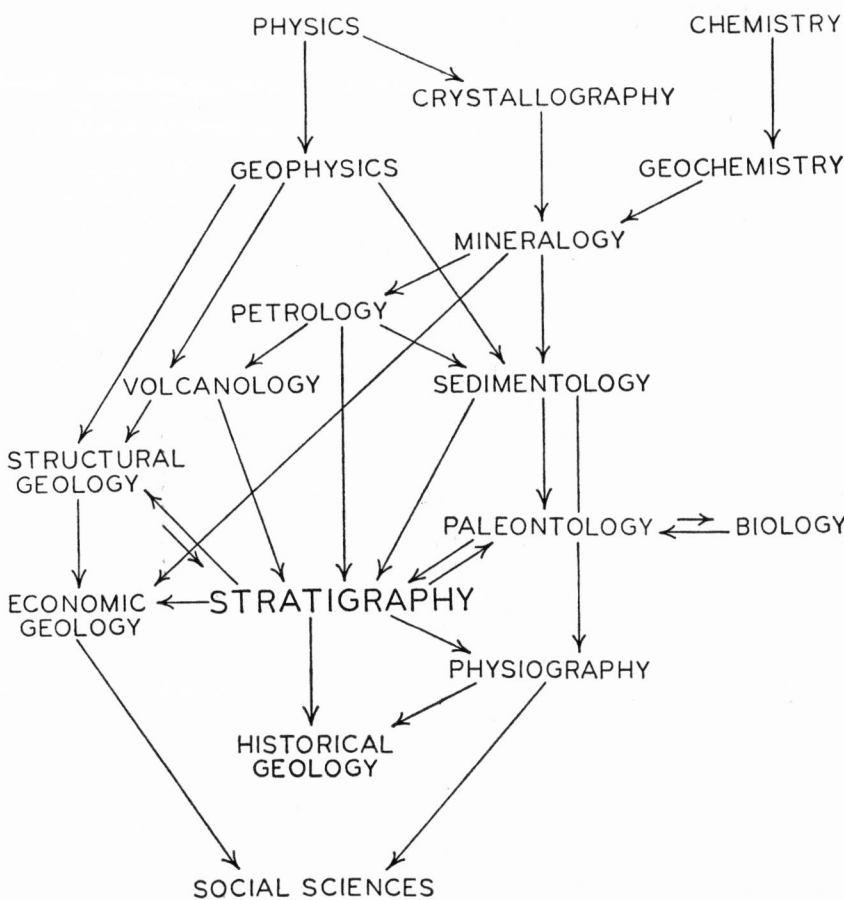

Figure 1. Diagram showing the connections between the principal branches of geology and related sciences. Arrows indicate the more important contributions that studies in one field make to those in another. Many other less important connections also occur. Stratigraphy is the focal point where most geologic knowledge is synthesized into the reconstruction of geologic history. (After Weller, 1947, J. Paleon., vol. 21, p. 571, fig. 1.)

cerned with time. Stratigraphic correlations serve to date most geologic events and to relate them all over the earth. The order of some geologic events and processes such as fluctuations of the strand line, successive igneous intrusions, metamorphism, and structural disturbances may be determinable in local areas with a minimum of aid from stratigraphy. Without more accurate dating, however, such local histories could not be related to each other, and geology would be little more than a hodge-podge of unconnected facts and generalizations. Figure 1 shows that stratigraphy constitutes a kind of focal plexus in which much of the information contributed by other geologic and related fields is coördinated, synthesized, and systematized into a meaningful whole.

The part of stratigraphy that is concerned with the description and catalog-

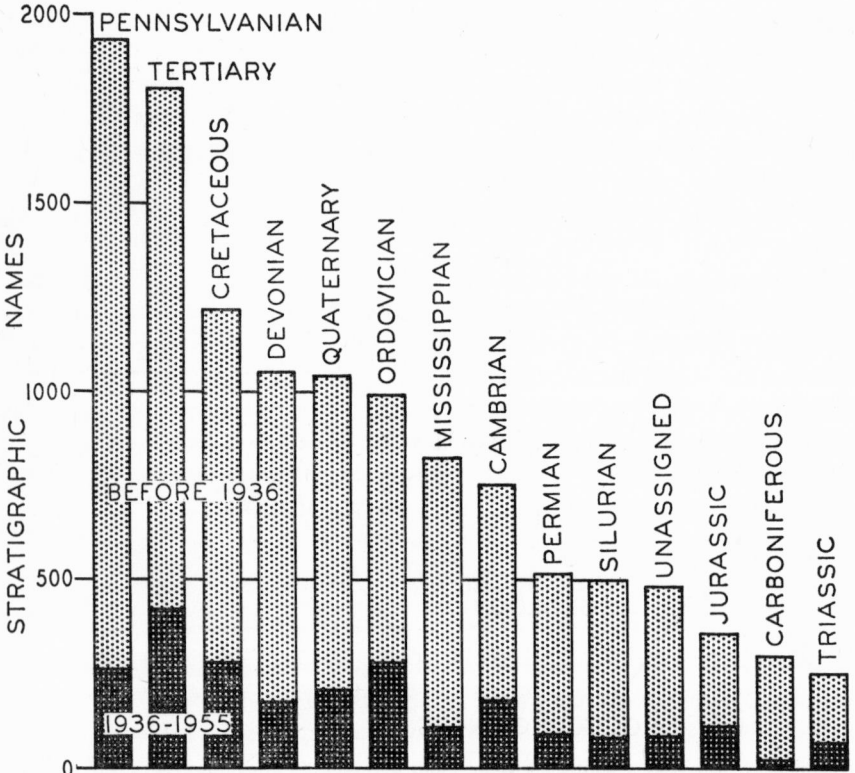

Figure 2. Diagram showing the number of names that have been applied to major stratigraphic divisions in North America. Some of these names have been abandoned, others are synonyms, and many have been very little used. Almost any of the obscure names might be recognized widely in the future and a stratigrapher needs to be familiar with all of the nomenclature applicable within the region where he works. Data for the period before 1936 from Moore, 1941, Geol. Soc. Amer., 50th Ann. Vol., p. 197, fig. 5. Names proposed from 1936 to 1955 from Wilson and others, 1957, U.S. Geol. Surv., Bull. 1056-A. In the latter, members, facies, and other minor stratigraphic divisions were not counted.

ing of formations with respect to character, sequence, age, thickness, and distribution is important but it can be overemphasized. Such information has become so voluminous (see Figure 2) that no individual can hope to absorb and remember more than a very small part of it. Data of this type are readily available in a great variety of reports, maps, lexicons, and correlation tables. Much more important are the applications of the few and remarkably simple principles that govern stratigraphic procedures and thinking, and the interpretation of stratigraphic data. An adequate understanding of these principles, and also of sound stratigraphic practice, will insure more thorough and accurate stratigraphic work, avoid unnecessary complications, and lead to more significant interpretations. The latter particularly should be stressed because without them stratigraphy does not fulfill its potentialities. If followed to its logical conclusions, stratigraphy becomes dynamic and calls into full exercise all of the scientific abilities of the best geologist.

TIME

Geology is unique among the sciences because it is historical. In no other science does time play so significant a part because, as in physics, chemistry, or biology, for example, it is only one of several almost equally important factors. In geology, however, time provides a frame of reference that is essential to the interpretation of extremely diverse types of study involving all the materials and inhabitants of the earth and all the forces and processes that have shaped it. These studies have interest in themselves, but many of them are physical, chemical, or biologic studies until their relations within the time frame unite them as geology and give them greater meaning.

Estimates of Time

In the present stage of its development, geology is more concerned with relative time and the sequence of events in the history of the earth than with the actual dating of these events. Nevertheless, the human mind desires definite dates that give perspective to history. Many attempts have been made to determine the age of the earth and the length of time that has elapsed since the happening of some particular event. Evidence upon which to base estimates has been sought in different directions.

In 1658 Archbishop Ussher of Ireland calculated, on the basis of calendarial cycles and the biblical account of Genesis, that the earth was created at 6 P.M. on Sunday, October 22, 4004 B.C. In the mid-eighteenth century the French naturalist, Comte de Buffon, observed the rates of melting and cooling of iron balls and estimated that 75,000 years had elapsed since the earth was molten. In England the physicist Lord Kelvin made calculations on the basis of a supposedly cooling and contracting sun and concluded that the age of the earth was between 20 and 400 million years with the lower figure favored. Other physical estimates were based on the theoretical retardation of the earth's rotation resulting from the tides.

Geologists generally have favored geologic evidence. Estimates most commonly were made by dividing the observed thickness of all sedimentary strata by an assumed average rate of deposition. In 1876 Dana figured 36 million years for the Paleozoic Era and in 1910 Schuchert suggested 30 million years since the beginning of the Cambrian Period. Other estimates ranged from 3 million to more than a billion years. Calculations made on the basis of the salt content of the sea varied from 50 million to 340 million years since the oceans first appeared. At the beginning of the twentieth century most American geologists accepted a figure of not more than 100 million years since the beginning of the Paleozoic Era.

Paleontologic estimates have been attempted based on rates of evolution. By comparing the amount of evolution exhibited by marine molluscs in the various Tertiary stages with the amount that has occurred since the beginning of the glacial period, Lyell in 1867 estimated 80 million years since the beginning of the Tertiary. This figure was reached on the assumption that the Pleistocene began 1 million years ago. In 1914 Matthew graded horse evolution during Tertiary time in terms of comparative units rather than in years. If he had made an assumption similar to Lyell's, his estimate would have been closely comparable.

Geologists have attempted to use rhythmic banding in sediments as a geologic clock on the assumption that these bands record annual cycles, sunspot cycles of about 11 years or precessions of the equinox of about 26,000 years. The results of greatest interest have been obtained from glacial varves that record annual cycles. Varve studies were begun by de Geer in Sweden in 1878, and a record was built up extending back for about 18,000 years. Similar studies elsewhere have been less successful. This method gives actual dates only if varves can be correlated with some recorded date in human history, as was possible in Sweden. Older rhythmic deposits with laminations similar to varves have been observed at various places in rocks as old as the Precambrian. Few of them are believed to be annual, but if their periods could be determined they might be used to measure some intervals of time although they would provide no dates.

Measurements of Time

All of the foregoing methods of attempting to determine the duration of geologic time, except varve counting, are dependent upon estimates, inexact measurements, and interpretations that cannot be substantiated. The discovery of radioactivity opened the way for another method of age determination that gave promise of reasonably precise measurements in terms of years. This depends upon the decay of uranium and other radioactive elements that proceeds at a uniform rate and produces stable end-product elements undergoing no further change. The commonest radioactive method has involved the determination of uranium-lead ratios. The relations of these elements, however, proved to be much more complex than was at first realized.

There are three radioactive series starting with two different isotopes of uranium and one of thorium, all with different half-life periods and all ending with helium and three different isotopes of lead. In addition there is a fourth lead isotope that is not a product of radioactivity and several other rarer radioactive lead isotopes.

Theoretically, the three radioactive series should make it possible to determine age from any one of several ratios such as Pb^{206}/U^{238}, Pb^{207}/U^{235}, Pb^{206}/Pb^{207}, Pb^{208}/Th^{232}, and so forth. Calculations based on different measured ratios should check each other and produce the same answers; unfortunately, they rarely do. Besides analytical errors, the gaseous products helium and radon, an intermediate in the radioactive series, may escape, and weathering, leaching, or secondary enrichment may have altered the quantities of the elements and isotopes. Some of these complementary age determinations differ by several hundred million years. Among the more recent and accurate measurements, some of the different ratios give ages that vary systematically. As laboratory skills increase, however, and greater experience is gained in evaluating the results, more and more satisfactory age determinations are sure to be obtained.

The half-life decay rates of the radioactive series range from less than 1 billion to nearly 14 billion years. Very small analytical errors, therefore, produce large errors in determined ages. These ages generally are expressed in terms of millions of years plus or minus a second figure, thus: 650 ± 75 m.y. The second figure is not a measure of the accuracy of the age but only an indication of the reproducibility of the analytical result. Under the best of circumstances, accuracy within a limit of several million years cannot be expected.

Uranium minerals suitable for geologic dating occur only in igneous rocks, chiefly pegmatites, and their determined ages indicate the time of crystallization of a particular igneous body. The transfer of such a date to the stratigraphic time scale is generally difficult and uncertain. The igneous rock may intrude strata of one age and be overlain by strata of another, but the time gap between these is likely to be great. In some situations the intrusions may be related to orogenic disturbances, and attempts at correlation have been made accordingly. The German geologist Stille has correlated mountain-making epochs throughout the world and believed that he could distinguish about forty of them, each supposed to have been about 300,000 years in duration (see Figure 3). His correlations, however, are not well established nor is his series of disturbances generally accepted.

Few uranium dates can be tied in closely to the stratigraphic record. They serve, therefore, only as general bench marks that confirm the great span of geologic time and roughly indicate the time intervals separating a few geologic events. The dating of other events is dependent on calibration by other means, and estimates commonly have been made on the basis of stratigraphic

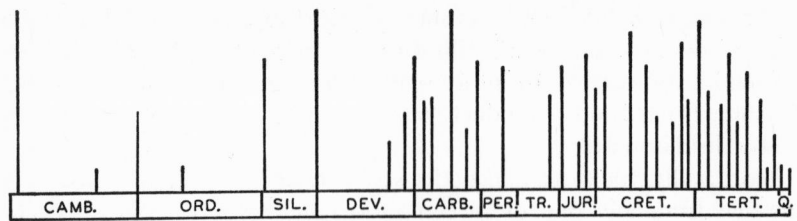

Figure 3. Stille's diagram illustrating his concept of the order and spacing of mountain-forming disturbances recognized in different parts of the world. The relative intensity of movements is indicated by the length of lines. (Adapted from Stille, 1955, Geol. Soc. Amer., Spec. Paper 62, p. 189, fig. 4.)

and paleontologic evidence of the types that have already been discussed.

Perfection of the mass spectrometer since 1938 has made the determination of isotope ratios relatively easy and accurate and has opened the way for age determinations based upon elements that are contained in sediments. The most extensive determinations have been made on carbon 14. The half-life period of this isotope is only about 5500 years, and dates based upon it cannot be continued very far back into the geologic past. Carbon dating is not effective much beyond the beginning of the last glacial age. For this time interval, carbon ratios suggest that certain recent geologic events are separated from the present by only about half of the time that had been estimated from other geologic evidence.

Carbon dating has been supplemented by ionium dating of deep-sea sediments, which measures time back to more than 1 million years. Analyses show that radium is deficient in sea water, and it is believed that a parent product, ionium or thorium 230, derived from uranium, is adsorbed by sediment and deposited as rapidly as it is supplied. Consequently the ratios of radioactive elements in newly deposited sediment are not in equilibrium because there is an excess of ionium. As time passes and ionium decays, the radium content of sediment at first increases until a maximum is reached and equilibrium between ionium and radium is attained. This requires about 8000 years. Thereafter the radium content decreases as both ionium and radium decay. The process continues for about 450,000 years until ionium attains equilibrium with uranium. Thereafter the radium content remains essentially constant because all three elements in the sediment are in equilibrium and uranium decays so slowly that a few million years make little difference in the rate of ionium production.

A curve indicating the radium content of sediment occurring at increasing depths can be constructed. Such a curve shows the rate of deposition and age of sediment for approximately the last 450,000 years. If the assumption is made that previous deposition occurred at similar rates, the age of sediment at lower levels can be calculated.

Dates for strata whose ages extend back into the Precambrian are now being determined from the potassium 40-argon 40 ratio. Dates so far obtained have been based on sedimentary glauconite and other authigenic potassium-bearing minerals. They seem to be somewhat short of expected dates, but this method gives great promise for the direct dating of many sedimentary formations. One possible source of present error results from the fact that potassium 40 decays to both argon 40 and calcium 40, and the relations of this branching ratio are not known with certainty. Possibly similar dating will be accomplished by measuring strontium-rubidium ratios although this method appears to be handicapped by the rarity of rubidium in sedimentary rocks. The ratio of potassium 40 to calcium 40 also may prove to be useful.

Geologic Time Scale

Estimates of the duration of time in millions of years represented by the main divisions of the stratigraphic column as now generally accepted are about as shown in Table 1.

TABLE 1. Estimates of the Duration of Time in
Millions of Years Represented by the Main
Divisions of the Stratigraphic Column

Pleistocene	1	Permian	25
Pliocene	11	Pennsylvanian	25
Miocene	16	Mississippian	30
Oligocene	12	Devonian	55
Eocene	20	Silurian	40
Cretaceous	70	Ordovician	80
Jurassic	25	Cambrian	80
Triassic	30	Total	520

The oldest known rocks, as indicated by radioactivity determinations, are pegmatites that intrude still older rocks in southeastern Manitoba, Canada, and in Southern Rhodesia, southeastern Africa. Their ages appear to fall somewhere within the range of 2.7 billion to 3.3 billion years. Calculations based on astronomical, physical, and chemical phenomena suggest that the age of our galaxy in the universe is about 6.5 ± 1 billion years, that the solar system is about 5.5 billion years old, and that a crust formed on the molten earth about 4.5 billion years ago. This last date, presumably, marks the beginning of geologic history.

BIBLIOGRAPHY

Ahrens, L. H. (1955), Oldest rocks exposed, Geol. Soc. Amer., Spec. Paper 62, pp. 155–168.
    Radioactive ages of very ancient rocks and meteorites are reported.
Ahrens, L. H. (1956), Radioactive methods for determining geologic age, in

Physics and chemistry of the earth, vol. 1, L. H. Ahrens, K. Rankama, and S. K. Runcorn (eds.), London, Pergamon Press, pp. 44–67.

Systematic variations in age derived from different isotopic ratios are reported.

Billings, M. P. (1950), Stratigraphy and the study of metamorphic rocks, *Bull. Geol. Soc. Amer.,* vol. 61, pp. 435–448.

Emphasis is placed on the importance of stratigraphy, sedimentology, and paleogeography in the study of metamorphic rocks.

Bowen, R. N. C. (1958), *The Exploration of Time,* London, George Newnes.

All methods of measuring past time are discussed.

Bradley, W. H. (1929), The varves and climate of the Green River Epoch, U.S. Geol. Surv., Prof. Paper 158, pp. 87–110.

This is an account of annual varves of Eocene age and their interpretation.

Curtis, G. H., and Reynolds, J. H. (1958), Notes on the potassium-argon dating of sedimentary rocks, *Bull. Geol. Soc. Amer.,* vol. 69, pp. 151–160.

Difficulties of radioactive dating and limitations and possible errors in potassium-argon dating are discussed.

Faul, Henry (ed.) (1954), *Nuclear geology,* New York, Wiley.

This symposium discusses, among other things, radioactive age determinations.

Haldane, J. B. S. (1945), A new theory of the past, *Am. Scientist,* vol. 33, pp. 129–145.

The possibility of more than one scale of geologic time is suggested.

Haun, J. D., and LeRoy, L. W. (eds.) (1958), *Subsurface geology in petroleum exploration,* Golden, Colo. School of Mines.

This symposium is similar to *Subsurface geologic methods,* edited by L. W. LeRoy, with extensive changes and revision of subject matter.

Herzog, L. F., Pinson, W. H., and Cormier, R. F. (1958), Sediment age determination by Rb/Sr analysis of glauconite, *Bull. Am. Assoc. Petroleum Geol.,* vol. 42, pp. 717–733.

Radioactive dating is reviewed and a report is given on a new method based on sedimentary glauconite.

Holmes, Arthur (1937), *The age of the earth,* London, Thomas Nelson.

This is an old but standard reference.

Holmes, Arthur (1947), The construction of a geologic time scale, *Trans. Geol. Soc. Glasgow,* vol. 21, pp. 117–152.

Geologic ages are estimated on the basis of radioactivity and thicknesses of sediments.

Kay, Marshall (1955), Sediments and subsidence through time, Geol. Soc. Amer., Spec. Paper 62, pp. 665–684.

Maximum known thicknesses of sediment and rates of subsidence are reported.

Krumbein, W. C., and Sloss, L. L. (1951), *Stratigraphy and sedimentation,* San Francisco, Freeman.

This textbook is devoted to stratigraphy and one type of stratigraphic analysis. See particularly pp. 428–447.

LeRoy, L. W. (ed.) (1950), *Subsurface geologic methods,* 2nd ed., Golden, Colo. School of Mines.

The many ramifications of subsurface geology are the subject of a symposium.

Libby, W. F. (1955), *Radiocarbon dating*, 2nd ed., Univ. of Chicago Press.
This is the standard reference.

Lipson, Joseph (1958), Potassium-argon dating of sedimentary rocks, *Bull. Geol. Soc. Amer.*, vol. 69, pp. 137–150.
The author explains method and reports dates determined from glauconite, feldspar, and sylvite.

Lochman, Christina (1956), Stratigraphy, paleontology, and paleogeography of the *Elliptocephala asaphoides* strata in Cambridge and Hoosick quadrangles, New York, *Bull. Geol. Soc. Amer.*, vol. 67, pp. 1331–1396.
Stratigraphic and paleontologic evidence is paleogeographically interpreted.

Moore, R. C. (1941), *Stratigraphy*, Geol. Soc. Amer., 50th Anniversary Vol., pp. 177–220.
Stratigraphic progress in America is reviewed.

Moore, R. C. (1952), Stratigraphical viewpoints in measurement of geologic time, *Trans. Am. Geophys. Union*, vol. 33, pp. 150–156.
Consideration is given to stratigraphic methods of determining time relationships.

Öpik, E. J. (1956), The time scale of our universe, Smiths. Report for 1955, Publ. 4232, pp. 203–226.
This is a broad review of the problem of time and the age of the universe.

Pepper, J. F., DeWitt, Wallace, Jr., and Demarest, D. F. (1954), Geology of the Bedford Shale and Berea Sandstone in the Appalachian basin, U.S. Geol. Surv., Prof. Paper 259.
This is an outstanding example of paleogeographic interpretation based on stratigraphic and petrologic evidence.

Urry, W. D. (1949), Radioactivity of ocean sediments. VI. Concentration of radio-elements in marine sediments of the southern hemisphere, *Am. J. Sci.*, vol. 247, pp. 257–275.
The ionium method of dating marine sediments is explained.

Wilmarth, M. G. (1938), Lexicon of geologic names of the United States (including Alaska), U.S. Geol. Surv., Bull. 896 (2 pts.), reprinted 1951 and 1957.
A complete annotated catalog of stratigraphic names published through 1935 with references, this is a basic stratigraphic source book.

Wilson, Druid, Sando, W. J., and Knopf, R. W. (1957), Geologic names of North America introduced in 1936–1955, U.S. Geol. Surv., Bull. 1056-A.
This supplements Wilmarth's Lexicon but is without annotations.

Zeuner, F. E. (1958), *Dating the past, an introduction to geochronology*, 4th ed., London, Menthuen.
In this standard reference work on geochronology see especially Chapters 2, 10, and 11.

2

Development of Stratigraphy

FEW things are more common in the world than rocks. Like many other common things they have not attracted as much attention or aroused as much interest as more unusual objects. Man and perhaps his immediate ancestors, however, undoubtedly have been interested in rocks for long ages. Rocks furnished the materials for some of the earliest tools, and rocks were used for construction purposes from very ancient times. Most prehistoric men probably knew more about rocks than many modern men because in the Stone Age some rocks were sought for implement making whereas others were not. Perhaps rocks were classified in this way. American Indians traveled many miles to places where superior flints could be collected or quarried for arrow points and tools. Certain areas are said to have been recognized as neutral ground where otherwise hostile tribes gathered periodically in peace to replenish their supply.

As civilization advanced, superior kinds of rocks were transported with enormous labor for long distances for the building of temples and palaces. Also rocks were obstacles to certain types of human endeavor such as farming and road building. Particularly in the construction of roads and canals, different qualities in rocks must have been noticed. Outside of these specialized concerns, however, little interest seems to have developed in such common things. Philosophers speculated regarding the origin of mountains but less attention was directed to the rocks of which the mountains are composed.

On the other hand, minerals and fossils contained in rocks were noticed and wondered about by many observant persons. They attracted attention because of their beauty, rarity, and usefulness or because they appeared to be inexplicable curiosities. The origins of mining are shrouded in the mists of antiquity, but mining was an important industry at many places and for many centuries before the true nature of ores or their associations began to be understood.

Fossils also were collected long before geology began as a science. A trilobite pierced and evidently used as an ornament by some prehistoric man was discovered in a European cave. A horn coral hollowed out to form a pipe was found associated with other Indian relics in this country. In China petrified bones, believed to be dragons' bones, and other fossils have been used as medicine for thousands of years.

Classical Geology

Several Greek philosophers and travelers left records showing that they noted certain geologic features and attempted to account for them. Some of their explanations are remarkably satisfactory considering the prevailing lack of physical, chemical, and biologic knowledge. Geologic observations and speculations, however, were unscientific because no attempts were made to check the theories and generalizations offered to account for them.

The Romans were a less philosophical and more practical people. They seem to have had little interest in the natural wonders of the world. What protoscientific literature they left consists largely of hearsay accounts and the collected opinions of previous writers, many of which are untrue if not preposterous.

Greek science was preserved, augmented, and carried through the Middle Ages by Arab philosophers. Had it not been for them some of the thoughts of earlier people would have been lost to the modern world.

The Renaissance

The Renaissance in western Europe was initiated by the revival of classical learning and the wider dissemination of education outside of the clerical groups. It was marked not only by great advances in the arts but also by the beginning of scientific observation. The scientific movement had its origin in Italy and rapidly spread northward. As far as geology was concerned, the first stage included a bitter controversy as to the nature of fossils. The contention was firmly held by many persons that fossils were artifacts which owed their existence to various occult processes. Even after their organic nature was generally admitted and the marine origin of some was recognized, the occurrence of fossils in rocks and on the land was largely ascribed to the Noachian deluge. It was common at this time to denounce as rankest heresy any opinion concerning nature if it did not conform to the most orthodox views then prevalent even though such views found no actual support in the scriptures.

The two greatest obstacles to early geologic progress were (1) an utter lack of appreciation of the span of geologic time and (2) man's viewpoint as a land creature entirely unacquainted with subaqueous and subterranean conditions and processes. Absolute faith in the biblical account of creation also inhibited geologic speculation. When attempts were made to explain geologic observations rationally, the supposed age of the earth, indirectly estimated from the scriptures, necessitated an enormous telescoping of events into a brief time interval of only a few thousand years at most. Such views inevitably resulted in the belief that one or more mightly cataclysms had shaken the earth, disrupting its surface, shifting areas of land and sea, and raising islands and mountains. Many believed that all geologic changes had a single cause and had occurred in one brief interval of time.

Superposition of Strata

Reports of early geologic observations in Italy are the first to indicate realization of the significance of stratigraphic superposition. This principle is the basis of all stratigraphy. It is so simple that any child can understand it and no elaborate explanation is now necessary. The fact is quite obvious to everyone that, in a pile of objects, a lower object must have been in place before a higher one could have been laid down upon it. This, of course, is true of rock layers. Each layer now is known to represent an interval of time, short or long, and these intervals of time are recorded in orderly succession from below upward in any ordinary stratigraphic section of rocks. The succession may be continuous or it may have been interrupted one or many times so that only a partial depositional record is preserved.

The significance of superposition or stratigraphic order was not recognized clearly in the earliest stages of geologic observation. As long as the belief was held that the earth had been created in a day, no important time differentiation of rock layers was possible. Until the seventeenth century, all explanations of rocks were based on philosophic reasoning, authority of the classical writers of antiquity, or the scriptures. No systematic observations were made to test these views. Later, however, as more rational explanations were sought for observed geologic features, the importance of time differentiation slowly became apparent. At first, distinction was made between mountains supposed to date from the original creation and those that had come into existence subsequently. Development of the time concept was the first and most essential step in the scientific emergence of geology and it led to the appreciation of the significance of superposition.

Geology in Southern Europe

The suggestion of a time sequence first appeared in explanations offered to account for the origin of mountains. Nicolaus Steno (1638–1686), a Danish physician who moved to Italy and settled in Florence, distinguished

(1) mountains produced by the uplifting or downdropping of strata, that is, faulted mountains, (2) volcanic mountains, and (3) erosional mountains. In 1669 he published a series of diagrammatic cross sections, the first geologic sections of which there is now a record, showing strata of two different ages (see Figure 4). He believed that subterranean forces destroyed strata below the surface, and collapse produced mountains and valleys. Then the sea entered the valleys and new strata were deposited. Further destruction of underlying beds resulted in more collapse and the formation of hills and smaller valleys.

Anton Lazzaro Moro (1687–1740) of Venice distinguished mountains of two classes. The first consists exclusively of unstratified rocks. The second consists of stratified rocks or contains stratified materials overlying unstratified rocks. According to Moro's reasoning, the second class must have had a later origin, and thus two different periods of mountain formation are indicated. This seems to have been the birth of the idea that later led to the differentiation of the so-called *primary* and *secondary* mountains.

The definite idea of a time sequence was transferred from mountains to the rocks themselves almost simultaneously in several European countries. For example, in England this idea was applied to gently dipping strata, now recognized as Mesozoic, that were observed to overlie older, more steeply dipping Coal Measures (see Figure 5).

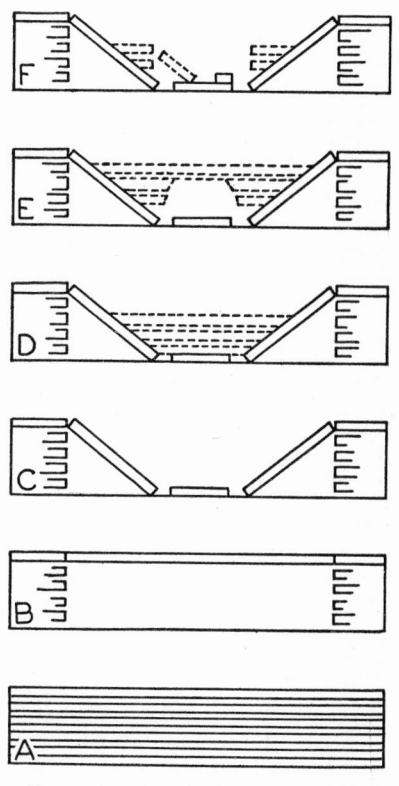

Figure 4. Steno's diagram published in his Prodromus of 1669. This shows his conception of the sequence of geologic events in Tuscany that produced strata of different ages now occurring in differently inclined positions. Steno believed that this resulted from the development and subsequent collapse of underground caverns. (Redrawn from *The birth and development of the geological sciences*, by F. D. Adams, 1938, p. 362, fig. 61, reprinted by permission of Dover Publications, Inc., New York 14, N.Y. [$2.00])

In Italy, Giovanni Arduino (1714–1795) of Verona and Venice distinguished three classes of mountains and four classes of deposits each composed of characteristically different materials. He concluded that the earth had been disrupted repeatedly by violent upheavals and subsidences. His classification is as follows:

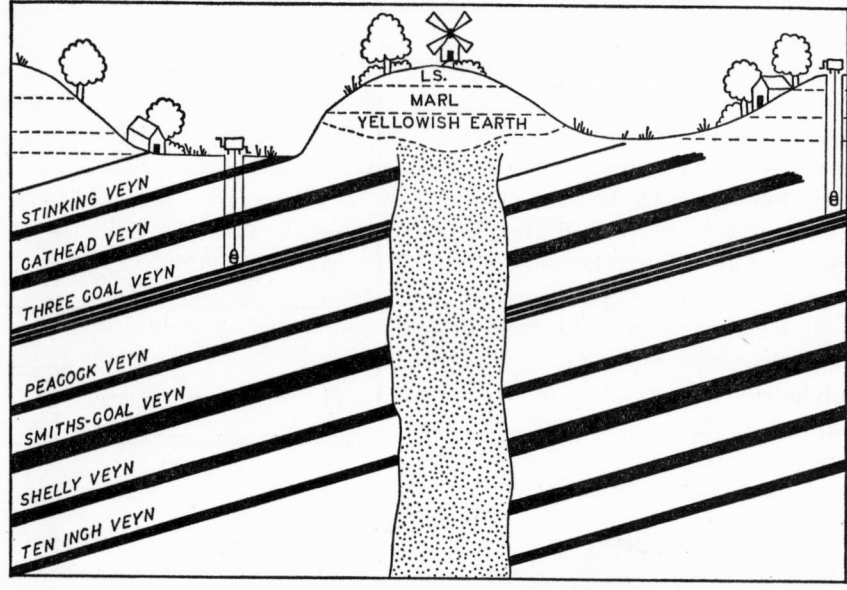

Figure 5.   Strachey's diagram of 1719 showing a very early representation of unconformable relations and a fault in the Coal Measures of Somersetshire, England, overlain
by Mesozoic strata. (Redrawn from the original, Phil. Trans. Roy. Soc. London, vol. 30,
pl. 2.)

1. Primary mountains, whose rocks contain metallic ores at many places
but lack fossils.

2. Secondary mountains, consisting of bedded and well-lithified rocks
which contain many marine organisms but are without ore deposits.

3. Tertiary low mountains or hills, consisting of fossiliferous but unconsolidated gravels, sands, and clays. Volcanic rocks are associated with these
strata.

4. Lastly, earthy and rocky materials washed down from the mountains
and overlying the other kinds of rock.

Geology in Northern Europe

Johann Gottlob Lehmann (1719–1767), professor of mineralogy and mining at Berlin and St. Petersburg, appears to have been the first geologist to
measure and record actual sections of stratified rocks. Similar studies also
were made by Georg Christian Füchsel (1722–1776), a physician in Thu-
ringia. The work of these two men strongly influenced later geologic ideas in
northern Europe. Lehmann recognized three classes of mountains as follows:

1. Urgebirge or primitive mountains, formed at the time of creation, include all of the highest peaks and great mountain ranges of the world. They
consist of unstratified or poorly bedded rocks that were deposited from vio-

lently agitated water. They contain veins and irregular masses of metallic ores formed at a later time.

2. Flötzgebirge or layered mountains consist of well-bedded strata with fossils. The rocks of these mountains were formed at the time of Noah's flood and consist of material washed down from the primitive mountains and deposited upon their sloping sides and in basins between them.

3. Mountains of the third class are fewer and less important. They were formed at a later time in restricted regions by various processes including the action of great floods and volcanoes. These Aufgeschwemmptgebirge or so-called transported rocks are largely unconsolidated.

In their general nature, the systems of Arduino and Lehmann closely correspond as follows:

Italy	Germany	Character of Rocks
Primary	Urgebirge	Igneous and metamorphic rocks of mountain cores
Secondary	Flötzgebirge	Dipping sedimentary strata on mountain flanks
Tertiary	Aufgeschwemmptgebirge	Unconsolidated and horizontal sediments

Peter Simon Pallas (1741–1811) was a German of French parentage who became professor of natural history at St. Petersburg under the patronage of Empress Catherine II. He traveled widely in both European and Asiatic Russia and studied particularly the Ural and Altai Mountains where he worked out a somewhat similar succession. He observed that granite forms the central part of great mountain ranges. This generally is flanked by vertical or steeply dipping beds of a considerable variety of rocks that would now be classed as crystalline schists. Like granite they are unfossiliferous but contain ore deposits. Next comes a great series of calcareous rocks rich in fossils that form secondary mountains on both sides of the main ranges. At first these beds are steeply inclined but farther from the mountains the dips become more gentle and they pass under thick clays and marls that form the Tertiary mountains or foothills. Pallas believed that the sea had never stood more than 600 feet above its present level, and that violent volcanic action resulting from the combustion of buried organic matter and pyrite was responsible for the upheaval of mountain ranges and the fracturing and contortion of the strata on their flanks.

The concept of a threefold division of rocks came to be widely accepted in the latter part of the eighteenth century. It marked a great advance in geologic thinking and constituted the first step in the advancement of stratigraphy. It directed attention to the physical and time relations of rock strata and introduced the idea of correlation. The development of other generalizations concerning more detailed aspects of stratigraphy followed, and subsequent progress was more rapid. Some notice began to be taken of possible past changes in geography, climate, and the organisms preserved as fossils.

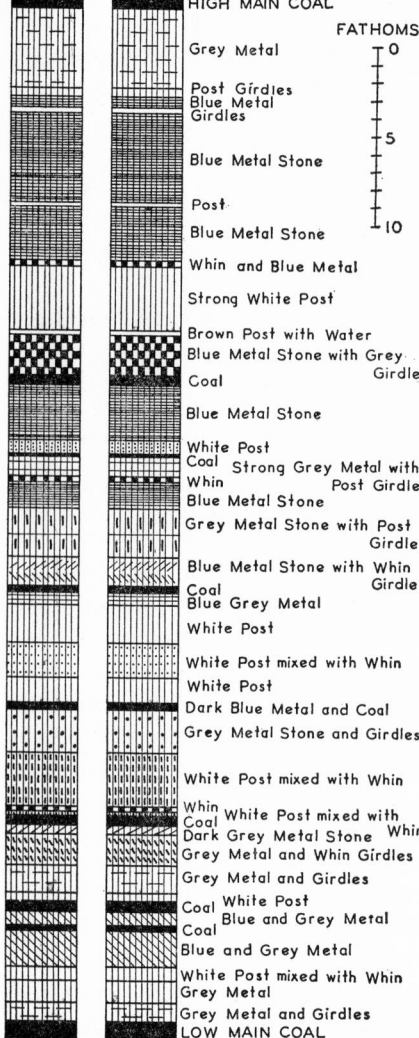

HIGH MAIN COAL

FATHOMS

Grey Metal

Post Girdles
Blue Metal
Girdles

Blue Metal Stone

Post

Blue Metal Stone

Whin and Blue Metal

Strong White Post

Brown Post with Water
Blue Metal Stone with Grey
Coal   Girdles

Blue Metal Stone

White Post
Coal   Strong Grey Metal with
Whin   Post Girdles
Blue Metal Stone
Grey Metal Stone with Post
                    Girdles
Blue Metal Stone with Whin
Coal   Girdles
Blue Grey Metal
White Post

White Post mixed with Whin
White Post
Dark Blue Metal and Coal
Grey Metal Stone and Girdles

White Post mixed with Whin

Whin White Post mixed with
Coal
Dark Grey Metal Stone Whin
Grey Metal and Whin Girdles
Grey Metal and Girdles
Coal White Post
Coal Blue and Grey Metal
Blue and Grey Metal
White Post mixed with Whin
Grey Metal
Grey Metal and Girdles
LOW MAIN COAL

Figure 6. Representation of part of the stratigraphic section penetrated by a coal mine shaft near Newcastle in England. This section appeared originally in the 1799 edition of *The Botanic Garden*, an epic nature poem by Erasmus Darwin. It is one of the earliest graphic sections published. The various kinds of strata are indicated by patterns very different from those now commonly used. Descriptions are in terms employed by the local miners and quarrymen. "Metal" is shale, "post" is sandstone, "whin" is dark-colored hard rock, mostly sandstone but possibly including some impure limestone, and "girdles" are layers or bands of any harder rock including perhaps discontinuous concretions. (Redrawn from Arkell and Tomkeieff, 1953, *English rock terms*, frontispiece, by permission of Oxford University Press on behalf of the University of Durham.)

Werner and Formations

The greatest figure in geology toward the close of the eighteenth century was Abraham Gottlob Werner (1750–1817), professor of mineralogy in the School of Mines at Freiburg in Saxony. His enthusiasm and the eloquence of his lectures transformed a rather obscure school into an important university that attracted students from all parts of Europe. More than any other man he raised geology to the level of a popular and useful science; for more than a generation he molded the opinions of a large group of loyal followers. Few other teachers of geology have acquired so much influence or earned so great contemporary fame.

Most of Werner's fundamental ideas were not original and he leaned heavily on the work of Lehmann. The system taught by Werner during his later years classified rocks as follows:

1. Urgebirge (Primitive), granite and other crystalline rocks, also including metamorphic rocks, without fossils.

2. Übergangsgebirge (Transition), mainly graywacke but also

some limestone and diabase. This was a new division consisting of stratified but generally highly deformed rocks; fossils present but not common.

3. Flötzgebirge (layered), consisting of a great variety of less-deformed layered fossiliferous rocks and basalt which Werner arranged in a supposedly universal stratigraphic order.

4. Aufgeschwemmptgebirge (Transported), unconsolidated sediments occurring at lower levels.

5. Volcanic rocks, including both extrusive igneous material and sediments altered by heat.

Werner believed that the earth developed gradually and suffered many changes. All rocks were formed in water except the last or volcanic group, but rocks of this type are rare and unimportant. The original earth was covered by a thickly turbid primeval ocean deep enough to submerge the highest mountains. The oldest rock is granite and upon it were deposited other crystalline rocks all precipitated from aqueous solution. Then the level of the ocean began to fall and other formations (Transition) were produced, partly by mechanical derivation from older rocks and partly by precipitation. The sea continued to subside and the great series of Flötz formations, mainly of mechanical origin, was deposited. All of the rocks up to and including those of this stage are universal formations deposited simultaneously over the whole earth except where mountains emerged from the shrinking sea. Later (Transported) formations, developed when sea level fell still lower, are local and discontinuous. Lastly, volcanoes erupted in a few restricted districts where heat was produced by the subterranean burning of coal.

Werner taught that the earth originally was a chaos with the primeval ocean constantly churned by great storms. Water level did not subside regularly but oscillated, and currents cut channels developing valleys between mountains. Conditions gradually ameliorated, and as the Transition rocks were deposited the earth became habitable and marine organisms appeared. Later the ocean quieted and modern conditions were approached. A final withdrawal of the sea left the earth as it appears today.

Material deposited in the ocean formed beds parallel to the surface upon which they lie. Therefore, strata dip outward on the flanks of mountains which were original topographic features and were not uplifted. Steeply inclined beds sometimes slid downward while still soft and unconsolidated and thus they were contorted and broken.

Because of the belief that almost all rocks, including granite and basalt, were formed in water, Werner and his followers came to be known as Neptunists. Inspired by their teacher's views, most of Werner's pupils interpreted rocks in accordance with his doctrines. These did not correspond with the conclusions of other geologists, particularly some who had studied certain parts of France and Italy. The main point of conflict that soon developed concerned the origin of basalt. Werner believed this rock to be aqueous in spite of the findings of several French geologists who had traced basaltic flows to their volcanic sources. Werner's influence was so great, however, that his views were accepted as the final authority by most of his pupils, who maintained them in the face of all conflicting evidence. His generalizations, based on very limited field work in Saxony, were much too sweeping but his emphasis on the physical characters of rocks led to more careful observations of them, and the breadth of his generalizations encouraged comparisons and correlations on a wide scale such as had not been made before.

The idea of formations, originated by Füchsel, was adopted by Werner. He believed that stratified rocks occur in an invariable order and that the formations characterized by their lithology can be identified everywhere. Correlation was established by lithologic similarity and stratigraphic order.

Two of Werner's favorite pupils eventually defected. In France J. F. D'Aubisson de Voisins demonstrated the volcanic origin of basalt. Also Christian Leopold von Buch at last was similarly convinced but, in deference to his teacher, insisted that German basalts are different. In the course of his wide travels, von Buch also observed granite cutting through fossiliferous Secondary limestone in Norway. He realized, therefore, that all granite is not primitive. Likewise he correctly interpreted evidence showing that the Swedish coast has been uplifted, thus disproving Werner's contention that the earth's surface has always been stable.

Hutton and Uniformitarianism

Another great contemporary figure was James Hutton (1726–1797), a Scot who successively studied law, medicine, chemistry, and agriculture. He was never a professional geologist or teacher and consequently his direct personal influence was not comparable to Werner's. His conclusions regarding the processes responsible for the development of the earth, however, mark him as the first modern geologist. Nevertheless, it was not until after his death that his views, advocated by a few ardent converts, became widely known.

Hutton observed present-day erosion in river valleys and along the seacoast and concluded that all rocks have been formed of material derived from the wasting away of older rocks. His reference to a "succession of worlds, with no vestige of a beginning—no prospect of an end," was out of harmony with all preceding views and introduced the idea of a very ancient earth. His contention that the formation of all rocks can be explained on the basis of processes that are now in operation gave rise to the doctrine of *uniformitarianism*, now recognized as one of the most fundamental tenets of geology.

Hutton observed that at some places one series of strata rests on the upturned and beveled layers of another. He realized that both had originally been horizontal and that the first had been upheaved and eroded before the deposition of the other. Such relations record disturbances resulting from subterranean heating and expansion of the rocks. Thus, geologic history witnessed alternate periods of quiet deposition and episodes of earth movement.

Internal heat of the earth is proved by volcanoes, and to Hutton this was most important in the explanation of many geologic phenomena. For this reason his followers were termed Plutonists in contrast to the Neptunists. Hutton believed that sediments deposited on the sea bottom were heated and lithified by partial fusion and not by compaction and cementation as taught by Werner. Therefore, lithology is no indication of age. Complete fusion of sediments produced the igneous rocks that Hutton observed intruding older sediments. Volcanoes acted as safety valves that released internal heat and in part prevented earthquakes and upheavals of the land.

Hutton's great work *Theory of the Earth* was published in 1795 but has been read by few persons because of its turgid language and uninteresting style. His ideas were more effectively spread by the actions of his friends and particularly by a book, *Illustrations of the Huttonian Theory*, written by John Playfair which appeared in 1802. At first Hutton's views were bitterly opposed by the Neptunists but his ideas soon spread from Great Britain to the continent, and the accumulation of evidence gathered in many lands brought increasing support to the Plutonists. Sir Charles Lyell (1797–1875) was the most influential of Hutton's followers. He traveled widely, wrote extensively, and presented the doctrine of uniformitarianism most effectively. His *Principles of Geology*, which was published in three volumes between 1830 and 1833 and appeared in numerous later editions, was the first modern textbook of geology.

Geologists now do not believe all of the things that Hutton advocated. Uniformitarianism as presently understood means that the physical world, as far back as the geologic record can be read, did not differ importantly from the world as it exists today. Modern processes like erosion, deposition, and volcanic action may have varied in intensity from time to time, but the interpretation of earth history does not require the intervention of conditions or processes different from those that now can be observed.

Smith and Paleontologic Correlation

Meantime an English surveyor and engineer, William Smith (1769–1839), was developing the principle of paleontologic correlation and making the first extensive and detailed geologic map. His work in coal mines, canal construction, and marsh drainage revealed to him that different types of stratified rocks occur in a definite sequence and that they can be identified by the topography and soils produced and by the fossils they contain.

Up to this time, the source of fossils in collections was rarely recorded because it seemed to be of no importance. No one took much interest in

Smith's discovery until he convinced skeptics by naming the places where certain specimens had been found and predicting the occurrence of particular fossils at places that he had never visited.

Smith's professional duties carried him to all parts of England, Wales, and southern Scotland and he noted the rocks and fossils everywhere he went. In 1815 and 1816 he published a geologic map at a scale of five miles to one inch in several sheets, altogether nine by six feet in size, and descriptions of the formations with lists and illustrations of the fossils. Some of the names he introduced for formations are still in use. This monumental work earned for Smith the titles "Father of English Geology" and "Father of Stratigraphy." His observations and the conclusions he drew from them are among the best examples on record of practical scientific reasoning. It is remarkable that this was the accomplishment of a man totally without formal training in any of the sciences.

Actually Smith's was not the first geologic map although it was much more elaborate and detailed than its most noteworthy predecessor. In France, Jean Etienne Guettard (1715–1786), a botanist and keeper of the natural history collection of the Duke of Orleans, observed that many plants are restricted to certain types of soil. Directing his attention to the rocks, he found that similar rocks distinguishable by lithology, topography, soil, and botany outcrop in oval bands surrounding Paris. In 1752 he published a map showing these features and later extended his observations from Ireland to Spain and incorporated them on another map.

The value of fossils for identification and correlation of formations was not exclusively an English discovery. At the same time that Smith was making his observations, Baron Georges Léopold Cuvier (1769–1832), one of the most distinguished men in the history of French science, was conducting pioneer work in vertebrate paleontology. In association with Alexander Brongniart, he found that the remains of extinct animals occur only in certain stratigraphically restricted layers. From this he concluded that the earth had suffered a succession of widespread catastrophes each of which resulted in the extinguishing of an old fauna and the appearance of a new one.

Stratigraphic Principles

The foregoing brief account of the development of certain important geologic ideas shows that at the beginning of the nineteenth century the most fundamental principles of stratigraphy had been recognized. These are:

1. *Principle of superposition.* The recognition of the time significance of stratigraphic succession was first indicated by Steno in 1669 but not generally realized until after the work of Lehmann in Germany and Arduino in Italy in 1756 and 1759 respectively.

2. *Principle of uniformitarianism.* The lack of any necessity to call upon

strange and extraordinary forces to explain features of strata was first suggested by Hutton in 1788 and popularized later by Playfair and Lyell. This principle applies equally in other branches of geology but it is especially important in stratigraphy.

3. *Principle of paleontologic identification, correlation, and zonation.* The determination of time relations of geologic happenings indicated by similar fossils in different areas was first clearly formulated by Smith in 1790.

All modern stratigraphy is based on these three simple principles and nothing of comparable importance has been added since. Numerous other ideas or theories have contributed to stratigraphic progress from time to time, but their main applications are to other sciences or to other branches of geology. Darwin's theory of evolution has added refinements to correlation, and the principle of biologic adaptation to environment has aided stratigraphic interpretations. Also various physical principles such as those of hydrodynamics as applied to the erosion, transportation, and deposition of sediments, and chemical principles including those related to isotopes have contributed to stratigraphy. Most of these have been adapted from other scientific fields and applied to stratigraphic problems. They do not have the broad and fundamental importance of the three great principles outlined here.

The early stages of stratigraphic development were confused by misconceptions regarding the origins of both sedimentary and igneous rocks. When these were corrected and Hutton's views achieved general acceptance, progress in stratigraphic studies and interpretations was speeded up remarkably.

Structural complications such as those introduced by overthrust faults and overturned stratigraphic sequences caused much difficulty and resulted in serious misinterpretations before they were properly understood. Some much discussed problems such as the Precambrian versus Tertiary age of the salt deposits of the Salt Range in northern Pakistan hinge upon the disputed presence of an overthrust. Also such relationships have been pointed to in fairly recent time by a few fundamentalists to discredit the facts of historical geology and organic evolution.

The simplicity of the three great stratigraphic principles has caused some geologists, who are specialists in other fields, to consider stratigraphy such a simple layer-cake type of study that it is neither interesting nor worthy of much respect from a scientific standpoint. This might be true only if such aspects of stratified rocks as lateral uniformity and vertical consistency were equally simple or if exposures were everywhere sufficient to reveal all details of the strata and their mutual relations. It is fortunate perhaps for stratigraphers that this is not so. Lateral lithologic changes make the tracing and correlation of strata of equivalent age difficult and more or less uncertain. Differences in lithology and fossils may indicate either differences in age or differences in environment, and many mistakes in interpretation have been made. The recognition and evaluation of unconformities and other less important breaks in deposition are difficult and the fitting together of numerous incomplete stratigraphic sections offers many problems. Studies of this kind have been in progress for more than 150 years but it is not yet certain that a complete stratigraphic section has been pieced together.

The necessary application of theory to observed stratigraphic facts, as well as practical expediency, has led to situations in which interpretations by different individuals have varied widely. Thus it is commonly impossible, from the available information, to determine surely that one conclusion is superior to others. The most careful observation, clear thinking, good judgment, and the application of broad experience are required to solve many stratigraphic problems satisfactorily.

BIBLIOGRAPHY

Adams, F. D. (1938), *The birth and development of the geological sciences*, Baltimore, Williams and Wilkins, reprinted New York, Dover Publications.
This thorough review of geologic literature and ideas carries up to the beginning of modern geology.
Challinor, J. (1953, 1954), The early progress of British geology, I, *Annals of Science*, vol. 9 (1953), pp. 124–153; II, same, vol. 10 (1954), pp. 1–19; III, same, pp. 107–148.
The author presents a review of British literature from 1538 to 1802 with quotations and annotations.
Fenton, C. L., and Fenton, M. A. (1945), *The story of the great geologists*, Garden City, Doubleday, Doran.
This is a popular account of the development of geology from Werner to Chamberlin.
Fenton, C. L., and Fenton, M. A. (1952), *Giants of geology*, Garden City, Doubleday.
This is a revised second edition of the preceding book.
Geikie, Archibald (1905), *The founders of geology*, 2nd ed., London, Macmillan.
The period before 1850 is the main subject of this history of geology.
Gillispie, C. C. (1951), *Genesis and geology*, Cambridge, Harvard Univ. Press.
This book traces the development of geology and the contemporary conflict with religion in England from 1790 to 1850.
Grabau, A. W. (1920), *A textbook of geology*, 2 vols., Boston, Heath.
A condensed historical account of the development of geology is included. See vol. 1, pp. 24–28, and vol. 2, pp. 2–19.
Hawkes, Leonard (1958), Some aspects of the progress in geology in the last fifty years, *Quart. J. Geol. Soc. London*, vol. 113, pp. 309–321.
Emphasis is laid on the evidence that uniformitarianism has characterized geologic and biologic development at least since the Precambrian.

Institute for Government Research (1918), *The U.S. Geological Survey, its history, activities and organization*, New York, Appleton.

> The development of government surveys from 1804 through World War I is traced.

Lyell, Charles (1830 et seq.), *Principles of geology*, 3 vols., various editions.

> The early chapters present a good account of the development of geology.

Mather, K. F., and Mason, S. L. (1939), *A source book in geology*, New York, McGraw-Hill.

> Quotations are given from some of the most important geologic literature from Leonardo da Vinci to C. R. Van Hise.

Merrill, G. P. (1920), Contribution to a history of American state geological and natural history surveys, U.S. Nat. Mus., Bull. 109.

> Accounts are included of the early surveys that laid much of the foundation for geology in the United States.

Merrill, G. P. (1924), *The first one hundred years of American geology*, New Haven, Yale Univ. Press, revised from U.S. Nat. Mus. Ann. Report for 1904, pp. 189–734.

> Geologic investigations in North America are thoroughly reviewed.

Sagui, C. L. (1930), Economic geology and allied sciences in ancient times, *Econ. Geol.*, vol. 25, pp. 65–86.

> This is mainly an account of mining in Greek and Roman times.

Symposium (1947), Second symposium on the age of the Saline Series in the Salt Range of the Punjab, *Proc. National Acad. Sci. India*, sec. B, vol. 16, pp. 1–257.

> Nineteen papers present evidence and opinions regarding the Cambrian versus Tertiary age of the salt deposits.

Zittel, K. A. von (1901), *History of geology and palaeontology to the end of the 19th century*, trans. by M. M. Ogilvie-Gordon, London, Walter Scott.

> This comprehensive account lays particular stress on European accomplishments.

3

The Geologic Systems

THE earliest geologic classification was lithologic and structural. It was first applied to mountains and then transferred to the rocks that constitute the mountains. At the beginning of the nineteenth century this classification had the following form:

Italy and France	Germany
Tertiary	Transported
Secondary	Flötzgebirge
	Transition
Primary	Urgebirge

As paleontologic comparisons were made, it became apparent that these divisions did not correspond from region to region. In particular, a great series of formations in France was discovered to be intermediate in age between the Flötz and Transported strata of Germany. Also it was found that the Tertiary in Italy included younger strata than in France. The relations were approximately as follows:

Italy	France	Germany
		Transported
Tertiary		
	Tertiary	
Secondary	Secondary	Flötzgebirge
Primary	Primary	{ Transition
		{ Urgebirge

32

Gradually greater order was achieved and the meanings of some of the old terms were altered. Thus the recognition of divisions roughly comparable to the large geologic divisions as now understood evolved as follows:

Old Term	Modern Term
Transported	Quaternary
Tertiary	Tertiary
Secondary	Mesozoic
Transition	Paleozoic
Primary	Precambrian

This correspondence is not exact, and it varies somewhat from country to country, but the general similarity is close enough to demonstrate that a significant and practical basis exists for such a rock differentiation in the best-known parts of western Europe.

Each of the great groups consists of more or less numerous formations or other subdivisions. For many years the tendency to correlate strata on the basis of lithologic features, according to the Wernerian method, persisted. With increasing paleontologic knowledge, however, some of the lithologic correlations were disproved, and the realization developed that stratigraphic successions differ importantly in different areas. Studies in the several large Tertiary basins of Europe by 1830 had already revealed that they record different histories and preserve unlike sequences of strata. The gradually resulting reaction against Wernerianism detracted from the importance of formations in the minds of many European geologists. To this day such units are generally looked upon by them as more or less local stratigraphic subdivisions that receive little emphasis in correlation.

British Stratigraphy

A classification of geologic systems developed gradually as geologic studies multiplied. For many years the terms *formation, terrain, group, series,* and *system* did not have the graduated meanings that they hold today and were used more or less interchangeably. Division of the stratigraphic section into what are now known as systems, however, was largely the accomplishment of British geologists. For this reason the geology of England holds a position that, in a historical sense, is particularly important. The succession of major stratigraphic divisions long recognized in England is as follows (see Figure 7):

1. Precambrian schists.
2. Cambrian and Ordovician shales, limestones, and both intrusive and extrusive igneous rocks.
3. Silurian shale and limestone.

These three divisions constitute the Old Graywacke.

4. Devonian Old Red Sandstone, reddish and brownish fresh-water strata that are better developed in Scotland.

5. Carboniferous Limestone, formerly known as the Mountain Limestone.

6. Millstone Grit.

7. Coal Measures.

This and the last division constitute the Upper Carboniferous.

8. Permian Magnesian Limestone—grades westward into sandstone that was confused with the next younger division.

9. Triassic New Red Sandstone.

10. Lias, impure shale and limestone that forms a lowland area. The name is a corruption of the word *layers*.

11. The Oolite, an upland-forming limestone.

12. Oxford Clay.

13. Corallian Limestone.

14. Kimmeridge Clay.

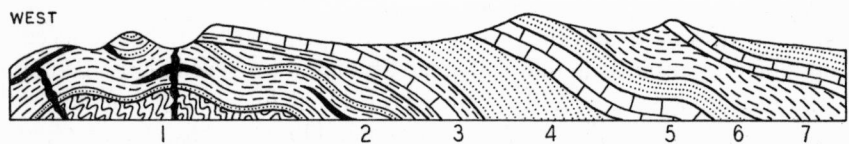

Figure 7. Much-generalized cross section of the stratigraphic succession in England extending from the Welsh coast to London. Observations of the relations of these strata contributed greatly to the early development of stratigraphic geology. The numbered units

This and the last two divisions form another lowland zone.

15. Portland and Purbeck Beds, mostly limestone.

Divisions 10 to 15 are Jurassic and they are the strata principally studied by William Smith.

16. Gault and Greensands.

17. The Chalk.

This and division 16 are Cretaceous.

18. Tertiary London Clay Group.

This succession is not complete according to modern standards, and most of these old formations are now subdivided.

THE STANDARD SYSTEMS

The recognition of geologic systems, or sequences of strata later accepted as systems, and the selection of names for them progressed in a very haphazard fashion over a period of 100 years, as shown in Figure 8. Most of the nomenclature, however, was established between 1822 and 1854. It closely paralleled and reflected contemporary progress in paleontologic correlation and stratigraphic discrimination. As might be expected, several of the younger systems achieved recognition earlier than older ones because they are more favorably exposed and less complex structurally.

Tertiary, 1759. This name, still in general use, was introduced by Arduino in his classification of mountains. Some consider the Tertiary to be a system but others subdivide it into two, four, or five systems. The comparable terms *Primary* and *Secondary* generally have been abandoned but still do appear in some European publications. In France particularly, Primary is now commonly employed with the same meaning as Paleozoic. In contrast the term *Quaternary* is of later origin.

Jurassic, 1795. Von Humboldt introduced this name for strata that outcrop in the Jura Mountains, part of the outer Alps that lie along the Franco-Swiss border. Originally it was applied to only a part of the present Jurassic System and it was later expanded to include other strata rich in ammonites that occur in western Europe and in England.

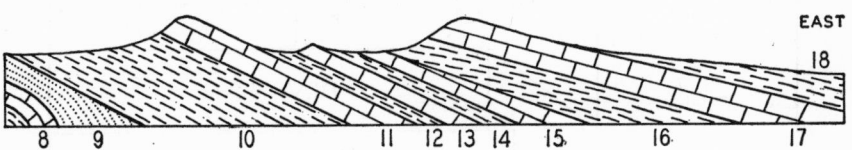

are identified in the text. (Constructed from *Geological map of England and Scotland,* 1948.)

Cretaceous, 1822. A Belgian geologist, d'Halloy, proposed several names for large groups of strata, but Cretaceous is the only one that was adopted by other geologists and has survived. It is a descriptive term derived from the Latin word for chalk and was originally applied to rocks extensively developed in the Paris basin.

Carboniferous, 1822. Conybeare and Phillips introduced this name in England where the threefold division of Mountain Limestone, Millstone Grit, and Coal Measures was recognized. The name was suggested by the coal deposits that had become increasingly important as the industrial revolution rapidly progressed in the early nineteenth century. At first it included the Old Red Sandstone that later was transferred to the subsequently recognized Devonian System.

Quaternary, 1829. Desnoyers proposed this name in France for post-Tertiary or modern strata whose fossils are living species occurring in the same latitudes. It parallels the older terms Primary, Secondary, and Tertiary.

Eocene, Miocene, Pliocene, 1833. These divisions of the Tertiary were originally defined and named by Lyell. They were not as much lithologic divisions or successions of strata characteristic of different regions as were most of the other systems. From the very start these had more specific time values because they were distinguished by paleontologic differences. At that time 2902 species of marine Tertiary fossils were recognized by the French paleontologist Deshays and 4639 species were known in the living Atlantic fauna. Distinctions were made according to the number of common species. The

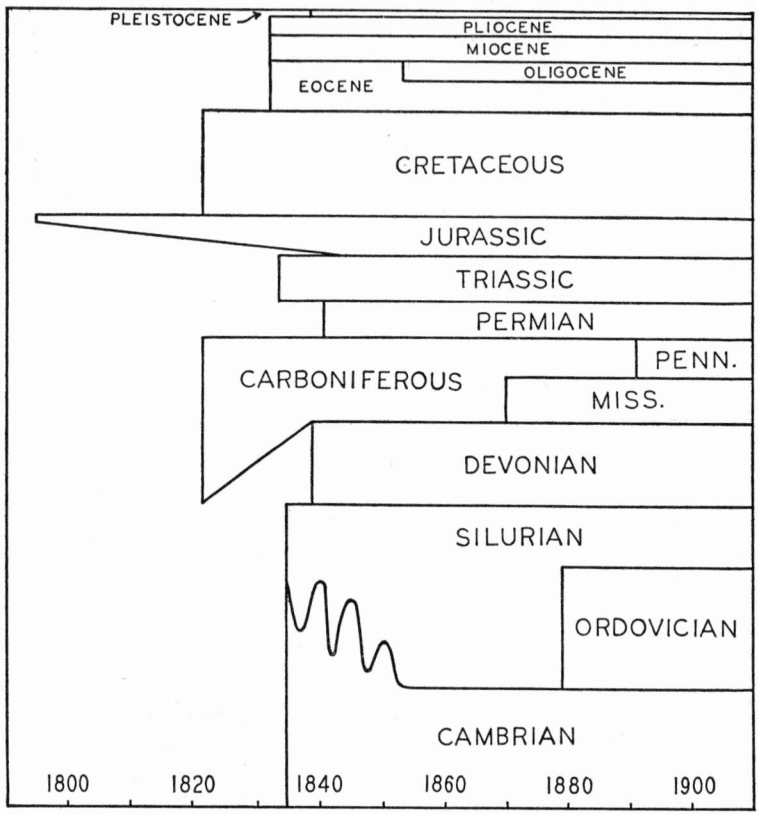

Figure 8. Diagram showing the relative dates of recognition of the large standard divisions of the stratigraphic section. Vertical scale is proportional to estimates of elapsed geologic time. (Modified from Moore, 1955, Geol. Soc. Amer., Spec. Paper 62, p. 548, fig. 1.)

Eocene fauna contained 3 percent of modern species, the Miocene 17 percent, the older Pliocene 50 to 67 percent, and the newer Pliocene 96 percent. The Tertiary of Italy was somewhat similarly divided into two parts equivalent to the Eocene below and the combined Miocene and Pliocene above. These three names mean "dawn new," "less new" and "more new." They are variously considered series of the Tertiary or separate systems.

Recent, 1833. Lyell used this term for deposits that have accumulated since the appearance of man. Originally the Recent included all post-Tertiary strata and was equivalent to Quaternary but later it was restricted to the post-Pleistocene of modern usage.

Triassic, 1834. The three divisions of this system in Germany, Keuper or Rhaetic, Muschelkalk (pelecypod limestone) and Buntsandstein (mottled sandstone), suggested the name to von Alberti, who first used it. The Triassic is represented by the New Red Sandstone in Great Britain, where Permian red beds were confused with the rocks of this system.

Cambrian, Silurian, 1835. Study of the Old Graywacke of Wales by Sedgwick and Murchison marks one of the classic chapters in the history of geology. Adam Sedgwick, a clergyman and professor at Cambridge University, and Sir Roderick Impy Murchison, a Scot who served as an army officer during the Napoleonic Wars, started their work at the bottom and the top of these complicated strata respectively. In the first account of their studies each distinguished a system that was named for an ancient Welsh tribe. Later, comparison of their fossils showed that these systems overlapped, and a bitter controversy developed regarding the proper division of strata between them. Sedgwick's Cambrian System included unfossiliferous beds in its lower part that are now known to be Lower Cambrian and Precambrian. Murchison claimed that all of the fossiliferous strata were part of his Silurian System. In this controversy Murchison possessed most of the advantages. He occupied a higher social position and he argued his claims in an elaborate and popular book; later he was appointed Director of the Geological Survey of Great Britain. Murchison's influence was so great that the Silurian, as he defined it, was rapidly adopted in foreign lands, and the disputed strata became known as the Lower Silurian. In many of the classifications of the middle nineteenth century the Silurian was considered to be equivalent to the old Transition. For example, Joachim Barrande, one of the greatest paleontologists of all time, included in the Silurian System all strata, in what is now Czechoslovakia, that range from the Cambrian to the Devonian. Other geologists recognized a Cambrian System but excluded from it Sedgwick's Upper Cambrian strata. Almost fifty years passed before the Ordovician System was proposed as a substitute for Sedgwick's Upper Cambrian and the greater part of Murchison's Lower Silurian.

Devonian, 1839. Before their quarrel over what is now the Ordovician System, Sedgwick and Murchison discovered that fossils in the upper part of the Old Graywacke of Devonshire are younger than the Silurian fossils of Wales. They also learned that similar fossils occur abundantly in New York State and, possibly to anticipate the recognition of a new system in America, they jointly named the Devonian System. Devonshire is a poor type locality because the strata there are metamorphosed, geosynclinal, very thick, structurally complex, and sparingly fossiliferous, and the contact with the Silurian was not observed. Either New York or Germany would have provided a much better type locality. The Old Red Sandstone of the foregoing English section is largely a non-marine lateral development of the Devonshire strata.

Pleistocene, 1839. This name, meaning "most new," was introduced by Lyell for late Tertiary strata that he had formerly termed newer Pliocene. In 1846 Forbes applied this name to deposits of glacial age and it was used so widely in this sense that Lyell in 1873 assented to the change in definition. The Pleistocene generally has been considered a series of the Quaternary System older than the Recent. There is a tendency now, however, to include the Recent in the Pleistocene. According to this arrangement, the Pleistocene is a system coextensive with the Quaternary, and the Recent becomes a stage.

Permian, 1841. Murchison's work on the Silurian in England brought him international recognition as the world's foremost geologist. He was invited by Czar Nicholas I to visit Russia with, it is supposed, the hope if not the purpose of discovering a new system. In this Murchison was successful because in the province of Perm, adjacent to the Ural Mountains, he found a great thickness of limestone overlying the Carboniferous with fossils different from any previously reported. To these rocks he gave the name Permian System. He recognized that strata of similar age had long been known in England, where they constitute the Magnesian Limestone, and in Germany. The Russian strata, however, are developed quite differently and a general name had not been applied to them anywhere.

Oligocene, 1854. Beyrich proposed this name, meaning "slightly new," for strata that some geologists had been calling Upper Eocene and others Lower Miocene. The Oligocene is variously considered either a series of the Tertiary or a system.

Mississippian, 1870. Winchell introduced this name for Lower Carboniferous strata that are dominantly limestones in the Mississippi Valley. It was accepted by Chamberlin and Salisbury in 1906 and soon thereafter was widely recognized in the United States as a system. In Europe approximately equivalent beds are termed Dinantian from a city in Belgium but they are considered to be a subdivision of the Carboniferous and are not accorded the status of a system. In order to preserve harmony in a universal classification, R. C. Moore has proposed that the Mississippian be regarded as a subsystem of the Carboniferous.

Ordovician, 1879. This system, named from another old Welsh tribe, was suggested by Lapworth in England as a substitute for the Lower Silurian. Its general acceptance in England and the United States at about the beginning of the twentieth century brought to a fairly satisfactory conclusion the rather anomalous situation that had existed ever since the controversy arose between Sedgwick and Murchison. Similar acceptance has not been so complete in Europe and even today "Lower Silurian," in its old sense, still appears in some continental publications. The "Lower Silurian" of most American reports issued before 1900 is Ordovician.

Holocene, 1885. This name, meaning "entirely new," was agreed upon by a committee of the International Geological Congress for the post-Pleistocene. It is considered by most geologists to be a subdivision of the Quaternary System. The name is used much more in Europe than it is in the United States, where the equivalent term Recent generally is preferred.

Pennsylvanian, 1891. Williams introduced this name for the Upper Carboniferous as these rocks were recognized in North America. Like Mississippian, it was accepted by Chamberlin and Salisbury in 1906 and since then has been adopted generally in America but not in Europe. Suggestion has been made that the Pennsylvanian also be considered a subsystem of the Carboniferous.

As the foregoing brief accounts demonstrate, the succession of recognized geologic systems grew up without plan from the activities of many geologists working independently. Complete agreement regarding all systems has not been reached. The concept of a system gradually changed from a considerable thickness of strata well developed in a certain area to a large group that is distinct from other similar ones. The acceptance of favored units has not been entirely rational, and recognition probably has been influenced almost as much by prejudice as by actual geologic evidence that serves to set apart definite segments of the stratigraphic section. As time passed, some old systems were subdivided and intermediate new systems were recognized. Some boundaries were adjusted to conform more conveniently to physical and faunal discontinuities, but all boundaries are not yet agreed upon. The British, for example, include strata in the Upper Cambrian that almost everywhere else are considered to be Lower Ordovician. The systems now recognized, however, are in general convenient units in western Europe and the eastern United States but all of them cannot be differentiated satisfactorily in some other parts of the world.

OTHER SYSTEMS AND NAMES

The systems now recognized, and the names by which they are known, have been stabilized by custom, and no system proposed since the Ordovician in 1879 has attained nearly general acceptance. Other systems have been proposed and other names have been employed but none has achieved much recognition except locally. Some system names not included in the standard list are, however, important enough to make familiarity with them desirable.

Anthracolithic. This name was proposed by Waagen to include the Carboniferous and Permian because of the close relations and many similarities of these systems. It was derived from the Greek word for charcoal.

Canadian. Dana introduced this name for a new system separated from the

Lower Silurian (Ordovician) and termed the remainder of the Lower Silurian the Trenton System. Ulrich restricted and redefined the Canadian System making it approximately equivalent to the Beekmantown strata of early Ordovician age. For a time, such a system achieved limited recognition among Ulrich's followers but this name is now used for the lowest series of the Ordovician.

Carboniferous. For many years the United States Geological Survey considered that the Carboniferous System consists of three series, Mississippian, Pennsylvanian, and Permian. This usage, which was at variance with European practice, has been abandoned and the Survey now regards the three parts as systems.

Champlainian. The Geological Survey of New York was organized in 1836, and the "final" report of its accomplishments was published in four volumes in 1842 and 1843. The most important stratigraphic work was done by James Hall in the Fourth District of western New York where he described the rocks as constituting the New York System. In the northern district, Ebenezer Emmons described the Taconic System named from the Taconic Mountains. The nature of the Taconic System was long disputed. Emmons claimed, and it is now known, that it included strata older than any of those observed by Hall. The New York stratigraphic section, therefore, as then subdivided had approximately the following equivalents:

New York System	
Erie Division	Devonian
Ontario Division	Silurian
Champlain Division	Ordovician, plus
Taconic System	Cambrian, plus

Schuchert used Champlainian for Ordovician in his textbooks and other writings for many years because he contended that this name has priority and is preferable. Some other geologists followed his example temporarily but this usage is no longer recognized.

Comanchean. Hill designated Lower Cretaceous rocks as the Comanche Series in 1887, and Chamberlin and Salisbury elevated this series to the rank of system in 1906 thus restricting the Cretaceous to the Gulf Series of Hill. This system achieved scant recognition, and Comanchean is now used for the American Lower Cretaceous Series.

Dyas. In Germany the Permian consists of two parts, the Zechstein, equivalent to the Magnesian Limestone of England, and the Rotliegende red beds. Dyas, like Triassic, refers to the composition of the system. It has been little used for many years.

Diluvium. This is an old term for the Pleistocene in contrast to the Recent deposits formerly termed Alluvium.

Dinantian. This is the Lower Carboniferous, particularly of Belgium, and it is approximately equivalent to the American Mississippian. No corresponding name has been proposed for the Upper Carboniferous. Europeans generally do not consider the Dinantian to be a system, but the name has been used for a Lower Carboniferous system in Asia.

Epiric. Sherwood questioned the validity of a Permian System. He contended that the Lower and Middle Permian should be added to the Carboniferous and that the Upper Permian should be combined with the Triassic to form a new system. In 1928 he proposed the name Epiric System for the latter.

Eogene. This name, meaning "dawn born," includes the Eocene and Oligocene and is the Lower Tertiary. Some geologists consider it the earlier one of two Tertiary systems. The term Eocene was used long ago with nearly the same meaning.

Gotlandian. In Europe, this name has been used in place of Silurian in its modern or restricted sense. Some geologists have considered Ordovician and Gotlandian to be subdivisions of the old Silurian rather than independent systems.

Lipalian. Walcott introduced this name for a theoretical system of Precambrian marine strata that has not been discovered in any part of the world. He believed that all observed late Precambrian strata are non-marine and that, if their marine equivalents could be found, they would contain the fossilized ancestors of Cambrian faunas. The term also has been applied to the time represented by the sub-Cambrian unconformity, but this appears to be a misuse of the name because Cambrian beds in several regions probably overlie unfossiliferous strata that may be of Lipalian age.

Neogene. This is the complement to Eogene. It means "new born" and includes the Miocene and Pliocene. Some geologists consider it to be the upper system of the Tertiary. It also has been termed Neocene.

Nummulitic. This name, suggested by the large discoidal foraminifera abundant in early Tertiary limestones of the Tethys region, has been used in Europe in place of Eocene.

Ontarian. Emmons originally proposed this name in 1842 for what is now the Middle and Upper Ordovician. In 1890 Dana employed it for the Upper Silurian of Murchison and at the same time restricted the use of Silurian to what is now the Ordovician. This name has only historical interest.

Ozarkian. Ulrich introduced this name in 1911 for what was supposed to include part of the Upper Cambrian and part of the Lower Ordovician of ordinary usage. It was based on paleontology and is now impossible to define because of complex correlations some of which were not well founded. As recognized by Ulrich and his followers it had different stratigraphic limits in different areas. The introduction of this system accomplished nothing but confusion.

Paleocene. This name, meaning "ancient new," was proposed by Schimper in 1874 for the earliest Tertiary. It was based on paleobotanic distinctions. The Paleocene is recognized by some geologists as either a series or a system comparable to the other divisions of the Tertiary, but others consider these strata to be no more than Lower Eocene.

Paleogene. This name, meaning "ancient born," is a synonym of Eogene.

Permo-Carboniferous. The Permian System has always been a troublesome one and its boundaries are uncertain or controversial in many parts of the world. The term Permo-Carboniferous has been used in many areas for strata whose assignment to the Carboniferous or Permian is uncertain.

Permo-Triassic. This term, like the last, has been commonly employed for strata occurring where the Permian-Triassic boundary is believed to lie in the midst of an unfossiliferous red beds succession.

Rhaetic. This name has been used by some geologists in a systemic sense for strata supposed to be transitional between the Triassic and Jurassic systems.

Sinian. This is a Precambrian system in China that has generally been included in the Paleozoic because its strata appear to pass upward into the Cambrian without stratigraphic disconformity. Commonly the base of the Cambrian is drawn just below the first appearance of the *Olenellus* fauna. Some geologists contend that in the absence of a stratigraphic break it is unrealistic to exclude underlying unfossiliferous strata from the Cambrian, and they would lower the Cambrian boundary to include strata comparable to the Sinian.

Subcarboniferous. In many respects the stratigraphic successions of England and the eastern United States are similar and English names were used in the early days by many American geologists. In America three subdivisions of the Carboniferous identical to those of England were recognized. In 1852 Owen restricted use of Carboniferous to the so-called Millstone Grit and Coal Measures and introduced the name Subcarboniferous for underlying strata that in the Mississippi and lower Ohio valleys include no coal beds. The Subcarboniferous is equivalent to the present Mississippian System.

Tennesseean. In 1911 Ulrich divided the Mississippian into two systems, this being the upper one. It corresponds to strata commonly considered to be Upper Mississippian.

Waverlian. This is the lower of Ulrich's Mississippian systems. Similar division of the Mississippian has been recognized by others but the parts are not considered to be systems.

This list could be expanded greatly but few other comparable names are of much interest to American geologists.

PRECAMBRIAN SUBDIVISIONS

The problem of subdivision of Precambrian rocks into systems is much more difficult and the results are much less satisfactory because fossils are absent and correlations between different Precambrian areas are very uncertain.

Reliance in correlation has been placed mainly on lithology, structure, and different degrees of metamorphism. Similarities and differences of these types, however, cannot be depended upon for age determinations, and some geologists maintain that no subdivision of the Precambrian into systems is justified. Certain igneous and metamorphic rocks that were formerly classed as Primary have been discovered to be much younger. For example, some of the original Primary rocks of Italy are Cretaceous, and even rocks of Cenozoic age were identified as Primary at some places.

In 1863 Sir William Logan described two Precambrian systems in eastern Canada. The younger one consisting of schist and phyllite was named Huronian and mistakenly identified as Cambrian. The older, or Laurentian system, was composed of gneissic granite. Later studies showed that the Precambrian is much more complex. It is now known to consist of several great sequences of sediments, each of which in turn was more or less metamorphosed and granitized.

Van Hise described two Precambrian systems in the Lake Superior region in 1892. The older is the Archean, which is so highly metamorphosed that it is entirely crystalline. This name was originally proposed by Dana in 1872 and applied by him to the entire Precambrian. Van Hise's younger system is the Algonkian, previously named by Walcott in 1889. It consists mainly of less metamorphosed detrital sediments and lava flows. These divisions are now generally considered to represent eras rather than periods and they are commonly termed Archeozoic and Proterozoic respectively. The United States Geological Survey does not recognize Archeozoic, however, and refers all Precambrian rocks to the Proterozoic. In its restricted sense, the Proterozoic consists of two parts commonly considered to be systems. The lower is the Huronian and the upper was named Keweenawan by Brooks in 1876. The Archeozoic generally is not subdivided into systems, and some geologists refer all of its rocks to the Kewatinian System named by Lawson in 1885. Others, however, distinguish a younger system above the Kewatinian for which Miller proposed the name Tamiskamian in 1911.

The foregoing classification is applicable only to the Lake Superior district in the United States and the adjacent part of Canada. Reliable correlations with other parts of the world have not yet been made. Precambrian systems do not have the universal applicability that the younger systems are supposed to possess.

ERA NAMES

Sedgwick introduced the name Palaeozoic (spelled Paleozoic in America) in 1838 for all of the rocks included in the Cambrian and Silurian systems up to the base of the Old Red Sandstone and proposed the name Protozoic for all underlying rocks. These mean "ancient life" and "first life" respectively.

In 1845 Murchison applied the name Azoic, meaning "without life," to the unfossiliferous pre-Paleozoic rocks.

In 1840 Phillips expanded the application of Palaeozoic by including strata up through at least the Carboniferous System. He also introduced the names Mesozoic and Cenozoic (=Kainozoic, Cainozoic), meaning "middle life" and "recent life," with approximately their modern limits.

The three terms Paleozoic, Mesozoic, and Cenozoic have remained in use essentially unchanged up to the present time. Theoretical considerations and disagreements regarding the appropriateness of *zoic* or life terms for Precambrian rocks, however, have resulted in the proposal of a great variety of comparable names such as Agnotozoic, Azoic, Eozoic, Hypozoic, and Prozoic. The only ones now deserving consideration are the following:

Archeozoic, introduced by Dana in 1872, means "primitive life." At first it included all Precambrian rocks but later it was restricted to the older of two great Precambrian successions. The United States Geological Survey does not recognize Archeozoic.

Proterozoic, meaning "earlier life," was first used by Emmons in 1888 for all rocks intervening between the Archean and the Paleozoic. Some geologists have applied it to all Precambrian rocks and this is the sense in which it is recognized by the United States Geological Survey. This is a different name from Sedgwick's Protozoic, which has not been used for many years.

Only one other era name is worthy of notice. This is Psychozoic, meaning "reasoning life," introduced by LeConte in 1877. It was defined as the age of man's supremacy, equivalent to the post-Pleistocene or Recent. The egocentric idea that this name implies is totally unjustified and it received little recognition.

EON NAMES

The base of the Cambrian System, below which only very rare and obscure fossils have been discovered, provides a base line from which all geologic events are reckoned either forward or backward. The old unfossiliferous rocks are generally referred to as Precambrian, but the comparable term Postproterozoic has been little used for younger rocks. In 1930 Chadwick proposed the names Cryptozoic, "hidden life," and Phanerozoic, "evident life," for these two grand divisions. Neither of them has been much used.

BIBLIOGRAPHY

Evans, J. W., and Stubblefield, C. J. (eds.) (1929), *Handbook of the geology of Great Britain, a compilative work*, London, Thomas Murby.

This condensed but comprehensive description is devoted largely to stratigraphy.

Gill, J. E. (ed.) (1957), The Proterozoic in Canada, Roy. Soc. Can., Spec. Publ. 2.

A symposium of twenty-five short papers deals with the Precambrian and its problems of identification and correlation.

Leith, C. K. (1934), The pre-Cambrian, Geol. Soc. Amer., Proc. 1933, pp. 151–180.

The Precambrian and later geologic records are compared in regard to life, conditions of sedimentation, and means of correlation.

Snyder, F. G. (1947), The problem of the Lipalian interval, *J. Geol.*, vol. 55, pp. 146–152.

The problem of recognizing a base of the Cambrian System is considered.

Wheeler, H. E. (1947), Base of the Cambrian System, *J. Geol.*, vol. 55, pp. 153–159.

The author advocates placing the base of the Cambrian System below the first appearance of the *Olenellus* fauna.

Wilmarth, M. G. (1925), The geological time classification of the United States Geological Survey compared with other classifications, U.S. Geol. Surv., Bull. 769.

Extensive quotations are drawn from the more important publications defining and redefining the major geologic time terms.

Wilson, M. E. (1958), Precambrian classification and correlation in the Canadian shield, *Bull. Geol. Soc. Amer.*, vol. 69, pp. 757–774.

Twofold division is suggested because only one widespread unconformity has been recognized within the Precambrian.

Part II

MATERIALS OF STRATIGRAPHY

The nature of a complex substance or object cannot be appreciated adequately without a prior understanding of its components. Stratified rocks consist of sediments. Therefore a study of these rocks must begin with a consideration of the sediments. Most sedimentology has stressed the physical aspects of deposition, but deposition is only a part of the history of these materials. Every sediment had an origin and was transported and then deposited, and many sediments were lithified to produce consolidated rock. All of these processes are important for an understanding of stratigraphy.

The organic aspects of sedimentation generally have been neglected. These aspects are fundamentally important because organisms produced much sediment and influenced the nature of much more. Organisms preserved as fossils also furnish information concerning sedimentary processes and conditions that are not revealed by any other characters of the rocks.

All aspects of sedimentation have been more or less controlled by tectonism. Therefore, sediments and the resulting rocks cannot be completely understood outside of the tectonic framework that was largely responsible for their development and present nature.

Finally, the interpretation of sedimentary rocks and the reconstruction of their histories provide much of the information upon which the synthesis of geologic knowledge in stratigraphy is based.

4

Classification and Composition
of Sediments and Rocks

STRATIGRAPHERS and sedimentary petrologists observe the same rocks and sediments but they see them from somewhat different points of view. Stratigraphers are interested mainly in rock masses; their attention is devoted largely to observing gross characters, structures, and relations in the field. Sedimentary petrologists are much more concerned with details; mainly they study those features that require laboratory observations. Insofar as the descriptive phases are concerned, stratigraphy and sedimentary petrology are separate branches of geology.

When explanations of observed characters and relations of rocks and sediments are sought and interpretations are attempted, however, much community of interest becomes apparent. In the broader definitions of these fields, therefore, stratigraphy and sedimentary petrology overlap. Much benefit is to be gained from close coöperation by workers in these fields, and satisfactory solutions to many problems cannot be obtained by either type of study unsupplemented by the other. Stratigraphy particularly stands to gain by coöperative action because petrologic studies are likely to be valuable in confirming or denying conclusions based on more general stratigraphic observations. Such studies also may suggest other explanations and direct attention to features previously overlooked or neglected because their significance was not appreciated. On the other hand, the results of petrologic studies may gain greater meaning than they would otherwise possess by orientation in the more general stratigraphic picture.

Stratigraphic Observations

Stratigraphy is vitally concerned with the space relationships of rocks. In order that these may be determined, the characters of stratigraphic bodies must be observed, the same rocks recognized from place to place, and different rocks discriminated. The major objective of any study determines, of course, the detail with which observations should be made. Some studies will progress much more rapidly than others. Requirements may be satisfied by observing outcrops at more or less wide intervals and noting only their more generalized features. On the other hand, it may be necessary to locate and observe all outcrops and to measure and describe all stratigraphic sections in great detail. Also depending upon circumstances, more or less attention is devoted to subsurface records. With increasing thoroughness in the detail with which outcropping rocks and well cuttings and cores are examined, conventional stratigraphic studies pass over imperceptibly into the fields of petrology and paleontology.

A large part of a stratigrapher's time and energy commonly is expended in searching for good outcrops. An important measure of his competence is the speed with which he can find outcrops, cover territory, and collect all of the information necessary for the particular type of study that is in progress. He cannot allow himself to become distracted by unnecessary details. The cutoff point defining the practical limits of necessary details rarely can be anticipated for a new study. It generally is set initially on the basis of experience and judgment of probable requirements and is subject to later modification. During all stages of a study, however, an alert stratigrapher will make mental note of many incidentally observed features any of which may unexpectedly prove to be pertinent to his study and require more thorough investigation.

The observation of certain characters of rocks is standard practice in all types of stratigraphic studies. Those characters most commonly noted are all more or less obvious on rather casual inspection. They are useful primarily in the identification of stratigraphic units and in the drawing up of their generalized descriptions. The principle ones are:

1. General lithologic character in terms of the common rock types such as sandstone, shale, and limestone or transitional varieties such as shaly sandstone or calcareous shale. Mixtures and interbedding of different types of rock are noted.

2. Color in common terms such as light gray, brown, or greenish; also interbedding or mottling of different colors.

3. Types of bedding such as thin bedded, cross bedded, wavy bedded, and so forth.

4. Textural features such as fineness of grain, sorting of sand, and crystallinity of limestone.

5. Structural features such as massiveness of beds, presence of ripple marks, and concretions.

6. Weathering characters such as color alteration, type of surface forms developed, and degree of leaching.

7. Abundance and kinds of fossils.

8. Estimated thicknesses of stratigraphic units.

Descriptions of rocks in the foregoing terms are extremely superficial but they may be adequate for some types of uncritical stratigraphic work. Even so, such descriptions provide some general indications of rock genesis. Most of these features, however, deserve much more careful observation. As they are noted in more detail, they become increasingly more useful in their application to correlation, interpretation, and reconstruction of past conditions and events.

CLASSIFICATION OF ROCKS

Rocks are so variable in appearance, composition, and mode of origin that any comprehensive and systematic classification is bound to be arbitrary and complex. Petrologists who study rocks in detail have proposed a great multitude of names for them based on mineralogic composition, texture, genesis, type localities, and so forth. Mostly their classifications and names are un-

TABLE 2.   Classification of Rocks as Commonly Recognized by Stratigraphers in the Field

Igneous Rocks	Sedimentary Rocks	Metamorphic Rocks

Intrusive
  Of little direct concern in stratigraphy
Extrusive
  Lava flows
    Basalt
    Rhyolite
  Pyroclastic
    Volcanic agglomerate
    Volcanic ash, tuff
	Water-laid
	  Common types
	    Conglomerate, breccia
	    Sandstone
	    Siltstone
	    Shale, mudstone, clay
	    Limestone, dolomite
	  Special types
	    Coal
	    Bedded chert
	    Gypsum, anhydrite
	    Rock salt
	    Rock phosphate
	    Sedimentary iron ore
	Eolian
	  Dune sand, sandstone
	  Loess
	Glacial
	  Till, tillite
		Of concern in stratigraphy only insofar as their original sedimentary characters can be determined

suited to general stratigraphic use because stratigraphers must observe and identify various rock types in the field. Consequently stratigraphers generally employ a comparatively small number of common names modified by adjectives where appropriate. Most of these can be classified as shown in Table 2.

The vast majority of all rocks dealt with by stratigraphers are the common water-laid types. The others indicate special conditions and they may be particularly important in identifying depositional environments and in reconstructing geologic history.

The common sedimentary rocks are divisible into two classes: (1) land-derived detritals and (2) limestones. Petrographers are inclined to identify many limestones as clastic rocks. With rare exceptions, however, limestones do not consist of material that was derived from the land as solid particles, as were the constituents of other clastic rocks. This is an extremely important distinction because the distribution of other clastic rocks is closely related to land areas, but the distribution of limestone generally is not. To emphasize this distinction, the term *detrital* will be used for particulate sediments produced directly by erosion of the land and the term *fragmental* for clastic limestones consisting of particles that possibly have been moved from the sites of their origin and redeposited.

Detrital Series

The detrital rocks constitute a continuous series ranging in grain size from very coarse to very fine. The names applied to the various members of this series are determined in a general way by grain size. Table 3 shows the classification according to the Wentworth scale.

TABLE 3.   Classification of Detrital Sediments
and Sedimentary Rocks According to the
Wentworth Size Scale

Grain Size (in mm.)	Sediment	Rock
Greater than 256	Boulders ⎫	
64–256	Cobbles ⎬	Conglomerate
4–64	Pebbles ⎭	
2–4	Granules	Grit
1/16–2	Sand	Sandstone
1/256–1/16	Silt	Siltstone
Less than 1/256	Clay	Shale

Field names actually applied to the fine-grained detrital rocks do not necessarily follow this classification closely because accurate estimates of grain size and the proportions of constituents cannot be made without laboratory measurements. For example, many field geologists do not recognize siltstone but distinguish sandstone and shale, connected by intermediate types commonly termed "shaly sandstone" and "sandy shale," mainly on the basis of the absence or presence and degree of development of the thin lamination which is commonly considered a characteristic feature of shale. Many so-called sandstones and so-called shales consist predominantly of silt-sized grains. In field practice, therefore, sandstones and shales are inexactly identified on the basis of textural or structural features. In a practical test, the grittiness of sand can be detected by rubbing between the fingers and the grittiness of silt by gently rubbing between the teeth.

Rocks obviously too fine grained to be considered sandstone but lacking the lamination of shale may be termed *mudstones*. They generally contain much silt. Fine-grained materials lacking bedding and possessing some plasticity are commonly known as *clays*. They are likely to contain less silt and may be entirely silt-free.

Detrital Constituents

The principal constituents of detrital rocks may be classified as follows:

Primary Materials	Secondary Cement
Rock fragments	Silica
Mineral grains	Calcite
First cycle	
Reworked	
Clay minerals	

The three primary constituents of detrital rocks generally are concentrated in different sedimentary size fractions (see Figure 9). Pebbles and larger masses are almost exclusively multigranular rock fragments. Sand may consist of mixtures of discrete mineral grains and rock fragments although the former are likely to predominate and the latter may be wholly lacking. Silt is composed almost exclusively of mineral grains. The clay minerals occur only in the finest-grained sedimentary fraction.

Secondary cement is mineral matter deposited in the interstices between primary sedimentary particles. Both silica and calcite are common. Both may occur in the same rock although they demand different chemical conditions for their deposition and, therefore, record different episodes of diagenesis. Silica generally is the more common cementing mineral in the coarser sands; it is rare in fine sands and silts which include important proportions of clay minerals. Some fine sands are cemented with calcite that is uniformly oriented crystallographically throughout comparatively large areas. Ferruginous calcite and siderite may constitute the cementing material particularly in fine-grained detrital sediments.

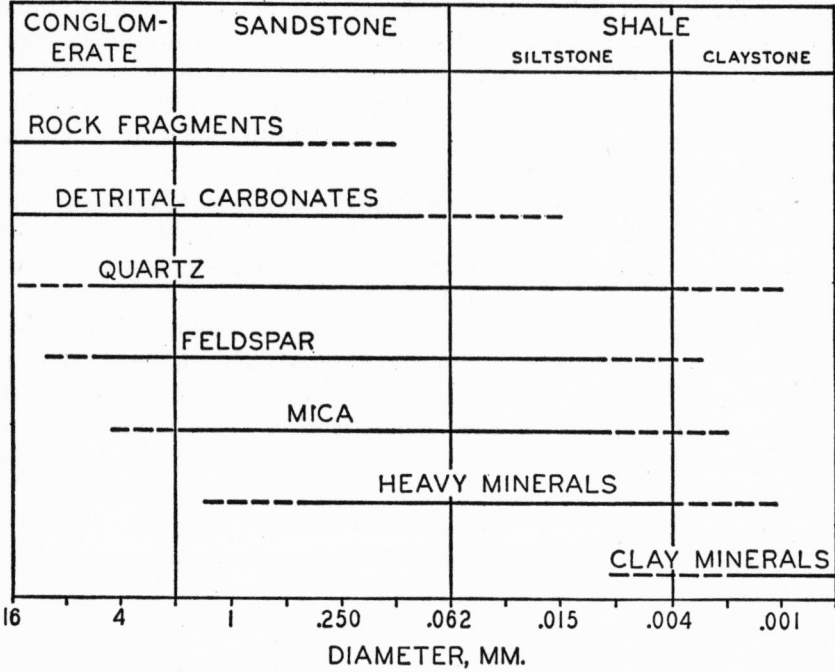

Figure 9.   Chart showing the common size range limits of different kinds of sedimentary particles. Notice that generally there is little overlap in the sizes of clay minerals and other mineral grains. (Adapted from *Stratigraphy and sedimentation* by W. C. Krumbein and L. L. Sloss, p. 103, fig. 4–15. San Francisco: W. H. Freeman and Company, 1951.)

Clay

Note should be made that the term *clay* is used in three quite different ways:

1. In its general nontechnical sense, clay is fine-grained sediment or rock that is characterized by being plastic when wet.

2. In its sedimentologic sense, clay is that fraction of a sediment or rock whose grains measure less than $\frac{1}{256}$ mm. in diameter. The material clay (sense 1) may contain variable proportions, ranging from none to more than half, of grains larger than clay size.

3. In its mineralogic sense, clay is the general name for minerals of several types of hydrous aluminum silicates, although other elements can substitute for some of the aluminum. They posssess more or less mica-like structure, occur in a very finely divided crystalline state, and generally are highly adsorptive. The clay-sized fraction of a sediment or rock may contain variable proportions, ranging from none to more than half, of non-clay minerals. The plasticity of material clay (sense 1) is due to the presence of clay minerals.

Shale

Shale generally is identified on the basis of its bedding, which is more or less closely spaced and even and provides planes of weakness along which the rock parts readily. The fine bedding or lamination of shale is a feature that is related to the presence of clay mineral particles even though other kinds of sediment may predominate. Either the clay occurs more or less concentrated in films that result in the parting of less clayey material in thin layers or, if more generally distributed through the sediment, horizontal orientation of the flaky clay minerals produces a type of fissility that is difficult to distinguish from true bedding.

Shales are the most variable of all sedimentary rocks. Sand, silt, lime, and organic material occur in various proportions with clay to form shales that differ widely in texture, type of bedding, hardness, and color. Argillaceous shales without impurities of these kinds are not common. Many shales are intermediate in composition between the other main types of sedimentary rocks and thus they grade into sandstone through sandy shale, into limestone through calcareous shale, and even into coal through carbonaceous shale. Organic material occurs more generally and more abundantly in shale or other clayey sediments than in any other common kind of rock. Also shale or other clayey material varies through a wider range of colors than other sedimentary rocks and is more likely than any other common kind to be greenish, red, or dark gray to black. Many shales include concretions.

Shales can be classified in many different ways as, for example, on the basis of (1) mineralogy, (2) texture, (3) color, (4) chemical composition, (5) structures, or (6) fossils. Although there are some relationships between these different kinds of characters, mostly they are independent variables. No single classification seems preferable to others, and different classifications may be constructed to suit different purposes. Efforts have been made to relate the physical and mineralogic characters of shales to environmental influences, but the results do not seem to have been particularly successful.

Sandstone

Most sandstones consist predominantly of quartz grains, but feldspar, rock fragments, chert, and clayey matrix are abundant in some varieties. A considerable number of other minerals that are resistant to weathering and abrasion also occur as minor accessory constituents (see Figure 10). These rarely exceed 1 percent and generally amount to less than $\frac{1}{10}$ percent of the rock. Because most of them have specific gravities greater than that of quartz, they are commonly termed *heavy minerals*. Finally, white mica in conspicuous thin flakes is present, particularly in some fine-grained sandstones and siltstones. Much of it probably is a secondary mineral that has been produced by the alteration and recrystallization of some of the clay minerals.

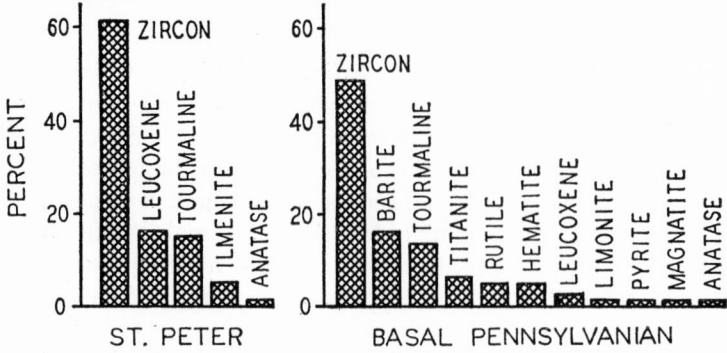

Figure 10. Histograms showing the variety and relative abundance of heavy minerals in the St. Peter Sandstone (Ord.) and basal Pennsylvanian sandstone in Wisconsin and Illinois respectively. If these rocks were not distinguishable by more obvious characters, sedimentary analysis would easily differentiate them. Generally a smaller variety of heavy minerals occurs in older than in younger sandstones. (After *Stratigraphy and sedimentation* by W. C. Krumbein and L. L. Sloss, p. 111, fig. 4–16. San Francisco: W. H. Freeman and Company, 1951.)

Four types of sandstone defined by their composition commonly are recognized, as shown in Figure 11. These are:

1. *Quartz sandstone*, which consists predominantly of quartz grains.

2. *Arkose*, which contains an appreciable amount of feldspar, mainly potassic, and very little clay. It generally is light gray to pink or even reddish owing to the presence of orthoclase. It is a product of the decomposition of granitic rocks.

3. *Graywacke*, which includes important proportions of clayey material and rock fragments in addition to quartz and sodic feldspar. It is commonly dark colored and appears to have been produced by the erosion of metamorphic and basic igneous rocks. The name *graywacke* has been used in so many ways by petrographers and others, however, that much confusion has resulted. It was originally employed to identify dark-colored, tough, impure, clayey sandstone and it still carries this general meaning.

4. *Subgraywacke*, which differs from graywacke in having a smaller proportion of clay matrix and generally greater porosity, and from arkose in containing more rock fragments. These rocks are intermediate between quartz sandstones and graywackes or arkoses. They are the most common kind of sandstone and it is unfortunate that a more distinctive name is not available for them.

The important differences between these types of sandstone are related to (1) the kinds of rock from which they were derived, (2) the amount of weathering that has contributed to the relative maturity of the sediment,

(3) the degree of sorting that they have undergone, (4) the rapidity of their deposition, and (5) the site of deposition. Thus arkose and graywacke had different origins. Both consist of immature sediments that were very little weathered. Both were rapidly deposited near the place where they originated. Most arkose appears to have accumulated under subaerial or shallow marine conditions whereas much graywacke probably was deposited in deeper ma-

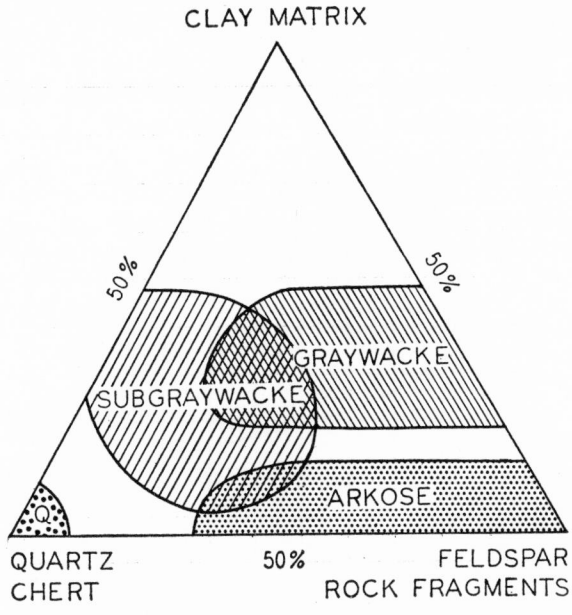

Figure 11. Three-component triangle showing the characteristic compositions of the four principal kinds of sandstone. In the overlapping areas subgraywacke contains more feldspar and fewer rock fragments than graywacke and more rock fragments and less feldspar than arkose. (Data from Pettijohn, 1957, *Sedimentary rocks.*)

rine water. Subgraywacke is less immature, generally of mixed origins, and better sorted during transportation or at the time of deposition; it accumulated under a wide variety of fluvial or shallow-water conditions farther from its site or origin.

Quartz sandstone is mature. It generally had a long history as a sediment but little of its history can be determined. Most sandstones of this type are marine and many were deposited in a transgressing sea. Both subgraywacke and quartz sandstone, but particularly the latter, probably consist of material that passed through more than one cycle of erosion, transportation, and deposition.

Conglomerate

Conglomerates are consolidated gravels. They vary in composition with respect to size, shape, and the kinds of rock constituting the coarser fractions and also the type of matrix. Most conglomerates consist of very poorly sorted material which may range from boulders to the finest sediment. They accumulated in many different situations; gravel ordinarily does not clearly indicate any particular environment.

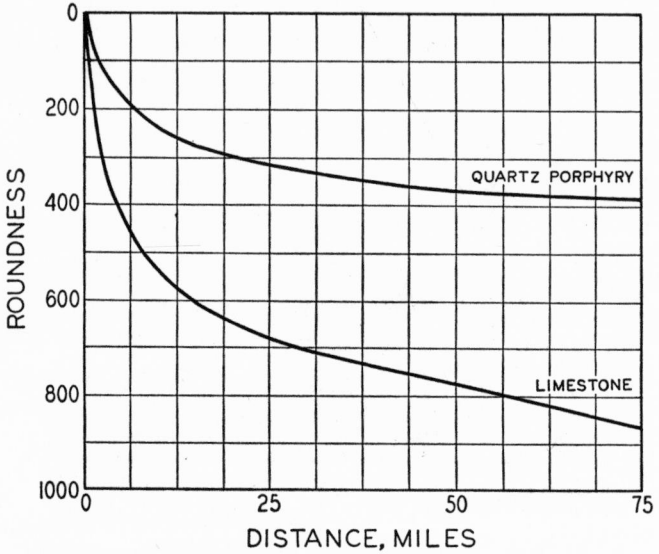

Figure 12.   Curves illustrating the rather obvious fact that resistant rock fragments are worn and rounded more slowly than easily abraded ones. (Modified from Kuenen, 1956, *J. Geol.*, vol. 64, p. 361, fig. 21.)

Gravels are of two general types: (1) depositional gravels that result from the accumulation of transported coarse material and (2) lag gravels, produced by the action of water or wind which removes fine sediment and leaves the coarser material behind to be concentrated on the surface. The first type indicates the slackening of currents strong enough to move the largest rock fragments. The second records the action of currents incapable of transporting the coarser fraction of an original deposit. Most conglomerates are of the first type, but in ancient deposits distinction is likely to be difficult if not impossible. So-called *pseudoconglomerate* is produced by various kinds of shearing action that fragments rocks and may even round the fragments, or it consists of concretionary aggregates that may resemble some conglomerates closely.

Rounding of the pebbles, cobbles, and boulders of gravel or conglomerate generally is dependent upon (1) the hardness and toughness of the rock fragments and (2) the distance they have traveled (see Figure 12). Exceptions are gravelly material deposited directly from glacial ice and the deposits of mud flows and turbidity currents. Although rounded pebbles have been cited as characteristic of stream gravel and flat pebbles have been considered indicative of beaches, such distinctions do not appear to be reliable. Pebble shapes are much more likely to be determined by the relative dimensions of the original angular rock fragments and their dominant planes of weakness. Beach pebbles are moved back and forth repeatedly by waves and may become well rounded without much actual transportation. Like sand, gravel may be a second or multiple-cycle deposit and rounding may be related to episodes antedating its final movement and deposition.

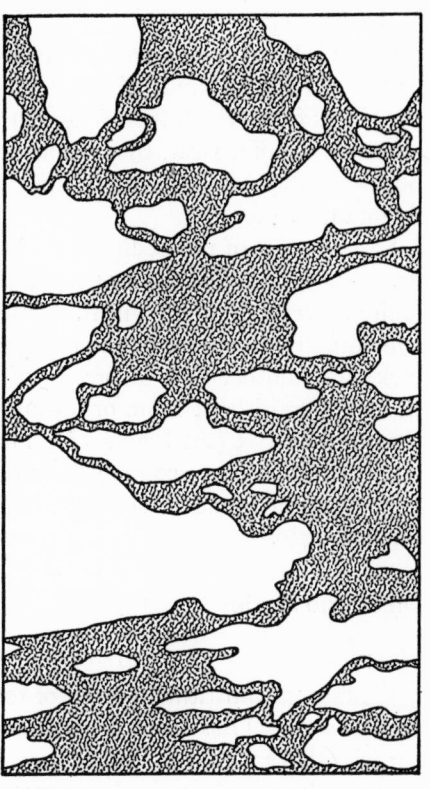

Figure 13. Polished core section showing irregular lighter-colored, more calcareous nodule-like masses in darker, less calcareous matrix. The origin of these masses is conjectural. They may have been produced by the burrowing of animals in unconsolidated sediment (see Figure 77, p. 233). This particular rock, however, is wholly lacking in recognizable fossils. Compare also with Figure 40, p. 115. Lower part of Ireton Formation (U. Dev.) of Alberta, Canada. (Drawn natural size from photograph by R. G. McCrossan.)

The source rocks generally are more easily identified for gravel than for finer sediment. Environments of deposition, however, are more clearly indicated by the form of bodies of conglomeratic rocks and the characters of fine-grained matrix and associated sediments than by the kind of rock fragments and their shapes. Thus linear bodies are characteristic of stream channel, beach, and bar deposits, whereas shallow neritic gravel is likely to be patchy and thin, and alluvial fan deposits may cover considerable areas and accumulate to great thickness. Distinction may be possible between current-laid and wave-worked gravel because the latter is likely to be washed free of mud and silt.

Breccia is a rock consisting of angular fragments of pebble and larger sizes. Commonly this term carries implications of tectonic origin, and one of the most familiar types of breccia is that produced by fracturing in the planes of faults. Some breccias, however, are sedimentary as, for example, those which occur in talus deposits, and others are of pyroclastic origin. These may be considered special kinds of conglomerate that have accumulated very near the places from which their fragments were derived. If they should be transported and suffer wear, they would grade into more typical conglomerates. Such transition would be most rapid, of course, if the fragments were of easily abraded kinds.

Several types of non-sedimentary breccias may be confusing because their occurrences resemble those of stratified deposits. Chief among these are mylonite breccias developed in the planes of low-angle thrust faults, and collapse breccias produced by the removal of soluble layers such as gypsum and rock salt. Another type of breccia of doubtful origin occurs in many limestones. It consists of more or less angular limestone fragments enclosed in limestone matrix (see Figure 13). This may record a brief interval of emergence in which limy sediment became consolidated and was broken up but not moved or rounded. It might be considered a kind of intraformational conglomerate.

Limestone Series

Limestone

Limestones constitute a series of rocks that in some respects parallels the detrital series. Thus most limestones consist of fragmental or precipitated particles that range from coarse to very fine. The various types of limestone, however, have not received common names probably because their differences generally are not apparent on casual observation. Also many limestones are more or less recrystallized or otherwise altered so that original textures may not be preserved. In a very general way, however, some comparison between detrital rocks and limestones can be made (see Table 4) although

TABLE 4.   Comparison of Limestones According to Texture
with Rocks of the Detrital Series

Detrital Series	Limestone Series	
	Descriptive Name	Technical Name
Conglomerate	Conglomeratic limestone ⎫	
Grit	⎧ Fragmental limestone ⎬	Calcirudite
	⎩ Coarsely crystalline limestone ⎭	
Sandstone	⎧ Crystalline limestone ⎫	Calcarenite
	⎩ Finely crystalline limestone ⎭	
Siltstone	Fine-grained limestone	Calcisiltite
Clay	Lithographic limestone	Calcilutite

the grain size of a limestone does not necessarily indicate its original texture.

Limestone pebbles and cobbles are common in some conglomerates. Limestone fragments of these sizes generally are enclosed in a matrix of detrital materials. If limestone predominates in these coarser size ranges, the rock is properly called a limestone conglomerate. If the matrix is limestone, the rock is a conglomeratic limestone regardless of the composition of the coarser fragments. The latter, however, are commonly also limestone and generally they do not exceed pebble size.

Calcareous sand or finer sediment is not a normal product of terrestrial erosion. The abrasion of large limestone fragments in stream beds and upon beaches probably produces small particles that are soon dissolved and disappear. Almost all lime sand consists of broken shells and other organic debris on beaches or in very shallow strongly wave-agitated water in situations where detrital material is not present in important quantities. Probably the limestone pebbles of most conglomeratic limestones are of local origin. Lime mud is predominantly a biochemical deposit produced by algae and perhaps bacteria. So far as is known, inorganic limestone is rare. Oolites are believed to be inorganic, and some peculiar limestones like the Minnekahta (Perm.) of the Black Hills and similar strata in Wyoming, which occur in the midst of red beds, may be very fine-grained chemical precipitates.

Limestones are fundamentally different from detrital rocks because lime is carried in solution, and waves and currents strong enough to keep particulate matter in suspension are not necessary for its distribution. Calcium carbonate is uniformly present dissolved in ocean water and can be carried unlimited distances. At present, lime deposition is restricted mainly to the warmer water regions of the tropical and subtropical zones. Similar temperature relations probably also were characteristic of much of its deposition in the past. Some lime deposits in deeper and colder water, however, are produced by corals and other organisms but their distribution is patchy. Deep-sea calcareous deposits, such as *Globigerina* ooze, accumulate very slowly; no ancient deep-sea sediments of this type are certainly known to occur in the present continental areas of the world.

Limestones also differ significantly from detrital rocks because they react differently to diagenic processes. Thus limestones generally have not been compacted greatly under the load of overburden by the simple closer crowding of their particles and the progressive reduction of pore space (see Figure 124, p. 311). Most limestones, however, are essentially lacking in the primary porosity of the original sediment even though adjacent sandstones and shales remain highly porous. Their common dense structure has resulted from the tight cementation of calcite grains by calcite introduced in solution, or by the alteration and consolidation of aragonite mud to form fine-grained calcite. Parts of some fragmental or oolitic limestones like the Salem (Miss.) of Indiana, however, appear to have escaped cementation and they have remained porous. Such limestones occur both as bedded deposits and as reef masses. Others have acquired secondary porosity as the result of partial solution by circulating ground water (see Figure 121, p. 308).

Calcite is an extremely mobile mineral because of its ready solubility. Recrystallization in limestone is fairly common and original textures may be obscured, altered, or destroyed particularly in dolomites. Fine-grained material is likely to develop coarser crystalline structure either in its entirety or between the larger grains. The origin of very fine-grained limestones is doubtful. Most of them probably are local biochemical precipitates although some may consist of finely comminuted fragments derived from the mechanical breaking down of coarser organic debris. The general undersaturation of calcium carbonate in sea water, except in shallow tropical situations, however, provides good reason to doubt that fine grains or crystals can be transported far without being lost by resolution.

Dolomite

Complete gradation occurs from practically magnesium-free limestone to rock consisting almost exclusively of the mineral dolomite. Calcareous mate-

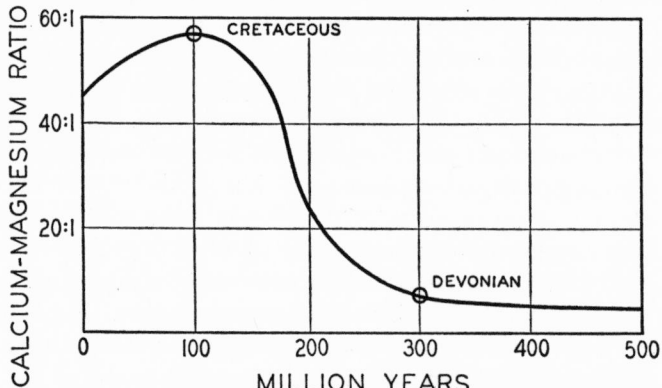

Figure 14.   Curve showing how the relative abundance of dolomite varies with geologic age, based on data by Daly and Chilingar. General observations in the central United States suggest that this curve should rise more sharply at the beginning of the Devonian Period. (After Fairbridge, 1957, Soc. Econ. Paleon. and Miner., Spec. Publ. 5, p. 161, fig. 12.)

rial of organic origin in some comparatively recent sediments may contain 8 percent or more of magnesium. This element originally is held in solid solution in calcite, but the mixture is mineralogically unstable and it is reorganized readily into discrete calcite and dolomite crystals. A higher magnesian content is almost certainly the result of replacement and the progressive appearance and growth of dolomite crystals within limestone. This substitution seems to be accomplished on a volume-for-volume and not a molecular basis. The time of dolomitization is not known with certainty. It probably occurred most commonly soon after the deposition of calcareous sediment, and the magnesium almost certainly was withdrawn from solution in sea water. Some primary dolomitic limestones have been reported but the actual existence of such rocks is doubtful except possibly in association with evaporites. Although dolomites of all geological ages occur, they are much more common and more widely distributed in the Silurian and older systems than in the Devonian and younger ones (see Figure 14).

Mixed Rocks

Many sedimentary rocks consist of variable mixtures of detrital materials and calcium carbonate. Distinction should be made in this class of rocks between those which have calcite only as introduced chemical cement and those which include sedimentary lime particles. The calcium carbonate content of the former type has no significance so far as the early history of the rock is concerned unless it was derived by the solution and redeposition of calcareous material originally present in the sediment. This rarely can be determined. Calcareous cement commonly reflects only conditions that existed during diagenesis. Lime also can accumulate in the soils of semiarid regions where moisture is drawn upward by capillary action and evaporates to form caliche. Sedimentary lime mixed with detrital material, however, provides important information concerning depositional environments.

The proportions of detrital sediment and lime in mixed rocks are difficult to estimate. Impurity is much more apparent in rocks with shaly bedding, resulting from variable mixtures in adjacent layers, than in mixtures that are homogeneous. Chemical analysis or study of insoluble residues may be necessary to determine even the approximate ratio of constituents. In fine-grained dominantly detrital rocks, acid testing generally is required to establish the occurrence of lime. If the acid is diluted, this test fails to detect dolomite.

Leached Strata

Just as calcium carbonate can be introduced into sediments after deposition, so also it can be removed by solution. Leaching is accomplished by the downward movement of ground water and occurs only in a terrestrial environment. It generally is part of the normal weathering process. Leaching is active almost everywhere beneath the present land surface except in the most arid regions, and in many areas it has been in operation for a very long period of time. Similar leaching occurred beneath land surfaces in the geologic past.

Under humid conditions and in well-drained situations, lime is removed by the general ground water circulation. Thus outcropping rock may be leached and only the insoluble residues remain. This is the way most limestones are reduced to residual clay. A very sandy limestone, however, may be altered to material that has all the appearances of an ordinary noncalcareous sandstone. Examples are the Dutch Creek (Dev.) and Rosiclare (Miss.) sandstones of southern Illinois, whose outcrops pass into quite different types of rock in the subsurface. Very argillaceous or silty limestone may be reduced by leaching to a lightweight porous and spongy material which is easily compressed but not broken when struck with a hammer.

In poorly drained situations, particularly in unconsolidated argillaceous material, a *weathering profile* may develop consisting of upper leached zones and a lower zone where lime is concentrated commonly in impure calcareous nodules as shown in Figure 15. Examples are many Pennsylvanian underclays and Pleistocene interglacial soils.

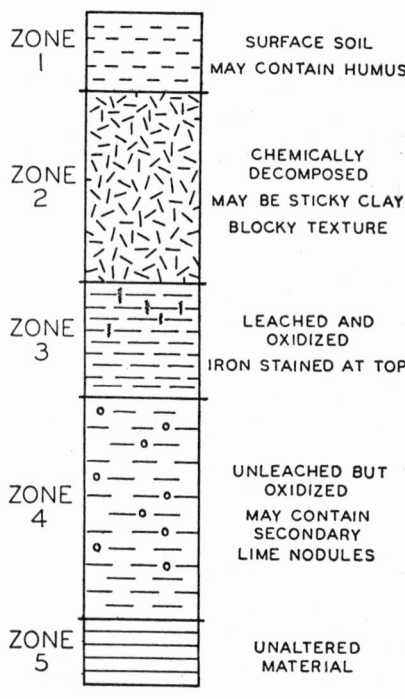

Figure 15. Column showing the characteristic zones of a maturely weathered soil profile. Relative development and thickness of weathered zones depends upon (1) elapsed time of soil formation, (2) situation with respect to drainage, and (3) kind of parent material. Weathering profiles are rarely well preserved in pre-Pleistocene sediments. The underclays beneath Carboniferous coals, however, show zonation very similar to this succession.

Floating Sand Grains

Some limestones, otherwise comparatively pure, contain more or less abundant disseminated or so-called floating grains of quartz sand scattered through them. Similar sand may be present in impure limestone or shale where it is much less conspicuous. Floating quartz grains generally have been accepted as identifying "clastic" limestone under the assumption that quartz sand required waves and currents for its transportation and, therefore, that comparably sized calcite grains were similarly transported. This is almost certainly true for some mixtures of this type. Floating sand is generally in the form of well-rounded and frosted grains of the kind that is commonly interpreted as eolian. There is at least the possibility that quartz in some limestones of this kind was carried to the place where it now occurs by wind.

Carbonaceous and Bituminous Rocks

Organic matter may occur in any kind of sediment. Few newly deposited modern marine sediments contain less than one-half of one percent or more than 10 percent. The range in terrestrial sediments is greater and varies from practically nothing to nearly 100 percent in peat. Large amounts generally are indication of fresh-water marsh conditions. Fine-grained near-shore marine sediments average 2½ percent and open-sea sediments about one percent (see Figure 51, p. 153). Also organic matter generally is two to five times more abundant in fine-grained muds than in sands.

Alteration of Organic Matter

Appreciable amounts of organic matter may be deposited with sediment but under favorable circumstances most of it is consumed as food by animals or undergoes bacterial decay. Normally it is oxidized and transformed into carbon dioxide and water and completely disappears. If the supply of oxygen is limited, methane may be formed. Therefore, much of the organic matter that survives and becomes a constituent of sedimentary rock owes its existence to some interruption of this process, generally accomplished by either (1) sedimentary deposition so rapid that destruction is not completed or (2) the development of anaerobic or toxic conditions that inhibit most organic action.

After decomposition ceases, at a depth of a few feet in most deposits, organic matter remaining in sediments is subject to dynamic action and suffers further alteration. The chemistry of organic matter is so complex and the difficulty of extracting it from sediments and rocks is so great that little is known about its actual composition or the details of its alteration. In a general way, however, organic matter is progressively deoxidized and dehydrated, and compounds richer in carbon or in hydrogen are produced (see Figure 17, p. 67). In some cases this process can continue to the development of graphite or practically pure carbon.

Different types of organic matter fare differently in both organic and dynamic environments and some are considerably more stable and resistant to change than others. Animal tissues that contain much protein decompose more rapidly than vegetable and are less prone to leave a carbonaceous residue. The cellulose of plants cannot be used as food directly by animals but it is readily decomposed by bacteria. It is believed to be almost completely eliminated during the peat stage of the coalification process. Lignin, which makes up about half the dry weight of land plants, is more resistant. Waxes, fats, and resins persist with little change in most sedimentary rocks. Some special degradation products such as fusain also resist further alteration. Most organic matter probably is not transported far from its place of origin without destruction. Resinous particles like spores and also fusain, however, can be carried long distances and occur in all types of sedimentary rock including some otherwise pure limestones.

Coal is the most easily studied organic material associated with sedimentary rocks. It constitutes a series whose members are ranked according to their carbon ratios (proportions of fixed carbon to fixed carbon plus volatile matter as determined by proximate analyses), moisture content, and heating values (see Figure 128, p. 317). Observations show that, in the same sedimentary basin, stratigraphically lower coal beds generally have larger carbon ratios than upper coals. This relation exemplifies Hilt's law, which states that the proportion of fixed carbon varies directly with the depth of burial, and is a reflection of dynamochemical alteration influenced by both increasing pressure of overburden and increasing temperature. Likewise, carbon ratios increase from an area of gentle structure toward an area of pronounced folding as in the Appalachian region (see Figure 16). Finally, they also increase

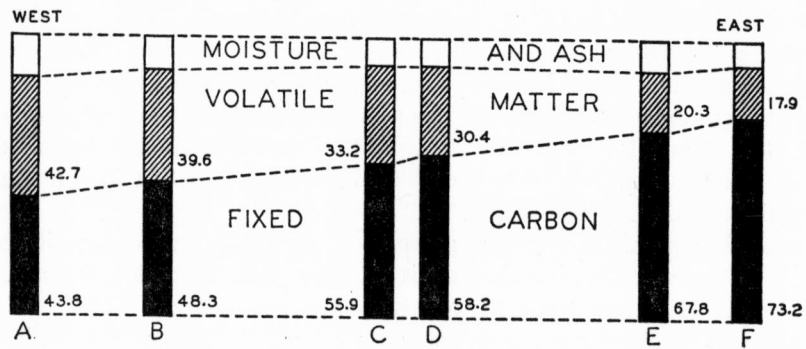

Figure 16. Diagram showing increasing rank of Pittsburgh coal as it is traced for a distance of about 130 miles from a point 25 miles west of Wheeling, West Virginia, to near Cumberland, Maryland. The suggestion has been made that such metamorphism in coal is related to increased structural disturbance, but any connection of this kind also has been vigorously denied. Nevertheless, evidence does exist that pressures greater than those resulting from weight of overburden may develop in structurally disturbed areas and that these pressures have affected coal composition. (After Campbell, 1930, *Econ. Geol.*, vol. 25, p. 681, fig. 1.)

to some extent in older strata. Thus most Paleozoic coals are of at least bituminous rank whereas most Tertiary coals are lignites except near igneous intrusions or in areas highly deformed structurally.

Animal remains deposited with other sediment presumably follow a somewhat similar course. Because they do not occur in accumulations comparable to peat and coal, however, they cannot be studied and analyzed in the same way and the nature of progressive changes is less certain. Also there seems to be good reason to conclude that pressure, temperature, and time act similarly on the more dispersed organic matter that constitutes a minor part of many sedimentary rocks. Obviously there is an important difference between the degradation processes that produce carbonaceous matter like coal—that is, enriched in carbon—and bituminous substances like petroleum. Dynamochemical alteration of the latter does not involve depletion of hydrogen to the same extent as in coal (see Figure 17). Nevertheless, petroleum exhibits a series of comparable changes. Thus oils from older and deeper strata and more structurally disturbed areas are commonly lighter in gravity, more paraffinic in quality, and, therefore, relatively richer in hydrogen.

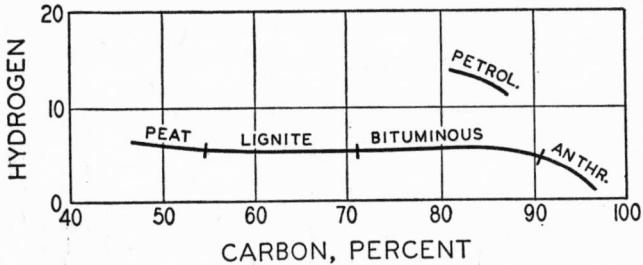

Figure 17. Curves showing the relative hydrogen content of coals and petroleum as related to carbon. Hydrogen is fairly constant or decreases only very slightly with increasing rank of coal. This indicates that hydrogen and carbon are lost at almost equal relative rates during the process of coalification until the anthracite stage is reached. In petroleum, however, the proportion of hydrogen generally increases in the lighter and higher grades. (Data from Francis, 1954, Coal, p. 323, fig. 7.14, and Tomkeieff, 1954, Coals and bitumens, table, fig. 2.)

Petroleum does not appear to be a product derived from land-plant vegetation as is coal. Whether the carbonaceous and bituminous substances owe their dissimilarities to original differences in the kind of organic material buried in the sediments, to environmental differences that influenced early decomposition, or to some other cause is not known. It does not seem likely, however, that differences in dynamochemical action are responsible.

In summary, the amount and kind of organic matter present in sedimentary rocks is the balance between that produced by organisms and deposited and that destroyed by organic and dynamic processes. This is dependent upon a variety of factors of which the most important are (1) abundance of organisms, (2) kind of organic material available, (3) distance to site of deposition, (4) environment of deposition, (5) type of sediment, (6) rapidity of deposition, (7) weight of overburden, (8) heat, (9) amount of structural deformation, and (10) age of rocks.

Because of partial dynamochemical decomposition, organic material is somewhat less abundant in most consolidated rocks than in corresponding sediments. Marine sandstones are likely to contain very little organic matter but terrestrial sandstones may include considerable amounts. In spite of the abundant life recorded by most limestones, these rocks generally possess a minimum organic content although there are many exceptions. Shales, both marine and fresh-water, are the rocks which as a class are richest in organic material.

Color

Although there is a general correlation between increasing amounts of organic matter in rocks and darker color, it is not close, and organic content differing by a factor of five may make little appreciable difference in color, as shown in Figure 18. Most rocks whose dark colors result from the presence

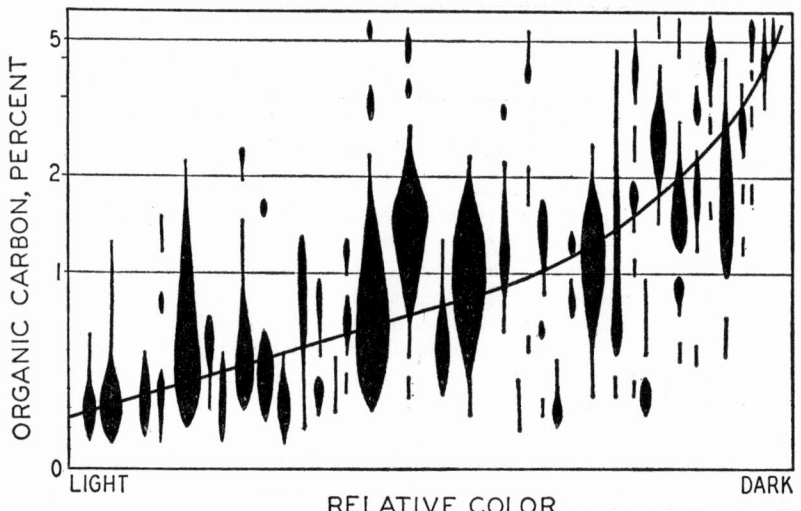

Figure 18. Diagram showing relations between the organic carbon content of sediments and their lightness or darkness of color. Although a general correlation is apparent, correspondence is not close. (Adapted from Trask and Patnode, 1937, *Drilling and production practice 1936*, p. 376, fig. 4, by permission of American Petroleum Institute.)

of organic matter contain the degraded carbonized remains of plants. Many bituminous rocks may be either light colored or dark because carbonaceous matter also is present. The Green River Shale (Tert.) of Colorado and neighboring states has attracted much attention because it is a rich oil shale but much of it contains little carbonaceous matter and is not dark colored.

Some dark sedimentary rocks owe their color to very fine-grained disseminated iron sulfide. This substance probably was produced by the reduction of sulfates by bacteria acting on organic matter shortly after deposition.

Its presence presumably indicates some depletion of the original organic content of the rocks.

Chert

Much chert occurs as secondary concretionary nodules in limestone, but regularly bedded chert is present in some formations and others consist of great thicknesses of chert interrupted only by shaly partings. Such formations as the Arkansas Novaculite (Dev.-Miss.) of Arkansas and Woodford Chert (Dev.-Miss.) of Oklahoma and the Monterey Chert (Tert.) of southern California include enormous amounts of silica. Any explanation of their origin encounters the problem of its source.

Some thick chert formations are associated with other rocks considered to be characteristic of a geosynclinal environment. The suggestion has been made that the silica is of volcanic origin derived either directly from siliceous submarine emanations or indirectly from the alteration of submarine lava flows. In either case the silica is supposed to have been precipitated as a gel that later was dehydrated and transformed to chert. Among the objections to this theory are the following: (1) The great chert formations are not known to be associated with evidence of important submarine volcanism, and (2) such presumably geosynclinal lava flows as those which occur in the Catoctin and Unicoi formations (Precamb. and L. Camb.) of the Appalachian region are not known to be accompanied by important chert deposits. A more probable explanation is that the silica was produced by the normal weathering of silicate minerals in igneous rocks on nearby land. The silica then may have been transported in colloidal form to the sea, where decrease in alkalinity caused its precipitation as a finely divided sediment rather than a gel. Later diagenetic changes resulted in the development of chert.

Other explanations relate thick chert formations to the alteration of diatomite and the silicification of limestone and other rocks. Careful study of the Monterey Chert suggests that originally it consisted largely of diatoms. If this is true, it may not be necessary to seek an extraneous source of silica. The extensive chertification of Devonian limestones in southern Illinois and western Tennessee suggests that the Arkansas Novaculite and Woodford Chert, which probably include strata of similar age, also resulted from the siliceous replacement of limestone. Tuff beds occur in the stratigraphic section of Arkansas and Oklahoma, but they do not give evidence of long-continued volcanic activity or provide an adequate source for all the silica. Similar tuff deposits have not been recognized in Illinois or Tennessee.

Bedded chert in some limestone formations such as the Kinkaid (Miss.) of southern Illinois and western Kentucky is similar in character to nodular chert in this and other nearby adjacent formations. There seems to be no necessity, therefore, to account for it otherwise than as the replacement of lime by silica. The difference in requirements appears to be that chemical conditions were uniform throughout certain beds rather than localized about various centers which became the site for growth of chert concretions. This replacement may have occurred at or close below the sea bottom shortly after the deposition of calcareous sediment.

More or less bedded chert also can develop by the alteration of sandy strata, particularly those in which sand was cemented by calcite. This also seems to involve the replacement of lime by hydrated silica and probably was accomplished by circulating ground water. In southern Illinois two cherty zones in outcropping Upper Mississippian limestone correspond to sandy zones encountered in nearby wells.

Although primary chert of more or less nodular form has been reported at numerous places, no completely satisfactory or conclusive evidence for its existence has been presented. Probably most if not all chert was produced by the alteration of original sediments of calcareous or organic siliceous nature. This alteration may have occurred very soon after deposition or much later, and chert of more than one generation certainly is present in some formations. Consequently the occurrence of chert generally is believed to be indicative of post-depositional conditions and processes although the original nature of some sediments undoubtedly predisposed them more than others to chertification. The characters of sediments that rendered them more or less susceptible to siliceous replacement and the physical and chemical factors involved in this alteration are, however, poorly understood. As previously noted, the source of large amounts of silica necessary for extensive replacement remains an unsolved problem.

Evaporites

Bedded deposits of gypsum, anhydrite, and rock salt constitute the evaporitic rocks. A variety of other less common minerals are associated but these rarely occur except as very minor constituents. The evaporites, as their name implies, generally have been produced by precipitation from solutions concentrated by evaporation. They are neither detrital sediments nor do they owe their existence to any kind of biologic action.

The most obvious and adequate source of the evaporitic rocks is the mineral matter carried in solution by sea water, and most of them have been derived either directly or indirectly from this source. At the present time the sea is estimated to contain dissolved matter in the quantities shown in Table 5.

When sea water is evaporated, lime soon begins to precipitate, and when the original volume has been reduced to 20 percent, essentially all has been eliminated from solution. Gypsum begins to precipitate when the volume has been reduced to about 25 percent. About two-thirds of the calcium sulfate has gone down when the volume of water reaches 15 percent, but additional precipitation continues to a volume of about 3 percent. Sodium chloride begins to appear in the precipitate when the volume of the solution has been reduced to 10 percent, and at a volume of 4 percent about two-thirds of it has been thrown down. Other salts, particularly magnesium chloride and sulfate, begin to precipitate almost simultaneously with common salt but amounts are small until the volume of water remaining is only 2.5 percent of the original. At a volume of about 1.5 percent, complex salts begin to crystallize. Over 20 percent of the total original mineral matter is still dissolved in this concentrated brine.

TABLE 5.   Quantities of the Principal Mineral Substances Dissolved in Sea Water

	Cubic Miles	Percent	Ratio	Depth of Water per Foot of Solid
Calcium carbonate	15,000	0.3	0.4	22,000
Calcium sulfate	200,000	3.6	4.6	1,800
Sodium chloride	3,900,000	77.8	100.0	83
Other salts	900,000	18.3	23.5	350
Total	5,015,000	100.0		67

The foregoing quantities of salts and series of precipitates shows that (1) the evaporation of sea water should produce a natural progression of different precipitates overlapping to some extent but occurring in a definite order, and (2) the different products of evaporation should occur in certain definite proportions to each other. Many evaporitic deposits, however, do not show this progression or do not occur in these proportions. This indicates that a simple hypothesis of evaporating sea water is not adequate to account for them. Furthermore the great thicknesses of some evaporitic deposits demand depths of water that appear to be prohibitive.

Theories of Origin

The commonest explanation for the deposition of evaporites postulates that a more or less extensive flooded area in an arid region, possessing restricted or intermittent connection with the sea, was so situated that water lost by evaporation was replenished but return circulation of concentrated brine did not occur. Such a situation might have existed either in a fairly stable shelf sea or in a subsiding basin with free circulation prevented by sedimentary bars, growing organic reefs, or tectonically produced and maintained barriers (see Figure 19). The physical relations of actual evaporite deposits generally are inadequately known, but the Permian salt of Kansas may illustrate the shelf type whereas the Silurian salt of Michigan almost certainly is related to the structural history of the Michigan basin (see Figure 180A, p. 486).

Variations with regard to the marine connections of an evaporite basin, whether constant or intermittent, and climatic fluctuations would determine the nature and succession of evaporites. Normally these should start with a thin limestone, be followed by a thicker deposit of gypsum or anhydrite, and be terminated by thick salt. Because of continuous precipitation, each member should be contaminated by small quantities of the preceding ones. Also

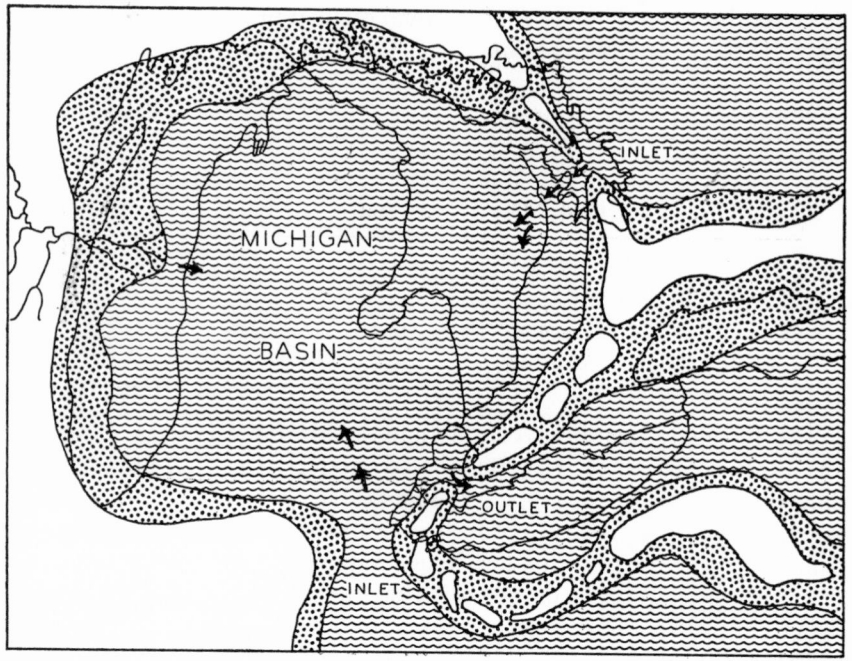

Figure 19.   Paleogeographic map of the Michigan basin region during Salina (Sil.) time. Fluctuations in relative sea level caused shorelines to advance and retreat. At times of lowered water level communication of the basin area with the neighboring more open sea was greatly restricted, and excessive evaporation caused precipitation of salt. The barrier that enclosed the basin on the east may have consisted of organic reefs (compare with Figure 186, p. 496). (After Briggs, 1958, J. Sediment. Petrol., vol. 28, p. 55, fig. 11.)

detrital sediments might be introduced anywhere in this series. Such concentration by evaporation and precipitation, however, might be interrupted at any point so that the sequence need not continue to completion. Moreover fluctuations in the introduction of marine or fresh water might result in the cyclic alteration of different evaporites such as is reported in the Stassfurt deposits of Germany.

The occurrence of gypsum or anhydrite without underlying limestone, which is common in the Permo-Triassic red beds of the west, or the occurrence of salt without antecedent gypsum or anhydrite, which appears to be the situation in some parts of Michigan and New York, shows an important deviation from this pattern. The great purity of some evaporites also seems to exclude the possibility that these have been produced by the direct evaporation of sea water. Finally, the general absence from evaporites of all fossils, such as might be expected to record the presence of pelagic organisms carried into an evaporite basin with sea water, has been called to notice.

These and other anomalies seem to necessitate some modification of the general barrier theory as applied to the origin of many evaporite deposits and suggest that some may have developed in quite different ways, as follows:

1. Surface evaporation and circulation of progressively more concentrated brine resulted naturally in the lateral segregation of different evaporites (see Figure 20). This might occur in a very shallow bay connected with a tideless sea that was not swept by violent storms.

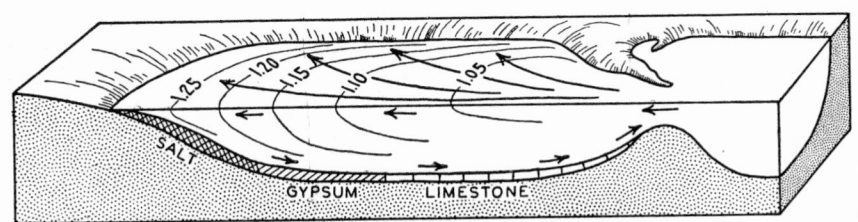

Figure 20. Schematic diagram showing water circulation in an evaporite basin, lines of equal brine density, and corresponding distribution of evaporite deposits. (After Briggs, 1957, Mich. Acad. Sci., vol. 42, p. 120, fig. 2, by permission of the University of Michigan.)

2. After partial concentration, the resulting brine may have been drawn off into another restricted basin where further concentration and precipitation occurred. This would serve in some degree to segregate later from earlier precipitation products.

3. Connection with the sea was not maintained and a salt lake wasted away by evaporation. As it shrank in size, later precipitates would be confined to smaller and smaller areas and consequently they would produce relatively thicker but less extensive deposits.

4. Salts were derived from connate water and adsorbed substances present in older marine sediments. They were leached by rain and delivered to an inland basin unconnected with the sea. Deposits of this type need not be near or associated in any way with contemporaneous marine strata.

5. Salts were derived from older evaporites and delivered to a similar inland basin. Under these circumstances fractional solution, particularly of rock salt, might result in purer evaporite deposits.

6. Salts were derived directly from the weathering of igneous rocks and

accumulated in an inland basin. This might produce evaporite deposits quite different in composition from those derived from sea water.

7. Brine brought to the surface by capillary action evaporated and salts accumulated at the surface. These were then transported and concentrated by the wind as in the gypsum dunes near Alamogordo, New Mexico. It is very unlikely that any rock salt deposits had this origin.

8. The action of sulfate solutions altered limestone to gypsum. This process is reported to have occurred in the Salina Formation (Sil.) of New York. Such gypsum is not a true evaporite and no similar process can account for salt deposits.

All evaporite deposits demand the existence of arid conditions so that evaporation loss exceeds the contribution of fresh water introduced by streams or furnished directly by rain. This loss amounts to as much as five feet of water per year or even more in some arid regions at the present time. Although aridity may have been more widespread at some times during the geologic past than at others, arid regions probably have always been localized much as they are today. They are determined by geographic conditions and generally owe their existence to mountain ranges that stand as barriers to moisture-bearing winds. Evaporites are present in all geologic systems from the Cambrian onward and they are being formed today.

Evaporites may or may not occur with red beds. Association with red beds commonly identifies evaporites precipitated in extensions of shallow shelf seas. Those deposited in sinking basins are much more likely to constitute parts of non-red sequences including important marine limestones. Evaporites rarely developed in actively subsiding geosynclinal belts.

Gypsum vs. Anhydrite

Calcium sulfate forms bedded deposits of both gypsum, $CaSO_4 \cdot 2H_2O$, and anhydrite, $CaSO_4$, and these two minerals are known in various degrees and conditions of association. The occurrences are such that one or the other mineral appears to be primary at certain places but at others it may be secondary, having been produced by alteration of the other. The physical chemistry of calcium sulfate in complex brines is not well understood. Experiments have indicated, however, that in a saturated solution of sodium chloride, calcium sulfate crystallizes out as gypsum at lower temperatures, and as anhydrite at higher ones. The conversion point has been determined variously to be between 77° and 86° F.

Some outcropping gypsum deposits pass into anhydrite in the subsurface and they are believed to have resulted from hydration of the latter mineral. This alteration involves a volume increase of about 60 percent and the contorted and otherwise disturbed structures of some gypsum deposits are attributed to such induced swelling. The alteration of gypsum to anhydrite is less certain. Mineral relations in the cap rock of some salt domes suggest that increased pressure and temperature have resulted in the dehydration of gypsum. If such an alteration does occur, it is accompanied by a volume decrease of about 37 percent.

The common evaporites become plastic under pressure. Rock salt particularly exhibits much evidence of flowage, as shown by highly contorted stratification. This may result in the extreme thickening and thinning of beds. It is responsible for the development of salt domes which occur in several widely scattered parts of the world, and for the concentration of great masses of salt in diapiric structures such as those in the northern part of western Pakistan and in Iran.

Rock Phosphates

Phosphates are a very minor constituent of the mineral matter dissolved in sea water, but they are necessary for the growth of planktonic plants, which provide the first link of the food chain supporting most marine animals. Rapid multiplication of these plants depletes the supply in near-surface water but it is renewed by currents rising from the depths. The most abundant marine faunas in the world today occur at places where persistent currents of this type reach the surface.

Some marine animals concentrate phosphorus in their hard parts, and phosphatic nodules of inorganic origin appear to be forming at some places on the modern sea floor. Consequently marine strata and particularly limestones may be expected to contain small quantities of phosphorus. The occurrence of bedded deposits, generally associated with limestone, which may contain up to 80 percent or even more calcium phosphate, however, requires special explanations. The largest deposits of the United States occur in the Phosphoria Formation (Perm.), in southeastern Idaho and neighboring states, which is estimated to contain more than five times as much phosphorus as occurs in the present sea. This phosphate is believed to have accumulated slowly over a long interval of time at the edge of a deep basin lying to the west where rising currents maintained the phosphorus content of surface water and thus provided an unusually favorable area for planktonic life. The phosphate deposits consist mainly of pellets and nodules concentrated in more or less extensive beds. These are believed to have obtained their phosphorus partly from the decay of organisms that fed upon the plankton and partly by direct precipitation or replacement from sea water.

Other important phosphate deposits occur in Tennessee and Florida. The Tennessee deposits are of several types. Some consist of small brownish grains, associated with Ordovician limestone, whose cross-bedding suggests a shallow-water origin. They are in part at least replaced because small fossils are present among them. Similar oolite-like bodies occurring at the base of the Chattanooga Shale (Dev.-Miss.) may have been derived from the

Ordovician and redeposited. Replacement deposits in Silurian limestone possibly were developed by the leaching of overlying basal Chattanooga phosphate. The Florida deposits consist of nodules and pebbles, which seem to have originated as residuum partly by leaching of phosphatic limestone and partly by replacement, concentrated and deposited in an advancing sea.

Phosphatic nodules occur more or less sparingly in many stratigraphic zones, some of which also contain glauconite. They are believed generally to indicate very slow sedimentary deposition or concentration of phosphatic material at unconformities.

Sedimentary Iron Ore

Many sediments contain appreciable amounts of iron, and some sedimentary rocks are sufficiently ferruginous to be considered ores. Iron occurs in them as hematite, limonite (or other hydrous oxides), siderite, pyrite, marcasite, glauconite, as well as other less common secondary minerals. The iron in all of them originally was derived largely from the weathering of basic igneous rocks.

After it is freed from complex silicate minerals, iron may be transported as soluble ferrous salts or as colloidal ferric oxide. The ferrous compounds are readily oxidized and then hydrolyze to produce ferric oxide. As most flowing water and also most standing water in which deposition might occur contains free oxygen, most iron probably was transported in the form of hydrated colloidal ferric oxide. Whereas this may be deposited as limonite in fresh water, salt water under some conditions appears to be an effective dehydrating agent, and in marine environments iron oxide probably was deposited mainly as hematite. In the presence of organic matter and carbon dioxide, colloidal ferric oxide may be reduced and transformed to siderite. If hydrogen sulfide from decaying organisms occurs, iron may be deposited as a sulfide.

Except for recent bog limonite, most sedimentary iron ores appear to be related to marine deposits. The common minerals are hematite, as in the Clinton ores (Sil.) of Alabama and more northern states, and siderite, as in the black band ores and clay ironstone (Penn.). Pyrite and marcasite also are abundant but they rarely are considered to be iron ores. All of these at some places have replaced calcite but at others they may be primary deposits. The question as to whether or not some ores have resulted from the replacement of calcium carbonate has not been answered satisfactorily. If they have, the replacement probably altered calcareous sediment under somewhat peculiar conditions very soon after its deposition on the sea floor.

The Lake Superior iron formations (Precamb.), and similar ones in other parts of the world, are believed by most geologists to be sedimentary, but they are quite different from any younger ores and the mode of their formation is not agreed upon. An unorthodox but possible suggestion is that they were produced before the earth's oxidizing atmosphere became stabilized and that the transportation and deposition of iron was controlled by alternate epochs of reducing and oxidizing conditions.

Siderite oxidizes in place during weathering and it is transformed to limonite. The sulfides also oxidize to limonite but their iron commonly is moved and deposited at or near the surface of porous rocks, forming a hard and resistant crust. Sulfuric acid, which also is produced, is neutralized by lime, and gypsum crystals of considerable size may develop particularly in shale.

Other Rocks

Eolian Deposits

Wind-blown sand probably is not uncommon in the stratigraphic section. Sandstones of many different ages consisting of well-rounded and frosted grains have been interpreted as eolian although some, like the St. Peter (Ord.), are obviously water-laid deposits. Many sands, particularly the purer ones, have had a long and varied history. Their most prominent characters do not necessarily identify the latest episodes that affected them. Evidence of the depositional environment of well-sorted sand must be sought in its structures rather than in its texture. Prominent and irregular cross-bedding is the most distinctive feature of dune sand (see Figure 32, p. 105). It is most likely to occur in sandstones that are parts of non-marine successions. Sandstones containing marine fossils obviously are not eolian deposits. Even though sand accumulated in dunes along a seashore, advance of the sea almost certainly resulted in reworking of the sand and the development of a transgressive marine deposit.

Although lime sand forms dunes today along some tropical and subtropical coasts, very few limestones have been interpreted as eolian. The best-known examples occur on islands like the Bahamas and Bermuda, where Pleistocene dunes have been identified consisting of oolitic sand, fragmented shells, and coral debris. Actually, calcareous coastal dunes have a better chance of preservation than those composed of quartz sand because they may become crusted over with a surficial cemented layer that provides some protection against erosion and reworking. Such a layer can be produced by alternate wetting by rain and drying, which results in a small amount of solution of the calcareous material and redeposition as cement in pores.

No loess deposits have been identified in ancient sediments. If they should occur, they probably would consist of massive well-sorted silt with only minor evidence of bedding. A few local formations of this type are known, as, for example, in the Kinderhookian Series (Miss.) in the upper Mississippi Valley. Such an origin of these particular silts, however, is unlikely because at some places they contain marine fossils.

Glacial Deposits

Glacial deposits have been reported in every geologic system and in many parts of the world. Mostly these supposed tillites are of questionable origin and many of them undoubtedly have been misidentified. The occurrence of heterogeneous gravel in an argillaceous matrix is no sure indication of glacial origin. Mixtures of this kind may be produced by mud flows and turbidity currents or they may be tectonic breccias of several different types. One of the most controversial deposits occurs in the Johns Valley Shale (Carb.) of Oklahoma, which has been considered glacial, a breccia beneath an overthrust fault, and the result of turbidity deposition. Reasonable interpretation of formations of this kind requires consideration of other features in addition to composition and texture.

Glacial till is very poorly sorted. It consists predominantly of fine material in which are distributed at random coarse rock fragments ranging possibly up to large boulders. Pleistocene glaciers at some places moved whole hills. For example, a small coal mine was formerly worked in western Illinois in one huge erratic mass. Glacial pebbles and larger rock fragments of many kinds are unweathered and occur indiscriminately mixed. They are more characteristically faceted than rounded but, contrary to general report, plainly striated specimens are not abundant. The matrix likewise is unweathered. It commonly is calcareous and consists largely of sharply angular fragments of rocks and minerals. Clayey material was derived from ground-up clayey rocks.

Till commonly is associated with other evidences of glaciation such as varved clays and striated rock pavements. Similar evidence accompanying possible ancient consolidated till contributes greatly to the sureness of identification. Although glacial deposits may be very restricted areally, as in the case of valley glaciers, the extensive occurrence of till-like material is significant because other similar deposits are likely to have been much more locally developed.

Metamorphic Rocks

Metamorphism of many sediments begins as soon as they are deposited and may continue more or less intermittently until sedimentary material has been so greatly changed that its original nature cannot be recognized. Processes such as compaction, cementation, and some types of recrystallization and replacement, that convert fresh sediments to consolidated rocks, generally are termed *diagenesis*. In contrast, more drastic alteration induced by heat and pressure, greater than the changes resulting solely from deep burial, produces different types of structures and new mineral associations. It is distinguished technically as *metamorphism*.

Most high-rank metamorphic rocks such as crystalline schist, gneiss, and perhaps even granite have been so altered that their possible sedimentary origins are uncertain. The sedimentary nature of many low-rank metamorphics is clear, however, and some of them can be traced laterally into their unmetamorphosed equivalents in other areas. The stratigraphic study of metamorphic rocks is very difficult because generally they occur in regions of great structural complexity. Also variable metamorphism has produced different types of rock from equivalent and originally continuous strata so that tracing and identification by lithologic similarity is accomplished with much uncertainty. Fossils commonly are destroyed or preserved so poorly that they provide little assistance in distinguishing strata or in dating them. Nevertheless, careful and detailed studies in some metamorphic regions like New England are gradually bringing to light much stratigraphic information of great interest.

Igneous Rocks

Intrusive igneous rocks are of little concern in stratigraphy except as (1) they were the source of sediments, (2) they complicate stratigraphic situations by introducing structural confusion and metamorphic alteration, (3) they record episodes that require integration into general geologic history, and (4) they include radioactive minerals that can be dated. Extrusive igneous rocks like lava flows, on the other hand, constitute more or less tabular rock bodies that may be interbedded with other stratified formations. Although they differ importantly in origin, they are as truly strata and they conform to the principle of superposition as perfectly as any sedimentary deposit.

Pyroclastic rocks are igneous derivatives comparable in some ways to detrital rocks, but erosion played no part in their production. They might be classed as eolian sediments because their materials descended from the air although wind was not responsible for their origin. Some pyroclastic material undoubtedly occurs where it originally settled but water was a more or less important agent in the transportation and deposition of much material of this kind. Volcanic eruptions commonly are accompanied by torrential rains, and huge mud flows may result. Also some tuffaceous strata were deposited in bodies of standing water which occurred within the areas of ash falls; others consist of volcanic ash that was moved and deposited by streams. Originally all pyroclastic material was unweathered. Most of it was glassy or very finely crystalline and sharply angular. It was susceptible to rapid weathering, however, and many deposits are considerably altered. The exact mode of deposition of many pyroclastic strata is uncertain unless sedimentary structures and textures such as cross-bedding and good sorting or the admixture of other kinds of sediment indicate an aqueous environment.

BIBLIOGRAPHY

Biggs, D. L. (1957), Petrography and origin of Illinois nodular cherts, Ill. Geol. Surv., Circ. 245.
> All specimens studied, from Cambrian to Mississippian in age, were developed by the replacement of limestone or dolomite.

Bramlette, M. N. (1946), The Monterey Formation of California and the origin of its siliceous rocks, U.S. Geol. Surv., Prof. Paper 212.
> Chertification occurred after deposition, by the solution and redeposition of silica derived from diatoms and tuff.

Campbell, M. R. (1930), Coal as a recorder of incipient rock metamorphism, Econ. Geol., vol. 25, pp. 675–696.
> Relations of fixed carbon, volatile matter, and moisture provide a delicate index.

Castaño, J. R., and Garrels, R. M. (1950), Experiment on the deposition of iron with special reference to the Clinton iron ore deposits, Econ. Geol., vol. 45, pp. 755–770.
> Iron was precipitated and replaced calcium carbonate in shallow, well-aerated sea water.

Coleman, A. P. (1926), Ice ages, recent and ancient, New York, Macmillan, reprinted 1929.
> Supposed glacial deposits of many ages in all parts of the world are uncritically described.

Dapples, E. C., Krumbein, W. C., and Sloss, L. L. (1953), Petrographic and lithologic attributes of sandstones, J. Geol., vol. 61, pp. 291–317.
> Classification by minerals and sorting relates different types of sandstone to origin, transportation, and deposition.

Dunbar, C. O., and Rodgers, John (1957), Principles of stratigraphy, New York, Wiley.
> Chapters 8 to 14, pp. 159–255, deal with sedimentary rocks and their interpretation.

Folk, R. L. (1959), Practical petrographic classification of limestones, Bull. Am. Assoc. Petroleum Geol., vol. 43, pp. 1–38.
> Eleven principal types of limestone based upon constituents are distinguished and recrystallization is discussed.

Goldstein, August, Jr., and Hendricks, T. A. (1953), Siliceous sediments of Ouachita facies in Oklahoma, Bull. Geol. Soc. Amer., vol. 64, pp. 421–442.
> Chert is an original deposit in a geosyncline derived from submarine weathering of volcanic ash.

Grabau, A. W. (1913), Principles of stratigraphy, New York, Seiler, reprinted 1924.

Chapters 6, pp. 269–300, and 9 to 15, pp. 339–690, are devoted to the classification and description of sediments and rocks.

Grabau, A. W. (1920), *Geology of the non-metallic mineral deposits other than silicates*, vol. 1, *Principles of salt deposition*, New York, McGraw-Hill.
Comprehensive consideration is given to salt deposits and theories for their formation.

Grim, R. E. (1942), Modern concepts of clay materials, *J. Geol.*, vol. 50, pp. 225–275.
The author discusses structures and occurrence of clay minerals, their relations to water and plastic properties.

Harlton, B. H. (1953), Ouachita chert facies, southeastern Oklahoma, *Bull. Am. Assoc. Petroleum Geol.*, vol. 37, pp. 778–796.
Chert was produced by replacement of other rocks at the time of structural disturbance.

Hatch, F. H., and Rastall, R. H. (1938), *The Petrology of the Sedimentary Rocks*, 3rd ed., revised by Maurice Black, London, Allen and Unwin.
Chapters 2 to 14, pp. 27–262, are devoted to classification and description of sedimentary rocks.

Hough, J. L. (1958), Fresh-water environment of deposition of Precambrian banded iron formations, *J. Sediment. Petrol.*, vol. 28, pp. 414–430.
Banding probably is related to alternate cooler and warmer seasons of the year.

Krumbein, W. C. (1947), Shales and their environmental significance, *J. Sediment. Petrol.*, vol. 17, pp. 101–108.
Shales are classified on physical properties, regional characters, and extent.

Krynine, P. D. (1948), The megascopic study and field classification of sedimentary rocks, *J. Geol.*, vol. 56, pp. 130–165.
Classification is based on mineralogy and texture; structure and colors also are considered.

LeBlanc, R. J., and Breeding, J. G. (eds.) (1957), Regional aspects of carbonate deposition, a symposium, Soc. Econ. Paleon. and Miner., Spec. Publ. 5.
Papers are by John Rodgers, N. D. Newell, and J. K. Rigby, R. N. Ginsburg, R. C. Moore, and R. W. Fairbridge.

McKelvey, V. E., Swanson, R. W., and Sheldon, R. P. (1953), The Permian phosphorite deposits of western United States, 19th Intern. Geol. Congr., Algiers, Rept., pt. 11, pp. 45–64.
Deposition occurred at margin of deep marine basin from rising currents by chemical and organic processes.

Miser, H. D. (1934), Carboniferous rocks of Ouachita Mountains, *Bull. Am. Assoc. Petroleum Geol.*, vol. 18, pp. 971–1009.
For discussion of Johns Valley Shale and its erratic boulders see pp. 992–1009.

Pettijohn, F. J. (1957), *Sedimentary rocks*, 2nd ed., New York, Harper.
Chapters 3, pp. 99–156, and 5 to 10, pp. 229–497, are devoted to the classification and description of sedimentary rocks.

Schopf, J. M. (1952), Was decay important in origin of coal? *J. Sediment. Petrol.*, vol. 22, pp. 61–69.

Decay was the first step in the formation of coal.

Scruton, P. C. (1953), Deposition of evaporites, *Bull. Am. Assoc. Petroleum Geol.*, vol. 37, pp. 2498–2512.

Theoretical current dynamics and depositional patterns in evaporite basins are considered.

Sloss, L. L. (1953), The significance of evaporites, *J. Sediment. Petrol.*, vol. 23, pp. 143–161.

Evaporite deposits of west Texas, Michigan, and Williston basins are compared and classified.

Taliaferro, N. L. (1933), The relation of volcanism to diatomaceous and associated siliceous sediments, Univ. Calif. Publ., *Bull. Dept. Geol. Sci.*, vol. 23, pp. 1–56.

Silica of diatomites and cherts was derived mainly from contemporaneously produced volcanic ash.

Thom, W. T., Jr. (1934), Present status of the carbon-ratio theory, in *Problems of petroleum geology*, W. E. Wrather and F. H. Lahee (eds.), Tulsa, Am. Assoc. Petroleum Geol., pp. 69–95.

This is a thorough review of evidence that carbon ratio of coal is a measure of low-grade metamorphism in sedimentary rocks.

Twenhofel, W. H. (1947), Environmental significance of conglomerates, *J. Sediment. Petrol.*, vol. 17, pp. 119–128.

Conglomerates only show the competence of some transporting medium.

Twenhofel, W. H. (1950), *Principles of sedimentation*, 2nd ed., New York, McGraw-Hill.

Chapters 7 to 13, pp. 282–541, describe sediments and their formation.

Twenhofel, W. H., and collaborators (1932), *Treatise on sedimentation*, 2nd ed., Baltimore, Williams and Wilkins.

Chapter 5, pp. 187–602, is devoted to descriptions of sediments.

Twenhofel, W. H., and Tyler, S. A. (1941), *Methods of study of sediments*, New York, McGraw-Hill.

Laboratory and field methods are briefly explained.

Tyler, S. A. (1959), Sedimentary iron deposits, in *Applied sedimentation*, P. D. Trask (ed.), New York, Wiley, pp. 506–523.

The nature and occurrence of different kinds of sedimentary iron ores are reviewed.

Whitlatch, G. K., and Smith, R. W. (1940), The phosphate resources of Tennessee, Tenn. Div. Geol., Bull. 48.

The deposits are described; for stratigraphic relations and origin see pp. 33–49, 301–310, and 355–360.

5

Textures, Structures, and
Colors of Sediments
and Rocks

In ADDITION to their mineral and chemical composition, the nature and
characters of sediments and stratified rocks are determined by their textures
and bedding. The general appearance of sediments and rocks also is strongly
influenced by their colors and is modified by various types of more or less
minor structures.

TEXTURES

The textures of sediments and rocks are largely dependent upon (1) the
sizes of grains or particles, (2) their degree of uniformity or sorting, (3) their
shapes, and (4) their packing and cementation. The detailed observation
and investigation of these features fall within the realm of the sedimentary
petrologist and requires microscopic or other types of laboratory examination. Knowledge of them, however, is of great value to the stratigrapher,
and it is in this field that petrology can make one of its most useful contributions to stratigraphy.

Coarseness

The classification of detrital rocks is based on the sizes of the predominant
or most conspicuous grain particles and other features largely dependent

upon these sizes and their variations. A somewhat similar classification of carbonate rocks can be made on the same basis, but the differences are less noticeable and less significant.

Detrital material has been moved from its source of origin to its point of deposition by one or another of the three common transporting media: water, wind, and glacial ice. Except in the case of ice, size of the particles moved is generally an important index to the potency of the transporting medium because progressively more power is required to move increasingly large particles. Sedimentary material is deposited where transportational potency falls below the minimum that is required to move it (see Figure 53, p. 156).

The transporting power of water and air increases with increasing current velocity and greater turbulence. Also transportational efficiency is a direct function of the density and viscosity of the medium. Therefore, ice is more efficient than water, and water is more efficient than air. The density of a water medium is increased by the presence of suspended silt and clay. In very muddy fluids greater viscosity increases efficiency still more (see Figure 21). These variable hydrodynamic factors necessitate identification of the trans-

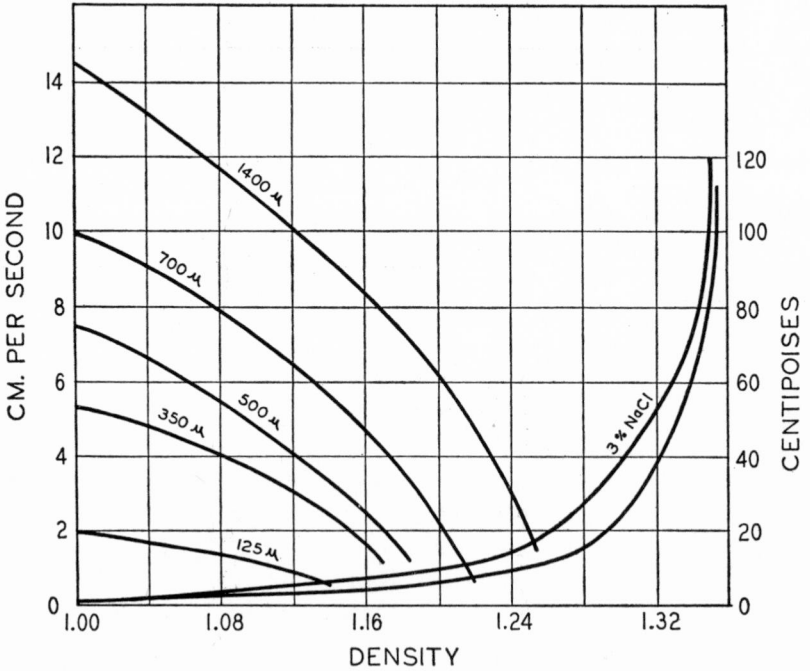

Figure 21.   Diagram showing experimental results of the settling of sand grains in clay suspensions of different densities and the viscosity of the suspensions in fresh and salt water. (Adapted from Kuenen, 1951, Soc. Econ. Paleon. and Miner., Spec. Publ. 2, p. 25, fig. 7, and p. 27, fig. 9.)

porting medium before transportational processes and history can be evaluated.

The foregoing factors are equally significant with respect to detrital and carbonate sediments insofar as either kind has been transported. Transportation, however, has played a much less important role in the history of carbonate sediments. Mostly they originated in the sea and found their final resting places at or near their points of origin (see Figure 22). Some carbonate sediments are related to general fresh-water environments similar to those of the sea. Very few were ever introduced into the terrestrial environment where they became subject to either fluvial or eolian currents. Conse-

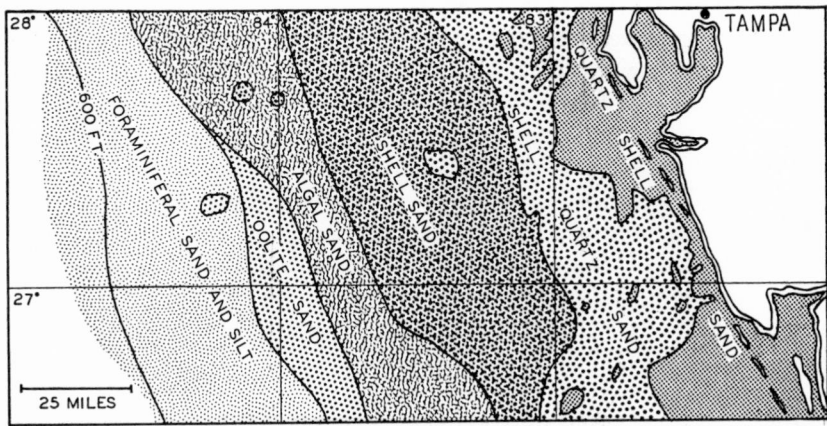

Figure 22.   Sediment zones of the sea bottom off the west coast of Florida. Coarse detrital sediment (quartz sand) is mainly restricted to shallow water generally less than 100 feet deep near the coast. The outer zones of calcareous sediment probably are related to depth conditions as they existed during late Pleistocene time when sea level is estimated to have stood about 200 feet below its present level. (After Gould and Stewart, 1955, Soc. Econ. Paleon. and Miner., Spec. Publ. 3, p. 5, fig. 2.)

quently the turbulence of wave action probably has been a much more important mechanism than current action in the transportation and sorting of most carbonate sediments.

The sizes of particles in many coarse carbonate sediments probably are more nearly an index to the maximum power of turbulence than to the potency of currents. In these sediments the larger particles may have remained relatively undisturbed whereas the smaller ones were winnowed out and moved away. This may explain, for example, the sorting in some crinoidal limestones. Transportation of coarse carbonate material is evident only in those beds that contain abundant broken and abraded shells or show cross-bedding or other types of bar or current structures. Even in these the coarser particles may have been moved only very short distances.

Exceptions to the foregoing principles are furnished by coarse material that has been transported frozen in floating ice, entangled in the roots of floating vegetation, or carried in the stomachs of large animals. Erratic pebbles or even small boulders whose presence in fine-grained sediments cannot be explained by any ordinary means of transportation are rare but they have been found in rocks of many ages. Peculiar formations like the Levis Conglomerate (Ord.) of Quebec and the Johns Valley Shale (Carb.) of Oklahoma also present the anomalous association of large blocks of foreign rock enclosed in fine sediment. They have been interpreted as tectonic breccias related to overthrust faulting, talus accumulations beneath submarine fault scarps, and turbidity current deposits.

Size Distribution

Almost all sediments consist of mixtures of particles of different sizes. These mixtures may have a wide range between maximum and minimum sizes or they may be relatively homogeneous. Sedimentary petrologists have devised means of analyzing sedimentary mixtures and measuring certain parameters that best express their characters. These are (1) the average, mean, or median size, (2) the range, distribution, dispersion, or spread of sizes, (3) the skewness or symmetry of size variation, and (4) the kurtosis or concentration of sediment within a certain size fraction. For purposes of comparison these parameters can be expressed numerically, and sediments can be graphed by histograms and various types of size frequency curves like those in Figure 23.

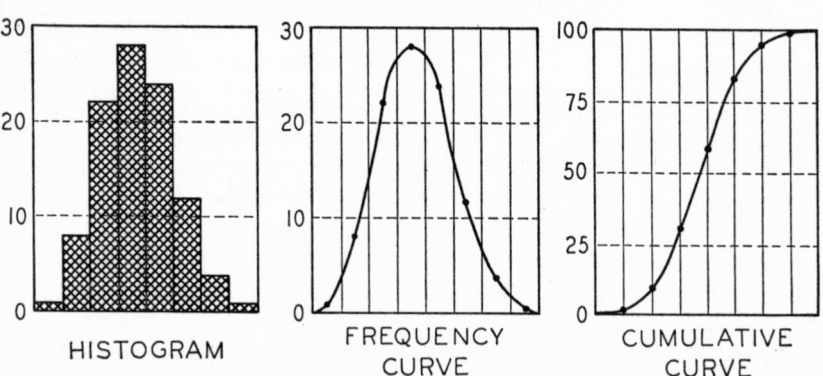

HISTOGRAM   FREQUENCY CURVE   CUMULATIVE CURVE

Figure 23.   Histogram, frequency curve, and cumulative curve showing the size distribution of particles in a hypothetical sediment separated into eight arbitrary size classes. Distributions of many kinds involving measurements or counts can be graphed in these ways.

Size studies of sedimentary mixtures have been made for purposes that are both descriptive and interpretative. Descriptive studies have been motivated by desires (1) to devise improved systems of classification and nomenclature and (2) to discover characters useful in correlation. Interpretative studies have sought (3) to investigate the dynamics of sedimentary transportation and deposition, (4) to determine sedimentary genesis, and (5) to analyze the influence of mixtures on porosity and permeability. Although much has been learned about these matters, the practical results of such studies have been somewhat disappointing.

The sizes of particles present in any sedimentary mixture are dependent upon a variety of factors as follows:

1. Nature of source rock. Rocks differ greatly in their response to the destructive action of weathering and erosion. Some, like many igneous rocks, limestone, and quartzite, tend to break into blocky fragments. Others, like many sandstones and shales, are readily reduced to much smaller particles. Also depending upon the degree of weathering, igneous rocks may yield either blocky fragments or resistant crystal grains and clayey alteration products.

2. Original sizes of available particles. Regardless of the kind of source rock, none can furnish particles to sediments larger than those which have been made available to transportation by weathering and erosion. Thus a friable sandstone or a soft shale is very unlikely to contribute to the formation of a conglomerate even though physical conditions and processes are favorable for the transportation and accumulation of pebbles.

3. Kind of transporting medium. The transporting efficiency of glacial ice, water, and wind decreases in this order. Glaciers can move enormous blocks of rock. Water cannot transport large boulders except under somewhat unusual conditions that are likely to be temporary and to prevail for only short distances. Wind action under all ordinary conditions does not effect the movement of particles coarser than sand size.

4. Wear and solution during transportation. All transported material is subject to wear, and, if the medium is water, solution may be important. Both wear and solution reduce particle size, and the farther sediment is transported the smaller its particles become. Different rocks and different minerals are variously susceptible to wear and solution. The softer and more soluble particles, of course, suffer most and the harder and more insoluble ones are least affected. Also the larger particles are more strongly abraded during transportation and are reduced in size more rapidly than smaller ones. Thus reduction in sediment size during transportation is related to (1) hardness and toughness of the source rock and its weathered products, (2) distance traveled, and (3) sizes of transported particles.

5. Sorting. Although this term is used to describe the size distribution of particulate matter without regard to its history, actual sorting involves division and separation of a mixture into unlike parts. Sorting of sediments is accomplished during transportation by the differential movement of sediment that results in the more rapid and farther transportation of smaller,

less compact, and lighter particles than of the larger, more compact, and heavier ones. Sorting is favored by action of the less viscous transporting media. Glacial ice accomplishes little or no sorting whereas eolian sediment

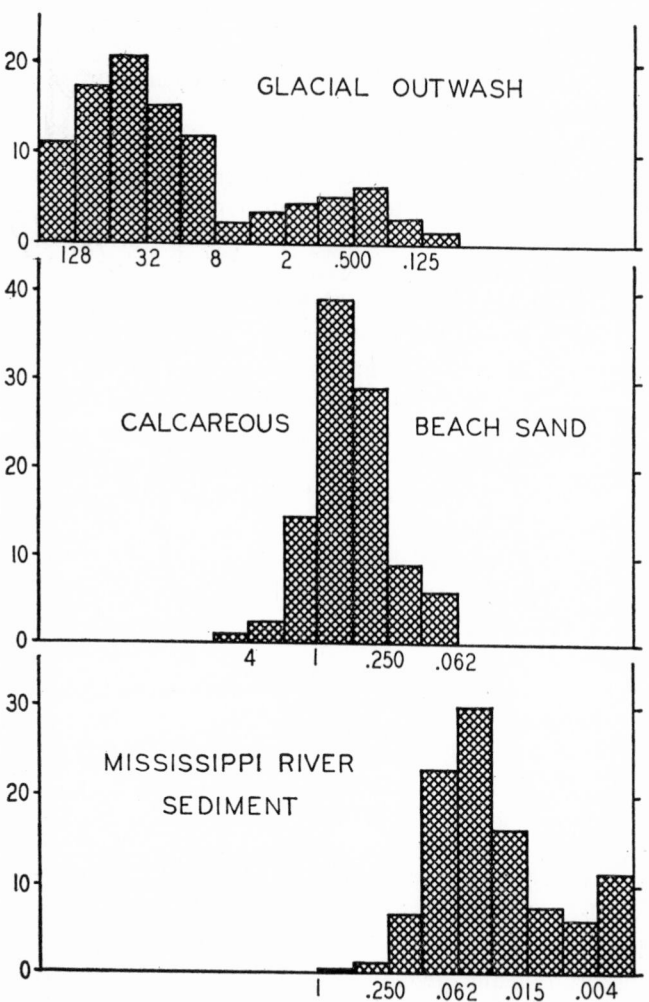

Figure 24.   Histograms showing size distributions in three different kinds of sediment. The size range of a sediment and the form and symmetry of its histogram reveal features that are more or less characteristic of the sorting accomplished during transportation and at the site of deposition. These histograms are arranged according to the same base scale and their positions shifting to the right show increasing fineness from outwash to river sediment. The beach sand is best and the glacial outwash is least well sorted. (Data from Pettijohn, 1957, *Sedimentary rocks*.)

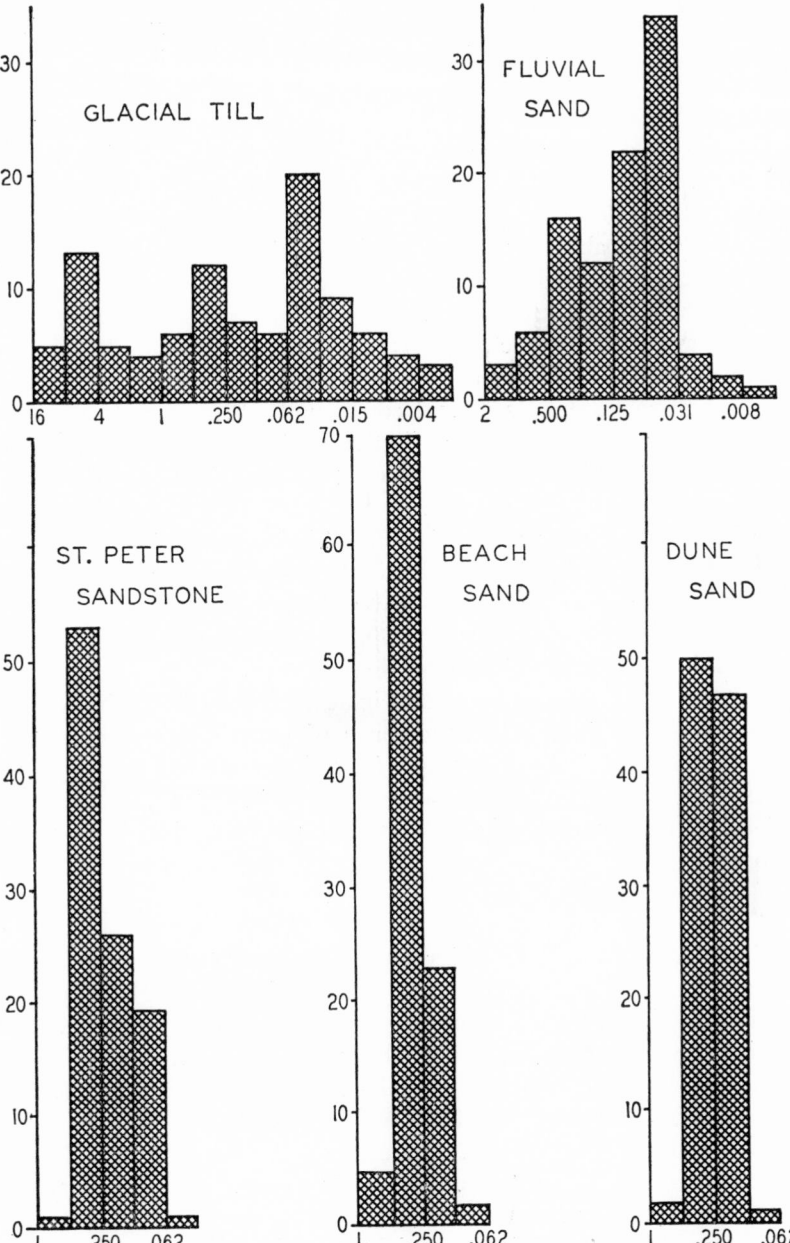

Figure 25. Histograms drawn to a single scale contrasting poor sorting in glacial till and fluvial sand as compared to beach and dune sand and the St. Peter Sandstone (Ord.). The apparent better sorting in the beach than in the dune sand shown here probably results from the class intervals selected for representation. (Data from Pettijohn, 1957, Sedimentary rocks.)

is likely to be best sorted—that is, it consists of the most homogeneous material (see Figures 24 and 25). In water, good sorting is promoted by a combination of turbulence and current action.

6. Depositional environment. Deposition is the final stage of the sorting process at which a coarser, more compact, and heavier fraction of the moving sediment comes to final rest. Except for the fraction that includes the finest of all sediment, a deposit consists of abandoned material that the transporting medium was unable to move farther. Deposition commonly follows after the introduction of a sediment into a new environment of less transportational efficiency, as in the delivery of ice-borne material to outwash streams, of fluvial material to the quieter waters of lake or sea, or where shallow-water sediment is washed upon a beach by waves and built into dunes by wind. In each of these examples sediment comes under the influence of a more effective sorting medium or more effective sorting action, and a more perfectly sorted deposit is the result. Reversal is not possible unless sediments of different types are mixed.

The foregoing factors are so variable and their interrelations are so complex that the interpretation of size distribution in many sediments is subject to much and serious uncertainty. Many sedimentary deposits consist of mixed material derived from very different rocks occurring in different areas, and the sedimentary histories of these parts may be quite unlike. Some such mixtures show bimodality (see Figure 24, glacial outwash, p. 88) or polymodality—that is, the preponderence of material is concentrated in two or more noncontiguous size grades instead of one. Bimodality also may result from the peculiarity of sediment transport in streams where a coarse fraction is moved by rolling along the bottom whereas a finer one travels in suspension.

Shape

Sedimentary petrologists have developed two concepts regarding shapes of particles: (1) sphericity or approach to spherical form and (2) roundness or the smoothing of edges and corners from angular fragments. Roundness is increased by wear. In particles of equal size and hardness, it is an index to distance traveled if it is entirely the result of stream action. Similar or greater roundness, however, may result from prolonged agitation on a beach with little or no lateral transportation. Sphericity is increased by rounding but it is dependent to a large extent on the original shapes of sedimentary particles and their cleavages.

Roundness is most rapidly attained by particles of larger sizes and less resistant materials. Limestone pebbles become well rounded in the course of only a few miles' travel whereas harder rock like quartzite is rounded much more slowly. Well-rounded quartz sand generally records a long geologic history. It has probably passed through several cycles of erosion, transportation, and deposition. The maturity of a sediment is defined in terms of its rounding, sorting, and freedom from unstable minerals and clay as shown in Figure 26.

Sphericity plays an important role in deposition. Highly spherical particles are most compact and settle most rapidly from suspension. Thus they are separated from platy particles like mica flakes of similar weight and density which accumulate with more compact particles of smaller size. Highly spherical particles also are rolled more easily along a sedimentary surface by water or air currents. Approach to spherical shape in sand grains has been

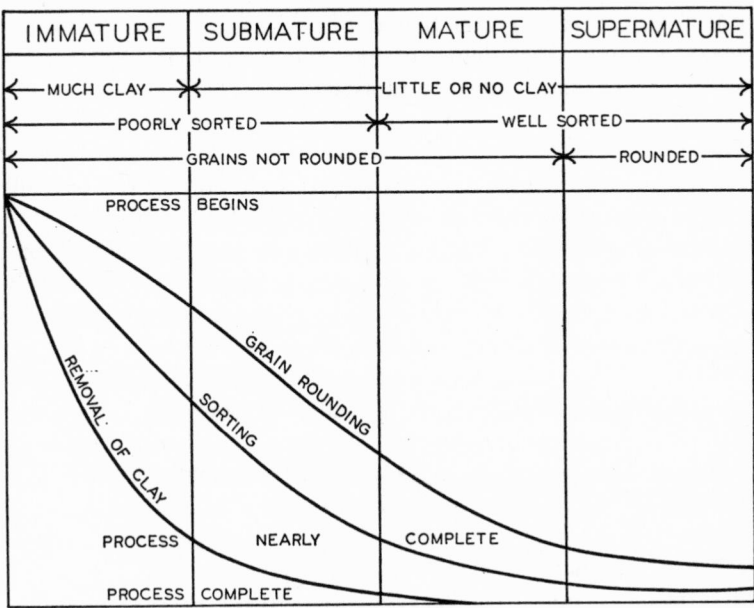

Figure 26. Textural maturity of a sediment is attained by the removal of clay-sized particles, the sorting of large grains, and their rounding. These processes advance at different rates. The stage of textural maturity is determined by the degree to which these processes have approached completion. See also Figure 139, p. 341. (Modified from Folk, 1951, *J. Sediment. Petrol.*, vol. 21, p. 128, fig. 1.)

considered an indication of wear during eolian transportation because of the common concentration of such sand in dunes. This concentration, however, may be partly an effect of sorting resulting from the rolling transportation of much dune sand.

Grains of many sandstones have been enlarged by mineral matter derived from solution and deposited in optical continuity with them. They commonly show reconstituted crystal faces and such sandstones sparkle in the sunlight. Secondarily enlarged sand grains are angular regardless of the shapes of their nuclei. Erosion and transportation of such sand may again produce rounded grains, but the overgrowths generally can be recognized (see Figure 111A, p. 294). Grains of this kind are a sure indication of a previous sedimentary stage in the history of a sand.

Some pebbles and larger rock fragments possess more or less characteristic shapes that serve to identify them as having inhabited particular environments. Noteworthy are the flattened and possibly striated surfaces produced by glacial grinding and the sharply angular forms and polished surfaces resulting from the sandblast action of wind in desert regions. Distinction also has been made between the flattened form of beach pebbles and the more spherical shape of stream gravel. Shapes of pebbles, however, are so strongly influenced by the original shapes of rock fragments that identification on this basis should be made with great caution.

Surface Texture

The surface textures of sedimentary particles are noteworthy only insofar as they differ from those that most commonly occur. The differences may be in the direction of either greater roughness, commonly produced by pits, grooves, and scratches, or greater smoothness. Both appear to be mainly the results of processes that have acted upon the particles during transportation, that is, wear and solution, but the differences from ordinary surfaces suggest that they owe their existence to some other contributory factors.

Grooved pebbles and boulders of glacial origin are familiar objects but most glacial erratics do not show these features and they are easily erased by subsequent stream wear. Also grooves can be produced by the action of ice unassociated with glaciers, as in rivers or upon lake shores, by tectonic grinding, and possibly in other ways. Nonglaciated pebbles, however, are not likely to possess flat planed surfaces.

A high degree of polish has been imparted to the surfaces of some pebbles. This may have resulted from solution in the case of some limestone pebbles, from sandblasting, or from movement of hard rock fragments in a finely silty or clayey matrix as in some Tertiary gravels in the Mississippi embayment region. The so-called *gastroliths* or gizzard stones of the Cretaceous may have acquired their polish in the stomachs of large reptiles.

The frosted surfaces of some well-rounded quartz sands, of which the St. Peter (Ord.) is a good example, have been attributed to wear during eolian transportation. This interpretation may be correct because, theoretically, the buffeting of sand grains propelled by wind should be more severe and effective in their abrasion than that of grains moved by water. The latter have less momentum and the liquid medium provides a cushioning effect. This interpretation has been denied, however, and the suggestion made that frosting has resulted from solution or the beginning of secondary enlargement.

Packing

Spheres of equal size can be regularly packed in various ways so that the intersphere voids constitute a maximum of 47 or a minimum of 26 percent of the total volume. This is the porosity of the aggregate. Sediments do not consist of particles that are spheres or of equal size so these relations are not duplicated in nature. Sediments cannot be regularly packed nor, as they are deposited naturally, are they likely to assume an arrangement that corresponds to the tightest possible packing. Rearrangement may occur, however, and the packing may be improved and become tighter producing a more compact, more dense, and less porous aggregate that possibly is more cohesive.

Well-sorted, coarse, compacted sand has a porosity of about 37 percent. Without cement it is an incoherent mass. Finer sedimentary particles are likely to be more irregular in shape and less closely packed. More pore space is generally included. Clayey silt is 50 percent or more porous. Irregular grains may develop an interlocking structure so that the sediment will hold its form. Clay minerals present in a sedimentary mixture bind it into a more or less cohesive body.

Cementation

The cementation of sedimentary particles by mineral matter deposited in the pores is one of the important processes transforming loose sediment into consolidated rock. Cementation may be slight or it may be so complete that no pore space remains unfilled. The common cementing minerals in sandstone are quartz and calcite. These may occur separately or together. Quartz commonly forms overgrowths on the sand grains and seems to be more abundant in older than in younger sandstones. Quartz cement is rare in sandstone that includes much clay. Dolomite may occur instead of calcite or replace it. Other cementing minerals are known but mostly they are rare except for limonite, which appears to be confined to the zone of oxidation near the surface, and siderite, which cements concretions in some shales.

The grains of fragmental limestones are cemented with calcite. Such cementation is likely to be nearly complete and most limestones are relatively nonporous. Calcite shows much less tendency than quartz to form crystal overgrowths.

The source of cementing minerals is uncertain. The silica in sandstone may have been derived by solution from the sand grains at their points of contact. This conforms to Riecke's principle that solubility increases at points of stress. Such derivation of much cement, however, has been denied. Calculations for nineteen sandstones show that intergranular space, including that occupied by cement, averages less than 25 percent. This is much less than the probable approximate original porosity of the sand—37 percent—

and suggests that closer packing has resulted from solution. Many sandstones, however, contain more silica cement than could have been provided by this process (see Figure 27). Most fragmental limestones consisting of fossil debris or oolites show little or no evidence of intergranular solution (see Figure 124, p. 311). Their cement and the calcite in many sandstones must have had a different origin. There is, nevertheless, nothing to indicate that cementing minerals were not derived from nearby sediments.

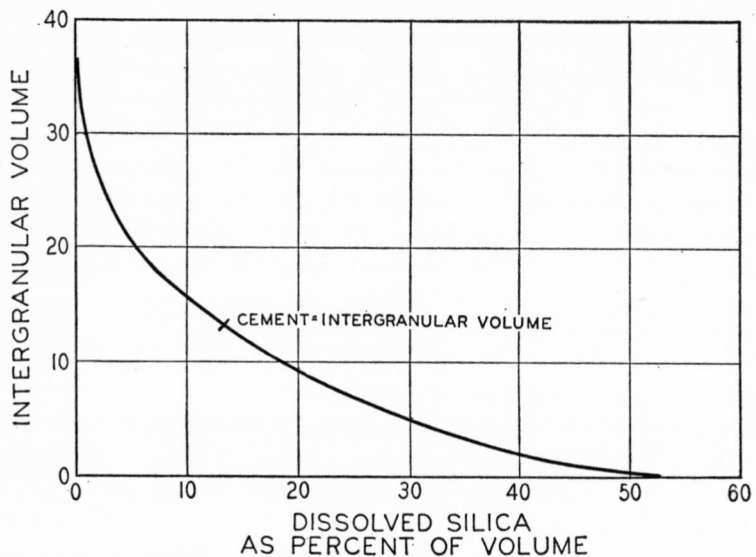

Figure 27. Reduction in intergranular volume rather than in porosity is a measure of the compaction of well-sorted sandstones. This reduction results from solution at grain contacts and closer crowding of the grains. The deposition of cement between the grains reduces porosity further. The curve of this graph shows the approximate relations between the amount of silica dissolved at grain contacts and the remaining intergranular volume. At a value of about 13 percent the deposition of all dissolved silica in the pores would completely eliminate porosity. Completely cemented sands with greater intergranular volume probably contain cement derived from an exterior source. Less than 13 percent intergranular volume in any well-sorted sandstone probably indicates that part of the silica dissolved at grain contacts has been removed in solution from the stratum. (After Weller, 1959, *Bull. Am. Assoc. Petroleum Geol.*, vol. 43, p. 297, fig. 15.)

The interplay of physical and chemical processes involved in cementation is not adequately understood. Near the surface, pore water may evaporate and deposit cementing substances as in the casehardening of outcrops and the formation of beachrock from calcareous sand in the intertidal zone (see Figure 122, p. 309). The factors involved are (1) chemical composition and concentration of solutions, (2) temperature, (3) pressure, and (4) pH values. In the long geologic history of a buried sediment these may have altered repeatedly with respect to one another and resulted in changes and even reversal of cementing action. The paragenesis of cementing minerals has not been the same in all sediments and various types of replacement are known to have occurred.

Compaction

Compaction is another process that has been highly important in the diagenesis of sediments. All porous sediments are subject to compaction as they are buried beneath later deposits and come to bear the increasing weight of accumulating overburden. Compaction results in decreasing porosity and reduced volume or thickness of strata.

The relations of solid matter and pore space in sediments and rocks commonly are expressed in percent porosity. In stratigraphy, however, volume or more specifically thickness relations are more important. These are two different functions of the same factors and they are related as follows:

$$porosity = \frac{volume\ of\ voids}{total\ volume}$$

Conversion of porosity to volume and vice versa for material of any original porosity can be computed according to the following formulas:

$$V = \frac{1 - P_o}{1 - P_c} \qquad P_c = 1 - \frac{1 - P_o}{V}$$

in which V is volume, P_o is original porosity, and P_c is porosity after compaction.

The relations of porosity and volume or thickness in two compacting sediments originally having 80 and 50 percent porosity respectively are shown in Tables 6 and 7.

TABLE 6.   Porosity-Volume Relations in Originally
80 Percent Porous Sediment

Percent Porosity	Volume	Volume	Percent Porosity
80	1.00	1.00	80
70	.67	.90	78
60	.50	.80	75
50	.40	.70	71
40	.33	.60	67
30	.29	.50	60
20	.25	.40	50
10	.22	.30	33
00	.20	20	00

TABLE 7.   Porosity-Volume Relations in Originally
50 Percent Porous Sediment

Percent Porosity	Volume	Volume	Percent Porosity
50	1.00	1.00	50
40	.83	.90	44
30	.71	.80	37
20	.62	.70	28
10	.56	.60	16
00	.50	.50	00

All sedimentary particles in an aqueous environment adsorb films of water at their surfaces. As particle size decreases, surface area increases proportionally and, therefore, the amount of absorbed water also increases. Adsorbed water films serve to separate and hold apart the sedimentary particles. Consequently finer-grained sediments are deposited with greater original porosity than are coarser ones (see Figure 28). Most shales probably accumulated as mud with original porosity of 60 to 90 percent.

The compactibility of any sediment depends upon its porosity. A layer of 90 percent porous mud can be compressed to one-tenth of its original thickness. In contrast, a layer of 37 percent porous sand cannot be compacted to much less than two-thirds of its original thickness.

The natural compaction of clayey sediments appears to be divisible into four successive stages. In the first, adsorbed water films are squeezed out from between the particles until these come into contact with each other. This occurs at a porosity of about 45 percent, at which point most of the plasticity of the sediment is lost. In the second stage, particles move against each other to effect more perfect packing, and porosity is reduced to about 37 percent. This is the point at which mud begins to be transformed to shale. In an originally 80 percent porous mud, thickness has been reduced to less than one-third. Next, the soft clay minerals are squeezed into interstices between the grains of more resistant minerals until the latter come into contact with each other. Studies of cores from wells show that during this stage the porosity of shale decreases more or less regularly with depth. In many ordinary shales, compaction by this process seems to be completed when porosity is reduced to about 10 percent. Last, the more resistant mineral grains are deformed or broken until all porosity is eliminated.

Sandstones are not compacted in a similar manner. They do not pass through the first three stages, in which much water is squeezed out and the mineral grains are extensively rearranged. If pressure were applied rapidly and increased greatly, the compressive strength of sand would soon be exceeded and result in crushing of the grains. Much of the compaction in relatively pure sandstones, however, appears to have been accomplished slowly by solution at the contacts between grains, which produces tighter packing. This process occurs in response to pressure, but the amount of solution accomplished probably is related more closely to chemical conditions and time than to the intensity of pressure. Redeposition of silica, as inter-

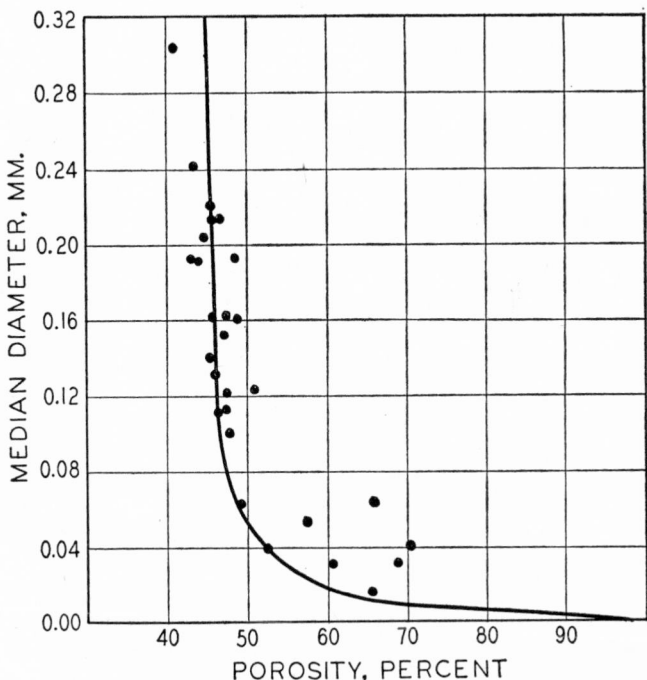

Figure 28.   Graph showing relations between the median grain size and porosity in recently deposited sediment. The curve records Trask's experimental results of 1932. The dots represent actual measurements of San Diego sediments. In sandy material porosity averages about 47 percent and variation in size makes very little difference in porosity. In sediments below fine sand size (0.06 mm.) the porosity increases rapidly. This results from the greatly increased surface area of the sedimentary particles and the increasing volumetric importance of adsorbed water films. See also Figure 112, p. 297. (After Hamilton and Menard, 1956, Bull. Am. Assoc. Petroleum Geol., vol. 40, p. 757, fig. 1.)

granular cement, increases the strength of sandstone and prevents crushing where it might otherwise occur.

Little is known about the compaction of limestone. The ready solubility of calcium carbonate suggests that limestone might react like sandstone but more rapidly. Studies of many limestones, however, reveal that few of them show evidence of much intergranular solution and tighter packing, or of crushing. Limestones of low porosity generally seem to owe their consolidation to cementation by calcium carbonate introduced from some external source.

Differential compaction of sediments can produce structures that are unrelated to any crustal deformation (see Figure 29). Some anticlines and domes, important as oil producers, have been formed by this process above reefs and buried hills. Compaction also is of much interest in stratigraphy because its proper evaluation may influence interpretations regarding the development and histories of depositional basins, the structures of sand bodies (see Figure 110, p. 293), and other sedimentary relations.

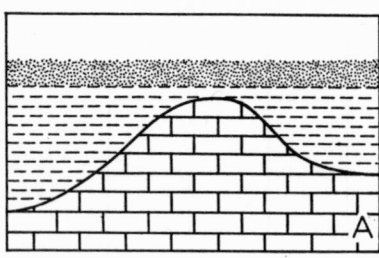

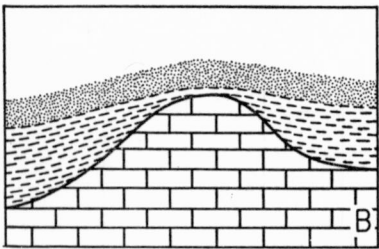

Figure 29.   Diagrams illustrating the development of compaction structure over a buried hill. The horizontal strata shown above the unconformity in A have been compacted by one-third or reduced to two-thirds of their original thickness in B. In nature, of course, this would be a continuous process progressing gradually as sediments accumulated. Therefore compaction structures may be expected to die out upward in the stratigraphic section.

Porosity and Permeability

Porosity is a fundamental property of sediments and sedimentary rocks. To some degree it is an index to certain forces that have affected them. Porosity also determines the amount of fluid that strata can contain and is of great economic importance particularly in relation to water supply and oil production.

Permeability is a kindred but different property that determines the ability of any porous body to permit fluid to pass through it. This ability is related to the intercommunication and continuity of pore space and the size of pores. Depending on the pattern of porosity, equally porous substances can differ greatly in permeability. In general, permeability decreases as pore space becomes finer, and if the pores are very small the decline in permeability is relatively much more rapid. Permeability is important economically in connection with the extraction of fluids from porous strata. Also it may be a significant geologic factor because compaction of sediments necessitates the expulsion from them of great quantities of water, and the ease with which this can be accomplished is governed by permeability.

If sediments were homogeneous, continuous deposition and compaction might be looked upon as furnishing the essentials for a system in which sediment settles steadily through a stagnant water layer. An equally valid concept is that, under these circumstances, water displaced by compaction rises through the column of accumulating sediment. Whichever viewpoint may be taken, the shortest and easiest avenue of escape is upward. In nature, however, sediment is not homogeneous and some layers are certain to be more permeable than others. Under these circumstances, lateral movement of water will occur. In a natural stratigraphic sequence some layers, such as shales, will yield much water on compaction but, because they are relatively impervious, they will drain into both overlying and underlying more permeable strata such as sandstones. In this way foreign solutions are introduced into coarser strata, through which they move, and the resultant chemical changes may determine the nature and sequence of cement deposition or other modifications.

Organic Textures

The textures of many limestones and some dolomites and shales are determined or strongly influenced by the fossil material they contain. Insofar as this consists of very small fossils or fossil fragments that have been transported, the textures are comparable to those occurring in detrital sediments. They are likely to be somewhat coarser under identical current or wave conditions, however, because many fossils or fragments are porous or hollow and, therefore, lower in density than inorganic mineral grains. Larger fossils are much more easily moved than pebbles of comparable size for this same reason or because, like many shells, they are concavo-convex or relatively thin and flat and thus deviate greatly from the compact form of pebbles and most smaller rock and mineral fragments. Fossils have not necessarily been moved, however. Some coarse-grained limestones lack fine material because this has been swept away by currents that were not competent to move the larger constituents.

The textures of many limestones are obscured by the presence of calcareous cement that has eliminated much of the porosity of the original sediment. Rock of this type breaks across the grains and cement alike and shows little more than calcite cleavage faces. Its texture generally cannot be determined without the preparation of thin sections and microscopic study. Considerable portions of some limestones consist of larger masses built by colonial organisms such as corals, stromatoporoids, and bryozoans. Their textures depend upon the size and distribution and the internal organic structure of these masses. Similarly some calcareous algae contributed importantly to limestone. Their detailed structures generally are not well preserved, but, as in some Precambrian beds, their presence may be indicated by various types of peculiar fine concentric layering. Other algae produced nodular masses mostly of small size that are now bound together in a calcareous matrix of different appearance. Limestones of this type, particularly after weathering, may resemble conglomerates. All of these textures and structures are likely to be more or less destroyed by recrystallization. This is especially true of dolomite, which may retain few of the original features of the sediment. Some dolomites, however, acquire a porous texture resulting from the selective solution of calcareous fossils in a dolomitic matrix.

Many fine-grained modern sediments contain innumerable tiny pellets that have been identified as the faeces of various invertebrates. They consist of sedimentary material bound with mucous and exhibit many different forms although oval ones are most common. Generally they are no larger than oolites and repeatedly have been mistaken for them. Similar pellets have been found in limestones. They have been reported most commonly from beds of early Paleozoic age but this may mean no more than that these strata have been examined more carefully than others. Faecal pellets also may occur in shale although few have been described. Perhaps compaction in muddy sediment results in their general destruction. There is some evidence that pellets of this kind have been altered preferentially to glauconite or replaced by phosphate or iron sulfide under post-depositional conditions.

The occurrence of fossils in shale has both interfered with and contributed to the development of lamination. Calcareous shells or fragments interrupt the continuity of fine-grained sediment. If fossils are abundant and have been flattened by compaction, they lie parallel with the bedding and may provide rough parting surfaces. Otherwise the bedding and parting of shale is likely to be poorly developed and such strata are texturally inhomogeneous. Most notably calcareous shales are not well bedded. In some highly carbonaceous shales, most calcareous fossils have been destroyed and removed by solution. Impressions of them may remain, however, along which parting readily occurs. Also carbonaceous plant remains provide surfaces where adjacent shale layers are weakly adherent and splitting is likely to follow them.

STRUCTURES

The more or less minor structures which characterize various sediments and sedimentary rocks may be divided into three groups: (1) bedding structures that are largely of physical origin and owe their existence mainly to processes operating during or shortly after sedimentary deposition, (2) nonbedding structures involving chemical deposition, rearrangement, or solution that mostly occurred after sedimentary deposition, and (3) structures that are related to the activities or the remains of organisms. Mostly these structures are larger-scale features than the textures previously discussed. They are very commonly mentioned in stratigraphic descriptions but their thorough investigation generally requires laboratory study.

Physical Structures

Bedding

Bedding is a type of structure characteristic of most sediments and sedimentary rocks. It is produced by variations of material or by orientation of particles at or along planes disposed approximately parallel to the surface of deposition. Bedding may be apparent in discontinuity of material, change in grain size, difference in color, and tendency to weather differentially or split more easily along these planes. Bedding may result from inequalities or interruptions of sedimentary deposition, from compaction and lithification, or possibly from later alteration of sediments. Most properly the term *bedding* is applied to the original structures of deposition, but later alteration may result in the development of planar structures, including fissility, which closely simulate original bedding. Some of these may be related to bedding characters too subtle to attract notice under ordinary conditions. The actual origin of some bedding structures may be very difficult to determine.

Bedding may be closely or widely spaced, distinct or obscure, evenly parallel or angularly disposed, smooth or irregular. Individual strata set off by bedding planes may be uniformly thick and continuous for long distances or lenticular and unequal in thickness, horizontal or strongly inclined. They may be truncated in various ways by minor or major erosion surfaces.

Several attempts have been made to systematize and closely define terms used to describe bedding. This is difficult because of the extreme variability of bedding and the existence of all intermediate types. No system has gained much following. Most terms are used qualitatively and distinctions generally are vague and relative. A single stratification unit that is not divisible on the basis of subordinate bedding planes is known as a *stratum, bed, lamination,* or *lamina.* It seems useful to recognize *stratum* as a general term. The words *bed* and *lamination* commonly carry thickness connotations, the latter being used for layers below some arbitrary thickness of perhaps about half an inch. *Bed,* however, also suggests more perfect parting along bedding planes and in this sense a bed might consist of laminations.

Some sedimentary deposits are non-bedded, such as glacial till and loess, and some may have had their original bedding destroyed, as have the underclays of coals. Lack of bedding produces so-called *massive* sediments or rocks that appear to be nearly homogeneous throughout. The terms *massively bedded* and *thick bedded* are practically synonymous and describe stratification units perhaps three to four or more feet thick. *Flaggy bedding* implies ready parting of well-consolidated sandstone or limestone in fairly even-surfaced layers a few inches thick. *Fissility* characterizes shales that split evenly into thin layers of uniform thickness in contrast to hackly chips and irregular fragments. Upon weathering, some hard, homogeneous-appearing, highly carbonaceous shales split into thin, somewhat elastic laminae a sixteenth of an inch or so in thickness. They have been termed *paper shales*.

Bedding is most conspicuous in sandstones and limestones whose strata are separated by partings or beds of shale. As detrital rocks become finer grained, their bedding is likely to become thinner, probably because of slower deposition, and less distinct because it is not evidenced by marked variations in grain size (see Figure 30). Increase in the argillaceous content

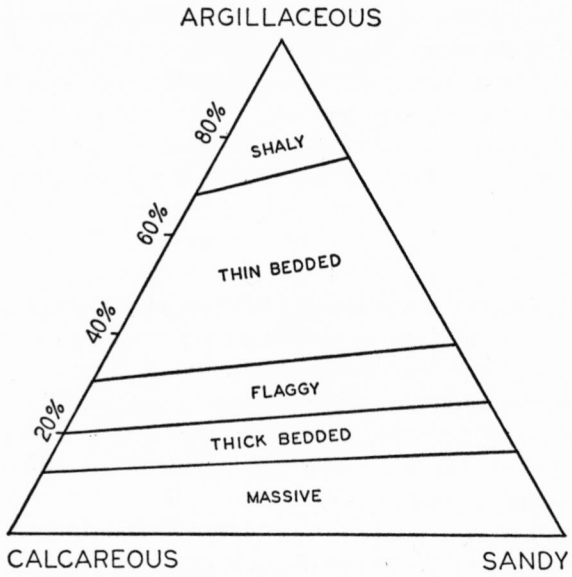

Figure 30. Triangular diagram showing the approximate general relations between composition and thickness of bedding in consolidated sediments. Obvious bedding commonly is produced by the occurrence of more or less shaly partings. In homogeneous sediments without such partings there may be little apparent bedding regardless of the composition. (Modified from Alling, 1945, *Bull. Geol. Soc. Amer.*, vol. 56, p. 751, fig. 6-D.)

of limestones has somewhat similar results. Shales generally are the thinnest bedded of all rocks, indicating probable slow deposition in quiet environments. Their structure, however, may be related in part to compaction and the resulting horizontal orientation of the tiny flakes of their clay minerals. This process appears to require much time for its completion; it may also involve mineralogic changes and reorganization. Most Paleozoic shales are well laminated whereas many younger ones are not. Tertiary argillaceous beds may be massive and almost structureless. The differences probably are related to the alteration of original clay minerals to mica-like *illite,* which greatly predominates in the Paleozoic rocks.

Several other types of structure may be mistaken for bedding. Such *pseudo-bedding* generally occurs in massive homogeneous sedimentary rocks that lack obvious evidence of true bedding. For example, parallel shear planes developed in quartzitic sandstone or dense limestone in disturbed areas of faulting or strong folding may be very deceptive. Others are associated mostly with weathering and are confined to the surface or near-surface zone. They include close jointing and spalling parallel to an outcrop surface, best developed in porous, finely fragmental limestone and produced perhaps by the freezing and expansion of pore water; the firm cementation of friable sandstone in layers also parallel to an outcrop surface, probably resulting from evaporation of pore water drawn to the surface by capillary action; and color banding of the diffusion or Liesegang type that seems to have been produced by oxidation working inward from outcrops, bedding planes, and joint surfaces.

Cross-Bedding

Cross-bedding is true bedding that resulted from interrupted or variable sedimentary deposition on inclined surfaces. It is unfortunate that the term *false bedding* has been employed for this structure.

Sedimentary surfaces very rarely are exactly horizontal. In some situations appreciable slopes occur, as on the flanks of buried hills and reefs, but generally slopes are so gentle as to be inconsequential. Also crustal movements after the deposition of sediment, including uplift, subsidence, and various types of tilting and warping, have altered the attitude of strata so that the exact original inclinations cannot be determined. Rapidly changing local conditions, such as those that are commonly associated with current transportation and deposition, however, are likely to result in the development of irregular bedding and dipping strata that vary considerably both in steepness and in direction of inclination within small areas. If alternate deposition and erosion occurs, minor unconformities are developed that transect the bedding in a discordant manner and furnish planes of reference by which the approximate original inclination of the bedding may be judged.

Cross-bedding is well developed only in the coarser sediments consisting of particles that were rolled along the bottom by current action. It is a common structure in sandstones, particularly those of fluvial origin. Sandstones deposited in standing water are much more likely to be regularly bedded. Cross-bedding is far less common in limestones but it is developed in some fragmental and oolitic strata. Cross-bedding is very rare in shales.

Cross-bedding characteristically consists of *sets* of beds that are similarly shaped and approximately parallel. The sets are of limited and generally moderate thickness and are separated from other sets by stratigraphic planes more persistent than those between the individual cross-bedded layers. The sets may be of considerable lateral extent or they may be extremely local lenses or wedges. Individual cross-beds within the sets ordinarily are concave upward and become thinner and finer grained in their lower, more gently dipping portions. This form and the common truncation of cross-beds above by erosion planes are recognized as one of the surest ways to determine top and bottom directions in strata that have been much disturbed and perhaps stand vertically or are overturned. Observations should be carefully made, however, and checked by other evidence if possible because cross-bedding relations are not uniformly clear. The beds of some sets dip at a nearly equal angle from end to end and appear to be cut off abruptly below as well as above. Also rare cross-bedding that is convex upward may be encountered.

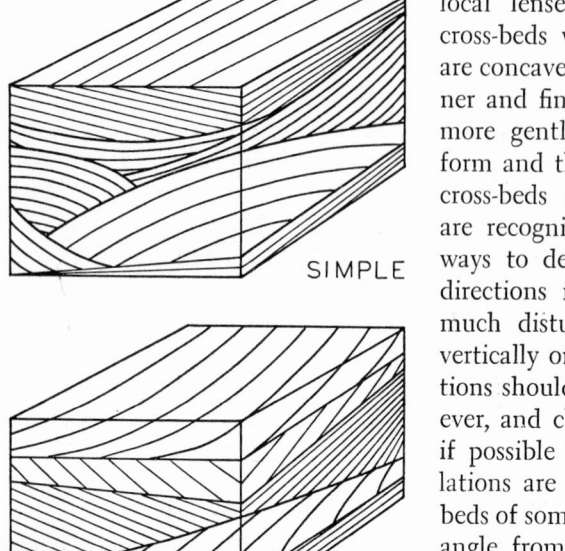

SIMPLE

PLANAR

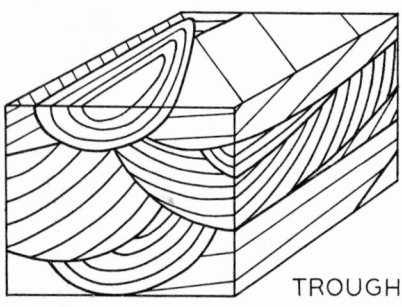

TROUGH

Figure 31. Three types of cross-bedding that are commonly described. Actually, much cross-bedding is difficult to classify. Generally it is seen in cross section and the same structure may present notably different patterns depending upon the orientation of the exposure. (After McKee and Weir, 1953, *Bull. Geol. Soc. Amer.*, vol. 64, p. 387, fig. 2.)

Both descriptive and supposedly genetic classifications of cross-bedding have been presented (see Figure 31). The descriptive classifications do not seem to be particularly useful because there are no sharp distinctions between the various types. These structures generally are seen in cross section and the same set of beds may look quite different depending upon the orientation of the section. Genetic classifications are uncertain because features possibly identifying eolian, fluvial, marine, and lacustrine cross-bedding do not appear to be certainly distinctive and differences are not adequately understood. Theoretically, eolian cross-bedding should be steeper than aqueous cross-bedding because the angle of repose of sand is greater in air than in water (see Figure 32). It is generally agreed, however, that distinction in rocks made on this basis is not certain. Reported dips vary to a maximum of about 43 degrees but mostly they are less than 30 degrees. If sediments have been compacted, of course the inclination is reduced. Eolian cross-bedding is likely to be more irregular than aqueous as to shape of sets and dip direction because of the great variability of winds. Regular sets with nearly parallel surfaces and beds dipping constantly in one direction are almost surely aqueous.

The direction of cross-bedding records direction of the current that produced it because deposition occurs only on lee slopes. Fluvial cross-bedding indicates the direction of flow of streams but many irregularities may result from eddies and meandering, and complete reversal of dip may occur in tidal channels. It is unsafe to project cross-bedding directions for long distances in seeking the source of sediments because the courses of transporting streams may have changed direction importantly and unpredictably.

Figure 32. Cross section of part of a modern sand dune showing nature of the cross-bedding. At some places dips approach 40 degrees. (After McKee, 1957, Bull. Am. Assoc. Petroleum Geol., vol. 41, p. 1726, fig. 22.)

Graded Bedding

Graded bedding is a term used to describe the textural sequence in individual beds which grade from coarser at the bottom to finer at the top, as shown in Figure 33. Grading is fairly common in sedimentary rocks of all ages. It is recognizable in strata whose particles range in size from very coarse to very fine. The thickness of graded beds generally bears a rough relationship to the coarseness of the sediment with coarse beds likely to be thick. This structure is obvious in coarse-grained strata but in the very fine-grained ones it may be megascopically unrecognizable except as it is indicated by color differences. Graded beds commonly occur sharply set off from each other in continuous sequences that may reach great thicknesses with scores or hundreds of repetitions or they may be present as isolated units in otherwise ungraded sediment. Graded bedding is ordinarily associated with detrital sediment. Some of the best examples occur in material deposited in geosynclinal environments. It also is developed, however, in some limestones and in strata deposited in other situations.

The most perfect graded beds resulted from deposition of suspended sediment in bodies of standing water where the coarsest particles settled rapidly and were followed by successively finer and finer material. Deposition of this type indicates a quiet and possibly deep water environment quite different from that characterized by cross-bedding, and these two types of structure rarely are associated. Successions of graded beds may have resulted from (1) seasonal alternations of conditions, (2) alternations of longer period, (3) repeated storms that produced quantities of new land-derived sediment, (4) storms that interrupted continuous sedimentation and periodically

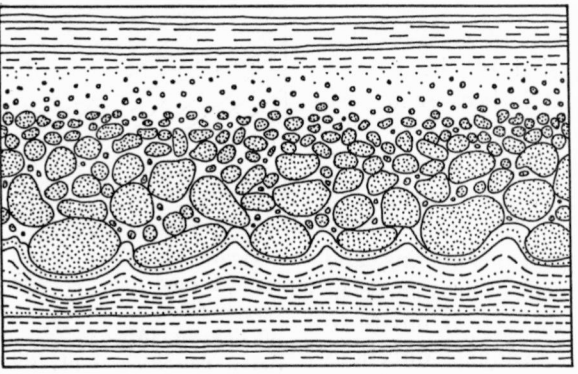

Figure 33.   Generalized drawing of well-graded sediment with pebbles up to one inch in diameter in the uplifted Ventura basin, California. The Upper Pliocene here is more than 6000 feet thick and it contains foraminifera that rarely occur at present at depths of less than 900 feet. The vertical grading of a conglomerate and its presumed deposition in such deep water have been presented as evidence that this is a turbidity current deposit. (After Natland and Kuenen, 1951, Soc. Econ. Paleon. and Miner., Spec. Publ. 2, p. 100, fig. 20.)

stirred up unconsolidated bottom material, (5) successive submarine landslides, and possibly other causes. Single graded beds may have formed in any of these ways and also from slackening of the speed of flowing water. One of the best-known types of graded bedding is exhibited in annual glacial varves.

Graded beds that include pebbles and larger rock fragments seem to require a more restricted explanation because such coarse detritus cannot be held in any ordinary aqueous suspension. Many of these beds probably were produced by deposition from currents of decreasing competency. Beds of this kind, however, could not be expected to follow each other repeatedly in sequence.

Turbidity currents (see Figure 34) are favored as the probable agency responsible for much graded bedding, particularly where it occurs abundantly in thick stratigraphic sections. Turbidity currents responsible for such deposits are believed to have resulted from great submarine slumps of unconsolidated sediment set off perhaps by earthquakes. Sediment set in motion in this way may be churned up with water to form a thick muddy fluid, much denser than sea water, that gathers momentum and flows swiftly downward across the bottom. A fluid of this kind is capable of sweeping along pebbles and, under some conditions, larger rock masses contained in the slumped sediment. Its density aids in sustaining a suspension of much coarse material

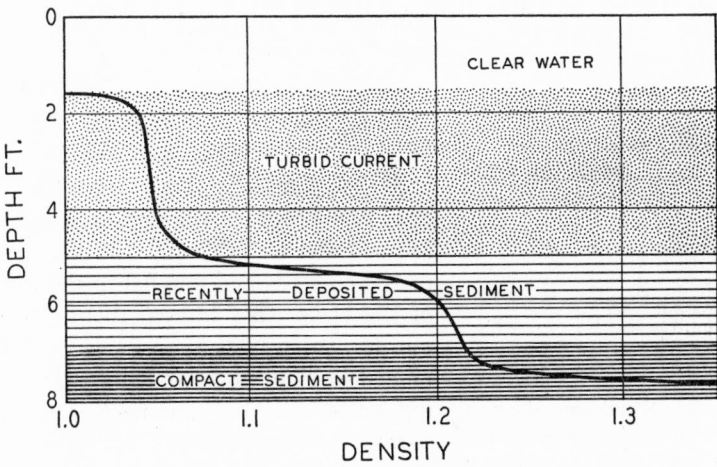

Figure 34. Diagram showing the vertical distribution of density from clear water downward to compacted sediment in Lake Mead at the mouth of Virgin Canyon of the Colorado River valley in November, 1948. A bottom-flowing turbidity current three and one-half feet thick carried enough sediment in suspension to form a newly deposited layer about one foot thick. The zero depth is an arbitrary level at an unspecified distance below the surface of the lake. (After Gould, 1951, Soc. Econ. Paleon. and Miner., Spec. Publ. 2, p. 45, fig. 5.)

that ordinarily would settle out rapidly from any water current of comparable speed and turbulence. Experiments indicate that grading results from the rapid transportation of coarse material in the lower portion of such a current and the later settling of finer sediment from its upper part. The presence of graded beds common in the sediments recovered in some deep-sea cores (see Figure 35) seems to be best accounted for in this way. Turbidity currents also provide an explanation for the occurrence of coarse material on the deep-sea bottom far from any land.

Graded bedding has been much employed in the identification of tops and bottoms of structurally disturbed strata particularly in the Precambrian. Caution must be exercised, however, because, as in the case of cross-bedding, structures showing reversed relations have been observed.

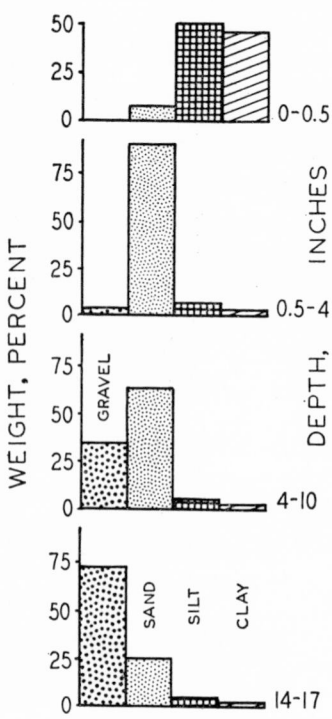

Figure 35. Histograms showing size distribution in segments of a core sample taken in Monterey submarine canyon off the coast of California at a depth of more than 5000 feet. Progressive coarsening downward and the occurrence of gravel have been accepted as evidence of turbidity current deposition. (After Shepard, 1951, Soc. Econ. Paleon. and Miner., Spec. Publ. 2, p. 63, fig. 8.)

Ripple Marks

Ripple marks are produced on the surfaces of incoherent sediments of sand and silt size but are very rare on argillaceous mud. They consist of two general types: (1) *asymmetrical* or so-called *current ripples* and (2) *symmetrical* or so-called *oscillation ripples* (see Figure 36). Where most perfectly developed, they consist of straight parallel wavelike ridges and hollows with wave lengths of a few inches and amplitudes of an inch or less although both larger and smaller ones also occur. With rare exceptions they are oriented at right angles to the direction of the currents and parallel to the direction of the waves that formed them. Most current-formed ripples are irregular and are arranged in somewhat curved and anastomosing patterns. They are fairly common in sandstones of all ages but also occur in limestones. Wave-formed ripples are less abundant but more regular and they also mark both sandstone and limestone surfaces of all ages.

Almost all current-formed ripples are asymmetrical. They develop between certain critical velocities of both water and wind movement by the transportation of sedimentary particles with the current. Ridges are built with a gentle up-current slope, a rounded crest, and a steep lee slope. Grains of sediment are rolled up the gentle slope and across the crest and deposited on the lee slope of the ridge, which moves slowly forward with the current direction. Ripple marks are formed on the beds of streams and larger bodies of standing water in which currents of sufficient strength are active. The size of these ripples probably is determined by sediment size and current velocity but the relations of these factors are not well understood. Current ripples generally are good indication of shallow water although asymmetrical ripples of apparent current origin have been discovered on the sea floor at depths of more than a mile. Eolian ripples resemble aqueous ones except that amplitude as compared to wave length is much less. They are rarely preserved in consolidated rocks. Symmetrical ripples have been observed to form parallel to current direction on muddy sediment in very shallow water.

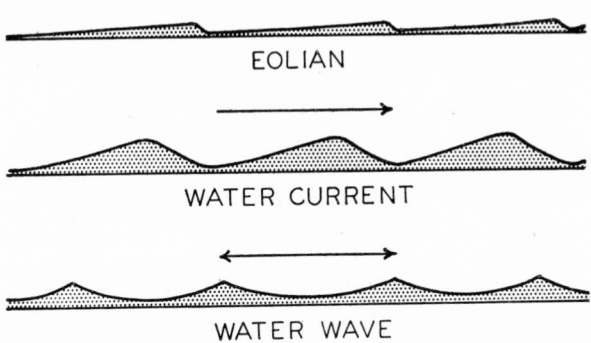

EOLIAN

WATER CURRENT

WATER WAVE

Figure 36. Characteristic profiles of the three principal types of ripple marks. (After Kindle in Twenhofel, 1932, *Treatise on sedimentation*, p. 643, fig. 79.)

Most symmetrical ripple marks, however, are related to wave action and occur only in aqueous sediments. Waves are produced by circular motions in the water which gradually pass into backward-and-forward motions at the bottom. These sweep sediments first one way and then the other and build up sharp-crested ridges separated by concave troughs. Ripples of this type are stationary. Their sizes probably are related to the sizes of surface waves, depth of water, and coarseness of sediment but the influences of these factors are not adequately understood. Minor ridges may develop in the troughs between the major ones, perhaps as the result of a change in the size of waves. Symmetrical ripples can be formed on suitable bottom sediments at any depth reached by appreciable wave action. They have been reported in the open sea at depths of 600 feet or more. Asymmetrical ripples are formed by waves or symmetrical ripples are altered to this form under some circumstances that are not understood. These seem to occur most commonly in very shallow water particularly in the zone of breaking waves.

At some places giant ripple-like structures have been observed that are much beyond the size range of ordinary ripple marks. Both symmetrical and asymmetrical forms occur but all are reported to have rounded crests. Some of them are believed to have been produced by swift currents that moved ridges of sand. Others may be submarine dunes. These explanations do not seem adequate to account for those that mark some limestone surfaces in situations where the former occurrence of powerful currents appears improbable.

Ripple marks are most likely to be found on the surfaces of thin bedded or flaggy strata or on some of the more gently inclined types of cross-beds. They were commonly preserved by the deposition of argillaceous sediment in thin films along which parting of the rock layers occurs or by thicker layers of mud now forming beds of shale. Symmetrical ripples are useful in determining the orientations of steeply dipping or overturned strata because they and their counterpart impressions are quite unlike. Asymmetrical ripples are not similarly useful because they and their impressions are so nearly identical in form that distinction between them may not be possible.

Mud Cracks

All colloidal sediments shrink on drying because removal of water causes their particles to be drawn closer together. Mud cracks developed by this process are common in the argillaceous sediments on modern mud flats, and identical structures are preserved in some consolidated rocks. The cracks generally are widest at the top and narrow downward until they disappear. Their width and depth and the size of the irregular polygonal blocks or columns which they separate depend upon (1) the original porosity or water content of the mud, (2) the amount and kind of clay minerals present, (3) the thickness and homogeneity of the mud, (4) the degree of desiccation, and possibly other factors such as salinity of water and rapidity of drying. Large cracks and columns are most likely to form in thick layers of highly colloidal mud that has dried thoroughly.

Mud cracks rarely develop on tidal flats except in very thin layers because such areas are not exposed continuously enough to permit deep drying. Therefore these structures are most characteristic of sediments and rocks deposited above tide level. Distinct mud cracks do occur, however, in rocks of marine origin including limestone. They may record minor fluctuations of sea level.

The statement has been made that edges of mud-cracked columns tend to curl upward in a fresh-water environment and downward if sediment was deposited in salt and particularly super-saline water. Observations show that this is not an entirely reliable criterion for differentiation. Curling of either type very rarely is noticeable in mud-cracked rocks.

If the drying mud is inhomogeneous and contains thin layers of different texture, parting is likely to occur along these planes. Slight reworking of mud-cracked layers may result in the incorporation of chips, plates, and small flaggy fragments in overlying sediment to produce a peculiar type of conglomerate. So-called *edgewise conglomerate* consists of irregularly disposed and commonly steeply dipping small slabby fragments of limestone in a limestone matrix. It occurs at many places, particularly in Cambrian and Ordovician strata, and may have had such an origin.

In order to be preserved, mud cracks must be filled with sediment of a different type before the muddy layer has the opportunity to absorb water and swell to its former state. Generally the material occupying ancient mud cracks is coarser textured than the mud. It is most likely to be sandy or silty sediment deposited very rapidly by water or swept across the desiccated surface by the wind. Because mud cracks mark one side of a stratigraphic contact and diminish in width downward, these structures are useful in orienting structurally disturbed strata.

Surface Markings

Many different kinds of markings occur on the surfaces of sedimentary rocks and are preserved as casts at the bottom of overlying strata. Some are of uncertain origin but others can be identified as (1) the tracks and trails of animals, (2) pits produced by rain or hail, (3) impressions of salt or ice crystals, (4) minor erosion features, (5) grooves made by the dragging parts of floating objects, and so on. Some may have been impressed on a more or less firm sedimentary bottom under water but others required subaerial conditions. Almost all except the trails of marine animals indicate either exposed or very shallowly submerged surfaces. Some of these markings also are serviceable to determine the top or bottom of a bed.

Under favorable circumstances, markings of all these types may be preserved in consolidated rocks. Three general requirements seem necessary: (1) The sediment must be fine grained and generally somewhat argillaceous in order that the form of a marking may be retained. Sand is a poor medium for the preservation of surface markings although a thin layer of sand underlain by mud may provide suitable conditions. (2) The sediment must be damp but generally not saturated with water. Thus the most favorable situations are mud flats such as the alluvial surfaces of flood plains and deltas, the beds of ephemeral ponds and lakes, and the intertidal zone adjacent to the seashore. (3) The markings must be buried promptly because they are very easily destroyed. Preservation is favored if overlying sediment, generally sand or silt, is different from the underlying layer. Conditions required for the formation and preservation of surface markings indicate that most of them record the temporary atmospheric exposure of sedimentation surfaces in depositional areas.

Contorted Bedding

Irregularities and contortion involving more or less thin layers of sediment or only a single plane of contact between contrasting types of sediment have been observed at many places. They have attracted considerable attention because of their seemingly anomalous relations to both underlying and overlying undisturbed strata. Various explanations have been offered to account for these structures, most of which can be classified in one or the other of two types. Both are related to gravitationally induced pressure with movement in one case acting predominantly horizontally and in the other in a downward direction.

Complex small- to medium-scale folding that is suggestive of lateral compression, accompanied perhaps by the breaking, displacement, or discontinuous drawing out of certain beds, may mark moderate slumping of largely unconsolidated sediments generally in a subaqueous environment (see Figure 37). Material so disturbed overlies unaffected sediment and may be buried subsequently by other undistorted strata. Slumping may involve only thin surface layers or large masses of plastic sediment. In the latter case all bedding features may be destroyed and great blocks derived from more con-

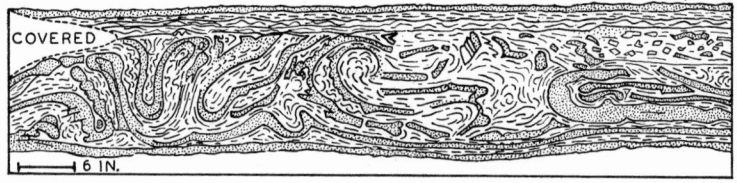

Figure 37.   Sketch of slump structure observed in the Pico Formation (Plio.) of Ventura County, California. This formation also contains graded beds interpreted as turbidity current deposits. (After Crowell, 1957, *Bull. Geol. Soc. Amer.*, vol. 68, p. 1002, fig. 10.)

solidated strata may be moved and irregularly incorporated in the disturbed mass.

Slumping also may be accomplished by gliding along certain more plastic layers without noteworthy distortion of underlying or overlying sediments. These distortions may be confined to one or more zones a few inches to a few feet thick.

Fine-grained sediments settling from suspension are deposited on both level and sloping bottom areas. Steep slopes upon the flanks of reefs or other prominences provide precarious resting places for this material and unequal loading or overloading is almost certain to result eventually in slumping. Gravity-induced lateral movements are not confined to such situations, however, but may occur on very gently inclined surfaces. Slumping is known to have taken place, for example, at angles of less than two degrees.

Some highly porous colloidal clays possess a property termed *thixotropy* or the ability in various degrees to change suddenly from a solid to a more or less liquid condition. Such clays by a gelling or setting process build up an internal structure that provides them with considerable strength. This structure, however, can be destroyed almost instantly by a sudden shock such as an earthquake. Changes of this kind in susceptible layers of shallowly buried sediment probably have resulted in slumping at many places.

Slumping in layered sediments commonly produces contortions and more or less tight folds that extend at right angles to the direction of movement and are inclined downslope. Somewhat similar structures may develop from drag induced in other ways. Thus plastic distortion beneath moving glaciers, turbidity currents, or stranded icebergs may show closely comparable features.

Load Casts

Rolled and billowed surfaces on the under side of sandstones are known as load casts. They develop at the contact between an overlying sand or silt and underlying clay and show more or less complicated infolding of the former material in the latter (see Figure 38). They are produced by gravita-

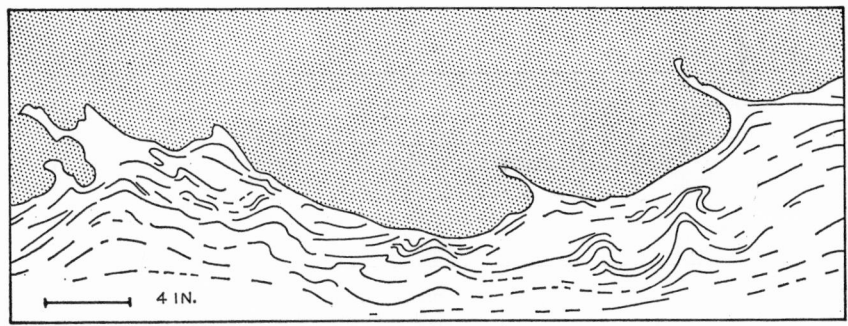

4 IN.

Figure 38. Load casts developed by the irregular settling of sand into underlying unconsolidated laminated silt. Cretaceous of Ventura County, California. (After Kuenen, 1953, Bull. Am. Assoc. Petroleum Geol., vol. 37, p. 1058, fig. 12.)

tional settling shortly after deposition. Highly porous clay is less dense than sand or silt, and slight inequalities in loading cause the latter material to sink unevenly into its plastic underbed. At the same time, and continuing until much later, the clay is progressively compacted and, as water is expelled, shrinks in volume and is further distorted beneath the less-yielding overlying stratum.

Structures of this type can be produced only at the contact of an upper denser and a lower generally more porous and plastic bed. They are especially likely to develop in rapidly deposited detrital sediments. Similar structures have been observed between lignites and overlying sands where settling seems to have occurred while the plant material was in a peaty condition. A somewhat analogous but much more spectacular and protracted process has been responsible for the development of salt domes.

The solution of beds of gypsum or salt causes collapse of overlying strata.

Brecciation may result but under some circumstances rolls, folding, and other structural irregularities develop that resemble the effects of slumping or load settling as just described. Much more rarely, solution of limestone may produce similar results in overlying shale. Structures of this type are confined to near-surface situations.

Uneven under surfaces of sands and siltstones have been produced in other ways. Casts of some erosion surfaces resemble the more simple types of flow and settling structures, but well-developed ones generally can be identified without much doubt.

Boudinage

Boudinage structure is a consequence of tension commonly produced by downslope creep in unconsolidated sediments that does not progress to the stage of more active slumping. Some thin layers that are more cohesive than the surrounding plastic mud may be drawn out and thinned at intervals (see Figure 39). Stronger layers, particularly the more calcareous ones,

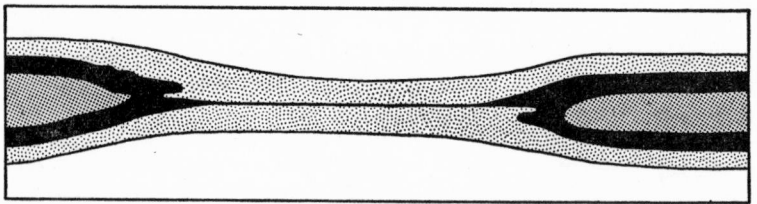

Figure 39. Artificial boudinage produced by the application of vertical pressure on layers of modeling clay and putty that differed in plasticity. All of the layers originally were equally thick. (After photograph by Ramberg, 1955, *J. Geol.*, vol. 63, p. 521, pl. 6, fig. F.)

may be broken into platy fragments that are moved apart and have the intervening spaces filled with overlying and underlying mud as shown in Figure 40. All gradations exist from slight movements of this kind to others that have brought about the rotation and complex displacement of the fragments of certain layers such as occurs as a result of greater slumping.

Chemical Structures

Concretions

The term *concretion* is used rather loosely for a variety of more or less rounded bodies chiefly of inorganic origin, occurring in all types and in all ages of sedimentary rocks, which are different in composition and generally harder and more resistant to weathering than their enclosing matrix. They are not pebbles, because they are not fragments of other rocks and have not been transported, but are closely related in their origin to the surrounding sediment. Generally they consist of more or less impure silica, calcite, siderite, or iron sulfide although a variety of other minerals are reported to form concretions or concretion-like structures. Mostly these other bodies differ in some way from the ordinary types of concretions.

Concretions occur in different shapes ranging from almost perfectly spherical through more or less symmetrically flattened or elongated forms to irregular masses consisting of rounded lobes arranged in almost every conceivable way. Most commonly they are somewhat flattened parallel with the bedding and at many places they are present intermittently at definite horizons or in restricted zones. They range in size from very small to very large but the very small ones generally escape notice and comment. Spherical concretions may be five feet or more in diameter and elongated ones may have lengths of twenty feet or more. Most, however, are measurable in inches.

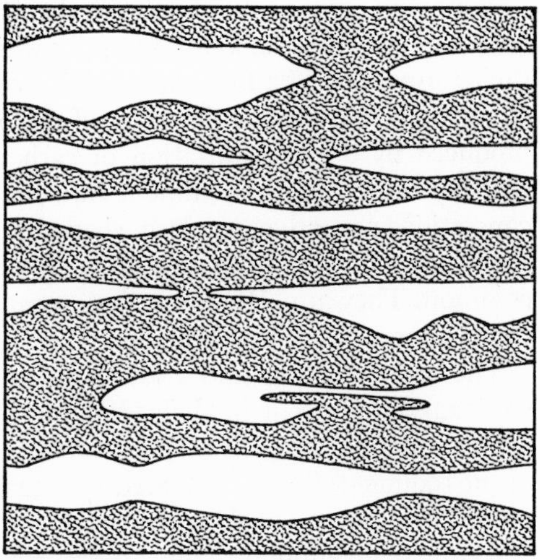

Figure 40. Polished core section, actual size, showing lighter-colored, more calcareous nodule-like masses enclosed in darker, less calcareous matrix. The form and relations of these masses suggest that they are remnants of once continuous layers that were thinned and pulled apart by gravitationally induced creep down a submarine slope before the sediment was consolidated. Compare the next to the lowest mass with Figure 39. Ireton Formation (U. Dev.) Alberta, Canada. (From photograph by R. G. McCrossan.)

Concretions may have clearly defined outlines and abrupt contacts with enclosing rock or their boundaries may be somewhat indistinct. Their surfaces may be roughened, pitted, or smooth. Some are slickensided and others are surrounded by cone-in-cone structure. They generally are very fine grained although iron sulfide concretions may be more or less coarsely crystalline. They may be homogeneous in composition, horizontally laminated, or concentrically banded.

All concretions appear to have grown outward from a center. Growth may have occurred on a subaqueous surface and been followed by burial, it may have taken place within sediments shortly after deposition or much later, or it may have come about within or at the surface of completely consolidated rock either below the water table or in the zone of weathering. Although there is general agreement that concretions originated in several varying ways, there is much difference of opinion as to their actual time and mode of development. Much of the evidence presented in support of supposed primary origin on the sea floor probably is inconsequential and appears to have been misinterpreted or overemphasized.

Concretions in Detrital Rocks

Most concretions fall into one or the other of two classes depending upon their composition, the kind of rock in which they occur, and the method of their formation. The first class consists of calcareous, more or less sideritic concretions that are characteristic of detrital rocks. They seem to have been produced by the concentration of carbonate material, moved in solution, that has cemented the sediment into hard nodular masses. Generally such concretions are rather regularly shaped and some have boundaries that are indistinct. Concretions in sandstone are of this accretionary type but are not common. They are little more than masses of sand firmly cemented by calcite in a more or less friable matrix.

The best developed and most abundant and varied concretions of the accretionary kind occur in shale. Judging by their relations to bedding, they formed or achieved their major growth at various stages during compaction of the sediment. Some originated very early in extremely porous fine-grained mud. They now are enclosed by much-compacted laminae that bend sharply and completely around them. An example is shown in Figure 41. Such concretions may contain excellently preserved uncompressed fossils whereas fossils in the shale are greatly flattened. At the other extreme are concretions preserving in their outer parts some indication of original bedding that continues with little change in thickness from the surrounding shale. These generally occur in very silty beds and are most likely to contain conspicuous organic nuclei that appear to have attracted and caused the precipitation of cementing material. The Pennsylvanian plant-bearing concretions of Mazon Creek in Illinois are good examples.

Concretions in shale appear to have drawn their cementing material from the surrounding sediment because some trace elements present in the shale are depleted nearby and concentrated in them. Concretions with carbonate material least contaminated by silt and clay were formed in relatively young uncompressed sediment and now show the most evidence of surrounding compaction. Some shale concretions contain a large proportion of siderite. These are easily oxidized to limonite in the zone of weathering and they may develop secondary shelly structures or become hollow because of the volume shrinkage that results.

Septarian concretions are similar to other shale concretions but they are characterized by the presence of irregular internal tension cracks that may or may not extend to their surfaces. The cracks seem to have developed at an early stage as a result of the shrinking and partial dehydration of material in a colloidal state. The cracks commonly are filled with coarsely crystalline calcite. Some of them contain other minerals including sphalerite and galena.

Impure calcareous concretionary structures have been produced by the downward movement of ground water and the deposition of material

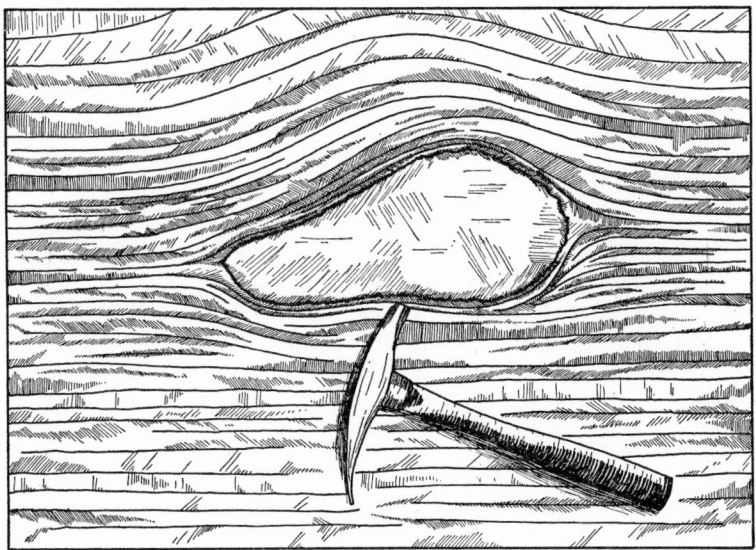

Figure 41. Calcareous concretion embedded in dark-colored shale whose layers conform to the shape of the concretion. Concretions at this locality contain beautifully preserved fossil fish that are very little compressed or distorted. Obviously these concretions developed very soon after deposition of the sediment and before appreciable compaction occurred. Bending of the shale layers around the concretions resulted from subsequent compaction of the shale. Cretaceous, Magdalena Valley, Colombia, South America. (After photograph by Weeks, 1953, J. Sediment. Petrol., vol. 23, p. 166, fig. 4.)

leached from an overlying zone. Examples are *loess kindchen* and nodules in the underclays of Pennsylvanian coals.

Chert Concretions

Chert concretions are characteristic of limestone and dolomite. Most of them seem to have resulted from the selective replacement of carbonate rock by silica. Nevertheless, a primary rather than a secondary origin of chert has been strongly advocated. According to this view, silica was deposited on the sea bottom as a hydrous gel that accumulated in masses which, after burial, were compacted and dehydrated to form chert. That such has been the origin of some chert cannot be disproved but there is little conclusive evidence in its favor. On the other hand, much chert certainly is a secondary replacement product and silica gel is not known to be accumulating anywhere on the floor of the modern sea. Such gelatinous masses as have been postulated would have been compacted to a much greater extent than is indicated by the shapes of most chert concretions. The very perfect and undistorted molds of fossils that are abundant in many concretions show no evidence of decrease in volume of the chert.

Chert and *flint* are practically synonymous terms although efforts have been made to establish different meanings for them. Two general types of chert do occur, but they are connected by complete intergradations. One, which may be designated *chalcedonic chert*, is glassy or waxy in appearance and breaks with very smooth conchoidal surfaces. It may include amorphous silica as well as exceedingly fine-grained quartz. This variety occurs in many colors ranging from grays to black, red, and greenish. In contrast, the other, or *novaculitic chert*, is less vitreous and has slightly roughened, splintery fracture surfaces. Its silica probably consists wholly of somewhat coarser but still very finely crystalline quartz and generally it is some shade of gray.

Although chert is very resistant to weathering, on long exposure it is bleached and becomes slightly porous and possibly somewhat coarser grained. Most unweathered chert contains small but variable amounts of finely disseminated calcite or dolomite. Prolonged leaching probably is important in its decomposition. Some is at last reduced to a fine siliceous powder. Chert nodules commonly are much more irregularly shaped than shale concretions although symmetrical and even spherical ones occur. Bedding rarely shows any indication of bending around them. Adjacent nodules may coalesce to form more or less continuous bands or layers and thus nodules pass into bedded chert. The shapes, sizes, colors, textures, and weathering characteristics of chert concretions may be very different in different limestone formations or zones. These features, therefore, are useful in the identification of some stratigraphic units.

Certain formations like the Devonian limestones of southern Illinois contain chert of more than one generation. The origin of the earlier chert is not known with certainty but there is much evidence that late chert is a product of replacement and all of it may have formed similarly but at different times. Certain beds of chert and limestone meet at well-developed stylolitic surfaces proving that silicification was later than stylolite formation. Outcrops also exhibit laterally continuous beds passing abruptly from limestone with scattered chert nodules into completely chertified layers without change in thickness or destruction of some of the textural features of the original limestone as shown in Figure 42. Active and comparatively recent and rapid replacement in other limestones is shown by silicification of parts of fossils exposed on the surfaces of outcrops which continue as calcite where the remaining parts are enclosed in rock. Chert nodules stand out in strong relief on some weathered outcrop surfaces but lose their identity and grade inward into almost unaltered rock. Nodules of this kind probably are growing at the present time. Analyses of some limestones have shown that the silica content decreases as chert nodules are approached. Mines, quarries, and diamond drill cores prove that chert becomes less abundant in many limestones at only a short distance below the surface. Also more chert is present in the residual soil derived from some limestones than could be furnished by them as they are constituted in an unweathered state nearby. On the other

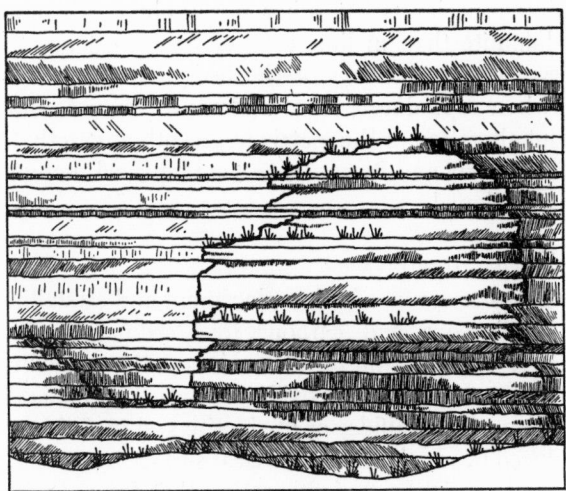

Figure 42. Outcrop of Bailey Limestone (L. Dev.) in road cut east of Thebes in southern Illinois. This formation consists of fine-grained, very silty limestone in thin even layers. It becomes silicified and is transformed to chert in the zone of weathering. This outcrop shows a knob of fresh unweathered limestone about five feet high projecting upward into secondary chert. The contact is sharp, and layers pass without reduction in thickness from the limestone to the chert. Evidence is provided here that chertification involved the introduction from some external source of much silica that replaced the limestone. (Drawn from photograph by Weller, 1944, Ill. Geol. Surv., Bull. 68, p. 92, fig. 16.)

hand some limestones appear to be as cherty far below the surface as they are at any outcrop.

Much chert almost certainly is a concentration of silica originally disseminated in limestone in the form of sponge spicules, radiolarians, diatoms, and possibly tiny grains of quartz. Some silica, particularly that constituting late chert, may have been transported in solution and some nodules lie along bedding planes that may have furnished a passageway for solutions. Much chert, however, is enclosed in essentially nonporous limestone. The silica that formed it probably moved by diffusion along crystal surfaces.

Silicification of carbonate rocks has been highly selective. The physical chemistry of this process is not adequately understood but evidently some differences in local conditions produced exactly opposite results. Thus in certain formations chert seems to have been reluctant to replace dolomite, and silica occurs disseminated in dolomitic layers but concentrated in concretions in the limestone layers. At other places chert concretions are more abundant in dolomite than in limestone of equivalent age. Chert may or may not preserve various textures of the beds that it replaces. Crystalline structure is nowhere reproduced. In some beds fossils and oolites have been silicified without alteration of the matrix but in others exactly the reverse occurs. If both the matrix and its contents were replaced, homogeneous chert commonly was developed.

Other Concretionary Structures

Pyrite and marcasite occur as both replacement and crystalline concretions generally in argillaceous and carbonaceous sediments. The crystalline masses seem to have made room for themselves as they grew by the displacement of surrounding material. Iron oxide concretionary masses have resulted from the oxidation of the sulfides or of siderite and probably are exclusively structures produced by weathering in the near-surface zone.

Coal balls are a special type of concretion that formed very early in the diagenesis of peat before plant structures were much decayed or had suffered appreciable compaction. They are more or less rounded calcareous masses, some of which consist partially of iron sulfide or silica, ranging upward to a diameter of about one foot. They occur closely crowded in nests or pockets in the upper parts of Carboniferous coal beds and are surrounded by slickensided films or masses of coal. In them, plant structures are beautifully preserved as the result of replacement, infiltration, and cementation by mineral matter.

Many other objects resemble concretions in some respects. These include phosphatic and manganese nodules, which are believed to form slowly on the sea bottom, crystalline rosettes of silica and gypsum, which replace limestone, oolites, and other structures. Like concretions they have grown outward from their centers as the result of some localized chemical reaction or some physical condition that is not adequately understood.

Stylolites

Stylolites are exceedingly irregular and completely interlocking columns of various lengths that project in opposite directions and meet along a very uneven surface. They are best seen in cross section where they produce a seam or suture that rises and falls abruptly like a steeply angular graph (see Figure 43). Stylolites are abundant in some limestones and occur in many dolomites. They are found rarely and poorly developed in some sandstones and are present in or at the surfaces of some chert beds and nodules.

Stylolitic surfaces generally extend nearly horizontally and commonly they appear to correspond with horizontal or gently dipping bedding planes. Some, however, are steeply inclined or even vertical and cut across the bedding. An example is shown in Figure 44. Stylolitic surfaces may be continuous over considerable areas or fade out and disappear rapidly in a lateral direction. They may join each other and coalesce or intersect and cross each other at low or more rarely at high angles. Stylolitic surfaces characteristically bear a film or thin layer of clay and other insoluble material.

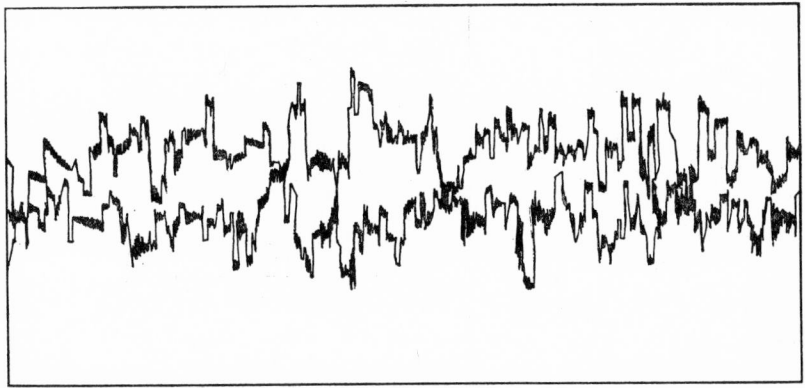

Figure 43.   Cross sections of two closely spaced typical stylolite seams in the Salem Limestone (Miss.) of southwestern Indiana as seen in a quarry wall. In places they meet and interfere. No scale provided. (After photograph by Stockdale, 1922, Ind. Univ. Studies No. 55, p. 65, fig. 32.)

Stylolites attain a length of six inches or more but generally are less than two inches long. Their sides are very steep or vertical and commonly fluted and they may appear to be slickensided. The tops of columns are hackly or more rarely flat and bear caps of insoluble material.

Stylolites have been produced by differential solution along both sides of a bedding plane, parting, fracture joint, or other type of contact surface. They develop in response to pressure; columns normally are elongated in the direction of the main pressure component. All rocks bear the weight of overlying material, and in areas of nearly horizontal strata and gentle structure stylolites are directed vertically.

The contention has been made that at least some stylolites originated in unconsolidated sediments and that interpenetration resulted from flowage induced by pressure. No convincing evidence supports this theory. Most stylolites certainly owe their existence to solution in solid rock. Proof is furnished by (1) good development only in soluble rocks, (2) transection of fossils and oolites, parts of which have been destroyed, (3) occurrence along joints transverse to bedding and at the contacts of calcite veins and wall rock, and (4) insoluble material in clay caps which is similar and approximately equal to that contained in thicknesses of limestone comparable to the lengths of columns.

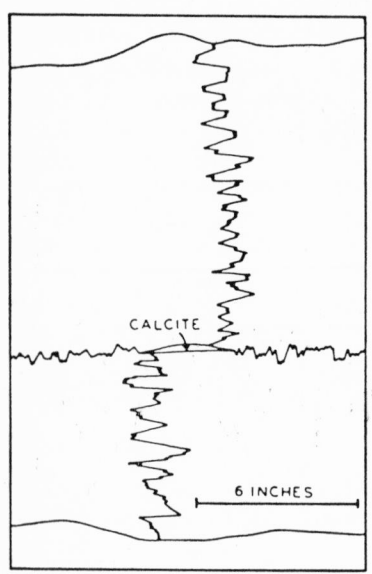

CALCITE

6 INCHES

Figure 44. Sketch showing both horizontal and vertical stylolites in the Pinery Limestone Member of the Bell Canyon Formation (Perm.) in the Guadalupe Mountains of west Texas. Many stylolites cutting transversely across the bedding were observed in the walls of McKittrick Canyon and at other nearby places. (After Rigby, 1953, J. Sediment. Petrol., vol. 23, p. 269, fig. 6A.)

Solution responsible for the development of stylolites occurred on both sides of a plane that originally was fairly flat and smooth. At some places solution was more active on one side and at others on the opposite. As it progressed this produced complementary recesses and projections and the penetration of each bed by columns of the other. The insoluble residue remaining after solution constitutes the argillaceous film that lies along the stylolitic surface.

Stylolites are best developed in pure limestones. The longest columns and most abundant stylolitic partings occur in crystalline or coarsely fragmental strata. The total amount of solution evidenced by stylolites is great in many limestones, and the thicknesses of some formations have been reduced by 25 percent or even more. This may be a factor of considerable importance in quantitative stratigraphic studies when the amount and thickness of sediments and rates of deposition are estimated.

Most strata cut by stylolite seams were originally very porous. The source of calcite that now cements them thoroughly and the disposition of the calcium carbonate removed in the development of stylolites are both uncertain. Possibly calcite dissolved at a stylolitic seam was deposited as cement nearby. This is questionable, however, because it seems unlikely that solution would have been so localized in a porous rock. Thin films of organic matter might have produced chemical disequilibrium and caused solution along these planes. Such an explanation would not apply to the development of stylolites along joint surfaces or at vein margins. The intersection of some stylolitic seams by others shows that solution probably was most active along different seams at different times.

Stylolites mark dipping planes in the flank beds of some Silurian reefs in Indiana. The columns are oriented vertically and rise at an angle to these planes recording the action of vertical pressure (see Figure 45). The columns of seams that follow dipping non-reef beds in some other areas are perpendicular to the seams and are believed to have developed before the strata were inclined. Vertical or steeply dipping seams that cut across the bedding probably were produced in response to lateral compression. They are rare except in areas of faulted or folded rocks.

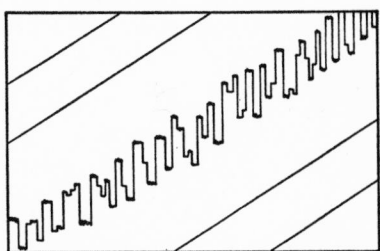

Figure 45. Schematic drawing of vertical stylolite columns observed by E. R. Cumings in the dipping flank beds of Silurian reefs in northern Indiana. Stylolites of this type are believed to have developed in inclined strata. No scale provided. (After Stockdale, 1922, Ind. Univ. Studies No. 55, p. 54, fig. 22.)

Stylolitic partings of very low relief occur rarely in some well-cemented sandstones, cherts, and quartzites. They probably were produced by solution of silica comparable to the solution of calcite in many limestones. The sutured contacts of quartz grains in many sandstones appear to be stylolites in miniature (see Figure 111B, p. 294). Larger stylolites in chert or at contacts between chert and limestone are relict structures developed before the silification of limestone and the formation of secondary chert.

Other Solution Surfaces

Structures occurring on the bedding surfaces and in zones of shearing parallel to bedding surfaces of some steeply dipping strata combine features of slickensides and stylolites; they have been termed *slickolites*. These surfaces bear irregular bands two to three inches wide extending along the strike that are polished and faintly grooved by down-dip slickensides and terminate below in shallow sutured pits (see Figure 46). Slight downward slipping of overlying strata accompanied by some solution is indicated. These structures have been observed in the flank beds of some Silurian reefs of the Chicago area and on steeply dipping Mississippian strata in western Illinois. In the latter area they record interstratal movement just the reverse of that normally occurring on the flanks of steep anticlines and synclines.

Solution of limestone almost certainly has occurred along some bedding planes without the development of stylolites. Some thin shaly partings between limestone strata therefore probably are insoluble residues similar to the material remaining at stylolitic contacts and not mud that settled during brief interruptions of calcareous deposition.

Geodes

Geodes are roughly spherical bodies, commonly hollow and typically lined with inwardly projecting quartz crystals. They occur in limestone much as chert nodules do and appear to have grown by expansion. They are most abundant and best formed in certain Mississippian formations throughout wide areas but they also occur in rocks of other ages. Their sizes range from an inch or less to more than a foot in diameter.

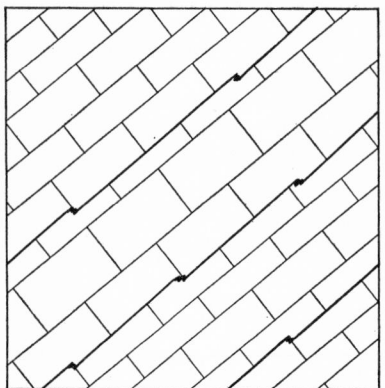

Figure 46.   Drawing showing the relations of slickolites to bedding planes as they would appear in transverse cross section. Slickolites are not likely to be observed except upon exposed bedding planes where they appear as roughly parallel slickensided bands.

Structures that appear to be incipient geodes suggest that these bodies have been produced by the fragmentation of certain fossils, particularly crinoids, and the growth of crystals between the fragments (see Figure 47). The fossils seem to have been progressively distorted and replaced by silica until all traces of organic structure were destroyed. The expansion of geodes has been explained as resulting from the force of crystal growth or—much less likely—from osmotic pressure developed by diffusion through an outer layer of silica gel.

The growth of geodes seems to have been accompanied by some solution

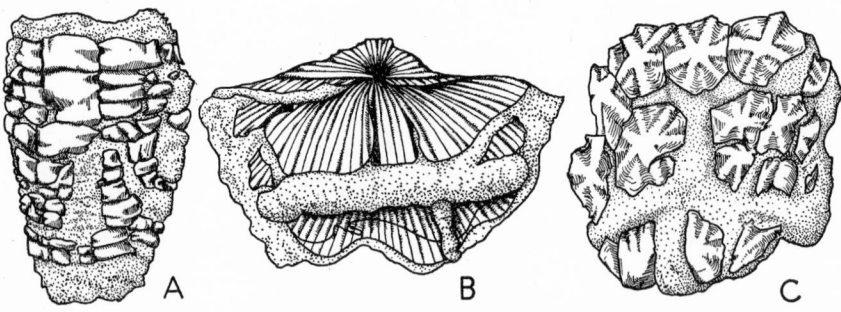

Figure 47.   Fossils showing fragmentation and expansion resulting from the growth of silica wedges in cracks. Specimens of this sort have been interpreted as early stages in the development of geodes. A, Crinoid stem, x1.5. B, Spirifer, x⅔. C, Crinoid, x⅔. A and B are from the New Providence Shale (Miss.), Button Mold Knob near Louisville, Kentucky. C is from the Tullahoma Formation (Miss.), White Creek Springs, Tennessee. (After photographs by Bassler, 1908, *Proc. U.S. Natl. Museum*, vol. 35, p. 146, pl. 20, fig. 8; p. 154, pl. 24, figs. 7 and 8.)

of surrounding limestone and the formation of poorly developed stylolite-like outer contacts. Well-formed geodes are not common in pure limestone, however, and some of the most perfect ones occur in somewhat massively bedded impure strata or in highly calcareous siltstone. The latter specimens indicate that some displacement of enclosing material probably was necessary for their growth. This may be evidence that geodes developed in unconsolidated sediment.

Quartz crystals lining the inner surfaces of typical geodes may be covered by later deposits of banded chalcedony, crystals of calcite, dolomite, and other less common minerals including kaolinite. These indicate important changes in the local chemical environment. Some geodes have been found containing oil. The growth of quartz crystals continued in some geodes until the central cavity was completely filled thus forming solid quartz spheroids.

Some rare geodes or geode-like structures consist of minerals other than quartz. Gypsum geodes have been observed in the Mississippian limestone of western Kentucky and calcite geodes also may occur. More or less spherical vugs in limestone lined with crystals resemble geodes, and distinction between these two quite different kinds of structure may be difficult.

Cone-in-Cone

Cone-in-cone is a type of shear structure produced by the development of irregular columns consisting of nested cones in impure calcareous material. It generally occurs in very argillaceous strata and forms layers or lenses, rarely more than four inches thick, or in zones surrounding concretions. The cones commonly have apex angles of from 30 to 60 degrees although some with broader and others with narrower angles have been reported. The diameters of columns are about half their height but this ratio is rather variable. The size of columns and the shape of cones generally shows little variation within individual layers.

Cone-in-cone commonly consists of 60 to 98 percent calcium carbonate that occurs in fibrous calcite crystals arranged vertically in the columns. The cones are separated by films or thin layers of clay along which parting occurs when specimens are broken. The surfaces of cones generally are marked with fine longitudinal striations radiating from the apex and much coarser irregular annular ridges and depressions. Many of the cones are incomplete or imperfect in their overlapping relations. Some large columns have smaller, less-well-developed columns of subsidiary cones within them.

The origin of cone-in-cone has been much debated. None of the several theories presented to account for it appears to provide an entirely adequate explanation, and little progress has been made in understanding these structures. Agreement is general that pressure has been an important factor in cone-in-cone development. Repeated comparisons have been made with pressure and shatter cones produced in other materials. Pressure responsible for cone-in-cone has been attributed to weight of overlying sediment, force of crystal growth, and expansion of concretions. Comparison has been made of cone angles with the angle of rhomboidal cleavage in calcite. Also solution has been called upon to account for the clay films on the supposition that they are insoluble residues.

Cone-in-cone layers certainly have been subjected to considerable weight of overburden and probably this is a sufficient pressure source. The origin of the calcite fibers remains unexplained. They must be secondary and they may have formed before the sediment was much consolidated or compacted. If the fibrous crystals were unoriented except along their long axes, shearing on the cleavage, probably produced incidentally to compaction, would have occurred in all directions. This may have become more pronounced as compaction continued and developed concentric patterns around fairly evenly spaced centers and thus produced the columns. The size of columns appears to be related to column length. Solution along the principal shear planes seems to explain the cones. Angles of cones may have been determined by the physical nature of the layer and the stage of compaction it had reached at the time calcite fibers formed or by the amount of subsequent compaction.

Cone-in-cone has been noted in formations of all ages from Cambrian to Tertiary. Gypsum cone-in-cone occurs in Kansas but it may be an alteration after calcite. Structures resembling cone-in-cone in British coal require a different explanation.

Oolites

Oolites are tiny spheroids generally no more than a twenty-fifth of an inch in diameter built up of concentric layers that commonly enclose a recognizable central nucleus. If abundant in a sediment, they provide it with a distinctive texture. Other similar bodies without concentric layering or without nuclei, and some foraminifera, are easily confused with oolites.

Many kinds of oolites or oolite-like bodies have been reported composed of different minerals and supposedly formed in different ways. The most common ones are calcite and occur in marine formations. At some places these are so abundant that they are the main constituent of limestone. Elsewhere they are associated with fragmental calcareous particles and may not be apparent except on close examination. They are rare in very fine-grained limestone and in dominantly detrital sediments. Some oolites of different composition, particularly siliceous and dolomitic ones, undoubtedly were produced by the replacement of calcium carbonate but the origin of others is more or less disputed.

Calcareous oolites generally contain recognizable nuclei which are mineral grains of various kinds, fragments of fossils, or other objects. The nuclei are of various sizes and shapes but as successive layers enclose them, more and more spherical forms develop. The concentric laminae are of unequal thicknesses and are distinguishable from each other because of slight differences of color, opacity, and crystal structure (see Figure 48). Some of the thicker layers may consist of radially directed calcite fibers. These minute structures, however, are likely to have been altered by recrystallization and some oolites have lost all traces of their concentric laminae in this way. Larger fossil fragments and the whole shells of tiny fossils in richly oolitic deposits may bear thin incrustations of similar laminae.

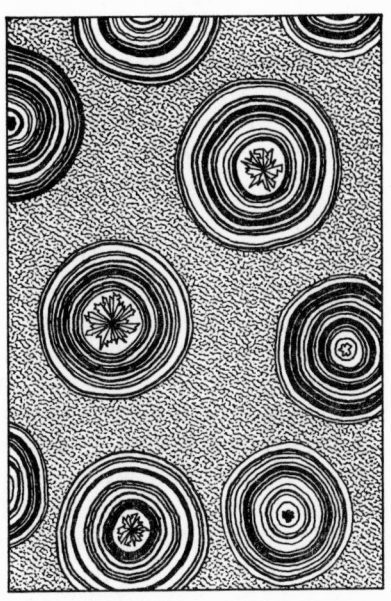

Calcareous oolites are being formed at present in the shallow warm clear waters of the Bahamas, the Red Sea, and elsewhere. They consist of aragonite, and probably the oolites of older limestones originally were similar but have altered to more stable calcite. Although algae have been mentioned as the agents responsible for the development of modern oolites, it is much more probable that oolites are inorganic and certain algae adhere to them just as these tiny plants live attached to or bore within many other objects. Sea water saturated with calcium carbonate and perhaps slightly more saline than ordinary seems necessary for the development of oolites. Also moderate turbulence of water appears to be required to keep the growing oolites in more or less constant motion and to

Figure 48.   Oolites enclosed in finely crystalline limestone from the Triassic of Germany. These oolites are about one mm. in diameter. They are unusual in that many of the nuclei about which the concentric layers grew appear to have recrystallized. (Drawing much generalized from photograph by Correns in Barth, Correns, and Eskola, 1939, *Die Entstehung der Gesteine*, p. 244, fig. 65, by permission of Springer-Verlag.)

permit calcium carbonate to accumulate uniformly over their whole surfaces. Size probably is limited by the lifting power of normal waves in shallow water. When oolites become so large that they remain motionless on the bottom they cease to grow. Larger bodies of somewhat similar form and structure, commonly termed pisolites, had a different origin. Some are algal bodies and others may have been produced by some kind of concretionary process within a sediment or a residual deposit.

Calcareous oolites and others altered by replacement occur in sedimentary rocks of the Precambrian and all later ages. Limestones with abundant oolites commonly are cross-bedded and exhibit other features indicating rapid deposition and wave or current action in shallow water. There can be little doubt that such strata record the existence in the geologic past of conditions similar to those now prevailing where oolites are being formed. Richly oolitic limestones generally are neither thick nor extensive laterally, indicating that oolitic environments of the past were temporary and local features of more extensive seas just as they are today. Oolites originating in such areas, however, may have been transported in greater or less abundance and deposited with other sediment in nearby areas.

Calcareous oolites are being formed in a few modern lakes, both salt and fresh, and in hot springs. So far as is known, oolites of this kind have rarely been preserved and they have not been identified in many ancient sediments. Siliceous oolites are present at many places but seem to be most common in the older geologic systems. They generally occur in chert or in zones where other components of limestones and dolomites have been silicified. Most of them were originally calcareous although there are some possible exceptions. Hematite oolites are abundant in some restricted stratigraphic zones such as the Clinton Group (Sil.) of the Appalachian region. Their original nature has been the subject of much argument but they occur with strata in which calcareous fossil shells have been replaced by iron oxide. The generally flattened form of these ferruginous oolites has been cited as evidence both for and against replacement. Dark-colored phosphatic bodies resembling oolites possibly formed on the ocean floor in areas of very slow sedimentary accumulation, but light-colored ones probably have been replaced, and larger pisolitic bodies are most likely concretionary.

Spherulitic structures much like oolites and pisolites occur in clay but they had a very different origin. They are present only in material of high alumina content like the diaspore of Missouri and bauxite. These are secondary structures developed during the protracted leaching that removed silica and purified what was originally more ordinary clay.

Organic Structures

Large and conspicuous organic structures such as reefs and bioherms are considered in Chapter 14. Smaller ones comparable to the physical and chemical structures described in the preceding pages are closely related to organic textures and have been mentioned (see p. 99). They consist mainly of (1) the internal structures of fossils themselves that become the structures of the rock if fossils are cemented to form solid limestone, and (2) types of bedding and parting especially in shale which are more or less strongly influenced by the presence of fossils. The development of many concretions also appears to have been related to the localized occurrence of organic material that created chemical conditions conducive to the diffusion and precipitation of several kinds of mineral matter.

COLORS

The color of a rock is one of the first things noted by an observer. Commonly it is also the rock's most intangible quality. The color is different depending upon whether a rock is wet or dry. When wet, colors are darker and more intense. Less striking but comparable differences depend upon whether a rock is viewed in bright sunshine, shade, or artificial light. The visual impressions of color in individual layers or rock bodies are influenced by the colors of adjacent rocks and other nearby objects. Also the quality of a surface, whether smooth or rough, affects its apparent color.

The color of a rock or sediment depends upon (1) the intrinsic colors of the minerals or rock fragments of which it is composed, (2) the sizes of these fragments and the closeness of their packing, (3) the amount and kind of organic matter present, and (4) the amount and degree of oxidation and hydration of iron compounds. Of these, the last two are generally much the most important.

Intrinsic Colors

The common stable minerals which constitute by far the greater part of most sediments and sedimentary rocks are light colored. Thus crystalline quartz and calcite are colorless or, if divided into fine particles, intensely white. Most clays if uncontaminated are white or very slightly greenish. Colored minerals like pink feldspar may be abundant in some sediments and color them but these minerals become white when pulverized. Only the ferromagnesian minerals and certain metallic oxides, which remain dark in a finely divided state, are likely to influence the colors of sediments importantly. Most sediments are fine grained and, therefore, they and sedimentary rocks of similar texture are very light gray or white if devoid of organic matter and iron compounds. Exceptions are rocks of the graywacke type containing abundant fragments of dark minerals and rocks, and unusual sediments like some beach sands in which dark heavy minerals are concentrated.

Chemical decay of rocks and minerals accomplished either at the place of origin of sediments or later is almost certain to alter or destroy original colors. Consequently sediments colored by their constituent minerals or rock fragments are most likely to be produced in arid or cold regions where chemical activity is at a minimum or by very rapid mechanical erosion elsewhere. Such sediment may be transported through or to a different environment where chemical alteration is likely to occur. Therefore, transportation and deposition also must be accomplished under arid or cool conditions or must be extremely rapid if sediments are to retain intrinsic colors.

Compaction somewhat alters the colors of fine-grained sediments and rocks. Closer crowding of the particles produces darker or more vivid shades.

Organic Matter

Most darkening of rock colors through shades of gray to black results from the presence of organic matter. Carbonaceous compounds derived from the degradation of plant tissues are most effective. After the early stages of this process the organic matter is intensely black. Bituminous compounds, on the other hand, particularly those that have evolved farthest as the result of dynamochemical action, have less influence on sedimentary colors. Most sediments contain some organic matter but the darkening that results is not closely proportional to the amount present (see Figure 18, p. 68).

The occurrence of appreciable organic matter in sediments implies (1) that organisms existed in some abundance in or near the area of deposition and (2) that their remains were not completely destroyed. The preservation of organic matter is in turn dependent both on the kind of matter present and on the conditions to which it has been subjected.

Tissues of the higher plants, particularly those with woody stems, are more resistant to bacterial decay and are less likely to be consumed as food than are those of animals and more primitive plants. Because most of the terrestrial environment now is dominated by the higher plants, their remains constitute the organic matter in terrestrial sediments to the almost complete exclusion of other kinds. Since late in middle Paleozoic time, when plants became adapted to many land environments, all terrestrial sediments except those produced, transported, and deposited under extremely arid or extremely frigid conditions are likely to have contained organic matter of this kind. Terrestrial organic matter, however, is subject to more or less complete destruction in areas of high temperature, high humidity, and good soil drainage where rapid bacterial action is favored. Consequently dark colors in terrestrial sediments resulting from high organic content generally indicate moderately low temperature or poor drainage at the site of deposition.

The food chain in the sea begins with tiny planktonic diatoms and algae and progresses through a more numerous and more complicated series of animal stages than it does on land. Most of these microscopic plants are eaten by animals but the remains of some sink to the bottom with other sediment. Larger plants with resistant woody tissues are essentially lacking in this aqueous environment. Consequently much less organic material derived from plants is potentially available for burial in marine sediments in comparison to that which might be contributed by animals than upon the land. The most important possible exceptions are provided by some shallow coastal areas where seaweeds are abundant. Finally, cool temperatures prevailing in the sea, except in shallow water of the tropics, are less favorable for rapid bacterial decay than the higher temperatures of most land areas.

Marine sediments, therefore, are more likely to contain easily digestible organic matter of animal origin than are sediments of the land. This is reflected by the host of scavenging creatures that live on or in sea-bottom sediments and obtain their nourishment by eating mud. Under favorable conditions their activity removes much of the organic material. This is most likely to be preserved if deposition is too rapid for scavengers to eat it all or if physical conditions are unfavorable for their existence. Most richly organic and therefore dark-colored marine sediments probably accumulated in areas where bottom scavengers were not abundant. Lack of water circulation and consequent oxygen depletion and the accumulation of carbon dioxide and hydrogen sulfide, resulting from the bacterial decay of abundant organic material, are most effective in reducing or preventing the activity of scavengers.

Moderately degraded plant material such as that which occurs in peat may impart a brown color to sediments and rocks. Such colors are not uncommon in the Tertiary strata of some regions and are present rarely in rocks as old as the Carboniferous. These colors do not occur in marine beds except possibly in some that accumulated in very shallow coastal zones adjacent to swampy areas on the land.

The presence of organic matter is important in the coloring of sediments and sedimentary rocks not only because it is a dark pigment but also because it serves as an effective reducing agent and prevents or destroys the bright colors that iron compounds might otherwise impart to them.

Iron Compounds

Iron constitutes about 5 percent of the rocks occurring at the surface of the earth. It is so abundant and ubiquitous that few sediments or rocks are entirely free from it. Also iron is peculiar among the other principal elements in that it exists commonly in two valence forms and passes easily from one to the other as the result of oxidation or reduction. Finally, most iron compounds are colored and some of the more prevalent ones are powerful, almost insoluble, pigments that persist indefinitely. Consequently iron is the most important substance giving colors to sediments and rocks in contrast to the shades of gray to black produced by organic matter.

Compounds of the two forms of iron have different properties that are important in connection with the transportation and deposition of this element and the colors it imparts to sediments and rocks. Simple ferrous compounds such as sulfate, carbonate, and chloride are variously soluble and generally greenish or bluish green in color. When in solution they are readily oxidized to ferric compounds. The sulfide is insoluble, black when finely divided but golden if crystallized. Colloidal iron sulfide and the crystalline form of marcasite oxidize easily, forming ferric oxide and sulfuric acid. Pyrite is considerably more stable.

The corresponding ferric compounds do not occur in nature because they hydrolize in the presence of water, producing ferric oxide and acid. Ferric oxide is practically insoluble but it is formed commonly as a colloid and it is easily transported in this condition. In the presence of organic matter and carbon dioxide or organic acids, colloidal ferric oxide is reduced and soluble ferrous compounds are produced.

Ferric oxide occurs in both hydrated and unhydrated forms. The hydrous oxides form a series and are known collectively as *limonite*. They have colors

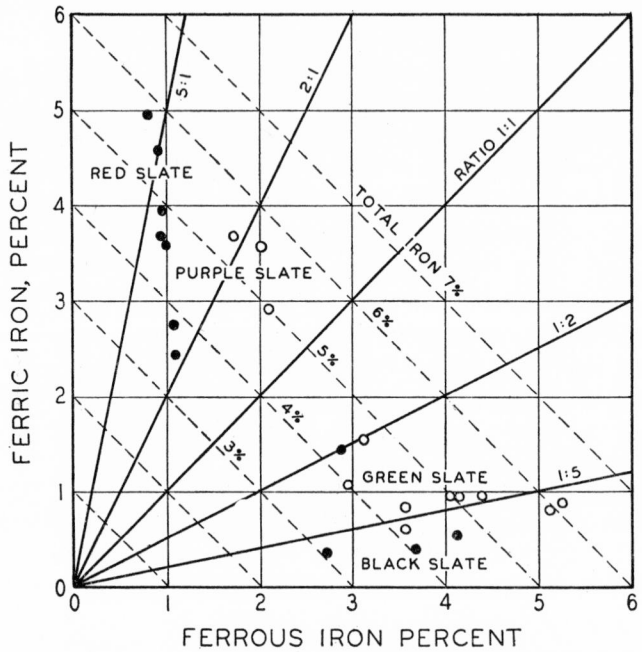

Figure 49. Diagram showing the relations of ferric and ferrous iron to color in metamorphic roofing slates from eastern New York and western Vermont. The purple slates that were studied are slightly less oxidized than the red ones. It is doubtful, however, that similar relations occur in red beds, where purplish colors may have been produced by greater compaction of the sediment. Green and black slates reveal no significant difference in their state of oxidation and the color probably is related to carbon content. (After Tomlinson, 1916, J. Geol., vol. 24, p. 158, fig. 2.)

ranging from ocher yellow to dark brown. The unhydrated oxide is *hematite* and it is red. These colors are very strong; tiny amounts of iron will color sediments and rocks brilliantly. Both oxides generally accumulate as films upon the grains of other minerals or in the areas between them. Also, however, they probably are chemically bound in some clay minerals.

Under some circumstances the water of hydration can come or go in ferric oxides. For example, field observations indicate that the hematite of red residual soil is hydrated during fluvial transportation, and brown limonitic sediment, characteristic of most modern alluvial deposits, is produced. In contrast, marine strata may be red but they are very rarely brown in an unweathered state. The inference is that brown oxide delivered to the sea by streams is either reduced to the ferrous state or dehydrated without reduction by the action of salt water. The physical chemistry of these reactions is not understood but they do not seem to be reversible under these general environmental conditions.

The kind of iron coloration exhibited is an index to the oxidation state of a sediment or rock (see Figure 49). Yellows, browns, reds, and purples indicate a high degree, and greens a lower degree, of oxidation. The former colors are unstable in the presence of organic matter and the latter are unstable in the presence of atmospheric or dissolved oxygen. The bright colors of ferric iron are common in older strata deposited under terrestrial conditions. They also occur, but are uncommon, in beds of marine origin. Alteration of one state to the other is shown in many rocks by mottling or change in color along joints and bedding planes. Greenish or bleached areas in otherwise reddish rocks indicate the local presence of organic matter or reduction by organic substances contained in circulating ground water. Similar brownish coloration in greenish or untinted rocks indicates oxidation by descending meteoric water.

Colloidal black iron sulfide, which may be present in amounts of 5 percent or more, contributes to the dark color of some rocks and sediments. It is generally accompanied by dark organic material. Rearrangement and crystallization of this sulfide as marcasite or pyrite may lighten the colors of some strata.

Red Beds

Red beds have attracted much attention because of their striking colors and the problems they pose concerning their origin. In the past the opinion has been widely, but probably erroneously, held that they are the product of a desert environment. Most modern deserts are not red, and if they are, like some large parts of the Sahara, they owe this color to the disintegration and decomposition of locally outcropping red rocks.

Red beds generally consist of alternating and intergrading clays or shales and sandstones. The most typical ones appear to be terrestrial deposits. They occur in all geologic systems from the Precambrian onward. The colors range from pinks and oranges through brilliant red to deep reddish purple. Colors commonly are concentrated in the finer sediments, and the sandstones are likely to be much paler or only brownish or untinted gray. Some red beds include gypsum and other evaporites but others contain limestone strata. A few marine limestones and shales of considerable thickness and areal extent are red or reddish. Most such limestones are impure and argillaceous.

The colors characteristic of red beds indicate a high degree of oxidation without hydration and the presence of little or no organic matter. Their existence has been explained variously as follows:

1. The color is intrinsic to the rocks that furnished sediments. If red granite were reduced by mechanical disintegration rather than by chemical decomposition, red beds might result. Among such sediments the coarsest should be reddest because the color of pink feldspar is lost or much less well marked in sediments of finer sizes.

The color may be inherited from older red beds. Thus the Navajo Sandstone (Jur.) of the southwest has been interpreted as a product of reworked Triassic red beds. If such sediments were transported far, the red coating probably would be removed from sand grains by abrasion, and iron pigment would be concentrated in the finer sediment. This explanation may account for some red beds. Observations show, however, that in fluvial transportation red colors commonly turn to brown as limonite is produced by the hydration of hematite. Possibly hydration of red oxide requires the presence of organic matter or is very slow and it may not be accomplished in arid regions.

2. The color is inherited from residual soil. Residual clays formed by the weathering and chemical decomposition of rocks in warm temperate to tropical regions of moist climate and good soil drainage are generally brown to red. Under these conditions organic material decays most rapidly and completely and it is not available for reducing ferric iron. Limestones and many kinds of igneous rocks particularly are likely to yield red soils. Alternate wet and dry seasons seem to provide especially favorable conditions, and some red beds probably are transported and redeposited red soil. Sediments derived from residual soil, however, are subject to the same conditions and processes that may alter the colors of material produced by the erosion of preëxisting red beds.

3. The color resulted from conditions at the site of deposition. Red beds may develop from non-red sediments at the time of deposition or shortly afterwards. Atmospheric oxygen may transform ferrous to ferric compounds, and hot dry summers might favor dehydration. Red sandstones as well as red clay or shale should be produced. Lack of organic matter or its rapid and complete decay would be required. Marshy conditions could not have existed but alternate wetting and drying, such as might occur in a region of seasonal extremes, seems to be demanded. This is one of the most favored explanations for the development of red beds but no place is known in the world today where action of this kind is taking place.

4. The color developed in buried sediment. Deep burial of sediment is attended by increasing pressure and rising temperature. These may result in the dehydration of brownish ferric oxide and the development of red beds. Both depth of burial and time may be important factors. If this process is

operative, all buried sediments containing ferric oxide should become red in time and only those with ferrous iron will not acquire this color. Sandstones should be red as well as clays.

Some movement and perhaps development of red iron oxide in buried strata is indicated by the occurrence of inclusions in the quartz cement of certain sandstones. A very thick succession of terrestrial Tertiary strata in the northern part of western Pakistan is suggestive because it shows complete gradation from dark purple reds below to light orange brown above. Later Tertiary clays in many other areas commonly are less strongly colored than older beds. Such color gradation, however, may have resulted from general climatic changes during the Tertiary Period. Furthermore Tertiary red beds commonly include gray sandstones.

5. The color developed after uplift and exposure. Oxidation of exposures generally alters ferrous iron to brown limonite, and the development of red oxides without the complete chemical decay of rocks is rare. Strata adjacent to burned lignites and outcrops swept by forest fires may be intensely red but they are not likely to be mistaken for true red beds. If the color of red beds developed near outcrops and at shallow depth, it should fade out and disappear close below the surface. This generally does not occur.

Red marine strata pose a different problem. An oxidizing environment at the site of marine deposition probably is rare except in some very shallow coastal areas and in the deepest parts of the ocean where sedimentation is slow and bottom life is scant. Some replacement of calcium carbonate by hematite certainly has taken place, but the nature of this process is not understood and it appears to have required special conditions that are not common. Most red limestone probably is colored by small amounts of precipitated colloidal ferric oxide or by red detrital clay. Red clay and shale may have inherited their color from residual soil washed into the sea from nearby land, or limonite, derived from the same source, may have been dehydrated by the action of sea water. In any case the main problem is to account for the persistence of ferric iron on the sea bottom where the abundance of marine life might be expected to provide organic matter and produce a reducing environment. Perhaps some combination of rapidly accumulating sediment comparatively rich in iron and conditions unfavorable for bottom life may have permitted ferric iron to escape reduction.

Green Colors

The pale greenish colors produced in sediments and rocks by ferrous compounds are much exceeded in intensity by the strong greens of glauconite and chlorite, which are much more likely to provide the pigments of noticeably colored rocks. Glauconite commonly occurs as sand-sized grains in sandstones and fragmental limestones of all ages from Cambrian to Recent. It is generally a primary constituent of shallow or more rarely deeper water sediments and appears to have formed on the sea bottom in areas of mildly reducing conditions and slow detrital deposition. Grains that are roughly pseudomorphic after foraminifera are common in Cretaceous and Tertiary strata and seem to have developed within the hollow shells of these tiny animals. Glauconite also occurs as smaller particles ranging downward to minute shreds and flakes in silt and shale.

Glauconite formation is not understood. The opinion has been widely held that it is an alteration product after biotite, but glauconite is an important constituent of many sediments that could never have contained this mica in abundance. Its principal mode of development probably involved the alteration of sedimentary clay to which was added material derived from solution in sea water. No glauconite is known to have originated in a freshwater environment. Some glauconite may occur as a secondary mineral, however, replacing others and constituting part of the cement in sandstone.

Glauconite varies from nearly black to vivid green. Most bright-green sediments probably owe their color to this mineral. It occurs as a minor constituent in considerable thicknesses of strata but may be concentrated in thinner zones where it is the most abundant mineral. Concentration of glauconite has been observed above numerous stratigraphic surfaces that have been interpreted as unconformities. In such situations it is likely to be associated with black phosphatic nodules.

The name *chlorite* is used for a family of related clayey minerals derived from the weathering of primary ferromagnesian minerals of igneous rocks. It also is a product of the diagenetic alteration of clay in sediments and has been observed partially replacing other minerals. Probably much chlorite in sedimentary rocks had this origin. It generally occurs in very tiny crystal flakes lying between or surrounding coarser sedimentary particles although larger masses and grains are not uncommon in some rocks. Chlorite is green with a color range from almost black to nearly colorless. Color is not as a rule conspicuous in the very fine-grained chlorite of most sediments.

Glauconite and chlorite may be difficult to distinguish. Both are soft minerals, and conspicuous grains of either are not likely to withstand the rigors of much transportation. Glauconite grains therefore are considered to be good evidence identifying marine sediments. Chlorite grains, however, do not have similar significance. Glauconite is not known in Precambrian rocks which contain several green minerals of similar appearance and possibly similar origin.

Bluish Colors

Many clays, shales, limestones, particularly fine-grained ones, and some tightly cemented sandstones of darker gray shades show slight bluish colors. In clays and shales these are more conspicuous if the material is wet. Organic matter generally is present but the source of the blue color is not known.

Some rocks are stained a vivid blue by copper or some other metallic com-pounds but such color ordinarily is very local. Although many rocks have been termed "blue," a true blue color is never seen in sediments and sedi-mentary rocks except as stains, and at best these rocks can be described accu-rately as only faintly bluish.

Color Changes Produced by Weathering

Many sedimentary rocks show different colors on outcrops and on freshly broken and unweathered surfaces. In dense nonporous rocks like most lime-stones the change generally occurs abruptly within a narrow surface zone but in porous rocks like many sandstones it is likely to be more gradual and ex-tend inward a considerable distance from the surface. The color difference in some rocks is great. A geologist accustomed to observing outcrops may have difficulty identifying familiar formations from cores or well cuttings and vice versa.

Most sediments consist of the end products of the chemical weathering of minerals. Because they have attained stability further changes of this type are not important. The sediments were deposited under a variety of condi-tions including particularly those related to oxidation or reduction, which determined the nature of their included organic matter and iron compounds. During the subsequent buried history of the sediment, these conditions ap-parently were preserved more or less unchanged. Uplift and erosion, how-ever, brought the sediments, or the now consolidated rocks, into contact with the atmosphere. Surficially at least they entered a very different environment and many of these rocks for the first time came under the influence of un-impeded oxidation. This is more generally true of marine than of terrestrial deposits.

Atmospheric oxidation has acted chiefly upon the organic matter and fer-rous compounds of exposed rocks. Both play important parts in giving rocks their colors. Oxidation of organic matter lightens grays. Many limestones, es-pecially oolitic and coarsely fragmental ones, are strongly bleached so that light gray or white surfaces overlie much darker interiors. Some dark-gray to black hard carbonaceous shales are similarly but less completely bleached. Their outcrops may convey an erroneous impression of true characters. Other black shales, however, seem to be wholly immune to this process.

Oxidation of ferrous compounds produces yellowish to brown colors and darkens the appearance of many rocks. Siderite generally is transformed to limonite in place without conspicuous migration of the iron or much periph-eral staining. Limestone with small amounts of irregularly distributed iron carbonate develops light-brown patches. This color extends farther into the rock than surface bleaching. Iron sulfide oxidizes first to ferrous sulfate and then to limonite. The first stage of this alteration may occur at some dis-tance from the outcrop surface. The soluble sulfate then transfuses slowly and is generally drawn toward the surface by capillary force. Further oxidation results in the staining of considerable volumes of sandstone, or limonite accumulates as a hard dark-brown cement at the surface and casehardens the outcrop. Similar action occurs in porous limestone; very commonly dolomites are slightly stained in this way. Also greenish and light-gray shales generally become brownish near an outcropping surface or a shallow joint.

Terrestrial strata exhibit less important color changes than marine beds. Many of them were deposited in an oxidizing environment and contain nothing that can be further oxidized. Red beds seem to be particularly stable and show little or no evidence of hydration that would transform reds to browns. Sulfides are likely to occur in marshland deposits and may be abundant in coal and associated strata. Oxidation products derived from them can move into nearby beds and discolor sandstones that might otherwise show no change.

Description of Colors

Because color is one of the important distinguishing qualities of sediments and rocks, it deserves careful consideration and accurate description. Random examination of only a few stratigraphic publications, however, furnishes ample evidence that colors are rarely observed or recorded adequately. Most descriptions are presented in such broad and relative terms that no more than a general idea of color is conveyed, and all too commonly even this is inaccurate or misleading. For example, the "blue shale" mentioned by many geologists is nonexistent.

Each person of necessity judges colors in terms of his own perception. This is not the same for everyone and some are color blind in various degrees. Even among persons with "normal" vision some are supersensitive to certain color differences. The perception of an individual also varies depending upon quality, intensity, and source of light and upon background colors. In addition, psychic factors undoubtedly are involved both in the perception of color, which probably varies from time to time, and in the identification and remembrance of colors. There can be small wonder, therefore, that determination of the color of a rock or sediment is difficult and its description by one person may be unsatisfactory to another.

All colors have two qualities, one defined in terms of wave length of light, which is the hue, and another defined in terms of intensity, or light and dark, which is the shade or tint. The second has two components: (1) the relative amount of light reflected by an object and (2) the relative amount of color not balanced to form white light. The actual colors of most objects are more or less complex mixtures of different hues in different shades (see Figure 50). Although the human eye can make comparisons and distinguish minute differences in colors, it is incapable of analyzing them or accurately measuring either of their qualities.

The infinite complexity of colors is beyond the power of any language to describe. Colors are characterized broadly as three primaries, blue, yellow, and red, and three intermediates, purple, green, and orange. These six hues intergrade and each covers a considerable segment of the spectrum. They

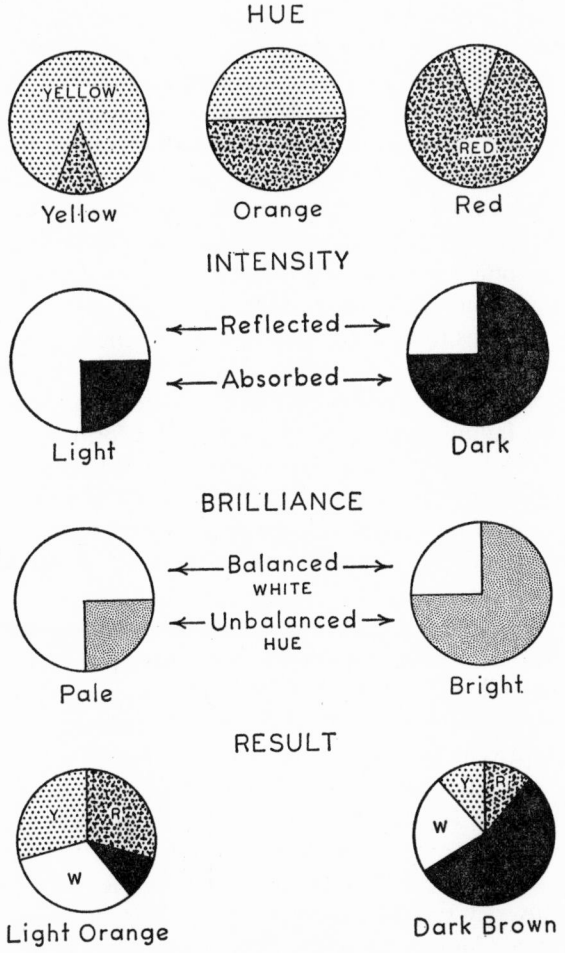

Figure 50. Diagram showing the relations of the elements of light which determine color in sediments and rocks. (Adapted from Krynine, 1948, *J. Geol.,* vol. 56, p. 144, fig. 8.)

have no shade distinctions. They are supplemented by a large number of unsystematized colors that are shades of hues named from flowers, minerals, and other substances, such as violet, ocher, chocolate, and carmine. Further distinction is indicated by adjectival modification, for example, bright purple, dark red, bluish gray, yellow orange, and olive green. In spite of all re-finements, however, most of these colors are indefinitely limited and they cannot be defined simply except by comparison with each other.

Various systems have been devised to distinguish colors more precisely. One designed for use by geologists is modified and simplified from the more comprehensive Munsell system. It is presented in the form of a chart com-posed of color samples intended for direct comparison with rocks. The sam-ples are arranged systematically according to hues and shades and are identi-fied by names and by formulas consisting of numbers and letters. Colors not represented on the chart can be recognized and identified by interpolation. This chart provides the means for attaining precision and uniformity in color designation. Unfortunately its obvious merits and usefulness seem to be out-weighed by the necessity of keeping it continuously at hand for comparison and the cumbersome nature of its names and formulas, that are very difficult to remember without extensive and continuous practice. It has been little used, and there seems to be slight prospect of its general adoption by geolo-gists.

The reception accorded to the color chart has been considered by some as a disappointing failure to achieve much-needed reform in color identifica-tion. Even though geologists may not desire to adopt its system, this chart is worthy of study because of its contribution to the closer observation and bet-ter understanding of rock colors. Closer attention to color is desirable but is no guarantee of the development of better nomenclature. One geologist who evidently became interested in detailed color discrimination described grays as *mouse, smoke, mineral,* and *confederate* and browns as *wood, army, malaga,* and *livid.* Precision here was lost because distinctions between these terms are incomprehensible to others. Quite evidently, close attention to col-ors must be supplemented by a carefully graded and generally recognizable system of descriptive names.

A practicable and understandable system of rock color designations can be devised using only a few common words. The basic ones are gray, brown, green, and red in this order of importance. Almost all sediments and rocks can be classified into one or another of these categories. Black and white are extremes of the gray series and require no modification. All others can be modified in terms of hues and graded as to shade. Thus fairly restrictive des-ignations such as *light bluish gray, medium yellowish brown,* and *very dark purplish red* can be built up that are subject to minimum misinterpretation. A few other adjectives may be useful in combination—olive green or choco-late brown—because they call to mind colors that are familiar to all. Terms like *buff, tan, drab,* and *maroon* are not nearly so explicit and generally should be avoided. This system provides about fifty readily understood color designations and is much superior to the prevalent haphazard and uncritical use of most color terms.

BIBLIOGRAPHY

Biggs, D. L. (1957), Petrography and origin of Illinois nodular cherts, Ill. Geol. Surv., Circ. 245.

All specimens studied, ranging in age from Cambrian to Mississippian, were developed by replacement of limestone or dolomite.

Bucher, W. H. (1919), On ripples and related sedimentary surface forms and their paleogeographic interpretation, Am. J. Sci., ser. 4, vol. 47, pp. 148–210 and 241–269.

Various types of ripples are described and modes of origin are discussed.

Choquette, P. W. (1955), A petrographic study of the "State College" siliceous oölite, J. Geol., vol. 63, pp. 337–347.

Evidence of siliceous replacement of originally calcareous Upper Cambrian oolites is presented.

Cloud, P. E., Jr. (1955), Physical limits of glauconite formation, Bull. Am. Assoc. Petroleum Geol., vol. 39, pp. 484–492.

Various detrital minerals were altered under normally saline and reducing conditions where deposition was very slow.

De Ford, R. K. (1944), "Rock colors," Bull. Am. Assoc. Petroleum Geol., vol. 28, pp. 128–137.

This review of the U.S. Department of Agriculture color chart includes an excellent discussion of color elements and discrimination.

Dunnington, H. V. (1954), Stylolite development post-dates rock induration, J. Sediment. Petrol., vol. 24, pp. 27–49.

The author reviews theories of stylolite development and presents evidence from limestones of Iraq and neighboring regions.

Evans, O. F. (1949), Ripple marks as an aid in determining depositional environment and rock sequence, J. Sediment. Petrol., vol. 19, pp. 82–86.

Wave and current ripple shapes and patterns are compared and their formation is explained.

Folk, R. L. (1951), Stages of textural maturity in sedimentary rocks, J. Sediment. Petrol., vol. 21, pp. 127–130.

Advancing maturity of detrital sediment is indicated by removal of clay, better sorting, and rounding of grains.

Goddard, E. N., chairman (1948), Rock-color chart, New York, Geol. Soc. Amer., 6 pp. and explanation, reprinted 1951.

More than 100 sample colors are arranged according to the Munsell system for direct comparison with rocks.

Goldstein, August, Jr. (1948), Cementation of Dakota Sandstone of the Colorado front range, J. Sediment. Petrol., vol. 18, pp. 108–125.

This article describes and explains siliceous and ferruginous cementation.

Gorsline, D. S., and Emery, K. O. (1959), Turbidity-current deposits in San Pedro and Santa Monica basins off southern California, Bull. Geol. Soc. Amer., vol. 70, pp. 279–290.

Coarse sediments slumped from deposits in submarine canyons and spread over basin floors are the subject of this article.

Grabau, A. W. (1913), *Principles of stratigraphy*, New York, Seiler, reprinted 1924.
> Chapter 17, pp. 696–722, is concerned with the structures of sedimentary rocks.

Grim, R. E. (1950), Some fundamental factors influencing the properties of soil materials, Ill. Geol. Surv., Rept. Invest. 146, pp. 5–11.
> An explanation is given of adsorption of water, ions, and organic matter by clays and its influence on their properties.

Hohlt, R. B. (1948), The nature and origin of limestone porosity, *Colo. School Mines Quart.*, vol. 43, no. 4.
> This is mostly concerned with the development of secondary porosity.

Illing, L. V. (1954), Bahaman calcareous sands, *Bull. Am. Assoc. Petroleum Geol.*, vol. 38, pp. 1–95.
> This thorough description of modern calcareous sediments concludes that oolites are inorganic.

Kelling, Gilbert (1958), *Ripple-mark in the Rhinns of Galloway*, Trans. Edinburgh Geol. Soc., vol. 17, pt. 2, pp. 117–132.
> This paper describes ripples and ripplelike structures in graywacke and attributes them to deposition, erosion, and structural deformation.

King, P. B. (1958), Problems of boulder beds of Haymond Formation, Marathon basin, Texas, *Bull. Am. Assoc. Petroleum Geol.*, vol. 42, pp. 1731–1735.
> The problem of the origin of coarse Pennsylvanian conglomerate in west Texas is reviewed; the author favors mud flows.

Krynine, P. D. (1950), Petrology, stratigraphy, and origin of the Triassic sedimentary rocks of Connecticut, Conn. Geol. Surv., Bull. 73.
> An exhaustive description of Triassic red beds interprets their origin by rapid erosion under warm humid seasonal climate and deposition in a subsiding river valley.

Kuenen, P. H. (1957), Sole markings of graded graywacke beds, *J. Geol.*, vol. 65, pp. 231–258.
> This article describes and interprets structures that occur in sediments other than graywackes.

Kuenen, P. H., and Menard, H. W. (1952), Turbidity currents, graded and non-graded deposits, *J. Sediment. Petrol.*, vol. 22, pp. 83–96.
> Sediment settling is considered in relation to various types of graded bedding and occurrence of sandy deposits of the deep sea.

McCrossan, R. G. (1958), Sedimentary "boudinage" structures in the Upper Devonian Ireton Formation of Alberta, *J. Sediment. Petrol.*, vol. 28, pp. 316–320.
> Limestone nodules in shale are interpreted as having been produced by compaction and lateral movement.

McKee, E. D., and Weir, G. W. (1953), Terminology for stratification and cross-stratification in sedimentary rocks, *Bull. Geol. Soc. Amer.*, vol. 64, pp. 381–390.
> Different types of cross-bedding are contrasted and classified.

Pettijohn, F. J. (1957), *Sedimentary rocks*, 2nd ed., New York, Harper.
> Chapters 2 and 4, pp. 13–98 and 157–228, discuss textures and structures of sedimentary rocks.

Rich, J. L. (1950), Flow markings, groovings, and intra-stratal crumplings as criteria for recognition of slope deposits with illustrations from Silurian rocks of Wales, *Bull. Am. Assoc. Petroleum Geol.*, vol. 34, pp. 717–741.

A variety of internal markings and structures is described and interpreted.

Stockdale, P. B. (1926), The stratigraphic significance of solution in rocks, *J. Geol.*, vol. 34, pp. 399–414.

The possibility that solution has materially reduced the thickness of many limestones and dolomites is emphasized.

Twenhofel, W. H. (1945), The rounding of sand grains; *J. Sediment. Petrol.*, vol. 15, pp. 59–71.

Rounding and frosting of sand grains are largely the result of eolian transportation.

Twenhofel, W. H. (1950), *Principles of sedimentation*, 2nd ed., New York, McGraw-Hill.

Chapters 4 and 5, pp. 542–641, deal with structures, textures, and colors of sediments.

Twenhofel, W. H., and collaborators (1932), *Treatise on sedimentation*, 2nd ed., Baltimore, Williams and Wilkins:

Chapter 6, pp. 603–782, is devoted to structures, textures, and colors of sediments.

Van Houten, F. B. (1948), Origin of red-banded Cenozoic deposits in Rocky Mountain region, *Bull. Am. Assoc. Petroleum Geol.*, vol. 32, pp. 2083–2126.

Consideration of the chemistry of iron oxides indicates that red beds were derived from red soil developed in a warm moist climate and not subsequently reduced.

Weeks, L. G. (1957), Origin of carbonate concretions in shales, Magdalena Valley, Colombia, *Bull. Geol. Soc. Amer.*, vol. 68, pp. 96–102.

Concretions formed during very early diagenetic stage before sediment was much compacted.

6

Physiography of Sediments

In its common usage, *sediment* is the term for finely divided solid material that has settled from suspension in a liquid. In geology, this meaning is extended to include all solid material of both mineral and organic nature that (1) is in suspension, (2) is being transported, or (3) has been moved by any means from its site of origin and has come to rest upon the surface of the earth either above or below sea level. Most sediment passes through a cycle that involves (1) formation, (2) transportation, and (3) deposition.

FORMATION OF SEDIMENTS

The great bulk of all sediment has been produced by the decomposition of rocks. This involves two processes, chemical weathering and mechanical disintegration. Commonly the processes operate together but, depending upon local conditions and circumstances, either may predominate. If one process has been dominant, the resulting sediment possesses distinguishing mineralogic characters that are readily recognized.

Chemical Weathering

Chemical weathering is accomplished by the action of carbon dioxide, water, and oxygen upon the unstable constituents of rocks. If carried to completion, it results in the production of stable substances. Thereafter these may pass through one or more subsequent cycles of erosion, transportation, and deposition with little or no further chemical change. Insofar as sedimentary rocks consist of stable minerals, they are not subject to further weathering. If, however, chemical weathering was not completed and sediments contain unstable minerals derived from parent rocks, weathering may continue until only stable substances remain. An important amount of chemical weathering may be accomplished while mineral matter is sediment in the course of transportation. Metamorphic alteration of sedimentary rocks can produce minerals that are unstable under atmospheric conditions and are again subject to chemical weathering in another cycle.

Chemical weathering is a process that is characteristic of the land. Although there seems to be no reason why some comparable weathering should not occur beneath the cover of water, subaqueous chemical weathering does not appear to be important and it is very rarely noted. Probably this is because (1) most susceptible rock is buried and protected beneath sedimentary deposits, (2) if such rock is exposed, mechanical abrasion is likely to exceed chemical decomposition, and (3) there is little or no downward circulation of water within submerged rocks or sediment to facilitate the necessary renewal of small amounts of carbon dioxide and oxygen that can act upon them.

Chemical weathering, like all chemical activity, is promoted by elevated temperature, and the presence of moisture is necessary for its efficient action. Therefore, the process is more rapid and important in warm regions than in cool, at low altitudes and latitudes than at high, and in humid regions rather than in dry. Very little chemical weathering is accomplished in arctic regions, high mountains, and deserts, even in those deserts located in the tropics.

Carbonation

Chemical reactions involving carbon dioxide are among the most important in nature. They are involved in almost all biologic activity and, together with hydration, are the principal ones responsible for rock weathering. The action of carbon dioxide on the complex silicates of rocks, mainly feldspars and ferromagnesian minerals, produces carbonates of the alkali and alkaline earth metals that are soluble and easily removed. Most of these carbonates are carried in solution to the sea.

Carbon dioxide probably was one of the most important constituents of the earth's early atmosphere. During all past ages, however, it has been removed and locked up in deposits of limestone and dolomite. Since life first appeared, carbon derived from atmospheric carbon dioxide has formed organic compounds, large quantities of which have been buried in the sediments. Both of these processes have served to deplete atmospheric carbon dioxide; were it not for renewal from volcanic sources, the supply probably would have been exhausted long ago.

Some measure of the quantity of carbon dioxide removed from the atmosphere may be obtained by considering the amounts of carbonate rocks and organic matter that have been formed and preserved. Thus carbonates in limestone, dolomite, and other sedimentary rocks have been estimated to contain 15,000 to 30,000 times the carbon dioxide now present in the atmosphere. Also the carbon in coal deposits and other organic sediments required up to 10,000 times the present amount of atmospheric carbon dioxide for its production. This suggests that carbon dioxide in the atmosphere was renewed about every 100,000 years.

At present carbon dioxide occurs in the atmosphere to the extent of about 3 parts in 10,000, and about 50 times as much is dissolved in sea water. Since at least the beginning of the Paleozoic Era, a rough balance of about these amounts probably has been maintained between carbon dioxide removed from the atmosphere and sea water and new carbon dioxide added to them. Fluctuations and temporary increases, resulting from epochs of exceptionally great volcanic activity that occurred intermittently in the past, possibly account for the large amounts of limestone that were deposited during such periods as the Ordovician, the Mississippian, and the Cretaceous. If this is the reason, two stages probably occurred. First, increased carbon dioxide in the atmosphere resulted in more rapid weathering of igneous rocks. Also, with increased partial pressure, more carbon dioxide dissolved in sea water, bicarbonate ion concentration rose, and larger amounts of lime were held in solution. Second, as the supply of new carbon dioxide decreased, dissolved carbon dioxide passed back into the atmosphere and excess lime was precipitated or became more readily available for use by organisms which caused its precipitation. Man's industrial activity has now upset the balance of nature to some extent. The return of carbon dioxide produced by the combustion of fossil fuels would double the amount present in the atmosphere in less than 500 years if it all accumulated there.

The chemical weathering of crystalline rocks, involving the carbonation of lime and magnesia derived from them, results in an increase in the mass of solid material that is first removed in solution and later deposited as sediment. The new rocks formed in this way, the limestones and the dolomites, consist of material that was about 55 percent derived from weathered older rocks and the remaining 45 percent is carbon dioxide contributed by the atmosphere. This means that in the development of the common carbonate rocks an increase of approximately 80 percent in both weight and volume has occurred.

Hydration

Hydration converts the unstable aluminum silicates of crystalline rocks to clay. It is a complex process that acts on complex compounds, mainly feldspars and ferromagnesian minerals, and produces a variety of complex clays. This reaction accompanies carbonation and in simplified form can be represented thus:

$$2Al(Na, Si)Si_2O_8 + 2Al(Ca, Al)Si_2O_8 + 3CO_2 + 6H_2O =$$

albite   anorthite

$$Na_2CO_3 + 2CaCO_3 + 3Al_2(Si_2O_5)(OH)_4 + 4SiO_2$$

kaolinite

Depending upon the kind of silicate minerals attacked and the kind of clay minerals produced, the hydration of aluminum silicates results in mass and volume increases ranging from about 10 to 35 percent and probably averages about 20 percent. The production of all sediments by chemical weathering, involving both carbonation and hydration, probably results in total mass increase of about 25 percent. Silica occurring as quartz is unaffected, and some weathering products remain in solution in the sea.

Oxidation

Oxygen is by far the most common element at and near the surface of the earth. It constitutes about half of all rocks available to observation, 89 percent of water, and 21 percent of the earth's atmosphere. Free oxygen probably was not an original constituent of the atmosphere but was produced by the decomposition of water vapor, at first through the action of ultraviolet light and later more importantly by the photosynthetic action of plants. Structures believed to record the existence of simple plants like algae have been found in very ancient rocks, dating back 2 billion years or more before the beginning of the Paleozoic Era. The fossil record suggests that the composition of the earth's atmosphere has not changed importantly since at least the beginning of Paleozoic time, and free oxygen, necessary for the respiration of animals, undoubtedly was present in the atmosphere much earlier. Perhaps the amount of free oxygen in the air is a rough measure of the unoxidized carbon contained in living organisms and the much greater quantity preserved in organic matter buried in the sediments and rocks.

Although oxygen is the most chemically active ingredient of the atmosphere, it is relatively unimportant as a strictly geologic agent. Its chief role is in biologic processes. Thus it is essential to metabolism but plays only a small part in the weathering of most rocks. Were it otherwise, the amount of oxygen in the atmosphere would be much less.

As a geologic agent, oxygen is concerned chiefly with the oxidation of some of the minor elements that are present in the rocks in a reduced condition. The most important of these is iron, more than half of which occurs in rocks in the ferrous state. Oxidation to ferric iron involves a mass increase of 22 percent. The amount of ferrous iron, however, constitutes less than 3 percent of all surface rocks. This increase, therefore, is negligible quantitatively in comparison to that resulting from carbonation and hydration. Next, but much less important quantitatively, is sulfur. Oxidation from sulfide to sulfate, and neutralization of the sulfuric acid that is formed, results in increase in mass of solid material ranging from about 15 to 25 percent depending upon the minerals involved.

Mechanical Disintegration

Incomplete chemical weathering, or the decomposition of unstable minerals that exist only as minor constituents, weakens rock, making it susceptible to mechanical disintegration and facilitating its erosion. Sedimentary rocks that consist wholly of stable minerals, however, are subject only to mechanical disintegration. For this reason, some sedimentary rocks like limestone under favorable climatic and topographic conditions are more resistant to erosion than much harder rocks like granite. Thus in some parts of the tropics where chemical weathering is relatively very rapid, limestones are likely to form the most conspicuous topographic prominences. Quartzite is the most resistant of all rocks. Other sedimentary rocks ordinarily are porous and less well consolidated and they yield to mechanical disintegration much more readily. In humid climates, limestone may dissolve more rapidly than other sedimentary rocks disintegrate.

Mechanical disintegration of rocks that also are susceptible to chemical weathering is likely to prevail in cool climates rather than in warm, at high altitudes and latitudes rather than at low, and in regions that are relatively dry rather than humid. For this reason geographic conditions generally exert inverse influences upon mechanical disintegration and chemical weathering. This, however, is not entirely the case so far as solution is concerned because obviously solution is promoted by humid conditions.

Abrasion

The most generally effective agent of mechanical disintegration is the abrasive action of sediment in transit, which is capable of wearing away the hardest rock. Abrasion also affects the sediment itself and sedimentary particles are worn to smaller and smaller sizes. The effectiveness of abrasion depends upon (1) hardness and cohesiveness of the rock, (2) hardness, size, and abundance of the sediment, (3) speed of transportation, and (4) transporting medium.

The resistance of rocks to abrasion does not depend simply on the hardness and toughness of their minerals. Some rocks composed of resistant minerals are fairly easily disintegrated because their grains are not tightly bound together. Thus porous sandstone consisting of resistant quartz is more easily eroded than essentially nonporous limestone whose much softer calcite grains are closely interlocked. Nonporous igneous and metamorphic rocks composed of relatively hard minerals are most resistant to abrasion and also generally to other types of mechanical disintegration. The most easily eroded of all rocks are shales and mudstones containing important proportions of soft clay minerals.

The effectiveness of abrasion is dependent upon the tools available: the moving sedimentary particles. Clear water flowing over bare rock is almost wholly ineffective, and abrasion increases with the amount of sediment that is transported. Hard and large sedimentary particles, of course, are the most efficient agents of abrasion but large particles wear away more rapidly than small ones.

The energy required to accomplish abrasion is provided by the movement of the medium that transports sediment. Therefore, with equal quantities and kinds of sediment, effectiveness increases with the speed. Also the speed of movement determines the quantity of sediment that can be transported by wind or water; with greater speed the effectiveness of abrasion may be increased still more.

The three major transporting media, air, water, and ice, differ importantly in their influence on abrasion. Air transport is potentially most efficient in its sand-blast action but it is limited to arid regions; ordinary winds are not capable of moving particles of larger size than sand. Water-borne sediment is much more generally effective. It includes particles of greater size ranging in some circumstances up to boulders. This sediment, however, commonly moves at less velocity than wind-borne material. Also it bears adsorbed water films which, on the sand- and silt-sized particles, act as cushions and lessen the effectiveness of impact. Glacial ice is capable of moving enormous blocks of rock, but movement is very slow and abrasion is accomplished by grinding under a considerable weight of ice rather than by impact. This greatly increases the effectiveness of glacial abrasion.

Frost Action

Water freezing in the cracks and pores of rocks exerts powerful expansive force that, if repeated many times, is capable of disintegrating the hardest rock. Almost all sedimentary rocks are porous in some degree and they are separated into layers by bedding planes. Metamorphic rocks generally possess some type of schistosity or planes of shearing, along which parting is likely to occur. Igneous rocks commonly are cut by fractures formed in response to strains set up during their periods of cooling. Also most rocks at and near the surface are broken by joints produced by more or less gentle warping or folding. All of these provide avenues for the entrance of water. Freezing enlarges and extends them.

Disintegration of rocks by frost action can occur, of course, only in areas subject to freezing temperatures. The process is not active in the tropics except at high altitudes. It is, however, important in temperate regions and those parts of the arctic that are not permanently frozen. The action is confined to a narrow surface layer only a few feet thick. In many regions it is supplemented by growth of the roots of plants that enter cracks in the rock and serve to wedge and hold them open.

Thermal Action

Alternate expansion and contraction of rock, resulting from heating by exposure to bright sunlight during the day and cooling off at night, set up strains that may cause spalling off of surface chips or layers. This is most effective in dense nonporous rock. It is restricted to surfaces of actual exposure because even a thin covering of soil or disintegrated material serves as protective insulation. Thermal action of this sort is not likely to be important except in arid regions or areas of high topographic relief where intense illumination is general and bare rock surfaces are extensive.

Solution

Solution is a process that possesses both physical and chemical attributes but its effects are mainly physical. Although it is very important in the disintegration and removal of many sedimentary rocks, the action of solution alone on metamorphic and igneous rocks generally is negligible. It is, however, the principal means of limestone destruction. Calcium and magnesium carbonates are dissolved and removed in solution leaving admixed insoluble material behind as residual soil. Solution acting on cementing minerals, mainly calcite, also weakens granular rock like sandstone, which thereafter is more readily disintegrated by freezing or by solar heating and is more easily worn away by abrasive action. Solution, of course, is most effective in humid regions. It may continue to considerable depths below the surface at least as far as ground water is in slow circulation.

Organic Sediments

Organic sediments differ from detrital sediments because they are not derived directly from either chemically weathered or mechanically disintegrated rocks. Two types can be distinguished: (1) sediments, mainly calcium carbonate, derived from mineral substances transported in solution and removed therefrom generally by organic action, and (2) more properly organic substances derived from the tissues of plants and animals that accumulate essentially in place or are transported in suspension like other sediments.

Carbonates

Carbonate deposits constitute one of the most important kinds of sedimentary rock. The mineral matter of which they are composed was produced by (1) the chemical weathering of unstable minerals mostly in igneous and some metamorphic rocks, and (2) the solution of either previously existing carbonate deposits of similar type or carbonate material dispersed in other kinds of sediment or sedimentary rock. This material was transported in solution, precipitated by one means or another, then generally moved as sediment for a short distance and deposited. Carbonate sediment other than gravel, produced by mechanical disintegration of limestone or dolomite on land, transported any appreciable distance and redeposited is very rare.

The chemical system connecting carbon dioxide in the atmosphere and precipitated calcium carbonate is complicated. Carbon dioxide occurs in (1) the molecular state, gaseous and dissolved, (2) carbonic acid, (3) carbonate and bicarbonate anions, (4) dissolved salts such as calcium carbonate and bicarbonate, (5) precipitated calcium carbonate, and (6) organic compounds. The carbon dioxide in all of these states is connected by reversible reactions and a change at one point in the system affects the equilibria in most of its other parts. The following equations represent the carbon dioxide system in a simplified form:

$$CO_2 \text{ (atmosphere)}$$
$$\updownarrow$$
$$CO_2 + H_2O \rightleftharpoons H_2CO_3 \rightleftharpoons H^+ + HCO_3^- \text{ (solution)}$$
$$\updownarrow \qquad\qquad \| \qquad\qquad$$
$$\text{organic carbon} \qquad Ca^{++} + 2HCO_3^- \rightleftharpoons Ca(HCO_3)_2 \text{ (solution)}$$
$$\text{compounds}$$
$$H_2CO_3 \rightleftharpoons 2H^+ + CO_3^- \text{ (solution)}$$
$$\|$$
$$Ca^{++} + CO_3^- \rightleftharpoons CaCO_3 \text{ (solution)}$$
$$\updownarrow$$
$$CaCO_3 \text{ (precipitated)}$$

Most limestones consist of variable proportions of recognizable, more or less fragmented remains of shells, other calcareous hard parts secreted by organisms, and crystalline cement or very finely divided calcium carbonate of indeterminate origin. Some of the fine material is organic debris broken down by wave turbulence in shallow water or by the action of scavenging animals. Some probably was precipitated in finely crystalline form by algae, and perhaps by bacteria, that extracted carbon dioxide from solution thereby reducing the solubility of calcium carbonate in nearby water. Some possibly was precipitated wholly inorganically. The constituents of limestone, therefore, are sediments of varied origin and crystalline cement. This is true except for parts of rigid structures like reefs that were built by firmly attached organisms growing in place and cannot properly be considered sedimentary.

Calcareous sediments generally were not transported for more than moderate distances. Many were deposited close to the places where they originated. Most sea water, except in very shallow and warm areas, is not completely saturated with calcium carbonate and at least the smaller particles probably are redissolved before they can be carried far.

Dolomites had origins similar to those of limestones and consist of similar material. Most of them owe their magnesian character to chemical replacement after the deposition of originally calcareous material.

So-called chemical deposits such as gypsum and rock salt were produced as crystalline precipitates by physical rather than by biologic processes. Sediments of this kind rarely were moved any appreciable distance from the places where they were precipitated.

Organic Compounds

Organic substances, derived from the partial decay of plant or animal tissues, may be important constituents of sediment in situations where they are not subject to oxidation. Two general types can be distinguished: (1) carbonaceous—solid black nonvolatile matter related to coal—and (2) bituminous, consisting of more or less liquid and volatile hydrocarbons related to petroleum. All organic matter contained in sediments and sedimentary rocks, however, is not strictly sedimentary.

More or less macerated plant debris is readily transported as sediment. Partial decay may have resulted in carbonization before the material was transported or after its deposition. Non-marine strata contain very little organic matter derived from animals and, therefore, plant material is identified in them most easily. Coal is an outstanding example although an important part of most coal beds moved little if at all from its place of origin. Much of this carbonaceous material was derived from the degradation of lignin, a constituent of woody plant structures that is relatively resistant to decay. Carbonized plant remains occur in many kinds of non-marine strata of Carboniferous and later ages.

The derivation of most carbonaceous material in marine strata is uncertain because generally it occurs in such a finely divided state that its original nature cannot be determined. Some land plant debris is carried to the sea and deposited with detrital sediment but probably most carbonaceous material in marine strata originated locally. In some areas and at some times seaweeds probably were the principal source but mostly perhaps this material consists of the remains of planktonic organisms, both plant and animal, that died and sank to the bottom. In the marine environment carbonaceous material commonly is preserved in important amounts only in mud and under conditions where oxygen is deficient or deposition of detrital sediment is relatively rapid (see Figure 51). Reducing conditions ordinarily occur close below the surface of mud bottoms and, once it is buried, organic material is likely to escape complete decay.

Carbonaceous material is a residue that remains after various more or less mobile compounds, produced during the decomposition of organic matter in an oxygen-deficient environment, have moved away. Methane gas, for example, evolves and escapes under ordinary conditions. Under others, higher and more complex bituminous hydrocarbons are produced. Part of this process may occur before organic material is buried, and some of the products formed may be adsorbed on the surfaces of sedimentary particles and travel with them. Mostly, however, the process appears to operate in buried material, and a separation of residue and mobile products is effected by subsequent hydraulic movement. Large quantities of bituminous compounds, like petroleum, have migrated and accumulated at localities and in strata more or less distant from their place of origin. Although such material is of sedimen-

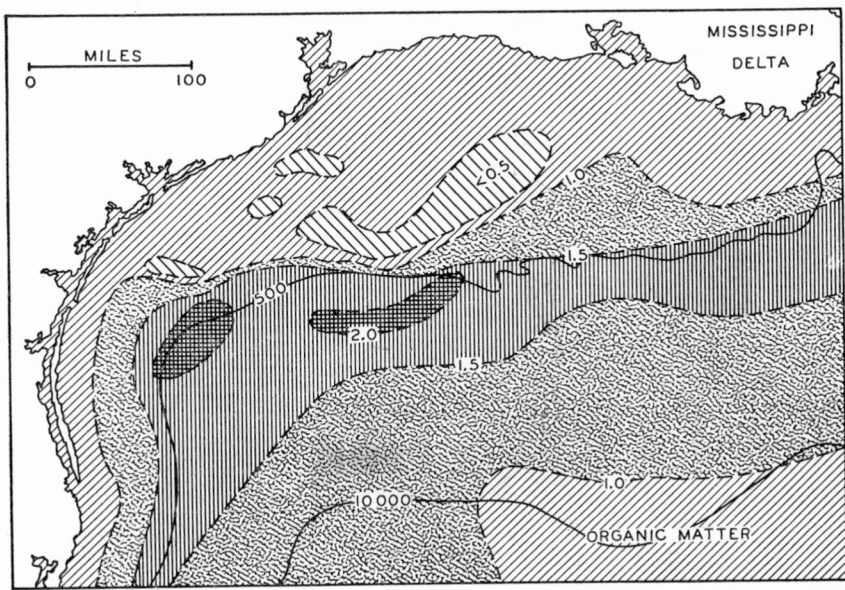

Figure 51. Map showing variations in the organic content of modern sediments in the northwestern part of the Gulf of Mexico. The greatest concentration of organic matter occurs in fine sediment close to or just beyond the edge of the continental shelf. Compare with Figure 211, p. 544. (After Richards, 1957, Geol. Soc. Amer., Mem. 67, vol. 1, p. 216, fig. 10.)

tary derivation, it is not properly part of the sediment where it now occurs because its formation and movement were not part of the ordinary sedimentary cycle.

The manner in which liquid bituminous hydrocarbons are formed is not understood. They are not produced in important quantities by the decomposition of all organic matter. There is no evidence, for example, that coal and petroleum are closely related because most coal-bearing strata are deficient in petroleum and much petroleum originated in rocks that contain no coal. Most petroleum appears to have been derived from organic matter deposited in marine mud, from which it was expelled by compaction of the sediment. Similar material originating in limestone generally has not migrated to a similar extent, and many limestones when freshly broken have a fetid odor that indicates the presence of volatile bituminous material.

Altogether the chemical processes involved in the conversion of newly dead organisms to the organic matter contained in consolidated rocks are ex-

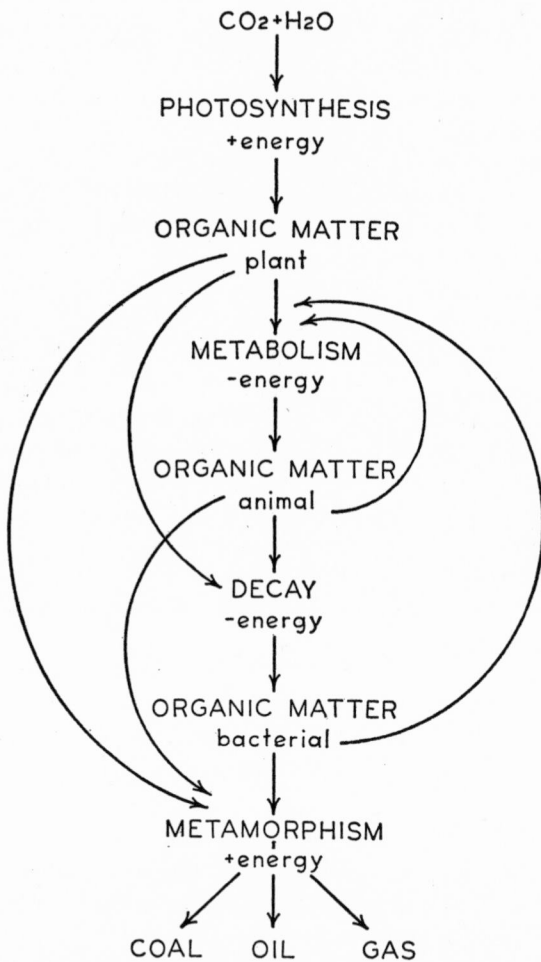

$CO_2 + H_2O$

PHOTOSYNTHESIS
+energy

ORGANIC MATTER
plant

METABOLISM
-energy

ORGANIC MATTER
animal

DECAY
-energy

ORGANIC MATTER
bacterial

METAMORPHISM
+energy

COAL   OIL   GAS

Figure 52. Diagram showing progressive stages in the process by which carbon dioxide in the atmosphere or dissolved in water has been converted to the fossil fuels.

ceedingly complex. Generally they include first several organic stages related to animal metabolism and bacterial decay and later dynamic processes resulting from the action of pressure and heat. Figure 52 shows in simplified form the progressive stages leading to the development of mineral fuels. Similar stages doubtless affect organic matter occurring in a more diffused condition in the sediments and rocks.

TRANSPORTATION OF SEDIMENTS

Sediments are transported varied distances ranging from negligibly small to very great. Thus vegetable material may no more than settle beneath the water surface of a swamp where the plants grew whereas dust from a volcanic eruption or an atomic explosion may completely encircle the earth in the upper atmosphere before descending to lower levels.

The movement of all sediment is determined by the interplay of gravity and one or another of the three media air, water, and ice. Gravity causes material to settle to a lower level but a moving medium deflects settling from a straight downward course and it may completely overcome the force of gravity for longer or shorter intervals of time and thus result in transportation. The effectiveness of a moving medium depends upon its density, viscosity, and speed. Material carried in solution is uncontrolled by gravity. It may be transported to any part of the ocean and remain in solution indefinitely.

Most sediment moves in an irregular and intermittent manner. It may pass from the influence of one medium to that of another several times before it is deposited more or less permanently.

By Flowing Water

Water is by far the most important agent responsible for the transportation of sediment. Distinction must be made, however, between transportation in (1) flowing water, as in streams, and (2) standing water, as in ponds, lakes, or the sea. The differences that characterize water in these two states are determined by the relative importance of (1) flowing, or the movement of water from place to place, and (2) turbulence, which does not necessarily involve such movement.

Sediment is transported by flowing water either as bed load or in suspension. These types of transportation intergrade, and sedimentary particles that are part of the bed load may pass more or less briefly into suspension by saltation. In this process particles are lifted from the bottom by upwardly directed currents and are carried forward during the time required for them to sink again. Thus they progress by a series of intermittent forward hops.

Bed-load transportation is of three types that succeed each other as current velocity increases. At low velocities, individual particles roll or slide along a relatively even bottom. Larger particles of sand and silt size are moved somewhat more easily than smaller ones because they offer larger surfaces to the pressure of flowing water (see Figure 53). At higher velocities, ripples form and the movement of individual particles becomes rhythmic, alternating between active and resting phases. Particles move up the upstream ripple surfaces and roll down the steeper downstream surfaces. There they are buried by other particles and remain until the ripple has progressed downstream and they are uncovered and move again. At still greater velocities, ripples disappear and the whole mass of bottom sediment mixed with water passes into flowing motion. Transportation of the bed load is accomplished by forward

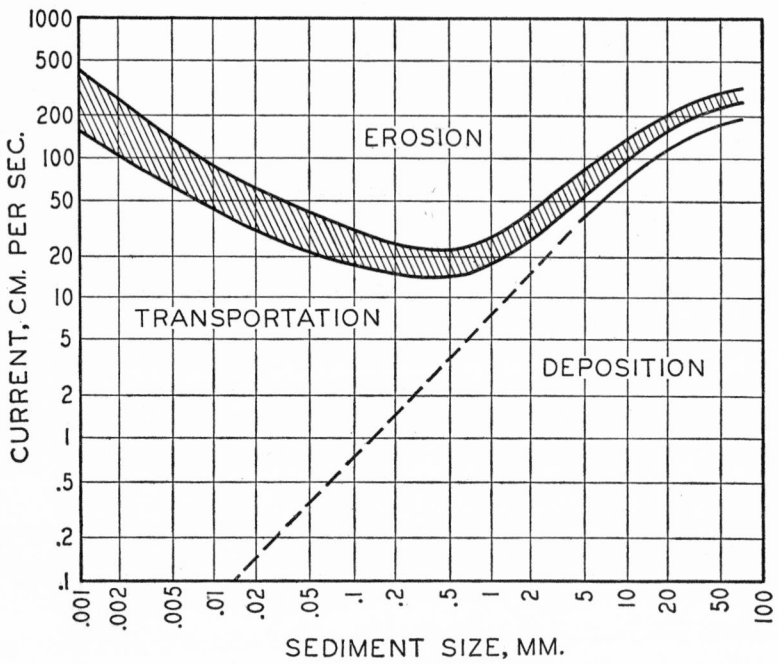

Figure 53. Curves showing the relations of erosion, transportation, and deposition of uniformly sorted sediments of various sizes to current velocity. The velocities are indicated here as occupying a band. This represents range of average velocity in streams more than one meter deep. Bottom currents cannot be measured accurately, and the actual bottom velocities probably are 10 to 20 centimeters per second slower than those indicated. Sedimentary particles about one-half millimeter in diameter are most easily moved. (After Hjulström, 1939, *Recent marine sediments*, p. 10, fig. 1, by permission of the Society of Economic Paleontologists and Mineralogists.)

current flow and is little affected by water turbulence. In most streams the bed load constitutes only a small fraction of the moving sediment, but the proportion becomes greater in streams with rapid fall such as those in mountainous regions.

Particles of all sizes ranging up to boulders travel as the bed load of streams but only the finer sediment is transported in suspension. These particles are raised from the bottom and their settling is delayed by turbulence which is produced by local and ever changing eddies within the water of a stream. Upward-moving currents in turbulent water must be balanced by downward currents but, because sediment concentration is greatest near the bottom, rising currents are more heavily laden and they distribute particles to all levels of a stream. The amount and coarseness of suspended sediment is determined by the degree of turbulence, which increases with current velocity and must overcome the gravitational settling of the sediment. The settling velocity of particles depends upon their size, shape, and density with respect to the water medium and the viscosity of the water (see Figure 21, p. 84). Settling velocities decrease much more rapidly than particle size; very fine sediment settles with extreme slowness even in tranquil water. The transportation of suspended sediment is of course accomplished by the forward motion of the stream. This sediment moves more rapidly than the bed load and thus a separation of coarse and fine material may be effected.

The transportation of sediment by flowing water generally involves repeated scouring or erosion of the bottom and temporary deposition of the eroded particles. More energy, as measured by current velocity, is required to erode sediment than to transport it after it has been put in motion. This differential increases rapidly with finer and finer sediment. Also as the quantity of suspended material increases, erosion of unconsolidated sediment declines but suspension is maintained more effectively.

By Mudstreams

Under some conditions much sediment may be transported in mass mixed with water in a more or less plastic or fluid condition. Collectively such sediment in motion may be designated *mudstreams*. Depending upon their physical nature and action, which is determined by their water content, mudstreams may be separated into (1) landslides, (2) mud flows, and (3) turbidity currents. There is no sharp division between these types.

Landslides develop when unconsolidated sediment or weathered mantle rock lubricated by water slumps downward under the force of gravity. They occur only on more or less steep slopes where the equilibrium of surface and near-surface material has been disturbed by erosional undercutting, by the absorption of unusual amounts of water, as after protracted rains, or by earthquake shocks. In landslides the material moves mostly along local shearing planes. The amount of moving material may be great but the distance it traverses is likely to be small. Landslides are of little importance in stratigraphy except as they initiate the transportation of sediment. Their deposits are rapidly attacked by erosion and rarely persist for any appreciable length of time. Landsliding is a process that with rare exceptions occurs only under subaerial conditions.

Mud flows differ from landslides in that more water is incorporated in the sedimentary mass, which moves as a plastic solid or very viscous liquid rather than along shear planes. Landslides are easily converted into mud flows if sufficient water is available. They develop both on land and beneath bodies of standing water. Almost all moving masses that begin as landslides in subaqueous situations become mud flows. Because mud flows are more mobile, they can move on less steep slopes and for greater distances than landslides. The momentum they develop may even carry them up small topographic rises. The high density and viscosity of mud flows makes possible the transportation of large blocks of rock on slopes much more gentle than any on which these could move by gravitational force alone. Movement within a mud flow mixes material thoroughly so that when it comes to rest it is a very poorly sorted deposit. Some mixtures of coarse and fine material identified as tillite almost certainly were produced by mud flows.

Turbidity currents are water currents so heavily laden with suspended sediment that their density causes them to flow downward along a sloping bottom in a body of standing water. They are of two types: (1) those developing where a heavily loaded stream enters a body of standing water and (2) those originating within a body of standing water as a result of slumping. The latter probably pass through brief stages that might be considered landslides and mud flows. As more water becomes mixed with it, the mud flow is converted from a plastic solid mass to a fluid condition.

Turbidity currents of the first type may transport large amounts of sediment over considerable periods of time (see Figure 34, p. 107) whereas those of the second type are irregularly intermittent but may be of huge proportions. These currents can move with great speed across very gently sloping bottoms and under some conditions they are capable of erosion. Their momentum allows them to travel great distances and to some degree they can ascend opposing slopes. Density slows the settling of larger sedimentary particles and turbulence serves to keep these in suspension. The deposits resulting from turbidity currents are characterized by graded bedding. Individual strata are likely to be continuous throughout large areas. Although no great turbidity currents have been observed, conclusive evidence of their existence appears to be provided by some sedimentary deposits and they are believed to be important agents in the transportation of much sediment to some portions of the deep-sea bottom situated far from any land.

In Standing Water

Currents occur in bodies of standing water, particularly the sea, generated by winds, tides, differences in temperature and salinity, and other causes. Three types can be recognized that interact and modify each other: (1) steady horizontal drift currents, (2) intermittent tidal currents, and (3) sloping convection currents. All of them may act upon bottom sediments and transport suspended material just as stream currents do. Generally, however, their velocities are much less than those of streams. Their boundary conditions also are less abrupt and, therefore, less turbulence is generated in them. Unless turbulence is augmented in some way only very fine sediment can be held in suspension. Such currents may prevent the deposition of sediment but rarely are they capable of erosion except where unusually strong tidal currents are confined to relatively narrow channels.

Waves generate a different kind of turbulence that is unrelated to currents. In wave motion, water molecules at the surface move in circular orbits whose diameters equal the height of waves. These orbits decrease downward exponentially in proportion to wave length and theoretically the ratio of orbit to depth is as $\dfrac{wave\ height}{2^n}$ is to $\dfrac{n \times wave\ length}{9}$. Thus at a depth of one wave length ($n = 9$) the orbit is $\dfrac{1}{2^9}$ or $\dfrac{1}{512}$ wave height. Actually the orbits become elliptical near the bottom and molecules there have little more than a backward-and-forward motion. This is the motion that builds up oscillation ripples on a sedimentary surface. Wave turbulence is capable of raising fine sediment from the bottom and keeping it in suspension. It cannot transport sediment rapidly, however, because the water molecules move forward only very slightly in the direction of the waves. Transportation is accomplished mainly by currents, even the slowest ones, that move wave-agitated water laterally. Conditions are much more complicated and turbulence is much greater in the zone of breaking waves that begins where the depth of water generally is somewhere between 1.5 and 3 times the wave height.

The salinity of the sea affects transportation importantly because electrolytes cause flocculation of fine suspended sediment and the resulting aggregates may settle relatively rapidly. Thus fine sediment is likely to remain suspended longer in fresh water than in salt and it may be transported greater distances.

By Air

The dynamics of sediment transportation by currents of air and water are the same. The chief factor of importance that differentiates these media is density. The density of ordinary sediment is 2.7 times that of water but it is about 2000 times that of air. Therefore, wind is a much less efficient agent of sediment transportation than water, and much greater current velocities are required to accomplish noteworthy results. On the other hand, the velocity of wind commonly exceeds that of water currents; high winds are capable of moving large amounts of fine material. Also wind moves across the land more widely and more continuously than water. Although the effect of wind appears negligible at most places, the total amount of sedimentary material moved certainly is very great.

Wind erosion can act only on dry material. Eolian transportation generally is inconspicuous except in arid regions or in areas of dry farm land where protective vegetation has been removed. After its deposition, wind-borne sediment in small amounts is difficult to identify. Most of it is soon moved again by water. When such sediment finally comes to rest, its eolian history rarely is apparent.

Size sorting of sediment is accomplished more efficiently by wind transportation than by water. The bed load consists almost exclusively of sand, and finer material is raised as dust that is carried in suspension faster and for greater distances. Some sand grains roll along the surface but most move principally by saltation. The swiftly moving grains that hop short distances impart their energy to others when they land. This lifts some grains into the air and serves to push others forward causing a kind of creeping motion to develop in a thin surface layer of the sand. The impact of grains is sharp and wear is relatively rapid. Corners and edges are rounded off and surfaces become frosted.

Dust and more rarely fine sand is carried upward by turbulent rising air currents and is shot upward by volcanic explosions. Some reaches high atmospheric levels where strong winds carry it swiftly for long distances. Later when it descends, the dust may filter down very slowly through air that is almost still. Some dust is so fine that it remains suspended until it is washed out of the air by rain. Storms of several days' duration with dust so thick that only near objects can be distinguished are not uncommon in desert regions. From time to time severe desert storms may darken the skies of almost an entire continent. Material from the dust bowl of the southwestern states has been traced as far as New England, and dust from the Sahara Desert reaches northern Europe. Much air-borne sediment falls directly into the sea.

During early Paleozoic and previous time, many land areas of the world were not as well protected from erosion and wind scouring by vegetation as they are at present. At that time wind action and eolian transportation certainly were more extensive and quantitatively important than they are today. They may have been relatively much more important and effective as compared with water action then than now. Possibly this may partially account for the commoner occurrence of cleaner sands in formations of early Paleozoic than of later ages.

By Ice

Ice in great masses such as glaciers is a plastic solid that flows from higher to lower levels and is capable of carrying large amounts of sediment. Besides its great viscosity, ice differs from water also in the extreme slowness of its movement and general lack of turbulence.

Glaciers acquire their load mainly from the surface over which they flow. They pick up loose material and break off rock fragments. There is almost no limit to the size of the masses they can move. In addition, abrasion beneath a glacier may be especially severe. Rock fragments pushed forward and weighted by overlying ice grind away the bed, and similar grinding action occurs between rocks embedded in the ice. Thus much finely divided sediment is produced.

After they are incorporated in the ice, rock fragments do not settle, and glaciers exhibit no selective action in their transportation of sedimentary material. All sediment moves almost equally slowly. Little or no sorting is accomplished. Glacial sediment characteristically consists of indiscriminately mixed rock fragments of all sizes and contains material ranging all the way from completely fresh to wholly weathered. Glacial sediment is subject to very little weathering during transportation.

Sediment in relatively small quantities is transported by floating ice. Icebergs broken off from glaciers and fragments of flow ice, that has picked up sediment from shore or shallow bottom, may float some distance before melting and dropping their solid loads. Pebbles and boulders carried in this way may sink among other sediments at places that they could not have reached by ordinary means. The occurrence of incongruous mixtures of this type, however, does not necessarily indicate floating ice because similar transportation can be accomplished by the drifting out from shore of large plants with debris entangled in their roots.

DEPOSITION OF SEDIMENTS

The nature of every sedimentary deposit depends upon a complex combination of factors that begins with (1) the kinds of rock that are subject to erosion, continues with (2) the degrees of chemical weathering and mechanical disintegration that affect these rocks and produce sediment and (3) the modifications of sedimentary material that occur during transportation, and ends with (4) the conditions that prevail at the site of deposition. When deposition alone is considered, it is important to recognize that, no matter what conditions characterize a depositional area, only those sediments that are delivered to or produced within it can accumulate.

The local factors that influence the deposition of sediment are equally complex: (1) The kind and quantity of sediment delivered to an area, as previously mentioned, is of chief importance. (2) Conditions that permit the deposition rather than the by-passing of this material are a consideration. These are not simple, but primary among them are depth of water in marine or lacustrine environments and gradient and volume of water in fluvial and related terrestrial environments. (3) The organic environment that controls the local production and preservation of organic sediment is a further factor. This determines the development of limestone and most organic material, both carbonaceous and bituminous. (4) another but generally less important factor is the physical environment that under some circumstances results in the formation of evaporites and other types of chemical sediments, like glauconite or phosphate nodules, or alters sediments as they accumulate, as possibly in the development of some red beds. (5) A last factor that is related to time rather than to location is the differences in the kinds of life that were in existence and that were capable of producing organic sediments. For example, in Precambrian time there were no animals that secreted calcareous shells or other hard parts such as became common later.

Depositional environments are difficult to classify in detail because they are influenced simultaneously by so many factors, are so varied, and intergrade so completely. The most obvious differentiation separates marine and non-marine environments but these are connected by littoral environments that share some features with both.

Marine Environment

The marine realm is much more important than the terrestrial as a region of sedimentary deposition. It occupies more than two-thirds of the surface

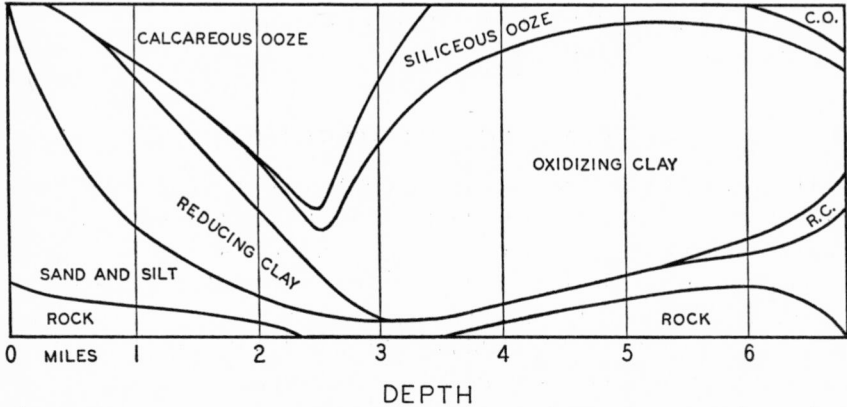

Figure 54.   Diagram showing relative proportions of the principal kinds of oceanic sediment as related to depth of water. This diagram does not show the occurrence of shallow-water calcareous sediment that probably is included with the sand and silt. The material indicated as "rock" includes gravel in near-shore areas and various kinds of crusted bottoms in deeper portions of the sea. (Data from Bruun, 1957, Geol. Soc. Amer., Mem. 67, vol. 1, p. 668, pl. 1.)

of the earth at present and is believed to have been still more extensive during much of the geologic past. Figure 54 shows the distribution of the principal types of oceanic sediment as they are related to depth of water.

Large bodies of sediment have been deposited above sea level in a variety of situations, but generally such deposition is temporary. Sooner or later most of this material is again eroded and carried onward to the sea. A prepon-

derance of the sedimentary rocks available to observation on the land today
are marine deposits.

Marine sediments and environments have been classified on the basis of
(1) depth of water, (2) nearness to shore, (3) penetration of light, (4) type
of benthonic life, (5) relations to topographic bottom zones, and (6) kinds
of sediment. No classification yet devised is wholly satisfactory because none
can be applied equally well to modern observed conditions and to the interpretation of ancient sediments. Most classifications distinguish a *neritic
zone,* recognition of which is strongly influenced by the general occurrence
at the present time of a land-margining continental shelf (see Figure 55).
This zone is variously defined as extending to (1) the edge of the steeper
continental slope, (2) a depth of 600 feet, (3) the limit of effective light

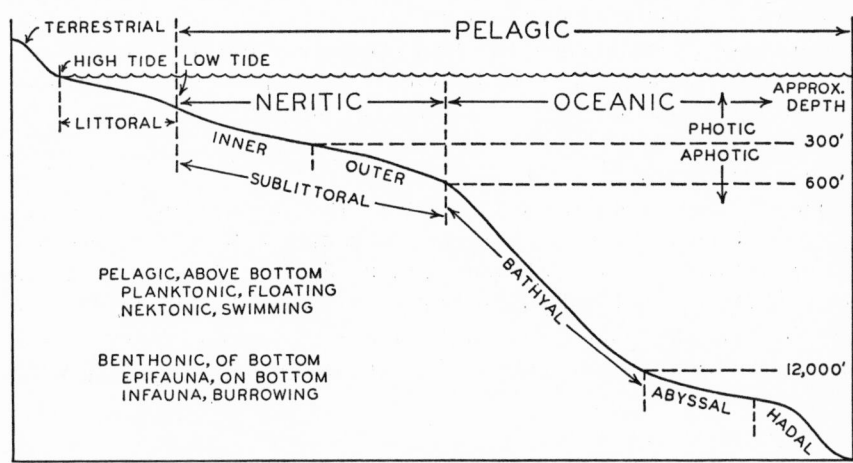

Figure 55. Schematic diagram showing the classification of marine environments. The
depth figures are approximate because agreement concerning them has not been reached.
The term *neritic* also is commonly used for the benthonic environments indicated here as
sublittoral. (Adapted from Hedgpeth, 1957, Geol. Soc. Amer., Mem. 67, vol. 1, p. 18,
fig. 1.)

penetration, (4) the greatest depth at which sediments are stirred by waves
at times of storm, or (5) the outer limit of abundant benthonic life.

A rough correlation exists between these various suggested limits of a neritic zone, and most marine sedimentary rocks available to observation seem
to have been deposited under conditions similar to those prevailing there.
These limits, however, do not serve to identify all neritic sediments, which
are extremely varied. The neritic zone has in fact been termed the zone of
variables. Comparisons between past and present neritic sediments are not
particularly significant for three reasons: (1) The modern neritic zone of

the continental shelf occurs along coasts facing the open ocean. It is exposed to great storms whereas many of the sedimentary rocks of the geologic past were deposited within the confines of sheltered inland seas where some of the physical conditions were very different. (2) Sediments today can be swept across the continental shelf and delivered to the deep ocean basins whereas the shallow landlocked seas of the past generally acted as traps from which relatively little sediment could escape to deeper water. (3) The present irregular pattern of sediment distribution on large parts of the continental shelf appears to be related to Pleistocene stages of lower sea level and has not yet become adjusted to modern conditions.

The classification of shallow marine sedimentary environments presented here is mainly lithologic. Although lithologic differences suggest differences in depth, these relations are doubtless variable. Almost certainly all of these shallow environments were parts of the neritic zone, but some of the following intermediate environment may have been neritic also. The *abyssal zone*, as commonly understood, is the bottom of the deep sea beyond the slope that descends from the edge of the continental shelf.

Shallow Sandy Zone

The effectiveness of waves and currents in the transportation of sediments decreases from the shoreline outward into deeper water (see Figure 56). Sediment that is moved slowly and with difficulty is left behind. In areas of active but relatively slow deposition, therefore, a natural gradient is likely to develop from gravel along a beach, to sand in very shallow water, mud in deeper water, and possibly calcareous material in situations beyond the reach

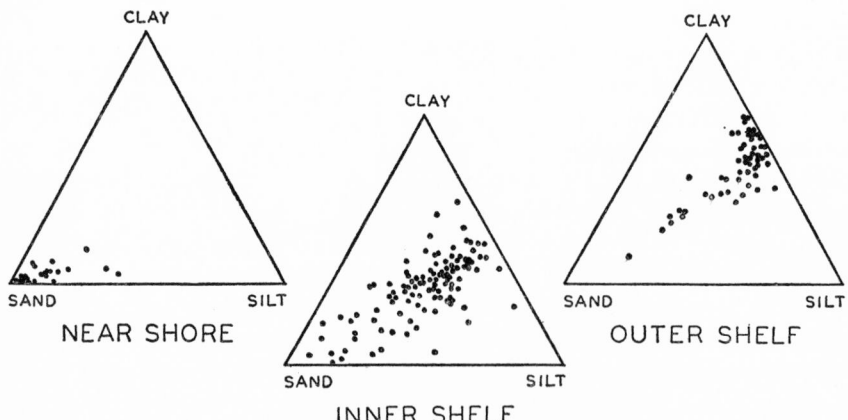

Figure 56.   Three component scatter diagrams showing differences in the composition of sediments in zones concentric with the Texas Gulf coast. See also Figure 131, p. 321. (After Shepard and Moore, 1955, *Bull. Am. Assoc. Petroleum Geol.*, vol. 39, p. 1501, fig. 26.)

of detrital sediments. The separation of sand and mud is accomplished by the action of wave turbulence, which holds fine material in suspension where it is susceptible to current movements, whereas coarser particles, if they are raised at all, return quickly to the bottom. This is an efficient sorting process, and marine sand generally is washed nearly free of mud and silt unless it accumulates at places where waves do not develop or is deposited relatively rapidly.

The action of waves tends to move coarser material toward the beach, and pebbles and sand are carried along the shore rather than into deeper water. Sand is not ordinarily transported in water more than thirty to forty feet deep and it characteristically marks a narrow near-shore zone (see Figures 189, 190, pp. 499, 500). Areally extensive sand deposits may indicate a corresponding zone of very shallow water or an unstable coastline. Most marine sandstones are either transgressive or regressive and vary in age in a direction normal to the ancient coast. Transgression occurs where sea level rises and the shore and zone of moving sand shift landward. Sand deposits are most likely to be preserved under transgressive conditions because, as water level rises, weaker turbulence and currents are unable to stir the sandy bottom, and finer sediment is deposited burying and protecting it. This is the only situation in which offshore sand bars are likely to escape destruction. Regressive conditions develop where sea level is stable, but a shallow bottom is built up gradually by continued deposition, or where sea level is slowly lowered. In either case the shore and sandy zone move seaward. Declining sea level exposes newly deposited unconsolidated sand to subaerial erosion and it is likely to be washed back into the sea by rain or dissipated by the wind.

Sand occurs on the modern sea bottom at places in deep water where its presence is difficult to explain by ordinary current transportation under conditions as they now exist. Some almost certainly is related to former lower stands of sea level. Elsewhere the depth seems to be much too great for this explanation. Turbidity currents are capable of moving coarse debris to such situations. Their deposits are characterized by graded bedding which shows a low degree of sorting. Deposits of this kind are to be expected in some ancient sediments that have been raised and are now exposed upon the land.

Shallow Muddy Zone

Muddy sediments not only exceed sand in quantity but are normally much more widely spread. Because they are carried in suspension, the distribution is determined by the direction and speed of currents rather than by depth of water.

A characteristic of clay that is of great importance in connection with its more or less permanent deposition is its agglomerating or agglutinating property. The electrolytes of sea water cause the particles to flocculate, and the resulting clumps generally settle more rapidly than do separate grains. When these reach the bottom and become reoriented and reorganized, attractive forces hold them together still more firmly. Thus currents and turbulence that are weak but capable of holding clay particles in suspension and transporting them may not be strong enough to pick them up again after deposition.

A near-shore sandy zone commonly grades outward into a zone of silty mud. Generally the silt content decreases as water deepens and the shore becomes more distant (see Figure 211, p. 544). Some silt is likely to be carried as far as wave action or currents stir bottom sediments, that is, to a depth that ordinarily does not greatly exceed 300 feet. The finest clay particles settle with extreme slowness. Some reach the bottom only at the greatest depths and in the most remote parts of the sea where practically no turbulence occurs.

Silt and mud may extend to the shore and merge into littoral deposits without the intervention of a sandy zone (see Figure 62, p. 182). This is not uncommon at protected places along a coast as in small sheltered bays and lagoons. Also mud may be entrapped by vegetation, as in mangrove swamps or areas of shallow water with abundant seaweed, where wave action and bottom stirring are inhibited.

Irregularities of deposition are common in areas of shallow water and muddy sediment and find expression in the development of alternating coarser and finer layers or the admixture of larger and smaller amounts of calcareous material. This may result from (1) intermittent periods of storm that influence the transportation of coarser sediment, (2) irregularity in the quality or quantity of sediment delivered to an area, (3) variability in the abundance or kinds of organisms living there, or (4) minor fluctuations of sea level. Interlayering, resulting from these causes, is likely to be seasonal or follow some cycle of longer period. Some mud flats exhibit very irregular, small, thin lenses of mud and silt, produced by the sorting but incomplete separation of sediments in the much shorter cycle of tidal ebb and flow.

Shallow Calcareous Zone

The distribution of calcareous sediment is limited by factors controlling the organisms that produce it. The growth of these organisms is favored by (1) warm water, (2) shallow depth, and (3) relative freedom from detrital land-derived sediments. At present large amounts of calcareous sediment are being produced and are accumulating importantly only in tropical and warm temperate regions where reef-building organisms thrive. The extent of limestones, however, shows that in the past calcium carbonate probably was deposited in much more extensive regions, and reefs were a less important source than they appear to be today.

Calcareous sediments range in size from coarse to very fine. They constitute a suite similar in most respects to detrital sediments. Waves and currents transport, sort, and deposit them like other sediments. Because most calcareous material originates on the sea bottom, however, it may escape the turbulence of a near-shore zone through which most terrigenous material must pass. On the whole, calcareous sediments are less well sorted and generally they do not exhibit well-marked gradation from coarse to fine material in zones extending parallel to a coast or corresponding to increasing depth of water. Very fine calcareous particles do not remain in suspension indefinitely like clay but redissolve. The transportation of such material is therefore

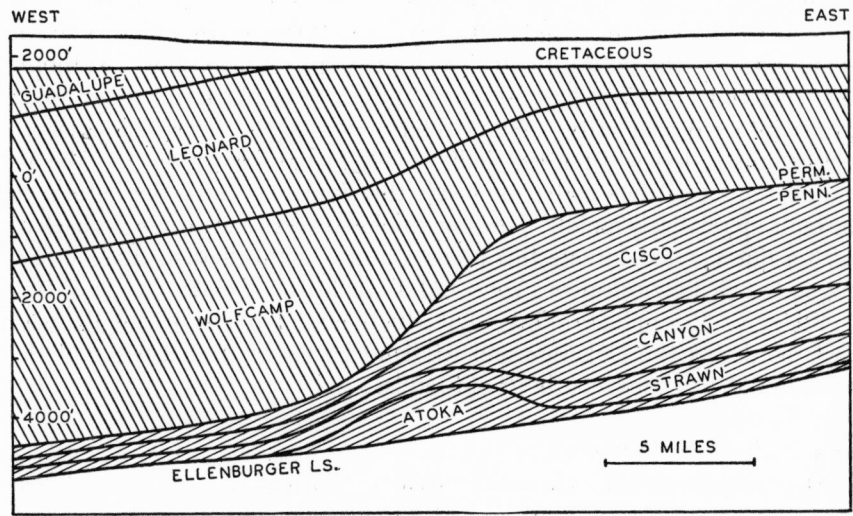

Figure 57. Generalized geologic cross section showing the relations of Pennsylvanian and Permian strata overlying the Ellenburger Limestone (Ord.) on the east side of the Midland basin of west Texas. The margin of the basin is marked by a succession of Pennsylvanian reefs. Sedimentation beyond them in the basin was very slow and conditions here gave rise to the concept of a starved basin. (After Adams and others, 1951, *Bull. Am. Assoc. Petroleum Geol.*, vol. 35, p. 2606, fig. 3.)

limited. Most calcareous sediment does not appear to have been transported far, and much of it probably accumulates close to its place of origin.

The production and deposition of dominantly calcareous sediment occurs at favorable places almost anywhere within the neritic zone. Calcareous deposits may extend to the shoreline and grade laterally into detrital sand. The presence of detrital sand grains, however, does not necessarily indicate a shore environment and shallow-water current action. Some sand can be carried long distances by the wind as, for example, off the northwestern coast of Africa, where fine sand from the Sahara Desert has been identified in deep-water sediments several hundred miles from shore.

More commonly the zone of calcareous sediment lies beyond the shallow-water muddy zone, or consists of more or less isolated patches surrounded by muddy sediment (see Figure 220, p. 581). Such patches, if they are small, may form *bioherms,* where local communities of lime-secreting organisms were able to persist in the midst of a generally inhospitable environment. The most favorable situations for lime accumulation occur rather far from land or some distance offshore from a low-lying coast where the land contributes little detrital material to the sea.

Just as rapid detrital sedimentation may limit the production and accumulation of important lime deposits in one direction, depth of water, or some other unfavorable condition, may limit them in the other. Thus at some place on the outward and downward sloping sea bottom, benthonic lime-secreting organisms become scarce and the zone of calcareous sediment passes into a deeper water zone of mud or very slowly accumulating ooze whose lime is derived from the shells of tiny planktonic organisms. The accumulation of calcium carbonate inside this limit may cause the bottom to be built up relatively rapidly. The growth of active reefs along and in back of such a line may accentuate this process, and a sharp division develops between the shallow calcareous zone and a much deeper outer one as shown in Figure 57. Examples of this kind of situation are provided by the Permian reefs bordering the Delaware and Midland basins in west Texas and the modern Bahama banks southeast of Florida.

Organic Reef Environment

Most calcareous sediment is produced by benthonic plants and animals. It consists of fragmented material and very fine-grained precipitated calcium carbonate that is transported and deposited like other sediment. Where reefs occur they are important sources of calcareous sediment. A considerable part of the reefs themselves, however, does not owe its existence to sedimentary deposition but is built up as a rigid structure by the activity of organisms that create and maintain an environment favorable for their growth. The reef environment, therefore, is different from that of the shallow calcareous zone and requires separate consideration. Reefs form a continuous zone along some coasts. Elsewhere they are scattered and completely isolated from each other. They rise from both calcareous and mud bottoms and also grow upward from topographic prominences in deep water far outside of the neritic zone.

The essential part of any organic reef is the rigid mass, rising above the sea bottom, composed of calcareous structures built by organisms that were firmly attached to solid underlying material. The framework of the mass generally is more or less discontinuous but the interstices are filled with calcareous sediment consisting of the remains of other organisms and debris derived from the fragmentation of the actual reef builders. This loose material is bound together by the cementing action of incrusting organisms and becomes part of the solid reef structure. The framework of modern reefs is formed chiefly of colonial corals, and the interstitial material is bound mainly by calcareous algae. Varyingly important similar roles in the growth of ancient reefs were played by other organisms including bryozoans, stromatoporoids, and sponges.

Few modern reef-building organisms flourish at depths of more than 250 feet although they may grow deeper in exceptionally clear water. Reefs, therefore, must start in shallow water and, under favorable circumstances, they grow upward until progress is stopped at the water surface. At present, reefs are restricted to regions of clear water where the temperature does not fall below 68 degrees. The northernmost actively growing reefs today occur at Bermuda in the Atlantic Ocean 850 miles due east of Charleston, South Carolina. The most southern coral islands are the Abrolhos off the west coast of Australia 250 miles north of Perth. The assumption has been common that ancient reefs were similarly restricted as to depth and temperature. This is uncertain, however, because the organisms that formed them were different from modern reef builders and it is not unlikely that they were adapted to somehwat different physical conditions.

As reefs grow upward, they encounter more and more wave turbulence and become subject to progressively more severe erosion. Growth commonly is so vigorous, howeverr that they reach low-tide level and maintain their tops there in spite of continuous battering by the waves (see Figure 184, p. 493). If sea level rises or the bottom sinks, reef growth may continue; reefs in various parts of the world have reached thicknesses of several thousand feet. Material produced by the wave erosion of reef summits, ranging from the finest sediment to large blocks of cemented reef rock, accumulates as talus aprons unless strong currents sweep it away and distribute it more evenly over the sea bottom.

Some modern corals grow in considerable abundance in deeper, colder water. Banks of them have been found in various parts of the world but they are best known along the Norwegian coast. There they occur at depths of from 600 to 900 feet where water temperatures range from 40 to 47 degrees. Elsewhere similar patches have been reported at depths of more than 8000 feet. Coral banks of this type attain diameters of more than a mile and some rise 200 feet above the surrounding bottom. It is not certain, however, that they are reeflike structures, and prominences rising above the bottom may only provide favorable places for coral growth. The banks generally occur in the midst of fine detrital sediment. The number of coral species is very limited and these cannot survive in shallow or warmer water. Many other kinds of animals occur in association with the corals but calcareous algae are absent. Ancient banks of this type might be mistaken for warm and shallow-water bioherms or organic reefs.

Evaporitic Environment

Evaporite deposits such as salt and gypsum are products of a highly specialized environment that does not constitute a zone but prevails in restricted areas. It results from excess evaporation, which concentrates the mineral matter dissolved in sea water and eventually causes its precipitation. This can occur only in shallow, more or less landlocked extensions of the sea, confined by barriers that prevent free water circulation, and in regions of arid and warm climate. Typical shallow-water sands and silty muds commonly accompany evaporites. High land or active erosion in nearby areas is not indicated, however, for the influx of fresh water would retard concentration of the brine, and salt and gypsum would be contaminated by much detrital sediment.

Supersaline conditions inhibit marine life, and the remains of organisms are rare or wholly absent from the sediment. During the concentration process, calcareous sediments may be produced inorganically. Their textures commonly are very fine but oolites and pisolites may occur. Dolomite generally is more common than calcium carbonate. Conditions within an evaporite basin fluctuate between greater and less brine concentration, and different kinds of strata succeed each other. They are likely to grade into red beds in one direction and into more normal marine deposits in the other.

Anaerobic Environment

Anaerobic conditions mark another specialized environment that occurs intermittently in restricted portions of the sea and does not form a zone. This environment owes its existence to abundant organic material whose decay depletes the oxygen dissolved in sea water. Distinction must be made between two types of anaerobic areas, one occurring in very shallow and the other in deeper water. In both situations water circulation is impeded to such an extent that oxygen is not supplied to the bottom as rapidly as it is consumed. Sediments deposited and preserved are characteristically black, and the remains of benthonic animals are absent or very rare.

The carbonaceous nature of black shales has been explained in various ways, one suggestion being that vegetable material or black soil was washed into the sea from adjacent low-lying land. The probability is greater, however, that the carbonaceous material had a local origin, and an important part of it may have been supplied by seaweeds that died, sank to the bottom, and partially decayed. Such plants rooted by holdfasts in the mud interfere with waves and currents and produce stagnation in the lower water layers. The surface water, however, normally is aerated, habitable for nektonic and planktonic organisms, and capable of transporting fine suspended sediment. Small animals can live among or attached to the upper parts of seaweeds.

Their remains and those of other creatures of the aerated surface zone may be preserved when they die and sink to the bottom.

Coarse seaweeds attached to the bottom and capable of damping waves are not abundant in water more than about 100 feet deep. If the foregoing explanation is correct, water of not much greater depth is indicated. It may have been much shallower. Such an origin of much carbonaceous matter is favored by (1) the great areal extent of some black shales like the Chatta-nooga (Dev.-Miss.) and its equivalents, and numerous thinner beds in the Pennsylvanian System whose organic content does not decrease in a direction away from the contemporary land; (2) the absence of recognizable land-plant fragments; and (3) the occurrence of black shales in Precambrian and

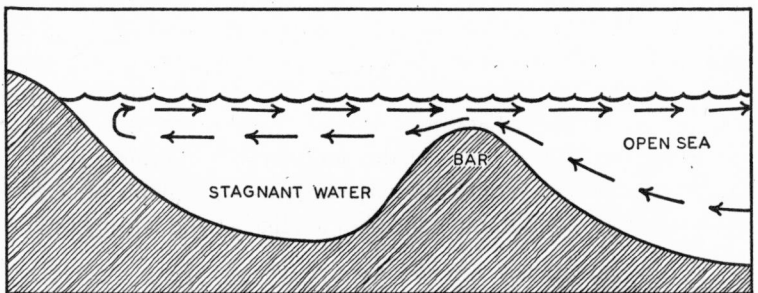

Figure 58. Schematic diagram showing how circulation of surface water in an enclosed barred or silled basin may leave the deeper water undisturbed. This is the explanation commonly offered to account for the accumulation of highly carbonaceous marine sediments.

early Paleozoic strata deposited at a time probably antedating extensive conquest of the land by plants. Strata of this type grade in one direction into near-shore sediments of various types such as silty and sandy shales and sandstones, or muds suggesting coastal swamp conditions. In the other direction they are transitional into more normal marine sediments, generally shales, containing less organic and more calcareous material indicating better aerated and deeper water. This type of anaerobic environment appears to require not only shallow water but also a humid climate that probably was relatively cool rather than warm because desiccation did not occur.

The other type of anaerobic environment occurs in more or less deep enclosed basins whose lower water becomes stagnant because it is dense and fails to mix with normal surface water (see Figure 58). Most basins of this kind are landlocked, like the Black Sea and some Norwegian fjords, or enclosed by reefs, as was the Permian basin of west Texas and the late Devonian basin in Alberta in western Canada. Free communication with the sea commonly is restricted to narrow or shallow passages where the bottom rises above nearby areas and forms barriers to the circulation of deeper water. Organic matter is supplied by planktonic organisms that die, sink to the bottom, and partially decay. The sediment in landlocked basins ordinarily is silty or argillaceous mud, but in those associated with reefs, variable amounts of calcium carbonate may contribute to the development of impure black limestone. The sediments of these basins are more or less sharply restricted laterally and are less likely than the black shales of shallow water to grade imperceptibly into normal marine deposits. Ordinarily they also are less extensive areally. Some large basins of the past, particularly those enclosed by reefs, appear to have received very little sediment. The black shale in them probably records deposition of extreme slowness. They have been termed *starved basins*.

Sediments deposited under other, relatively shallow-water conditions contain variable amounts of organic material and may be dark colored. These sediments are argillaceous or calcareous muds, but rarely sands. Some preserve organic matter because accumulation was too rapid to permit complete destruction by decay or the scavenging of mud-eating animals. Sediments of this kind are likely to be silty. Others record oxygen deficiency rather than complete exhaustion and probably contain only the most resistant organic compounds. Such sediments may contain the remains of a few particularly hardy benthonic animals and they are likely to be calcareous.

Intermediate Zone

Shallow-water sediments are separated from the deposits of the deep sea by an intermediate zone whose boundaries in most areas are indistinct. The sediments of this zone lack most of the features indicative of wave and current action, and the remains of benthonic animals generally are not abundant. Although modern sediments of this kind are commonly described as "blue mud," they vary considerably depending upon (1) their degree of oxidation, (2) their content of organic matter, (3) their nearness to land, (4) the kinds of material accumulating in adjacent shallow-water environments, and (5) the kind and abundance of planktonic organisms whose shells settle in different areas. Silt delivered by large rivers may reach this zone, and fine calcareous detritus from nearby reefs may be an important constituent. Also some patches of deep-water corals may occur.

The bottom within the intermediate zone is more generally and more steeply sloping than in most parts of either the shallower or deeper sea. Consequently slumping is likely to be common. Contorted bedding so produced, however, is not restricted to this zone because slumping also occurs on slopes in much shallower water. Altogether, sediments of the intermediate zone possess no characters that are unique or certainly distinctive.

Abyssal Environment

About half of the surface of the earth lies at the bottom of the deep sea where physical conditions are uniform and sedimentary deposition is very slow. Most deep-sea sediments consist of mixtures of very fine-grained inorganic mud and the shells of planktonic organisms. The sediments dredged from great depths owe their differences to variable proportions of these constituents. Three general types are recognized: (1) calcareous ooze, (2) siliceous ooze, and (3) red clay. They occupy areas having the approximate ratios of 4 to 1 to 3 respectively. Two kinds of calcareous ooze generally are distinguished, depending upon whether *Globigerina* and other pelagic foraminifera, or pteropods, which are tiny swimming molluscs, predominate. Similarly, siliceous oozes are of two kinds, containing either abundant skeletons of protozoan radiolarians or diatoms, which are single-celled microscropic plants.

The inorganic constituents of deep-sea sediments consist mainly of tiny clay particles produced by ordinary rock weathering and erosion. Both wind and water are responsible for their transportation. Much of this material occurring far from land may have been wind-borne before it settled into the sea.

Volcanic dust is a variably important constituent of deep-sea sediment and mostly it was transported through the air. It is, of course, commonest in regions of explosive volcanic action but otherwise its relative abundance probably is greatest in areas most distant from land that receive the smallest quantities of detrital clay.

Finally, cosmic dust in small amounts filters down through the atmosphere from outer space and has been identified in deep-sea sediments.

The nature of the organic fraction of abyssal sediments is determined by (1) the distribution of planktonic organisms and (2) the depth of water. All of the principal kinds of plankton are widely distributed geographically but their relative abundances vary in general with latitude. Thus foraminifera, pteropods, and radiolarians predominate in the warmer surface water between about 50 degrees north and 50 degrees south latitude whereas diatoms attain their greatest development poleward from this zone. For this reason most calcareous ooze is confined to the low and middle latitudes. Depth is important because the remains of planktonic organisms are subject to solution as they sink slowly in the sea, and solution continues as they lie unprotected on the bottom. Solution is most prolonged, of course, where deposition is slowest, in the deepest areas. Most calcareous ooze occurs at depths of less than 12,000 feet; very little calcareous material remains in sediment as deep as 15,000 feet. The siliceous skeletons are less soluble and radiolarian ooze occurs mainly below 14,000 feet. Diatomaceous ooze, however, is present at much shallower depths outside of the main range of calcareous plankton. Below 16,000 feet little organic silica remains, and red clay characterizes the deeper ocean floor.

The nature of abyssal sediments is complicated in some areas by the occurrence of coarser detrital material. Some, like desert sand in the Atlantic near northwestern Africa, probably was transported by the wind. Elsewhere turbidity currents are believed to have moved sand and silt for long distances across the deep-sea floor. There is, however, considerable difference of opinion concerning the prevalence of turbidity current transportation.

The various deep-sea oozes cannot be distinguished certainly from material that might have been deposited in much shallower water. The red clay, however, is believed to be unique. Sediments observed at a few places on islands in both the East and West Indies have been identified with it. If this is correct, these deposits establish the possibility that small portions of the deep-sea bottom may be elevated and converted into land.

Terrestrial Environment

Sedimentary deposition is much less general on land than in the sea. Most terrestrial regions suffer nearly continuous erosion, and deposition is confined to certain favorable areas that ordinarily occur at low elevations as related to local topography. These areas are small in comparison with the whole land surface and they are scattered. The conditions prevailing within them and influencing sedimentary deposition are extremely varied. Therefore, terrestrial deposits are more irregularly distributed and constituted than marine deposits. They generally represent only temporary stages interrupting the transportation of sediment to the sea.

Fluvial Deposition

Fluvial deposits include all sediments deposited from flowing water on the land. Their nature depends upon (1) the type of material available to transport, (2) the volume of flowing water, (3) the speed of currents, (4) the gradient of flow, (5) the nature and amount of sedimentary load and its distribution, (6) the size and shape of channels, and (7) the place of deposition. Some of these factors are interrelated, as are speed of flow and gradient, but the many possible combinations result in great complexity. Deposition occurs if the transporting power of a current fails, generally because of reduced velocity or volume of water. Therefore, it takes place when or where (1) lower gradient is encountered, as at the boundary between an upland area and a plain, (2) channels become smaller and shallower, as in a distributary system or on a flood plain beyond the main stream course, and (3) volume of water is reduced by decrease in supply, after a storm, or by loss from seepage into porous ground or from evaporation.

Most fluvial deposits can be classified as either channel or slack-water accumulations. Channel deposits generally are attenuated and much longer in one direction than in the other. They may curve and follow the meanderings of a stream, like some shoestring sands. Unconformable contacts between them and older strata ordinarily are clear. These deposits consist of poorly sorted sediments and show evidence of rapid but interrupted deposition. Coarseness may vary greatly, and cut-and-fill structures and irregular cross-bedding are common. Gravel and coarse sand are not likely to be transported outside of channels. Buried channels may be confused with beach deposits and offshore bars, which are somewhat similar in form and coarseness.

Flood-plain alluvium is the most perfect representative of terrestrial slack-water deposition. It generally consists of well-laminated and moderately well-sorted sediment, ranging from fine sand near stream channels, where natural levees may develop, to mud with decreasing amounts of silt at increasing distances away. The character of flood-plain sediments is likely to be influenced by climate. In humid regions organic material may occur in sufficient quantity to impart a dark color, or arid conditions may cause strong oxidation that perhaps accounts for the development of some red beds. River alluvium grades imperceptibly into sediment deposited in lakes, swamps, deltas, and the sea.

Fluvial deposits of transitional types—not strictly either channel or slack-water sediments—accumulate especially in arid regions upon the flanks of mountains and in intermontane basins. Steep alluvial fans are built up where current velocity is checked so abruptly in mountain streams that deposition of all but the finest sediment is very rapid. Systems of distributaries are developed at times of flood and the streams shift courses so often and so swiftly that no pattern of channels is preserved for long. Slack water does not border channels because there are no flood plains, but finer sediment may be deposited from the very shallow water of sheet floods. Mud flows also may develop whose high density and viscosity permit them to move large boulders.

Beyond the fans and pediment slopes, temporary and perhaps saline ponds and lakes form whose water disappears by evaporation. In them the finest sediment settles. The impermanence of shorelines results in the extensive intertonguing of fluvial and lacustrine deposits. Part of this sediment is likely to be whipped up by winds. The sand forms belts of dunes, but dust is transported farther and may settle to form loess like that in northern China. Extremely thick fluvial and basin deposits may develop particularly along the fronts of rising mountains. Ancient sedimentary accumulations of this type occur in the Tertiary formations of the Rocky Mountain region and the Triassic deposits of the Atlantic seaboard.

Lacustrine Deposition

Lake sediments are so similar to some of those deposited in the sea that distinction in ancient strata may be uncertain. Some features of the sea, however, are not duplicated in lakes—for example, size and depth—and neither very extensive nor very deep water lake deposits are to be expected.

Because of the small size and shallowness of most lakes, waves and currents are not strong and they are likely to be less effective in sorting and transporting sediments than in the sea. Also large bodies of calcareous material are rare. One of the most noteworthy differences concerns the faunas. The variety of organisms in fresh water is much restricted because several important groups such as the echinoids, brachiopods, corals, calcareous bryozoans, and cephalopods are exclusively marine. Where the remains of such animals occur abundantly, marine origin is established, but their absence is by no means proof of non-marine deposition. On the other hand, if fresh-water species can be identified, their presence generally is diagnostic.

Most lakes are only temporary features of the land destined soon to be filled with sediment or drained. Deposits in them are not likely to be thick. Where great bodies of sediment have accumulated, as in some intermontane areas, lacustrine and fluvial strata commonly are interlayered and differentiation may be difficult. Small lakes and ponds develop in many situations, as on river flood plains and near glaciers, and deposits in them merge more or less imperceptibly with those of other environments. On the whole, lacustrine sediments are hard to identify except where geomorphic features aid in establishing the existence of lakes in the relatively recent past.

Swamp Deposits

Swamp, marsh, or bog deposits represent a restricted and specialized environment that occurs only on the land or at the margin of the sea. Ordinarily they require (1) low topographic situation, (2) relatively humid climate, and (3) abundant vegetation. Ancient swamp deposits commonly are identified by the occurrence of vegetable debris in a partly decomposed condition. They are important because they include most coal beds. Three types of swamps can be distinguished: (1) coastal marshes, (2) low-moor bogs, and (3) high-moor bogs. Coastal marshes are part of the general littoral environment but both low-moor and high-moor bogs are terrestrial.

Low-moor bogs are confined to topographic depressions that are undrained or poorly drained and contain stagnant water in which vegetable material may accumulate as peat. Ordinarily beginning as ponds or small lakes, they are gradually filled in by the encroachment of vegetation about their margins. They are restricted to places where the water table lies at or above the surface of the ground and abundant inwash of sediment does not occur. They are discontinuous and generally small, but some may contain relatively thick peat or coal deposits. Thus Pennsylvanian coal up to nearly 100 feet thick has been mined from several ancient Missouri sink holes of moderate or small size. Low-moor bogs may develop throughout a wide range of latitude but they are rare in the tropics, where the decay of all organic material is very rapid.

High-moor bogs occur at present only in cool or cold regions where evap-

oration is retarded and decay is slow. They develop in flat or very gently rolling areas and are not dependent upon the position of the original water
table. In these locations vegetation, mainly moss at present, accumulates as
a spongey mass permanently saturated with water as in northern tundra
regions. These bogs may be extensive and continue without interruption
across gentle topographic undulations. Pennsylvanian coals, many of which
are continuous over thousands of square miles, probably record swamps of
the general high-moor type that differed from modern ones mainly in being
forested. Other coals, such as those in the Upper Cretaceous formations of

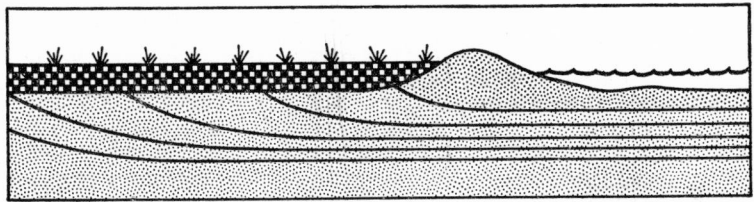

Figure 59. Diagrammatic reconstruction of a Cretaceous coal swamp developed behind a coastal bar or ridge. This is the type of situation in which peat is
believed to have accumulated at intervals during deposition of sediments of the
Mesa Verde Group. (After Young, 1955, *Bull. Geol. Soc. Amer.*, vol. 66, p. 196,
fig. 4a.)

the western states, seem to have had a somewhat different origin. They apparently developed adjacent to a shifting coastline in marshes that lay behind protective beach ridges made of sand as shown in Figure 59. These
probably were not salt marshes. In general, salt water does not provide a
favorable environment for the accumulation of thick or extensive peat deposits.

Glacial Deposition

Sediment transported by glacial ice cannot be deposited until the glacier
melts. Therefore, it is deposited in an aqueous environment and, speaking
most strictly, it forms an aqueous rather than a true glacial deposit. As loosely
and commonly interpreted, however, glacial deposits are considered to include all types of periglacial sediments, some of which, such as varved clay,
outwash gravel, and loess, clearly were not deposited from ice. Here an intermediate position is taken and attention is restricted to those materials that
are generally said to have been deposited directly from the ice, that is,
glacial till or boulder clay.

Till consists of wholly unsorted detrital material, much of it unweathered,
and includes fragments of all the rocks overridden by the glacier. It shows no
evidence of water transportation or reworking after liberation from the ice
although obviously water-laid deposits commonly are associated with it.

Generally it is composed of more or less argillaceous or sandy clay containing variably abundant pebbles and boulders, some of them very large. Till occurs (1) in ridgelike terminal or recessional moraines which mark the stationary margins of glaciers where rates of melting and ice advance were equal, and (2) in generally thinner layers of ground moraine where recessional melting occurred. Valley glaciers rarely leave much ground moraine, but a large proportion of the sediment transported by great continental ice sheets remains as ground moraine covering many thousands of square miles.

The thicknesses of till deposits vary. Thickness depends to some extent upon the topography of the underlying bedrock surface. Till plains were produced by the grinding down of hilltops during glacial advance and the filling of old valleys as a glacier melted back. At some places in the Great Lakes states glacial deposits, mainly till, range from 500 to more than 1000 feet in thickness. Till itself is unstratified but multiple glaciation, such as occurred during the Pleistocene Epoch, may pile till sheets upon each other, separated by weathered zones and wind- or water-laid interglacial deposits. Thus large-scale stratification may occur.

Much material transported by glaciers is reworked by meltwater and deposited in temporary lakes and ponds bordering the ice front, or in valleys that drained the melting ice. Such deposits show various degrees of sorting, but they consist of material derived from till and the genetic relations of Pleistocene deposits of this kind generally are fairly obvious.

Ancient till deposits, termed *tillite*, have been reported from almost every geologic system and in many parts of the world. Glacial deposits of Huronian and late Paleozoic ages seem to have been certainly identified but most others either are seriously questioned or are no longer interpreted as glacial. Unsorted sediments of quite different origin may resemble till closely in relatively small outcrops as, for example, submarine slumps, mud flows, and some tectonic breccias. Even faceted and scratched pebbles and striated rock surfaces may have other explanations. Without the aid of geomorphic features to supplement composition and texture, ancient consolidated deposits, some of which are metamorphosed, are very difficult to interpret surely.

Eolian Deposits

Ordinarily wind is not a primary agent of sediment transportation. Most of the material it moves has been processed previously by water and carried to favorable places where it became subject to wind erosion. Thus the sediment in most eolian deposits has had a somewhat more complex history than have other sediments. Eolian deposits are the only ones commonly accumulating in areas that are higher topographically than the immediate sources of the sediment. Wind-borne material also is deposited in lower situations, but there it is not likely to remain undisturbed and generally passes back into the regimen of water.

Eolian deposits fall into one or another of three distinct categories: (1) sand dunes, (2) loess, and (3) volcanic ash. The difference between the first two is primarily one of particle size, but this determines the method and distance of transportation and the form of the deposits. Both require a more or less uninterrupted supply of fresh dry material, provided by (1) beaches on windward coasts, (2) barren valleys of overloaded streams, and (3) deserts where rocks are continuously disintegrating.

Sand travels mainly by saltation and begins to accumulate in the lee of objects or other irregularities of the surface that interfere with the flow of air. Once started, a dune continues to grow until its crest reaches a level where

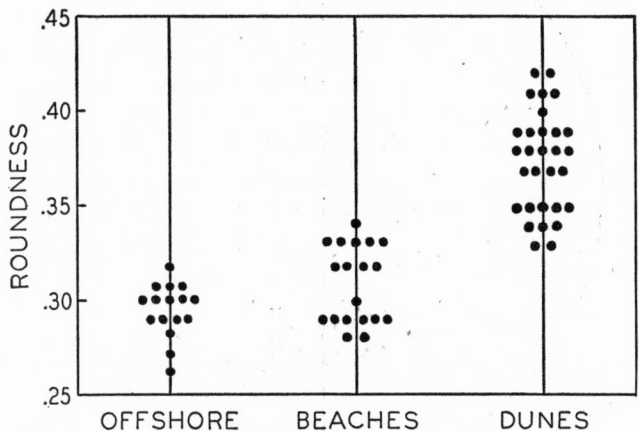

Figure 60. Diagram showing the relative roundness of sand grains occurring in different situations on the Texas Gulf coast. Each dot represents a studied sample. (After Shepard and Moore, 1955, Bull. Am. Assoc. Petroleum Geol., vol. 39, p. 1506, fig. 30.)

air currents are so strong that further accumulation is prevented. On the south shore of Lake Michigan dunes reach a height of 200 feet, and much higher ones are reported in the Sahara Desert. Dunes begin to form very near the source of sand. Whereas in arid regions they may travel long distances downwind, elsewhere their movement is limited to places where sand mobility is not neutralized by the growth of plants. Most dunes consist dominantly of quartz sand but composition reflects the source, and other material of sand size may be drifted into dunes. Thus in New Mexico gypsum dunes occur, and calcareous dunes formed of coral sand, oolites, and foraminifera have developed adjacent to some beaches in the tropics and more rarely as far north as the British Isles.

The most characteristic features of dunes are their composition and internal structure. They consist of well-sorted and generally rounded sand grains (see Figure 60) disposed in an irregular system of steep cross-bedding as shown in Figure 61. These features, where well developed, may be recognizable in sandstones of various ages as, for example, the Navajo Sandstone (Jur.) of Utah and Arizona. Other sandstones, like the St. Peter (Ord.) of the upper Mississippi Valley, composed of rounded and frosted grains but lacking conspicuous cross-bedding, probably are dune sands that have been reworked and deposited in water.

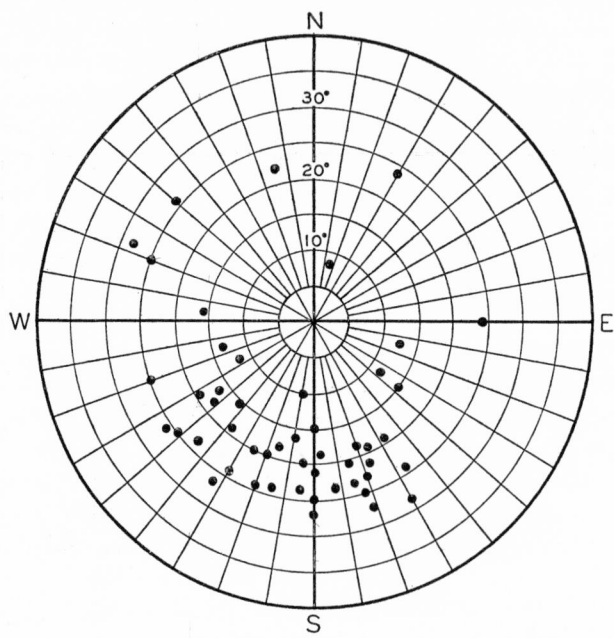

Figure 61.   Polar-coordinate diagram showing directions and angles of dip of cross-bedding in sandstone of the De Chelley Formation (Perm.) at Monument Valley, Arizona. (After Reiche, 1938, J. Geol., vol. 46, p. 925, fig. 5.)

Loess consists mainly of silt-sized particles carried in suspension by the turbulence of air. These particles may be transported continuously or by stages for long distances in the direction of prevailing winds and they accumulate slowly as an even blanket deposit where they settle among vegetation and are protected from further wind erosion. Two general types of loess can be distinguished depending upon whether the sediment was derived from overloaded streams or deserts. Sandy beaches do not provide a source of similar material.

The best-known loess deposits occur in North America and Europe and are products of Pleistocene glaciation. During summer when ice melted, rivers like the Mississippi were in flood and heavily loaded with outwash material. In winter, water volume decreased greatly and large expanses of the flood plains dried out and were attacked by wind erosion. Prevailing westerly winds moved large quantities of sand and dust eastward. The sand was piled in dunes upon the nearby lowlands but dust was carried farther and settled on the uplands to form loess. Adjacent to the principal outwash valleys loess deposits approach 100 feet in thickness at some places. With distance they become progressively thinner, more clayey, and finer grained until at last loess cannot be differentiated from other soil. This loess reflects its glacial origin, contains fresh unweathered minerals, and is abundantly calcareous.

The loess deposits of northern China, the greatest in the world, consist of dust carried southeastward from Mongolia and the Gobi Desert. As Asia had no Pleistocene continental glacier, this loess was derived mainly from alluvium contributed to the desert margin by streams flowing from the nearby mountains supplemented by deflation products of the desert surface. Wind erosion and sorting in the desert are still at work. Belts of dunes are growing, and much dust continues to be transported to the Yellow River valley. Loess is no longer accumulating, however, because agriculture has bared the land and erosion is now active in most areas. Chinese loess contains less fresh material than American loess and reflects its derivation from more normally weathered and eroded rocks.

Suggestions have been made that some loess is not eolian but alluvial or modified alluvial material. This certainly is not true of the great loess deposits just discussed. No discovery of pre-Pleistocene loess has been reported, but this is not surprising because thin loess layers probably could not be identified in ancient sediments and most loess probably would be reworked before final burial. The possibility exists, however, that some clay partings in coal beds are eolian and akin to loess.

Fine pyroclastic material is carried in the air like any other kind of dust, and tuff deposits are common in most volcanic regions. Many tuffs, however, appear to have been reworked and deposited in water. Examples that have not are rare among buried or consolidated strata and are uncertainly identified. The volcanic origin of beds of bentonite and metabentonite dating as far back as the Ordovician Period has been established by the presence of shards of volcanic glass, but generally they are associated with marine sediments and are undoubtedly water-laid strata.

Littoral Environment

The word *littoral*, referring to the shore, has not been defined consistently. It is used here to identify associated conditions and deposits characteristic of positions close above, but more generally close below, sea level. Littoral deposits are transitional. The sediments laid down in them share some of the features of marine and non-marine deposits. The main types of littoral sediments are deposited in or on (1) deltas, (2) coastal lagoons, (3) coastal marshes, (4) estuaries, (5) beaches, and (6) tidal flats, and as (7) offshore bars.

Deltaic Deposition

Rivers carry enormous quantities of sediment into the sea and build deltas that fill in large areas of water and convert them into land (see Figure

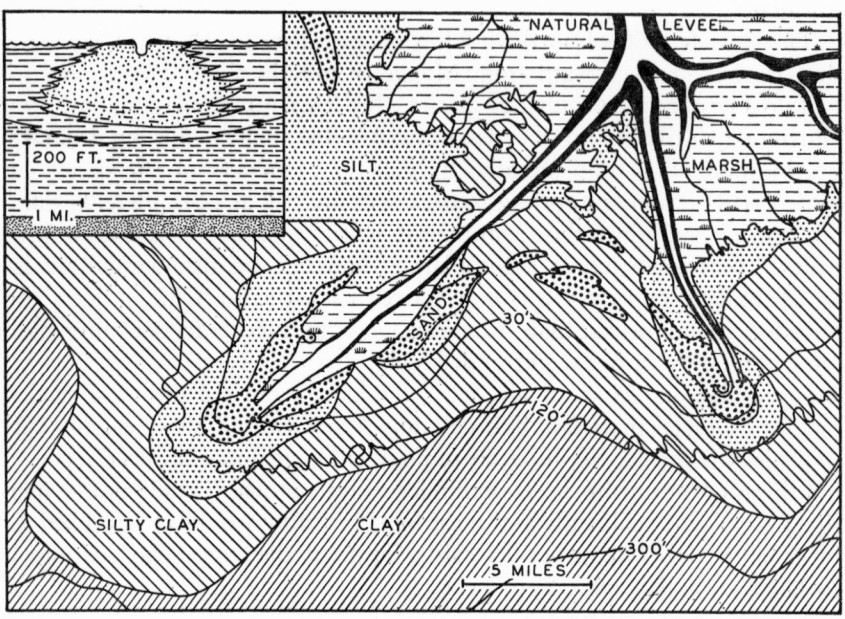

Figure 62. Map of part of the Mississippi delta showing relations of sediments to mouths of distributaries, shoreline, and depth of water. Inset is a transverse cross section through a distributary beyond the main delta front. This shows successively from below upward (1) pre-delta marine sand, (2) pro-delta marine clay antedating modern delta growth, and (3) deltaic deposits consisting of silty clay and an elongated barlike sand body built by the distributary. (After Fisk and others, 1954, *J. Sediment. Petrol.*, vol. 24, p. 77, fig. 1; p. 87, fig. 8; and p. 92, fig. 12.)

62). Deltas commonly have been described as consisting of regularly successive bottom-set, fore-set and top-set beds, but the great marine deltas that are growing now, and also those known from ancient sediments, generally do not have this ideal form. The theoretical pattern of delta growth rarely actually occurs because (1) relative sea level has been unstable, (2) most deltas have been built into shallow water, and (3) waves and currents modify delta form. Relative sea level that has oscillated with respect to the upper surface of a delta has interfered with the development of typical top-set bedding. Shallow offshore water agitated by waves and currents has spread sediment far and wide so that fore-set beds dip very gently at most places and there is little or no clear distinction between them and bottom-set bedding. Most large marine deltas possess upper surfaces that rise very gently landward and subaqueous extensions that dip equally gently out to sea.

Most important river systems are relatively stable for long periods of time. They follow and maintain topographic depressions leading to the sea, where sediment is delivered continuously to restricted areas and enormous deposits accumulate. The best-known areas of this type, the Mississippi delta of Louisiana and the Rhine delta of western Europe, appear to be subsiding slowly. The thicknesses of strata and the present position of shallow-water sediments deep below the surface are good evidence that much subsidence actually has occurred. Probably sedimentary loading has been important in the continuation of this movement. Surface sinking, however, also reflects progressive compaction of buried sediment, and the relative importance of these two factors at present is unknown. In any case the delta surface is unstable with respect to sea level. It alternates between slight building up and sinking so that shorelines here and there shift back and forth. In an actively growing delta, deposition prevails and as the sea is gradually filled in, the coast advances seaward.

Similar conditions seem to have controlled the growth of large deltas in the past. In this way the Catskill delta (Dev.) of Pennsylvania and New York grew westward in a subsiding area. It consists of sandy sediment deposited in very shallow water and is capped by non-marine deposits. The marine strata grade irregularly westward into finer-grained and somewhat deeper-water sediments (see Figure 159, p. 417) whose even bedding indicates that they were not affected by strong wave or current action. Some other ancient sandy sediments neither exhibit delta characteristics nor are known to be connected with strata of delta type. Several explanations for them can be suggested: (1) Associated deltas have been destroyed by erosion or are buried where they cannot be observed. (2) Sediment was delivered by small streams in quantities that did not match the dispersive power of waves and currents. (3) The sand was deposited mainly above sea level on a broad low and very gently inclined coastal plain. (4) The sand is reworked sediment deposited in a transgressive sea.

Deltas are not exclusive features of the margin of the sea. They can be formed wherever streams deliver sediment to a body of standing water. Many deltas occur in lakes and if they developed rapidly these are most likely to show theoretically typical delta structure. They are small, however, as compared to the deltas of great rivers that reach the sea. Lake deltas may be completely destroyed if lakes are drained. If preserved, few of them are large enough to constitute prominent stratigraphic features.

Other Littoral Deposits

Several specialized types of littoral deposits occur associated with deltas but they also are formed in other situations. If they can be recognized in ancient sediments, they serve to locate shorelines. Mostly, however, such deposits are likely to be restricted areally and thin. Also they are especially subject to reworking or complete destruction along unstable coasts. Consequently, most littoral deposits other than deltas are relatively unimportant in stratigraphy and many are difficult to identify with certainty.

Coastal lagoons generally are rather small bodies of very shallow water that lie behind barriers such as spits, bars, and islands built by longshore currents, and organic reefs. They are connected with the sea by narrow tidal channels. Unless important streams enter the lagoons, almost all sediment is carried inward by the tide and consists of material that has been sorted to some extent by wave action along the open coast. In such protected situations, waves are relatively unimportant and currents are gentle except in and near the channels. Sediments deposited in lagoons commonly are graded from sand in channels to silt and progressively finer mud in remote areas, but otherwise sorting generally is poor (see Figure 63).

The water in lagoons is likely to differ in salinity from the sea and to vary from time to time depending upon the local climate and whether or not streams flow into them. Consequently many lagoons provide an inhospitable environment for a variety of marine organisms. Some modern lagoons, however, support thickly populated banks of oysters that are adapted to such conditions, and a few species of burrowing animals may be abundant enough to prevent the development of bedding in the slowly accumulating sediment.

Coastal lagoons are not likely to be numerous in landlocked epicontinental seas, where longshore currents generally are negligible. They may occur, however, behind organic reefs. Because important tides are lacking in landlocked seas, circulation of water of normal marine salinity may be reduced. Lagoons are likely to be brackish to nearly fresh in humid climates, or supersaline in arid regions, where ideal conditions are provided for the development of evaporite deposits.

Coastal lagoons may grade laterally into or, as they are filled, be converted to marshlands. Also marshes occur along some low coasts where salt grass and other halophilic plants invade shallow water without confinement behind barriers, as in mangrove swamps. In these situations clayey sediment transported by very gentle currents filters through the living plants and is deposited with more or less organic matter as dark-gray or black mud. If little sediment is introduced, peat may develop in some favorable areas. Late Cretaceous coals of the Book Cliffs region of eastern Utah and western Colorado appear to have accumulated in coastal swamps behind sandy barrier beach

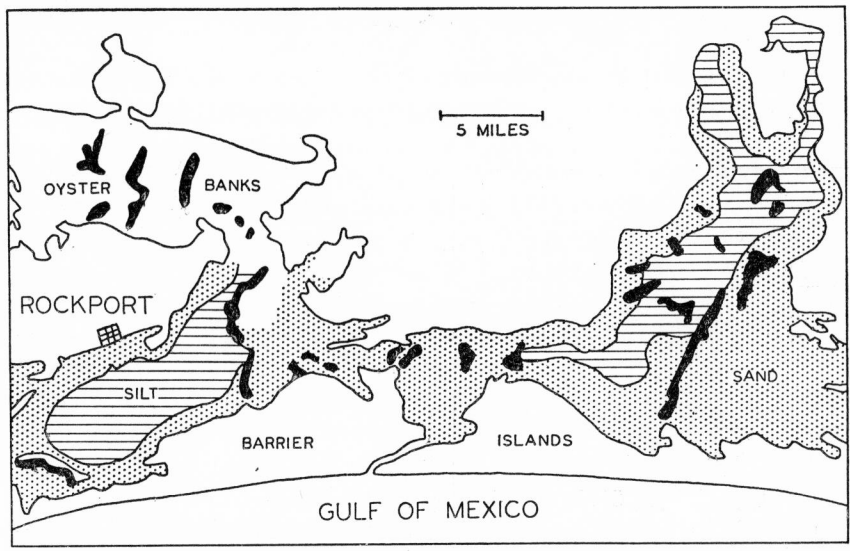

Figure 63. Map of part of the Gulf coast near Rockport, Texas, showing the distribution of sand, silt, and oyster banks in bays behind barrier islands. (Generalized from Shepard and Moore, 1955, *Bull. Am. Assoc. Petroleum Geol.*, vol. 39, p. 1484, fig. 15.)

ridges and they probably record an environment related to this type (see Figure 59, p. 177).

Tidal flats occur at many places along gently shelving coasts where shallow water reduces the effectiveness of waves. They are especially prominent in the more sheltered parts of bays. Sediment deposited on such flats, particularly near the mouths of streams, varies from sand to mud. Some sorting occurs and ripples may be extensively developed. Where deposition is rapid a peculiar type of small-scale interlayering of sand and mud occurs. Similar interlayering in ancient sediments has been observed and it may record an environment of this kind. If deposition is slow, burrowing animals commonly destroy most traces of the bedding. On the whole, if tidal flat deposits are preserved in ancient sediments, they probably cannot be distinguished surely from lagoonal sediments, or sands and muds deposited elsewhere in very shallow, fairly quiet water.

Estuaries are channels in which the tides ebb and flow. Some are the lower courses of rivers or smaller streams, but others only conduct water in and out of coastal swamps or across tidal flats. If sediment is brought into estuaries from the land, it is moved backward and forward repeatedly and the finer material is gradually carried out to sea. In estuaries that are no more than swamp drainage ways, sediment may be carried inward from the sea and the finer material settles at the slack water of high tide among the swamp plants. Along a subsiding coast, fine sand and silt may accumulate in estuaries and build up channel deposits very similar to those formed by streams in other situations.

Sand or gravel beaches are present along a large proportion of the seashores of the world. They are the products of wave action and mark most open coasts except where rocky cliffs occur or large rivers deliver more sediment to the sea than can be dispersed by waves and currents. Generally they are narrow strips, and their details are unstable and change with every storm. Waves winnow out the finer sediments, which are carried into offshore water, and also move coarser particles upward on the beach. Sandy beaches are most common. They consist of whatever material is available and supplied by longshore currents. Generally quartz sand is dominant but there are many exceptions. Some beaches have only calcareous fragments derived from broken shells and coral; others consist of volcanic sand. Gravel may occur abundantly along rocky coasts or where streams with steep gradients deliver pebbles to the sea.

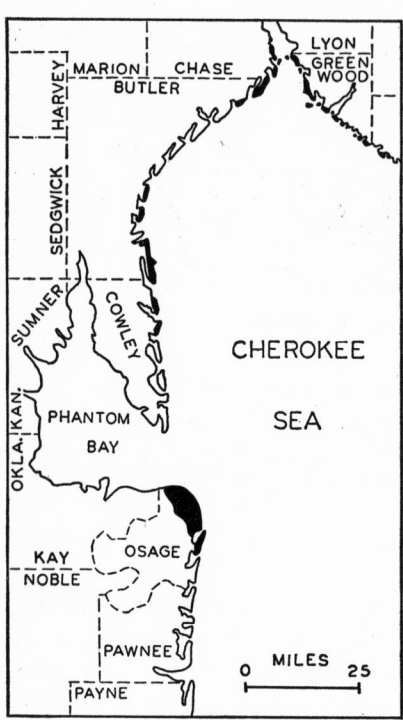

Figure 64. Paleogeographic map of area near the Kansas-Oklahoma state line showing inferred conditions during early Pennsylvanian time. Oil fields producing from the Burbank sand are shown in black. They are aligned in trends suggestive of coastal bars like those occurring along some modern shores. (After Bass and others, 1937, *Bull. Am. Assoc. Petroleum Geol.*, vol. 21, p. 60, fig. 15.)

Most beach deposits consist of conspicuously cross-bedded layers and show evidence of much localized erosion and deposition. Cross-bedding may dip either outward or inward from the coast, generally depending upon whether these structures were built respectively on the foreshore, between high- and low-tide levels, or on the backshore that is swept by the strong waves of storms. The beaches on many windward coasts are fringed by dunes consisting of sand blown inland from the shore.

Beach deposits are unlikely to be preserved in ancient sediments. Along rising coasts they generally are destroyed or greatly modified by erosion, and on subsiding coasts they are sure to be reworked. Some long narrow sand bodies of the shoestring type have been interpreted as beaches (see Figure 64), but such identification generally is doubtful.

Offshore sand bars occur along most beaches. They also are built by waves and they form at or near the line of breakers. Like beach structures, bars are unstable, changing from season to season and from storm to storm. Whereas they are sure to be destroyed and their sands reworked along coasts that are rising or being built outward by deposition, they may be preserved on subsiding coasts buried beneath later sediment. Some shoestring sands may be old offshore bars, but the differentiation of bars from stream channel deposits in ancient sediments is likely to be difficult.

BIBLIOGRAPHY

Bagnold, R. A. (1941), *The physics of blown sand and desert dunes*, London, Methuen.

> This is a comprehensive field and laboratory study of sand movement, structures developed, and forms assumed.

Cloud, P. E., Jr. (1958), Nature and origin of atolls, *Proc. 8th Pacif. Sci. Congr.*, vol. 3-A, pp. 1009–1024.

> This is a general review of evidence and theories.

Cooper, W. S. (1958), Coastal sand dunes of Oregon and Washington, Geol. Soc. Amer., Mem. 72.

> The form, development, and alteration of modern sand dunes are studied in detail.

Dunbar, C. O., and Rodgers, John (1957), *Principles of stratigraphy*, New York, Wiley.

> Chapters 1 to 4, pp. 3–95, deal with sedimentary processes and environments.

Grabau, A. W. (1913), *Principles of stratigraphy*, New York, Seiler, reprinted 1924.

> Chapters 5 and 26, pp. 209–268 and 982–990, discuss aqueous transportation and physical environments.

Grim, R. E. (1953), *Clay mineralogy*, New York, McGraw-Hill.

> Origin and occurrence of clay minerals in soils and in recent and ancient sediments are discussed in Chapters 13 and 14, pp. 330–368.

Guilcher, André (1958), *Coastal and submarine morphology*, London, Methuen.

> See pp. 76–118 for descriptions of coastal features and sediments.

Hatch, F. H., and Rastall, R. H. (1938), *The petrology of the sedimentary rocks*, 3rd ed., revised by Maurice Black, London, Allen and Unwin.

> Chapters 1 and 15, pp. 17–26 and 264–284, are concerned with depositional environments and modern oceanic sediments.

Hough, J. L. (ed.) (1951), Turbidity currents and the transportation of coarse sediments to deep water, a symposium, Soc. Econ. Paleon. and Miner., Spec. Publ. 2.

Papers are by H. W. Menard and J. C. Ludwick, P. H. Kuenen, H. R. Gould, F. P. Shepard, F. B. Phleger, and M. L. Natland and P. H. Kuenen.

Hough, J. L., and Menard, H. W. (eds.) (1955), Finding ancient shore lines, a symposium, Soc. Econ. Paleon. and Miner., Spec. Publ. 3.
Papers dealing with sedimentation in the Gulf of Mexico are by H. R. Gould and R. H. Stewart, P. C. Scruton, W. C. Thompson, F. P. Shepard and D. G. Moore, E. A. Lohse and D. L. Inman, and T. K. Chamberlain.

Hutchinson, G. E. (1957), A treatise on limnology, Vol. 1, Geography, physics and chemistry, New York, Wiley.
This is an exhaustive account of the physical environments of lakes.

Krumbein, W. C., and Sloss, L. L. (1951), Stratigraphy and sedimentation, San Francisco, Freeman.
See Chapters 6 and 7, pp. 148–223, for discussion of sedimentary processes and environments.

Kuenen, P. H. (1950), Marine geology, New York, Wiley.
Chapters 4 and 5, pp. 210–413, consider the sources, transportation, and deposition of marine sediments.

Laprade, K. E. (1957), Dust-storm sediments of Lubbock area, Texas, Bull. Am. Assoc. Petroleum Geol., vol. 41, pp. 709–726.
The author describes wind-borne dust and analyzes air turbulence that raises it.

LeBlank, R. J., and Breeding, J. G. (eds.) (1957), Regional aspects of carbonate deposition, a symposium, Soc. Econ. Paleon. and Miner., Spec. Publ. 5.
Papers are by John Rodgers, N. D. Newell and J. K. Rigby, R. N. Ginsburg, R. C. Moore, and R. W. Fairbridge.

Marr, J. E. (1929), Deposition of the sedimentary rocks, Cambridge, Univ. Press.
This is a simply written explanation of sediments and their environments.

Mason, Brian (1958), Principles of geochemistry, 2nd ed., New York, Wiley.
See particularly Chapter 6, pp. 145–183, and Chapter 9, pp. 215–238, for discussions of chemical conditions and processes affecting sediments.

Pettijohn, F. J. (1957), Sedimentary rocks, 2nd ed., New York, Harper.
Chapters 11 to 13, pp. 498–647, deal with the origin, transportation, and deposition of sediments.

Rich, J. L. (1951), Three critical environments of deposition and criteria for recognition of rocks deposited in each of them, Bull. Geol. Soc. Amer., vol. 62, pp. 1–20.
Emphasis is laid on the importance of wave base in a depositional basin. One environment above and two below it are distinguished.

Reiche, Parry (1945), A survey of weathering processes and products, Univ. of N. Mex., Publ. in Geol. 1.
Physical and especially chemical processes of weathering and the formation of soils are reviewed.

Rubey, W. W. (1951), Geologic history of sea water, Bull. Geol. Soc. Amer., vol. 62, pp. 1111–1148.
Author gives theoretical consideration to the origin of the oceans.

Rubey, W. W. (1955), Development of the hydrosphere and atmosphere, with special reference to probable composition of the early atmosphere, Geol. Soc. Amer., Spec. Paper 62, pp. 631–650.

Atmosphere and hydrosphere accumulated as H_2O, CO_2, CO, and N_2 derived from intrusive and extrusive igneous rocks.

Shepard, F. P. (1948), *Submarine geology*, New York, Harper.

Concern is mainly with the form and sediments of the continental shelves and processes influencing deposition there.

Shepard, F. P., and Moore, D. G. (1955), Central Texas coast sedimentation, *Bull. Am. Assoc. Petroleum Geol.*, vol. 39, pp. 1463–1593.

In a comprehensive study near-shore sediments are related to their environments.

Symposium on Organic Reefs (1950), *J. Geol.*, vol. 58, pp. 289–487.

Papers on both ancient and modern reefs are by J. E. Adams and H. N. Frenzel, Geoffrey Bond, R. W. Fairbridge, Assar Hadding, H. S. Ladd and others, M. N. Levet, and H. A. Lowenstam.

Teichert, Curt (1958), Cold- and deep-water coral banks, *Bull. Am. Assoc. Petroleum Geol.*, vol. 42, pp. 1064–1082.

Abundant modern corals occur in an environment different from that assumed to be indicated by ancient reefs.

Trask, P. D. (ed.) (1955), Recent marine sediments, a symposium, reprinted from 1939 edition with addition of Statement of progress in studies of recent sediments, 1939–1954, and bibliography by P. D. Trask, Soc. Econ. Paleon. and Miner., Spec. Publ. 4.

Thirty-four papers are devoted to (1) Transportation, (2) Relation of oceanography to sedimentation, (3) Deposits associated with strand line, (4) Near-shore sediments—Hemipelagic deposits, (5) Pelagic deposits, (6) Special features of sediments, and (7) Methods of study.

Twenhofel, W. H. (1937), Environments of origin of black shales, *Bull. Am. Assoc. Petroleum Geol.*, vol. 23, pp. 1178–1198.

Black-shale formation was related to lack of oxygen mostly in shallow, tideless, landlocked portions of the sea.

Twenhofel, W. H. (1950), *Principles of sedimentation*, 2nd ed., New York, McGraw-Hill.

Origin, transportation, deposition, and environments of sediments are considered in Chapters 2 to 4 and 6, pp. 10–166 and 199–281.

Twenhofel, W. H., and collaborators (1932), *Treatise on sedimentation*, 2nd ed., Baltimore, Williams and Wilkins.

Chapter 7, pp. 783–871, discusses depositional environments.

7

Paleoecology

FOSSILS are of great value to stratigraphy because (1) they aid in the correlation of strata occurring in different areas (considered in Chapter 15), (2) they furnish information regarding the depositional environments of sediments, and (3) their preservation indicates some of the conditions and processes that resulted in post-depositional alteration of sediments.

The relations linking organisms with environments are the subject matter of *ecology*. These relations can be observed directly in the case of living organisms whose reactions to different environments can be investigated. They are exceedingly complex, however, and even after long study, uncertainties remain regarding the influences and relative importance of some features of the environment. *Paleoecology* is the study devoted to the relations of fossil organisms and ancient environments. Here no experimentation is possible and even the general nature of some environments is not obvious. For this reason paleoecology involves the consideration of many obscure and poorly understood conditions and reactions and only recently has it become the subject of serious investigation. Because so little is known about it, the study of paleoecology provides an exceptional opportunity for fundamentally important research.

The interpretation of paleoecology is dependent upon evidence that is (1) physical and (2) biologic. The physical aspects of sedimentary deposition were considered in Chapter 6, and this chapter is devoted to the biologic aspects. These two general aspects of ecology are very closely related. In their study each supplements and serves as a check upon the other. The biologic aspects of paleoecology are especially important because (1) organisms are responsible for the production and modification of much sediment, and

(2) organisms generally are a more delicate index to variations in environment than are the physical characters of most sediments.

ENVIRONMENTS

An environment is a combination of mutually interacting physical and biologic conditions. It is not something that can be seen although some of its factors are visible or measurable. As a whole, a paleoenvironment can only be inferred from its results as these are exhibited in the form of sedimentary accumulations and fossil associations. Because the adjustments of organisms to their environments are so intimate and specific, the distributions and associations of fossil plants and animals reveal many differences in environ-

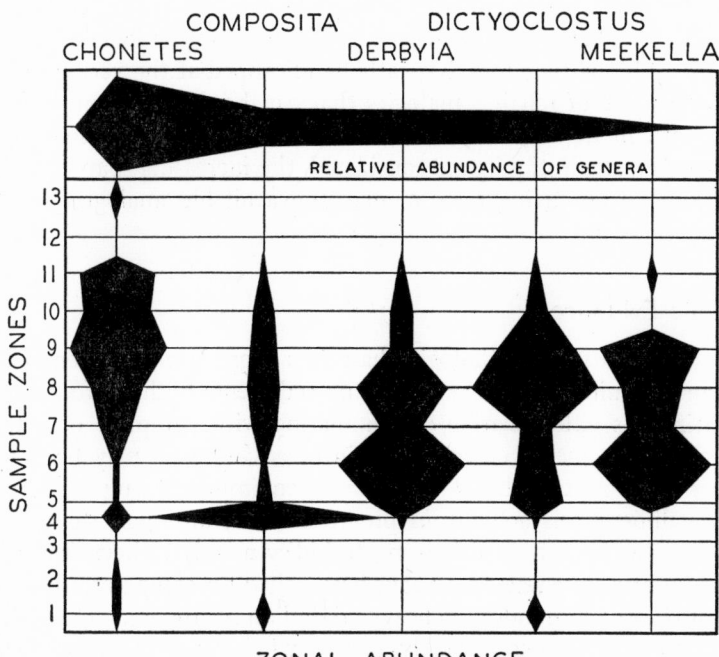

Figure 65. Diagram showing the relative abundance of several brachiopod genera collected from successive zones of the Florena Shale (Perm.) at a locality in eastern Kansas. Plotting is based upon weights of specimens totaling 100 percent for each genus. The relative total abundance of each genus by weight is indicated by the width of the upper horizontal bar. Weights were used instead of counts because many specimens were fragmentary. Differences in the abundance of genera in such zones as 4, 6, 9, and 11 indicate environmental differences not revealed by any features of the sediment. (After Imbrie, 1955, *Bull. Am. Assoc. Petroleum Geol.*, vol. 39, p. 662, fig. 6.)

ments that are not clearly indicated by any other evidence (see Figure 65). In interpretation, great care must be taken, however, to prevent the mixing of fossils from different succeeding zones each of which may contain a fossil assemblage with somewhat different environmental implications even though the strata are practically identical lithologically. Almost every stratigraphic unit, unless it is a very thin or restricted one, is likely to consist of a variety of such zones. The biologic character of a complex unit, therefore, is the sum of the characters of its zones and consequently it is a mixture. Such a mixture is almost certain to present a distorted and confused picture of detailed relations whose biologic interpretation is difficult or impossible.

In paleoecology, as in other phases of geology, the present is the key to the past. Thus ancient environments are interpreted in accordance with what is known of modern ones. The great majority of fossils accumulated under marine conditions, but unfortunately marine environments are less accessible and more difficult to study than terrestrial ones. Any ecologic analysis of a marine fossil biota, therefore, is greatly handicapped at the very start by the comparative lack of reliable analogies that can be drawn upon in its comparison with modern communities. Furthermore, as fossil assemblages of greater and greater antiquity are considered, the increasing span of time separating them from living ones renders the available analogies less trustworthy.

Lithologic Evidence

The degree to which lithologic characters suggest environmental details is extremely limited. For example, many sediments without fossils cannot be identified as either marine or non-marine with complete certainty. In some cases the aqueous or eolian origin of a sandstone may be doubtful. Also, for the most part, lithology indicates environment only while deposition of sediment was actually in progress. Thus, although shale suggests turbid water and a soft mud bottom, turbidity may have been intermittent and dominantly clear water may have been roiled for comparatively short intervals of time corresponding to heavy rainfall on nearby land, or to wave action resulting from exceptionally strong winds. The bottom, although muddy, may have been relatively firm or it may have been floored with slime so soft that it was capable of supporting only the tiniest organisms. Sandstone suggests shallow water and appreciable current action, but sand can be carried into deep water and deposition may have been slow, rapid, or distinctly intermittent.

Limestones are the least understood and in some ways the most puzzling sedimentary rocks. Granular beds consisting of disarticulated or comminuted organic fragments suggest an environment similar to that of sandstone. Such material, however, is rarely of terrestrial origin. It can be formed and accumulate in or near shallow water far from any sediment-producing land. Very little is known concerning the origin of extremely fine-grained limestone. It might have been produced by (1) minute fragmentation of organic debris, (2) secretion of structureless material by algae or other organisms, or (3) direct precipitation resulting from either organic or inorganic processes. Very few fine-grained limestones are suspected of having been produced by a decrease in the crystallinity of originally coarser-grained material. Fine calcareous sediment may have been produced locally or transported an appreciable distance. Probably many fine-grained limestones consist of material variously produced, derived, and transported. All of them certainly do not record closely comparable environments. Finally, the solubility of calcium carbonate makes recrystallization easy, and the original particles of many beds have been so altered that their original nature is obscured if not destroyed.

In spite of their many deficiencies, sediments furnish more adequate information concerning ancient bottom conditions than any other physical feature of the environment. If all of the details of sedimentary diagenesis were understood, which unfortunately is not so, the original condition of sediment that now exists as consolidated rock could be determined and this important environmental feature would be known. Other equally important environmental factors such as depth, temperature, and relative salinity are not equally recorded in the common sediments.

Biologic Evidence

Although most sedimentary rocks are essentially unfossiliferous, more or less abundant specimens occur in many marine strata. The presence of brachiopods, echinoderms, corals, cephalopods, and representatives of some less important groups, none of which is known ever to have included any non-marine species, generally is excellent evidence that the enclosing strata are normal marine deposits laid down in a basin connected with the permanent ocean. It should be recognized, however, that if non-marine species did occur in any of these groups at some past time, their differences might not be discovered. Non-marine fossils are much less abundant than marine, and non-marine species in some groups, such as the pelecypods and gastropods that inhabited both environments, generally cannot be differentiated unless their natural association with other certainly non-marine species can be established. Consequently, few invertebrate fossils are useful in identifying non-marine deposits.

The occurrence of vertebrates, except fish and other obviously swimming creatures, generally is good evidence of terrestrial deposition. Land-plant fossils are not quite so reliable indications of non-marine conditions. Stems, bits of wood, charcoal, and spores may be carried long distances from land. Although not common, they have been found in almost every kind of sedimentary rock including typical marine limestone. Delicate leaves, however, are not readily transported without damage. Some, probably derived from nearby sources, are preserved in marine or brackish water sediments but ordinarily they are a reasonably good index to non-marine strata.

Brackish- and fresh-water invertebrates are more difficult to identify. Many brackish-water assemblages include some species that serve to connect them with the normal marine environment. Certain transitional species of this kind exhibit various features of abnormal growth such as distortions of shape or dwarfing. Fresh-water assemblages are wholly lacking in typically marine species although some few species may occur in both brackish- and fresh-water deposits. Many Tertiary molluscs appear to be so closely related to living species that similarity of habitat can be inferred. Thus normal marine, brackish- and fresh-water Tertiary strata may be recognizable and pulmonate snails may identify terrestrial conditions. The kinship of older fossils with living species, however, is so remote that most analogies of this type are uncertain and unsafe. Faunal transition from normal marine to highly saline conditions generally is characterized by a rapid decrease in the number of species without the appearance of different ones to replace them. Abnormal growth of marine species also may mark the beginning of a transition of this kind.

A case in point with respect to uncertainty concerning the interpretation of fossils is provided by Paleozoic reef corals. These are particularly abundant in some Silurian formations and they extend into far northern regions (see Figure 186, p. 496). Their presence at such places has been accepted as evidence of subtropical conditions on the assumption that coral distribution at that time was limited by a minimum temperature comparable to that which marks the northern range of modern reefs. There are other good reasons for concluding that Paleozoic climates generally were mild and uniform in comparison with the present, but the drawing of a close parallel between factors limiting the growth of corals in ancient and in modern times is not warranted. Paleozoic reef-building corals are profoundly different from modern ones in many of their structural characters and paleontologists classify them in a wholly different and only remotely related group. Furthermore, some modern corals grow abundantly in deep cold water and ancient species may have been adapted to similar conditions.

Benthonic organisms provide the best information concerning sedimentary environments. They may be divided into two groups: (1) the sessile organisms incapable of movement that pass a sedentary existence upon or attached to the bottom, such as brachiopods, bryozoans, corals, and crinoids, and (2) the more or less vagrant creatures that habitually move about, or are at least capable of moving, in search of food and safety, either crawling upon or burrowing within the bottom sediment, such as snails, echinoids, trilobites, and many clams. The presence of planktonic or nektonic organisms as fossils, of course, provides little information regarding depositional conditions on the bottom.

Much agitated very shallow water, particularly near shore, is the characteristic habitat of a great variety of both sessile and motile animals that cling tightly to rocks and seaweeds. Such an environment is not likely to be recorded directly in sedimentary deposits because sediments rarely accumulate in situations of this kind or, if they do, they are almost certain to be destroyed later by erosion. Organic reefs are the principal exception. The remains of animals that thrive under these conditions, however, may be transported to an adjoining environment and preserved where deposition does prevail.

Few sessile animals can live in situations where deposition occurs at such a rate that they would soon be buried. Neither are they likely to prosper on unstable bottoms where sediment is actively moved about by currents. The presence of fossils of this kind, therefore, generally indicates an environment deep enough so that wave disturbance was not severe, currents were not strong, and deposition was not rapid. They are most characteristic of calcareous shale and limestone. Faunas of this type may have lived briefly at places where the environment was generally unfavorable and be preserved in thin fossiliferous zones enclosed in strata that contain few fossils or are barren. Favorable conditions also may have been interrupted briefly by catastrophic rapid deposition that brought sudden death and burial to all members of a community.

Vagrant animals have a wider distribution. They occur associated with sessile types but are capable of living where deposition is more rapid and bottom sediments are more disturbed. The species of these two general environments, however, are different. Vagrant creatures are the most abundant conspicuous benthonic inhabitants of shallow-water and near-shore situations in which sediments accumulate. Their fossils may dominate the silty shales.

Every species of organism is adapted to some preferred environment that is more or less definitely limited. The environment is not known accurately for most fossil species, but generalizations can be made with respect to many groups and types of fossils based on observations of their occurrence in the rocks and by analogy with living organisms. These generalizations are variously useful in the identification of paleoenvironments.

Land Plants

Most land plants possess well-differentiated roots, stems, and leaves. They are the only plants that are preserved as abundant and conspicuous fossils. With few exceptions, they identify terrestrial or fresh-water deposits. Details of cellular structure, if these can be observed, provide information with respect to some features of climate and may indicate whether it was wet or dry, equable or marked by seasonal extremes. Fruits and reproductive organs also suggest environments because spores require much moisture but seeds are capable of germinating in relatively dry situations. Most plants preserved as fossils grew in lowland areas. Very little is known of upland floras in periods older than the Tertiary because sediments rarely accumulated and were preserved in such places. Environmental interpretations based on lowland floras of course do not apply to other terrestrial regions.

Planktonic Plants

All pelagic plants are planktonic, most are microscopic, and, except for diatoms, few are likely to be fossilized. They are widely distributed in both fresh and salt water. Fossils are not commonly observed, however, except at places where detrital sedimentation was very slow and their remains accumulated in enormous numbers. These fossils give little information about sedimentary conditions except to indicate that deposition probably was slow.

Calcareous Algae

These benthonic plants require shallow, well-lighted, and relatively sediment-free water. They have been important as calcium carbonate producers and also as agents that bind loose calcareous material, as on organic reefs. Calcareous algae are rarely well preserved as fossils but their remains are believed to have been identified in limestones dating far back into the Precambrian. Several types of encrusting or nodular bodies in limestone are suggestive of these plants especially if microscopic study reveals obscure cellular structure.

Kelplike Seaweeds

Most of these plants are attached by holdfasts to hard objects on the sea bottom. Some can grow in water approaching 300 feet deep but generally they are characteristic of much shallower situations. A few break loose and thereafter lead a free-floating existence. Kelplike seaweeds do not have differentiated true roots, stems, and leaves and are poorly suited to preservation as fossils. Some so-called fucoidal structures have been identified doubtfully as seaweeds. In modern seas, flowering plants dominate soft shallow bottoms, and the kelps are restricted mainly to hard-bottomed or stony areas. Algae almost certainly occupied both environments, however, in pre-Tertiary times before the great differentiation of the angiosperms.

Foraminifera

The protozoans most commonly observed as fossils are foraminifera. Most species are marine benthonic forms and they are confined to more or less definite zones determined by temperature, salinity, and nature of the bottom (see Figure 66). Knowledge of the distribution of modern species

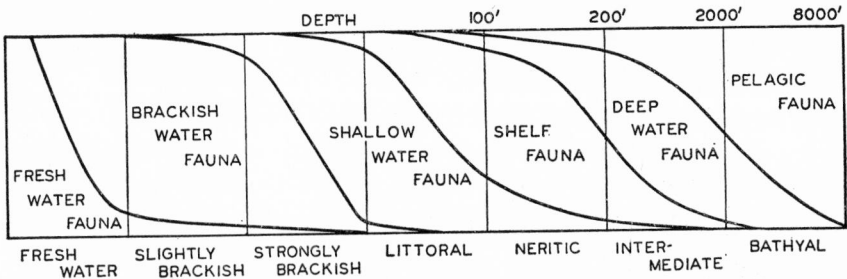

Figure 66. Diagram showing proportions of foraminifera grouped by genera and classified according to environmental occurrence recovered from modern sediments of the Gulf of Mexico. Late Tertiary foraminifera are so similar to modern ones that they provide fairly reliable evidence for environmental interpretations. (Greatly simplified from Lowman, 1949, Bull. Am. Assoc. Petroleum Geol., vol. 33, pp. 1954–1955, fig. 13.)

can be applied to the interpretation of Tertiary environments. Care must be taken, however, because the small size of these fossils makes their transportation easy, and specimens may be found in sediments that accumulated in situations very different from those inhabited by the living animals. The largest foraminifera occur in shallow, typically marine water of the tropics. Some species adhere to seaweeds or other objects raised above the sea bottom. Generally these can be identified because their shells show evidence of attachment. A few genera, such as *Globigerina*, are planktonic and are widely distributed without regard to conditions in deep water or on the bottom.

Sponges

Sponges are sessile benthonic organisms that inhabit many different environments in both shallow and deep water. Most of them occur in shallow, clear-water situations, but fossils are abundant at some places in very silty strata that appear to have accumulated rapidly. Sponge fossils, however, are not common except for disarticulated spicules. On the whole they provide little environmental information.

Corals

Corals are exclusively marine. They are adapted to a variety of environments but most of them require shallow and relatively clear warm water. Corals begin their growth attached to some hard object. Later they may break loose or grow outward over soft bottom sediment. Some solitary horn corals are common in argillaceous sediments, but deposition must have been slow or they would have smothered. Colonial corals generally are more restricted. Their fossils ordinarily indicate well-aerated shallow water uncontaminated with much suspended sediment. Reef-building corals mostly are restricted to depths of less than 250 feet. Reefs of greater thickness indicate either that sea level has risen or that the reefs grew upward as the bottom sank.

Graptolites

Graptolites are extinct, early Paleozoic, colonial fossils of doubtful zoologic affinity. Most commonly they have been considered hydrozoans although some similarity to hemichordates has been noted. Some members of one group of graptolites were attached to hard objects and grew upward from the sea bottom. They occur in various kinds of sediment. Little is known about their environmental implications except that sedimentary deposition probably was slow. Others were suspended from floating objects or developed floating organs, and these planktonic colonies had wide geographic ranges. They are preserved mainly in dark shale that appears to record the existence of oxygen-deficient bottom conditions inhospitable to most benthonic organisms.

Stromatoporoids

Stromatoporoids are fossils of another extinct group which are doubtfully identified as colonial hydroids. They occur as more or less large masses in calcareous strata, mainly limestone, and mostly of Paleozoic age. Their internal microscopic structures generally are imperfectly preserved but they seem to have grown as incrustations like some calcareous algae and bryozoans, and they were important in the building of some organic reefs. Stromatoporoids appear to identify shallow, relatively clear-water environments similar to those inhabited by colonial corals and calcareous algae.

Worms

Marine wormlike animals belong to several phyla. They are rarely preserved as fossils. Annelids are the most abundant, and many of them inhabit tubes or burrows in bottom sediments of widely different types. Worm tubes are most commonly observed in fine-grained sandstones that accumulated slowly. They also occur in shale and limestone but compaction and recrystallization render them much less conspicuous in strata of these kinds. Some worms built calcareous tubes attached to the shells of other animals or to seaweeds. Worms are of so many different kinds, however, and the traces of their existence are so difficult to differentiate that they are of little service in paleoecologic interpretation.

Bryozoans

Bryozoans are tiny sessile colonial animals and almost all that produce hard skeletons are marine. Their colonies grow attached to hard objects on the sea bottom, other animals, and seaweeds. Most fossil bryozoans occur in calcareous shale or limestone. In Paleozoic strata they are commonly associated with more or less abundant brachiopods. They prefer environments in shallow, well-aerated water without abundant suspended sediment.

Brachiopods

These bivalved animals are the most important fossils occurring in Paleozoic rocks but they were largely supplanted by molluscs in later time. Brachiopods have always been exclusively marine. Most of them were sessile creatures living on the surface of the sea bottom and attached by a fleshy pedicle to some hard object and also possibly to seaweeds. In some, the pedicle degenerated and these existed free upon the bottom but were incapable of movement. In a few, like *Lingula*, the pedicle became specialized as an organ of locomotion and these burrowed in muddy bottoms or perhaps moved clumsily upon the surface. Different brachiopods were adapted to so great a variety of environments that few Paleozoic fossil assemblages occur without representatives of this group. Most brachiopods, however, inhabited relatively clear water where the bottom was firm and stable. Their fossils are most abundant in limestone and calcareous shale.

Pelecypods

Pelecypods live abundantly in both marine and fresh water. Most of them are free motile animals that obtain their food by filtering suspended matter from the surrounding water. Many bury themselves in loose bottom sediment or plow through it by action of their so-called foot. After becoming established in favorable situations, some of them move very little but others are more or less continuously active. A few can swim swiftly for short distances. Some lead a sedentary existence, however, cemented to rocks or other resistant objects or attached by an adhesive byssus. Clams of this type occur closely crowded together in enormous numbers at some places. Pelecypods are adapted to a wide variety of environments and are abundantly represented in very shallow turbid water where many other kinds of organisms cannot live.

Gastropods

The gastropods are a group of highly successful animals that include water breathers in both marine and fresh water and air breathers many of which are terrestrial. Most of them are active although they move slowly on their so-called foot. Most marine gastropods live upon the bottom or among seaweeds but some are burrowers in loose sediment. The principal food of gastropods is vegetation, which they shred with a tongue-like organ equipped with rasps. Some, however, eat carrion and a few are carnivorous and attack living pelecypods. Gastropods occupy many marine environments but most prefer warm shallow water with abundant plants. Non-marine species inhabit streams, ponds, and lakes, and terrestrial forms occur in many damp shady situations in tropical and temperate regions.

Cephalopods

Cephalopods are the most active and highly organized molluscs. They are exclusively marine. Mainly predatory carnivorous animals, they all can swim effectively in pursuit of prey and to escape their enemies. Many shelled cephalopods that occur as fossils probably lived mostly on the bottom, and different species were adapted to different bottom conditions. Some of them, however, evidently were nektonic because their shells locally are common in dark sediment recording an environment inhospitable to most benthonic organisms. Some empty cephalopod shells float long distances and they may finally sink and be buried far from places where the creatures lived. For this reason, and because of their swimming habits, fossil cephalopods generally are less indicative of environmental conditions than many other animals.

Trilobites

Trilobites were exclusively marine animals that became extinct at the end of the Paleozoic Era. Most of them were benthonic creatures that crawled upon or burrowed shallowly in the bottom. They could also swim but probably few of them did more than skim along the bottom or rise occasionally short distances in the water. Trilobites were not equipped with pinching claws and therefore could not have been effective predators. Probably most of them were scavengers and surface mud eaters although they may have captured small slowly moving creatures. Trilobites occur in various types of fine-grained sediment, most of which appear to have accumulated in quiet water. Some species, however, were adapted to turbulent conditions on and adjacent to organic reefs. As trilobites grew they molted repeatedly and many of the molts were fossilized. Consequently fossils may seem to indicate more individuals than actually occurred.

Eurypterids

Eurypterids include the largest of the arthropods and they have been exceeded in size by few invertebrates belonging to other phyla. They were equipped with effective pinching claws and many of them probably were formidable predators that crawled about or swam close above the bottom. The fossil record of the eurypterids is exclusively Paleozoic. Specimens rarely occur associated with normal marine invertebrates and eurypterids seem to have inhabited marginal marine, brackish or fresh water environments where other creatures with preservable hard parts were not abundant.

Ostracods

Ostracods are tiny bivalved crustaceans that inhabit salt, brackish, and fresh water. They are most common in very shallow, more or less stagnant water although they occur in many other environments including the deep sea. They feed mainly on decaying organic material, and many of the shallow-water species can withstand conditions that are unfavorable to most other aquatic animals. The eggs of many ostracods can endure desiccation for a considerable length of time and will hatch when water is again available. Like foraminifera and molluscs, Tertiary ostracod species are so similar to modern ones that they serve to identify environments, but older species are much less useful.

Other Crustaceans

Most crustaceans are active animals. They inhabit all aqueous environments and occur in enormous numbers and variety. Except for ostracods, few kinds are well represented among fossils although several groups have had long geologic histories. These crustaceans do not furnish much paleoecologic information, but they have been of great importance in the organic economy of nature particularly in the sea. Tiny planktonic copepods eat diatoms and other minute organisms and they in turn constitute the food of many larger animals. Other small crustaceans besides the ostracods are free-swimming scavengers that live in very shallow water near the bottom and among seaweeds. The larger crabs, lobsters, and allied forms are bottom-dwelling scavengers and carrion eaters but they also attack other less active living animals. Some burrow in bottom sediment and others swim. Some have powerful claws that can crack the shells of gastropods and pelecypods. Crablike creatures were rare in Paleozoic time. The scavenging they now perform probably was accomplished by trilobites and a variety of other animals that are poorly recorded in the sediments.

Insects

Insects do not occur abundantly as fossils but they are known as far back in time as the Devonian Period and numerous specimens have been found at a few widely separated localities. They are mostly terrestrial and, like other land creatures, they are not likely to have been preserved in an environment similar to the one that they inhabited. The development of insects seems to have paralleled the evolution of land plants. Because of their small size, their occurrence generally is more intimately related to vegetative conditions than is that of larger animals. Therefore an insect fauna may provide useful indirect information concerning the flora of a nearby area and thus suggest other ecologic features such as climate.

Crinoids

Crinoids are a group of the echinoderms that includes only marine animals. Stalked crinoids were formerly much more numerous and varied than they are now. At some times and places in the past they were the principal producers of calcareous sediment that accumulated to form limestone. Modern crinoids of this type are mostly inhabitants of deep water but in the Paleozoic Era they were more or less abundant at many places in shallow water particularly where it was relatively free from detrital sediment and probably warm. Most of them were permanently fastened to the bottom by rootlike holdfasts. All obtained their food by filtering small particles from circulating sea water. Although most crinoids required a comparatively tranquil environment in well-aerated water, a few were adapted to other conditions including the turbulence of such places as organic reefs.

Echinoids

These constitute another group of the echinoderms. Most echinoids lead a free existence and are able to move about slowly. They are mainly inhabitants of shallow but fairly quiet water and are adapted to most types of bottom. Some live in agitated water near the shore where they seek crevices or other sheltered places and they may spend most of their existence in one spot. Others bury themselves shallowly in loose bottom sediment. The diet of echinoids varies. Some feed on fine suspended organic sediment; some are vegetarian; others are carnivorous and prey on small animals like worms and molluscs, which they crush with their powerful jaws; and there are those that are scavengers and mud eaters. Echinoids were less abundant than crinoids in the Paleozoic Era but since that time their numbers have increased and they have largely replaced the crinoids in shallow-water faunas.

Starfish

Starfish have existed since far back in geologic time and they are abundant in the sea today. Fossils are rare, however, because the bodies of these echinoderms disintegrate quickly after death and little can be determined from the scattered plates of their skeletons. Most starfish are shallow-water predatory animals that move over the sea bottom slowly in search of prey. Their food consists of almost any creatures they can capture and pelecypods are a particularly important element of their diet. Many modern starfish are very adaptable. They can withstand extreme conditions such as change in temperature, rough water, and even exposure to the air for short periods of time. They provide little environmental information.

Fish

Since at least the Devonian Period, fish have been the predominant predatory creatures of both marine and fresh water. Most of them swim swiftly and they inhabit water of all depths. Some spend much of their time resting on the bottom but mostly they are entirely independent of bottom conditions. Fish are not commonly preserved as fossils because when they die their bodies are rapidly devoured by scavengers and their remains are scattered. Marine and fresh-water species cannot be distinguished among fossils, and few fish are useful indicators of paleoecologic conditions.

Amphibians

The oldest-known amphibian fossils occur in Devonian strata. For a brief time these were the dominant animals of the land. Like fish, most amphibians have eggs, and young individuals are aquatic and breathe with gills. For this reason these animals cannot live far from fresh water, in which they breed. The aquatic larval stage has been suppressed in a few modern amphibians but whether or to what extent this may have been accomplished by fossil species cannot be determined. Fossils are relatively rare and do not furnish much information about environments.

Reptiles

The reptilian reproductive cycle, unlike that of most amphibians, does not include an aqueous phase, and reptiles have been freed from close dependence on water. They differentiated into many types and, especially in the Mesozoic Era, occupied a great variety of terrestrial environments. Much can be determined about the life habits of some of the specialized reptiles and, therefore, about the environments that they inhabited by observing their limbs, teeth, and other structures.

Mammals

Mammals succeeded reptiles as the dominant land animals after the end of the Mesozoic Era. They also differentiated rapidly and their types of limbs and teeth provide much information concerning the environments to which they were adapted. In this respect mammals are much superior to reptiles because of the greater specialization of many of their structures. Like other land vertebrates, however, mammalian fossils probably are generally preserved in strata uncharacteristic of the places where these animals actually lived.

Fossil Assemblages

One exceedingly important difference must be considered when assemblages of fossils are compared with communities of living organisms. This is the distinction that separates a dynamically active living population from a static dead one whose nature has been determined by the uncertain vicissitudes of preservation. Three features require particular notice: (1) The fossil record generally is very incomplete, (2) the circumstances of preservation make marine and terrestrial fossils unequally significant, and (3) the remains of organisms may be mixed so that they occur in unnatural associations. Figure 67 shows the relations of living animals to fossils and indicates the various ways in which the remains of organisms can be removed from or added to an assemblage of dead organisms or fossils.

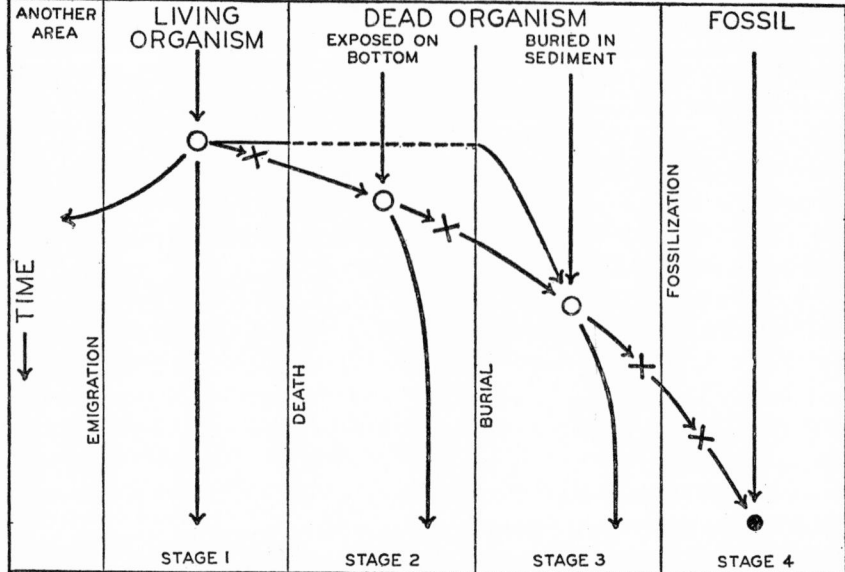

Figure 67. Diagram illustrating the relations of living organisms to fossils that may accumulate and be preserved within a restricted area. Arrows are flow lines indicating the passage from one stage to another that requires recognition. X marks a possible break in the sequence where organic remains may be totally destroyed.

Stage 1, the living organism. The organism may be native to an area or it may be an immigrant (upper arrow). If the organism is capable of movement, it may leave the area (arrow to left). If it reproduces asexually, it may remain living in the area indefinitely (lower arrow). If the organism falls prey to a predator, it disappears at X.

Stage 2, dead organism, exposed on surface. A dead organism or its partial remains may be one that lived within the area (arrow from left) or it may have been introduced from another area (upper arrow). It may be removed by action of currents or scavengers (lower arrow). It may be devoured by scavengers or decay completely and disappear at X.

Stage 3, dead organism buried in bottom sediment. The remains of an organism exposed on the surface may be buried by accumulating sediment (arrow from left). If, however, the organism was a burrower, it may have been already buried when it died and it did not pass through stage 2 (arrow from upper left). It may have been introduced from another area (upper arrow) or the bottom might be eroded and the organism removed (lower arrow). If the remains of this organism decays or is consumed by burrowing scavengers, it disappears at X.

Stage 4, fossil. The remains of an organism that escaped destruction in preceding stages becomes a fossil (arrow from left). Fossils, however, may be destroyed at X by solution, recrystallization of limestone, dolomitization, metamorphism, or some other process. Already fossilized specimens also may be introduced from another area (upper arrow). (Diagram suggested by R. G. Johnson.)

Incompleteness of Fossil Record

Only about one-sixth of all species of modern animals are estimated to be inhabitants of the sea. Of these not more than half live upon the muddy or sandy bottom that is represented by the vast majority of all abundantly fossiliferous rocks. Of the latter, not more than half possess hard parts that are likely to be preserved. Therefore, less than 5 percent of the species of living animals constitute that fraction of the modern fauna that can be compared with most ancient ones. The proportion of living plants that is likely to be preserved is even smaller.

About 1 million is commonly mentioned as the number of species of animals believed to be living in the world today but this may be an underestimate. Five percent of these, or about 50,000, constitute the reasonably expectable fossils of the future. Of course some others will be preserved rarely and under unusual circumstances. Such a number, however, greatly exceeds the number of fossil species that is known from any contemporaneously deposited sediments of the geologic past. Even after a generous allowance is made for new species that may be discovered in the future, the fossil record certainly is much more fragmentary than might be expected in comparison with the present.

The assumption can be safely made that every spot upon the earth is and always has been exploited to the fullest possible extent by the organisms then in existence that were able to reach it. Some fossil faunas probably present a reasonably complete record of an animal community so far as species equipped with preservable hard parts are concerned. Other communities, however, undoubtedly are very sparsely represented, and almost all of them lack recognizable traces of the numerous soft-bodied creatures that certainly existed. The absence of all fossils from any stratum does not mean that life was absent at that place when its sediment was deposited.

In long past ages land life was not as diversified as it is today, but there is little reason to conclude that the marine faunas are much richer or more varied now than they were in Ordovician time. Failure in the preservation of ancient animals and plants certainly has some meaning, and absence of the remains of organisms capable of fossilization or their complete destruction is fully as important as their preservation and presence at other places and at other times. The reasons for these differences in any instance, however, can rarely be determined. In contrast to many marine animals, all marine plants are poorly adapted to preservation in recognizable condition.

Thus most paleoecologic interpretations of marine communities must necessarily be based on notably incomplete biologic evidence. In consequence, special efforts must be made to utilize whatever evidence is available to its fullest possible extent and at the same time to make allowances for other features of the biologic communities that can only be inferred or guessed. In general terrestrial fossils are less satisfactory because they are too rare to provide much information concerning ecologic conditions of the land.

Relative Significance of Marine and Terrestrial Fossils

Many paleontologists have noticed a more or less close correlation between kinds of fossils and the kinds of rock in which they most commonly occur although this is rarely mentioned adequately in paleontologic reports (see Figure 68). Such correlation indicates that either (1) the fossil organ-

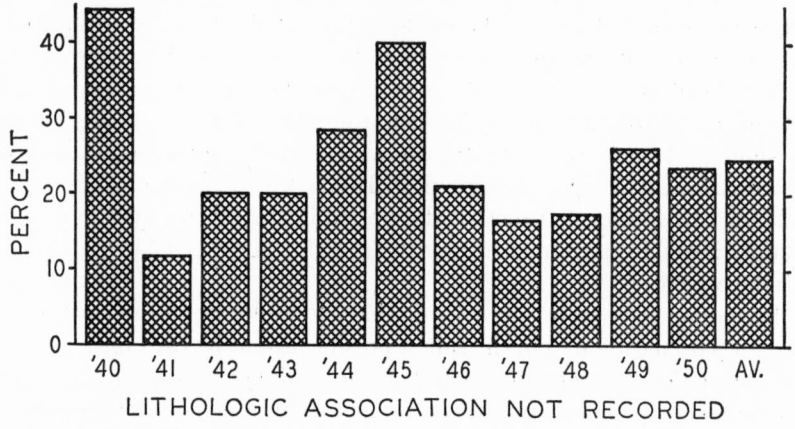

LITHOLOGIC ASSOCIATION NOT RECORDED

Figure 68. Diagram showing proportion of papers describing microfossils published in the *Journal of Paleontology* between 1940 and 1950 which make no reference to the lithologic associations of the fossils. Many other papers provide only incidental and inadequate information regarding association. Very few papers devoted to either macro- or microfossils make any mention of the occurrence of fossils of the other kind. (Data from Ellison, 1951, *J. Sediment. Petrol.,* vol. 21, p. 220, fig. 4.)

isms preferred a particular environment characterized by the entombing rock or (2) the rock represents an environment in which the fossil remains of particular organisms were most likely to be preserved. Actually these possibilities are both realized but in general they apply to different groups of fossils. If no such correlation exists, the implications are that either (1) the fossil organisms were adapted to a variety of environments and their possibilities of existence were not limited by the factors controlling the character of the sediment or (2) the organisms probably were native to another closely associated environment as, for example, the upper waters of the sea whose swimming and floating inhabitants after death sank to the bottom regardless of its nature.

Most rocks containing abundant marine fossils represent fairly tranquil environments. Generally those that do not can be recognized because the rocks are coarse textured and the fossils exhibit signs of transportation and are likely to be worn or broken. Marine fossils show the closest correlation with lithology. In rocks of any particular age, many species and even genera rarely occur in more than one particular type of rock. Such fossils have not moved far from the places where the organisms lived, and useful conclusions concerning physical environments can be reached on the basis of the type of sediment. Even if considerable transportation has occurred, the organisms commonly were native to an adjacent and closely related habitat.

Conditions on the land, where erosion is general, are very different. No chance exists there for most organisms to be preserved in the areas where they live because sediments do not accumulate. The only important exceptions are lakes, whose deposits are much like those of the sea and correlation between fossils and sediment can be made, and swamps, in which the remains of indigenous plants accumulate. Elsewhere the preservation of terrestrial fossils is largely a matter of accident, and enclosing sediment reflects an environment in which preservation is possible rather than the principal one in which the organisms lived. This is particularly true for fossil vertebrates. Also this is the reason why terrestrial fossils are much less abundant than marine and why the record of terrestrial life is much more fragmentary.

Fossils of Mixed Ages

The danger of mixing, caused by the uncritical or careless collecting of fossils from different stratigraphical zones, is obvious. Mixing also may occur naturally, however, and organisms from different environments may be brought together and preserved in a single stratum. Such mixed faunas are of three types: (1) those resulting from the reworking of fossils from an older stratum and their deposition with younger specimens, (2) those resulting from the transportation of organisms or their remains more or less horizontally from one environment to another contemporary one, and (3) those resulting from the sinking of organisms or their remains from an overlying environment to a benthonic one. Unless mixing can be recognized, conflicting evidence may cause confusion and the misinterpretation of local environments.

The mixing of fossils of different ages is not encountered commonly. It is probably a greater potential source of confusion with respect to age determination than to ecologic interpretation. If the older specimens have been derived from a consolidated formation, they are likely to be somewhat differently preserved and fossilized and thus distinction may be possible. In any case, larger specimens are commonly water worn and broken. The most troublesome mixtures are those containing microfossils such as foraminifera from unconsolidated late Mesozoic and Tertiary strata. Such mixed faunas may give very little indication of their composite nature. Generally they are recognized only when the different ages or different ecologic implications of some of the specimens are noted.

Fossils of Mixed Environments

The transportation and mixing of fossils of the same age presents a dissimilar problem. There is considerable difference of opinion as to how prevalent such mixing may have been. Although many worn and broken specimens may indicate transportation, this does not necessarily mean that the fossils were derived from one environment and deposited in another one. Also it is possible that the damage occurred without appreciable movement. For example, the disarticulated crinoids and broken bryozoans of bioherms in the Borden Group (Miss.) of Indiana may have been moved to some extent, but there can be no doubt that these organisms lived within the restricted areas of the bioherms, which were surrounded by a different environment inhospitable to them. Many marine formations record conditions that were remarkably uniform throughout large areas. The transportation of any but the smallest organisms or small fragments of their remains for long distances is improbable. Experiments indicate also that such objects as shells are much more likely to be buried by currents than to be moved considerable distances.

Some examples of transportation and mixing, however, are self-evident. Among them are the occurrences of terrestrial plant remains in strata containing marine fossils and the association of bones in fluvial deposits. Also the mixing of fossils originating in different environments or their transportation to a foreign environment can be expected under certain circumstances. The most noteworthy examples occur in the flanking beds of organic reefs and in the deposits of turbidity currents. In either of these cases the probability is greater that the recognition of displaced fossils would result from identification of the type of deposit on the basis of physical evidence rather than from the nature of the fossils. In general the mixing of fossils in sediments that accumulated on the nearly level sea bottom is very difficult to prove and ordinarily it can be doubted.

Stratified Environments

The definition of an environment is not easy. Strictly speaking the environment of every individual organism differs, however minutely, from that of every other. There is also the matter of scale as this involves the size of the organic community or the degree of similarity in the environment that is to be recognized. In a gross way three quite different environments can be distinguished: (1) the sea, (2) fresh water, and (3) the land. On the other hand, environments may be exemplified more precisely by (1) a small volume of mud below the bottom of the sea, (2) a small area of the sea bottom, (3) a small volume of water at intermediate depth, and (4) an equal volume of water near the surface of the sea. Each of these environments varies from place to place but each has certain significantly different physical attributes and is occupied by a characteristic association of organisms. Similar distinctions can be made with respect to environments in fresh water and on the land, but these find much less application in paleontology and paleoecology.

The four general environments of the sea that have been noted do not exhaust the possibilities of differentiation but they illustrate the contemporaneous stratification of environments that occurs everywhere. Most marine fossils are the remains of organisms that lived on or in the sediments of the sea bottom. Two groups can be recognized: (1) the infauna that inhabits the bottom sediment and (2) the epifauna that lives upon its surface. The remains of both groups are preserved together and both furnish evidence useful in the interpretation of sedimentary conditions. The remains of epifaunal organisms may be moved horizontally along the sea bottom, and under certain circumstances broken specimens may be concentrated in local deposits, particularly in very shallow water. In contrast, infaunal remains are much more likely to remain undamaged and undisturbed.

Less abundant fossils record the pelagic life of water above the bottom. Again two groups can be distinguished: (1) the nekton or creatures that swim freely and purposefully through the water and (2) the plankton or organisms that float or swim more or less aimlessly near the surface of the sea. After death the remains of both groups may sink to the bottom and some may be preserved as fossils with benthonic organisms. These fossils from upper environments provide little evidence regarding bottom conditions. Most fossils can be assigned to one or another of these four groups on the basis of their structural peculiarities, which indicate their mode of life, or by analogy with similar modern organisms whose ways of life are known.

The benthonic element of many fossil assemblages consists almost exclusively of the remains of epifaunal organisms. Pelecypods are the most abundant representatives of the infauna but their shells are rare or absent in many Paleozoic limestones. Fossil evidence suggests that extensive exploitation of the infaunal environment by molluscs was delayed until the Mesozoic Era. This appears to have been a major environmental conquest comparable perhaps to the successful invasion of fresh water by descendants of marine organisms. It seems to have occurred concurrently with the general expansion of pelecypods and their supplanting of the brachiopods as dominant shellfish of the sea. Worms undoubtedly have been numerous since Precambrian time but these soft-bodied creatures are ill suited for preservation. Their burrows or tubes, however, remain at many places in ancient sediments but are easily overlooked.

Most planktonic organisms are very small. Few are readily preserved under any ordinary circumstances. Therefore, their remains are not likely to constitute a conspicuous part of many fossil assemblages. The fossils of this type that are most commonly observed are the shells of foraminifera, such as *Globigerina* in relatively recent strata, and some graptolites in certain older rocks. Most nektonic animals achieve much larger size. They include fish, a few air-breathing vertebrates, and some cephalopods. The fossil remains of such creatures generally are not abundant and they may be fragmentary, but they are easily recognized as belonging to an environment different from that of the sea bottom.

Another type of fauna (not so easily recognized) that may be preserved with or without the remains of strictly benthonic organisms consists of creatures that lived on or among seaweeds some distance above the bottom. Its members belong to several of the same important groups that provide benthonic organisms. Their identification generally is dependent upon physical evidence more or less surely indicating that the sea bottom was inhospitable and necessitating the presumption that there must have been an overlying inhabited environment. Thus black highly organic shales commonly record a toxic bottom where few animals could live. Many of the fossils preserved in them may have sunk to the bottom from a higher zone. Seaweeds provide structures suitable for the attachment of sessile organisms and also a source of abundant organic matter that became incorporated in the sediment. Seaweeds and associated faunas may have been important in other environments also, but in the absence of black shale their existence cannot be so certainly established.

ECOLOGIC FACTORS

The ecologic factors that combine to produce the environment of any organism constitute an exceedingly complex system of interrelated variables. Some of them obviously are of great importance and are more decisive than others in determining the distribution of a species. Different species are variously influenced by the same factors, however, and any one may outweigh the others in a particular case. Because some factors are very closely related to each other, their relative importance may be difficult to determine. The most obvious and significant factors for both aqueous and terrestrial environments are shown in Table 8.

The distribution and continued existence of any population of organisms is dependent, not on the average or dominant conditions that prevail in any region or at any time, but upon the threshold of tolerance of the individuals of the population at their most susceptible stages with respect to each element of the environment separately. The balance between organisms and their environments is so delicate that any change in either physical or biologic conditions or relations is almost certain to be reflected by resultant changes in the local biota. Continuous change has resulted from evolution

TABLE 8.   The Principal Factors Affecting the Ecology of Aqueous
and Terrestrial Environments

Aqueous	Terrestrial
1. Salinity	1. Availability of water
2. Dissolved gases	2. Rainfall and atmospheric humidity
3. Temperature, seasonal range	3. Temperature, daily and seasonal ranges
4. Depth	4. Altitude
5. Light	5. Light
6. Turbidity	6. Topography
7. Currents and wave action	7. Wind
8. Bottom conditions	8. Soil
9. Food supply	9. Food supply
10. Organic associations	10. Organic associations

but this was slow. Most of the obvious differences between faunas or floras occurring in strata of approximately similar geologic age are the result of differences in environment and the accessibility of areas to migration and colonization by similar organisms. The actual ecologic factors that limited the distribution of any fossil species, however, generally are very obscure.

The problem of the paleontologist or paleoecologist is to recognize what if anything the fossils imply regarding these or other factors. Before this can be done, it is necessary to inquire into the nature of ecologic factors and to determine if possible in what ways they control or influence biologic activity.

Marine Environment

The almost infinite variety observable in the associations of plants and animals today is evidence of an equal variety in the ecologic conditions that are available for biologic exploitation. Many of these environments are more or less importantly conditioned by the organisms themselves, and the number of environments has multiplied as organisms have become more diversified from very ancient to modern times. The underlying physical factors to which organisms must become adapted if they are to survive, however, have changed little if at all since far back in the Precambrian.

The sea provides a general environment in which life is believed to have originated and from which organisms emigrated first into fresh water and then onto the land. This origin is indicated by (1) the much longer and more continuous record of marine life, (2) the greater diversity in the fundamental forms assumed by marine animals, suggesting longer continuous evolution, and (3) the osmotic equilibrium that exists between the sea and most protoplasm and organic body fluids, which seems to mark the latter as modified marine water.

The statement commonly is made that the sea provides an environment peculiarly favorable for life. It would be more correct to say that many organisms, and particularly the simpler and more primitive ones, are most perfectly adapted to living in the sea. If life originated under marine conditions, this is exactly what should be expected. In any event the sea provides a general environment that is sharply contrasted in several important respects with fresh-water and more especially with terrestrial environments, which necessitate special adaptations for successful habitation. Four features of the marine environment require particular notice.

1. Organisms living in water are not subjected to desiccation and they do not need to possess structures or habits designed to conserve body moisture, which is easily renewed from the surrounding medium. Terrestrial organisms generally either possess surface coverings that reduce evaporation or are restricted to living in relatively very moist situations. All of them must have access to water and means of furnishing water to all parts of their bodies. Fresh water is less favorable than marine, particularly for the less advanced organisms, because it tends to diffuse through organic membranes, and special means are required to prevent dilution of the body fluids. This may be accomplished by an impervious covering or a mechanism to eliminate excess water.

2. Water provides a medium nearly equal in density to living matter. Organisms can float or swim with little effort and do not require strong supporting structures such as skeletons. In this respect salt water is slightly more effective than fresh water. The possibility of swimming or floating, not necessarily near the surface, opens all parts of the sea to habitation. Thus the situation is very different from that presented by the atmosphere, into whose lower layers some organisms can rise temporarily. All terrestrial life is bound to a narrow zone close above or close below the surface of the land. The habitable space available to marine organisms has been estimated to be about 300 times as great as that available to terrestrial organisms and about 15,000 times that provided by fresh water.

3. The sea is much more uniform in all of its physical environmental characters, except pressure, than is fresh water or the land. Thus organic adaptation is less complex and, in spite of its great space, the sea provides fewer and generally less isolated habitats. This is reflected by the fact that of all the organisms living in the world today only about 15 percent are marine species. In general, evolution in the sea appears to have been less rapid than on land. Also many groups of organisms that have succeeded in adapting themselves to life on land have diversified much more greatly than comparable groups of marine organisms.

4. All main parts of the sea are broadly interconnected. The oceans are not separated from each other to the same extent as continents. Relatively isolated parts like the Baltic, Mediterranean, and Black seas are few and comparatively small. Completely isolated bodies of salt water like the Caspian Sea that can be compared to islands are neither numerous nor important. Thus the migration of terrestrial organisms across or around water bar-

riers is much more difficult than the migration of marine organisms that is impeded by less continuous barriers of land. This very important factor partly accounts for the world-wide greater uniformity of marine life and the larger number of terrestrial species that have evolved in more completely isolated situations.

Salinity

One of the most characteristic features of the sea is its salinity. Although nearly fifty elements have been identified in sea water, more than 99 percent of the dissolved material consists of chlorides and sulfates of sodium, magnesium, calcium, and potassium in this order of abundance. Sodium chloride is by far the most common compound and accounts for nearly 80 percent of it. All streams flowing into the sea carry mineral matter in solution, and the belief generally is held that long-continued contributions from this source, less the calcium and magnesium carbonates and sulfates and sodium chloride of limestone, dolomite, gypsum, and rock salt laid down as sediments, have been concentrated and remain dissolved in sea water. On the other hand, some theories regarding the origin of the oceans postulate that the water was originally salty. No evidence is known to indicate that the salinity of the sea has changed importantly since at least the beginning of the Paleozoic Era.

The salinity of the sea is remarkably constant. Throughout its whole extent there is little variation in the proportions of its dissolved solids. Salinity in the open sea below a depth of a few hundred feet everywhere approximates 35 permille. Surface water varies between 33 and 37 permille, the concentration being increased by evaporation in some areas and reduced in others by the admixture of fresh water falling as rain, entering from rivers, or produced by melting ice. Greater variations occur in some partly isolated water bodies such as the Baltic Sea, where salinity decreases almost to zero at its head, and the Red Sea, where the salt content may exceed 40 permille. In special situations such as small coastal lagoons and estuaries there is every gradation from abnormally high salinity to fresh water.

Aqueous organisms are sensitive to salinity because osmotic pressure varies with salt content. If their body fluids are not in equilibrium with the surrounding medium, water passes either into or out of their bodies. Most organisms can adjust themselves only within a narrow salinity range because of limitations to tolerable concentrations in their fluids. Consequently, salinity is an ecologic factor of great importance that determines their possible distribution. More adaptable organisms generally possess a mechanism permitting them to eliminate excess water from their bodies as rapidly as it is absorbed.

The great majority of all marine plants are thallophytes, whose parts are not differentiated into true roots, stems, and leaves as in the higher plants. Most are of microscopic size. They obtain all the materials needed for existence by absorption from the surrounding water, and even the largest do not require an elaborate vascular system to carry water and mineral substances to their various parts. Many of the larger plants are attached to the bottom or to other solid objects by holdfasts, but these are quite different functionally from roots. The lack of specialized woody structures in seaweeds renders them ill suited for fossilization and they are rarely recognizably preserved.

Nitrogen and phosphorus compounds are nutrients necessary for plant growth. They occur in solution in sea water in small amounts but are rapidly depleted. In many parts of the sea the small planktonic plants, like diatoms, lead a cyclic existence that varies with the seasons. Favorable conditions in the spring result in the rapid and enormous multiplication of individuals. This continues until the nutrients are depleted, generally by early summer. Further growth is limited by the rate at which nitrogen and phosphorous compounds diffuse upward from the deeps. Winter brings plant growth to a stop and nutrients accumulate until spring arrives and another cycle starts. More or less permanent upwelling currents maintain the fertility of the sea in some regions, particularly near continents where offshore winds cause the depleted surface water to drift away. Such places are likely to be especially rich in all types of marine life.

The food requirements of aqueous animals are simpler than those of land animals. Being surrounded by water they can obtain mineral substances by absorption and must consume organic matter only to meet their needs for energy and growth.

Dissolved Gases

Oxygen and carbon dioxide are the most important gases dissolved in water. Both are present in the air. They pass freely from the gaseous to the dissolved state and equilibrium is more or less maintained at the water-air interface. Like other gases their solubility varies inversely with temperature and the concentration of dissolved solids. They are diffused in very uniform proportions throughout the atmosphere but their occurrence in water is marked by great differences in concentration.

Free oxygen is necessary for the existence of most organisms, the principal exceptions being some of the bacteria. Oxygen in the sea is derived by solution from the air and from the metabolic activities of plants in the upper illuminated waters. It is consumed by animals and many bacteria and to a less extent by plants. The general distribution of oxygen in the sea is closely related to organic activity, and stratification commonly exists. Thus the oxygen content is high in surface water of the well-lighted zone, where plants are abundant and a condition of supersaturation may exist (see Figure 69). Plants are less active at lower levels and a larger proportion of the oxygen is consumed by animals so that concentration commonly declines. A minimum amount of oxygen has been observed at depths of some 1500 feet. Plants cannot exist abundantly below about 200 feet, and at greater depths little or no excess oxygen is produced. In deep water, animal life also becomes more sparse, less oxygen is consumed, and the concentration generally rises. Deep waters of the open ocean are replenished by surface water of the polar regions which sinks below the warmer, less dense water layers and carries oxygen down with it. Bacteria are very abundant in the upper layers of the bottom sediment and, where circulation is poor and abundant organic matter rains downward from the planktonic zone, oxygen is much depleted or entirely exhausted (see Figure 70). Such a situation is exemplified by the Black Sea. Most parts of the sea, however, are plentifully enough supplied with oxygen to support all of the life that is permitted to exist by other ecologic conditions.

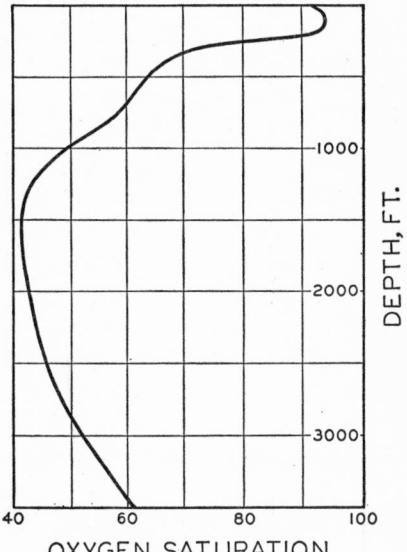

The chemical relations of carbon dioxide are more complex because equilibrium relations involve not only gaseous and dissolved phases but also simple solution and bicarbonate and carbonate molecules and ions (see p. 151). Carbon dioxide in the sea is obtained by solution from the atmosphere and as a product of the metabolic activity of animals and bacteria. It is utilized by plants in their photosynthetic processes for the production of carbohydrates. The concentration of carbon dioxide commonly shows stratification the reverse of that of oxygen. At the surface,

Figure 69. Curve showing percentage of oxygen saturation in water at various depths as measured in the Caribbean Sea off the north coast of Panama. Similar observations elsewhere have revealed somewhat different distribution, but the form of this curve is fairly characteristic. It clearly indicates the high oxygen content in near-surface water where planktonic plants are abundant. (After Schmidt, 1925, Science, vol. 61, p. 592.)

where plants are most active, concentration is low but it increases downward to about the same level where oxygen concentration is at a minimum. Below this, carbon dioxide is less abundant but water immediately above the bottom may be richly supplied with it as the result of the decomposition of organic matter in sediment by the action of bacteria. In general carbon dioxide tends to accumulate in the deeper parts of the sea where it is unavailable to plants until upwelling brings the deep water to the surface. Although rapid plant growth may nearly deplete carbon dioxide in surface water, only rarely does the deficiency of this substance constitute a controlling factor of the environment.

Normal sea water is weakly alkaline. At the surface it has pH values commonly ranging between 8.1 and 8.3 and these may approach 7.5 at intermediate depths. The variation in values is more closely related to carbon dioxide concentration than to temperature or salinity. Sea water, however, is a buffered solution. Relatively large variations in the carbon dioxide content produce only small differences in pH values. Except in special situations where the pH is influenced by other factors, such as the presence of hydrogen sulfide, variations in the alkalinity of sea water appear to have little effect upon the distributions of organisms.

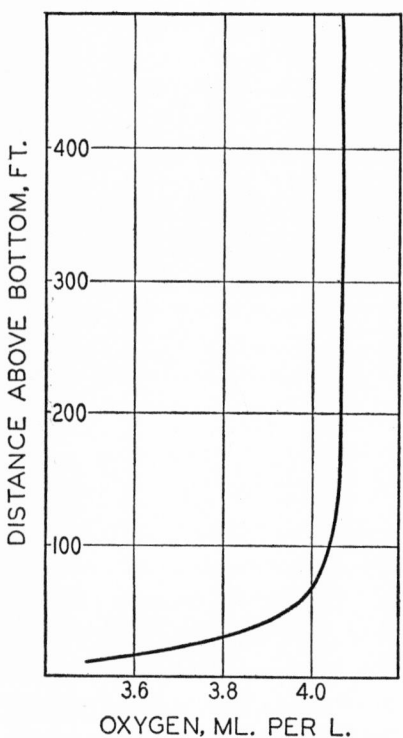

Figure 70. Curve showing decrease in oxygen content of water near the sea bottom where it may be more or less exhausted by bacterial processes. Generalized from measurements made in the Indian Ocean. (Data from Bruun, 1957, Geol. Soc. Amer., Mem. 67, vol. 1, p. 648, fig. 3.)

Hydrogen sulfide is one of the products of the bacterial decay of organic matter that occurs mainly in bottom sediments where reducing conditions commonly prevail. At most places aerated water overlies the bottom, and dissolved hydrogen sulfide gas is oxidized promptly to sulfuric acid, which displaces combined carbonic acid to form sulfates. In areas of poor water circulation and richly organic sediments, however, the oxygen is exhausted and hydrogen sulfide may accumulate. This substance is highly toxic to most organisms. If it accumulates in appreciable amounts, its presence and the lack of oxygen combine to produce conditions that exclude most forms of life. Many black shales appear to record the existence of situations of this kind.

Temperature

Temperature certainly is one of the most important factors of environment. It sets rather narrow limits beyond which life, as it occurs on earth, cannot exist. The ease and accuracy with which temperature can be measured, however, may have resulted in overemphasis of its importance in specific instances because some of its side effects, such as viscosity and density of water and solubility of both gases and solids, may actually be the controlling factors. Thus viscosity of sea water, which is important to all planktonic organisms, is twice as great at 32 as at 75 degrees. Because calcium carbonate, which is utilized by many marine animals for shells or other hard parts, is much more soluble in cold than in warm water, the development of such structures may be either inhibited or favored. On the other hand, metabolic activity is related directly to temperature and a rise of 20 degrees may result in doubling its rate.

All organisms thrive best at certain optimum temperatures which vary greatly for different species. Likewise there is much difference in the maximum and minimum temperatures that limit their existence. Here the time factor also is important because the limits vary depending upon the length of time extreme conditions can be endured. Generally the optimum temperature is much closer to the maximum and too great a rise in temperature results in swift and certain death. On the other hand, lowering of temperature slows metabolic activity and organisms may pass into a resting stage. Some animals can withstand temperatures lower than that at which body fluids freeze.

Temperatures in the sea range from about 25 to 100 degrees. This maximum is attained only in very restricted areas, such as tropical tide pools and small lagoons; maximum in the open ocean is about 85 degrees. This is a much smaller range than occurs in air, which varies at present between −85 and +150 degrees. Seasonal changes in surface temperature of the sea reach their maximum in the temperate zones but rarely exceed 25 degrees. Three-quarters of the ocean varies less than 10 degrees, and about one-third of it, located in the tropics, varies less than 5 degrees. Diurnal temperature variation is almost negligible, rarely reaches 1 degree, and is not noticeable below a depth of thirty to forty feet.

Temperature in the sea declines with depth but not regularly, and stratification is well marked especially in its warmer portions. There the surface water is bounded below by a *thermocline*, where temperature falls relatively rapidly and at some places attains a rate of 1 degree in twenty feet. If a well-marked thermocline exists it generally is encountered at depths ranging from 150 to 500 feet varying somewhat with the seasons. Below about 600 feet further decline is slow, and at any level at any place temperature is essentially constant at all times. Temperatures at the bottom of the deep sea everywhere are low. In some areas freezing temperature of sea water is nearly reached.

The relative uniformity and stability of temperature in different parts of the marine environment are reflected by the generally narrow adaptations of marine organisms in this respect. Certain organisms are adapted to each segment of the total range in temperature and many are closely restricted to these segments. Distinctions can be made both between warm- and cold-water organisms and between those that have narrow and wide tolerances. Optimum temperature and breadth of tolerance, however, are not necessarily the same at all stages in the life history of an organism. For example, the reproduction of many marine animals is more closely controlled by temperature than is their existence in either larval or mature stages. Also planktonic larvae of many benthonic species require temperatures different from those most favorable for adults. These and other divergences in tolerance and requirements influence the distribution of all organisms. In some populations reproduction is not possible and they are maintained only by the continual immigration of immature individuals.

Warm water provides an optimum environment for marine life. Metabolism is rapid and generations follow each other in quick succession. Under these conditions evolution might be expected to attain a maximum rate. Although no actual relation between rapidity of reproduction and evolution has been established, a greater variety and larger number of associated species occur in tropical communities than in less clement habitats. This is one example of the general rule that, with increasingly favorable physical conditions, the number of species in a community increases without a corresponding increase in the total population density, and, therefore, the community is less likely to be dominated by one or a few species.

Depth

The main physical effect of depth is increase in hydrostatic pressure of about one-half pound per square inch per foot of overlying water. This amounts to about 400 times atmospheric pressure at mean oceanic depth. Less important effects are slight decrease in viscosity and increase in density of water and slightly greater speed of chemical reactions. The influences of these effects on organisms are not known. Experiments show that some

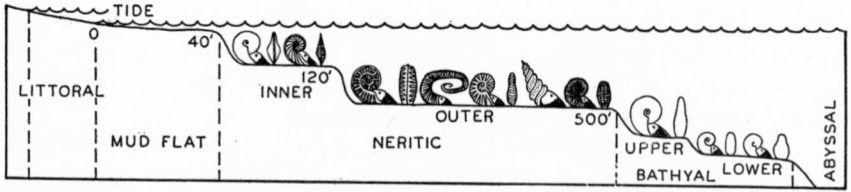

Figure 71. Diagram indicating the inferred depth preferences of several types of Cretaceous ammonites occurring in Texas. Conclusions were based mainly on the kinds of enclosing sediment and associated fossil faunas. The ammonite types are not, however, so sharply separated as this suggests because they intergrade to some extent. Nevertheless, the recognition of these types permits bathymetric conclusions to be drawn on the basis of the ammonites alone (see Figure 133, p. 325). (After Scott, 1940, J. Paleon., vol. 14, p. 317, fig. 8.)

shallow-water marine organisms are injured or fail to survive at 200 to 300 atmospheres but others are much more resistant. On the whole, considerable increase in hydrostatic pressure appears to have little effect on most organisms whose bodies do not contain free gases.

The stratification of different communities in the sea (see Figure 71) seems to be related more closely to other physical conditions that vary progressively with depth. The most obvious of these are decrease in light intensity and temperature. All plants, except bacteria, and most animals that feed upon them are restricted to shallow water. Also the distributions of many animals follow temperature zones without much regard to depth. Some are known that live near the surface in both arctic and antarctic regions but are deep-water species in the equatorial zone.

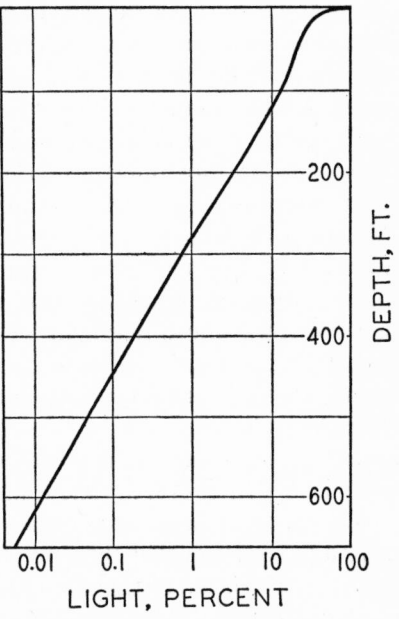

Figure 72. Curve showing the penetration of sunlight in the clearest oceanic water in terms of total incident energy. (After Holmes, 1957, Geol. Soc. Amer., Mem. 67, vol. 1, p. 119, fig. 6.)

Light

Light is of primary importance to plants because they depend upon its energy for photosynthesis. Therefore, in the sea, plants are restricted to the well-lighted shallow-water zone. In low latitudes bright sunlight penetrates clear water to a depth of about 300 feet in sufficient quantity to be used by plants (see Figure 72). Most plants, however, occur in much shallower water. Diatoms, for example, are present in maximum abundance at a depth of 25 to 30 feet. They are still abundant at 150 feet but in the next 75 their number is reduced one-half and at 300 feet only about one-fifth as many individuals occur.

The depth of light penetration in water depends upon four factors: (1) intensity of light falling on the water, (2) latitude, (3) time of day, and (4) clarity of water. Maximum penetration occurs when light falls from directly overhead. When it enters at an angle more light is reflected upward and the light that does enter follows a diagonal course and does not reach as great a depth. Thus the light of early morning, late afternoon, and at high latitudes is much less effective than direct overhead illumination. Light reaches only half the depth at 67 degrees of latitude as in the tropics.

Water absorbs light of different wave lengths differentially. The longer waves at the red end of the spectrum are filtered out rapidly. In clear water the shorter wave lengths penetrate more and more deeply. The longer waves are used by plants most effectively for photosynthesis. In more opaque turbid water the penetration of all wave lengths is reduced but the short waves also are filtered out promptly and those beyond the orange do not reach much below the surface. The clarity of water adjacent to most coasts is highly variable from place to place and from time to time depending upon the depth, the nearness to rivers, the type of bottom, and the kind of weather, but all is turbid to some extent. On the average, coastal water is only about one-tenth as translucent as the clear water of the open sea. Therefore, plant life is restricted to a much shallower zone in most coastal areas and at high latitudes than in the open tropical oceans.

Animals are not directly dependent upon light but because ultimately plants constitute the food of all animals light is necessary for their existence. Most marine animals are sensitive to light whether or not they are equipped with eyes. Many shun bright light and commonly seek shaded or sheltered places. Some hide during the day and come forth to feed at night. This does not necessarily mean that light is detrimental to them. The reaction may be one that makes them less conspicuous to their enemies or prey. Sedentary animals have no need for eyes. They simply wait for food to be brought to them by water currents and live as successfully in darkness as in light. Eyes are a great advantage to mobile creatures, however, and many different kinds of animals possess eyes in various stages of perfection.

The efficiency of the eyes of most animals is not known but there is little reason to conclude that they are much less perceptive of light than the human eye, which can distinguish illumination less than one-millionth as bright as sunlight. Faint shadows are discernible in very clear water at a depth of 1500 feet, and some light can still be seen at 2000 feet. Photographic plates indicate that a little light reaches 3000 feet but it is too faint to be seen by human eyes. Absolute darkness prevails deeper in the sea. Some of the benthonic animals inhabiting the deep twilight zone have much enlarged eyes but the eyes of others have degenerated and in a few they have completely atrophied.

Turbidity

Moderate turbidity has little direct effect upon organisms and is important principally because it reduces light penetration in the sea. It may result from either (1) suspended sediment or (2) the presence of abundant planktonic organisms. Turbidity is general in coastal waters whereas the open oceans are relatively clear. Water in the Sargasso Sea, southwest of the Azores in the North Atlantic, is the most translucent in the world today. There light penetrates twice as deeply as in the Mediterranean, which also is remarkably clear, and nearly twenty times as far as in Woods Hole Harbor on the Massachusetts coast. Areas of very clear water are deficient in planktonic organisms and suspended organic matter that settle to the bottom and constitute the food of many benthonic animals. Consequently, abundant bottom populations cannot be expected.

Excessively turbid areas are unfavorable to many forms of marine life, particularly most bryozoans and corals and numerous other sessile filter-feeding animals. Such turbidity may result from (1) the nearness of large rivers or (2) strong waves and currents above a shallow muddy or silty bottom. Abundant suspended sediment interferes with feeding and respiration, but reduced salinity or unsuitable bottom conditions probably accounts for the absence of some other organisms in turbid areas. Also sediment may accumulate relatively rapidly in such an area and render it unfit for many bottom-living organisms.

Waves and Currents

The tranquillity of the sea is disturbed by waves and currents. Some movement in the water is required to (1) maintain equable salinity, (2) reduce temperature variations, (3) carry dissolved gases and food to organisms, and (4) aid in the movement of organisms from place to place. Swift currents, however, or strong turbulence produced by waves is unfavorable for many forms of marine life. Nevertheless, a varied and highly successful group of organisms is adapted to disturbed conditions in very shallow water and near coastal situations.

Ordinary currents in the sea rarely attain a velocity of eight inches per second. This equals about half a mile per hour and it is close to the maximum recorded measurement of local current near the bottom. Currents of this strength are capable of eroding unconsolidated sand and silt and might exert dangerously strong pressure on delicate organisms living at the bottom. The Gulf Stream flows at a rate of about four miles per hour where it is constricted in the Florida Strait, but this is surface movement; speed is much less near the bottom. Turbidity currents may be much swifter and more powerful and they are likely to wreak havoc upon all bottom life. A current of this type produced by an earthquake in the Grand Banks region south of Newfoundland in 1929 attained a speed of more than fifty miles an hour on a slope of less than one-half degree and broke submarine cables 400 miles from its point of origin. Few areas on the sea bottom, however, except in very shallow water or at long intervals of time, are subject to currents strong enough to interfere seriously with most organisms.

On the whole, currents in the sea are more advantageous to marine life than they are harmful. They perform a particularly valuable service in facilitating the distribution of many organisms. Spores and the resting stages of plants and the eggs and larvae of animals are moved primarily by currents.

Thus planktonic plants and animals of the temperate and arctic zones survive from one season to the next and are dispersed widely. The larval life of benthonic animals averages about three weeks, and a current as slow as 100 feet per hour would carry them about ten miles. This is the principal way in which sessile animals can extend their ranges and such a rate probably is greater than the speed at which most bottom-crawling forms can migrate. Some ocean currents follow more or less circular courses within a single climatic zone. Others flow from warm to cold regions or vice versa. Organisms transported by a current of the latter type are likely to be carried into an unfavorable environment and perish.

Waves can be very destructive in shallow water and along exposed coasts. They stir the bottom actively to a depth of 50 feet or more and move pebbles and even cobbles along beaches. Most organisms cannot endure such conditions. Those that can generally live in crevices or other sheltered places, or are able to cling tenaciously to rock surfaces, or are cemented firmly to them. In spite of its rigors, however, this environment is favorable for hardy organisms because the water is well aerated and food commonly is plentiful. In the tropics this environment supports a specialized community of organisms that builds extensive reefs and prospers best in the most exposed situations. The severity of wave turbulence along some coasts is reduced by the abundant growth of kelp. Wave action in the open sea has little effect on planktonic organisms.

Bottom Conditions

Observations of modern marine benthonic faunas reveal that two periods in the life history of individuals are of supreme importance in the survival and distribution of the species constituting the population. These are the time of egg and sperm ripening and spawning and the time, immediately preceding metamorphosis, when the larvae sink to the bottom and seek a place to continue their existence.

The wastage accompanying the reproduction of most marine organisms is enormous. It is clearly indicated by the thousands to millions of eggs produced by a single female during her lifetime (see Figure 73) whereas no more than two need survive to maintain the population. Most of the eggs and larvae are consumed as food by other organisms. Many others, which fail to find a suitable environment for further growth, are also lost. A larva, however, that reaches a favorable spot, becomes established, and achieves a good start in its adolescent development has escaped the greatest hazards of its existence and has a reasonably good chance to reach maturity.

Most marine benthonic organisms are adapted to certain particular conditions of the bottom. Their larvae seek places where such conditions can be found. After settling, many larvae have the ability to postpone metamorpho-

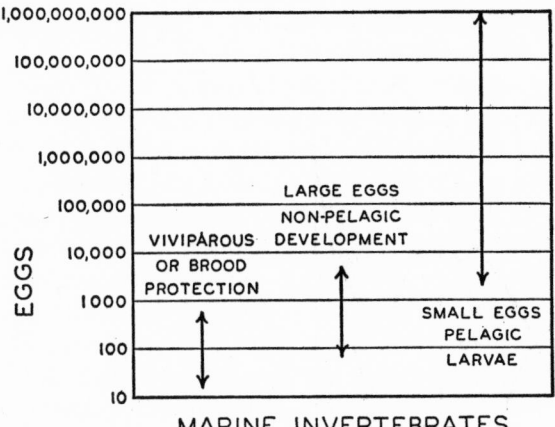

Figure 73. Diagram showing the ranges in number of eggs or young produced by marine benthonic invertebrates per female per breeding season. The wastage among pelagic larvae is enormous. (Adapted from Thorson, 1950, *Biol. Reviews*, vol. 25, p. 4, fig. 1, by permission of the Cambridge Philosophical Society.)

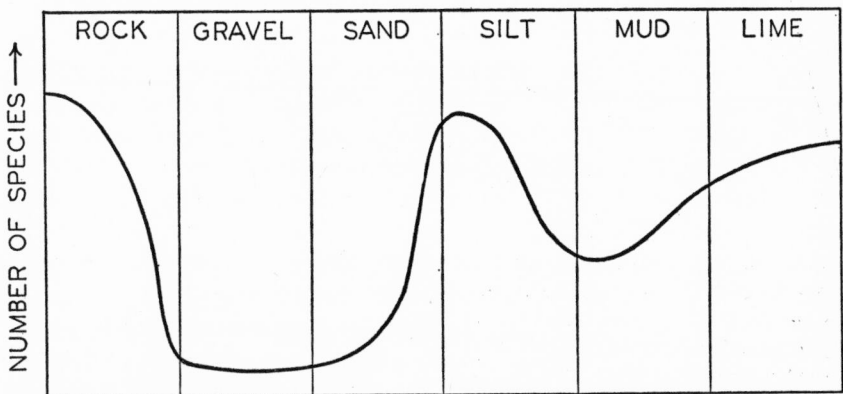

Figure 74. Much-generalized curve showing the relative diversity of marine benthonic faunas adapted to life on different types of bottom. A large variety of organisms lives on shallow-water rocky surfaces. An unstable gravel bottom is exceedingly unfavorable, and much sand also is unstable and lacks organic material. As sediment size decreases, a firmer bottom generally is provided and benthonic organisms are more abundant. Much mud, however, is too soft to support sessile organisms, whereas a lime bottom provides a favorable situation. In a consideration of this kind depth also is important but in this diagram only shallow water is considered.

sis for periods ranging from several days to a few weeks if they do not immediately come upon a favorable situation. Larvae are attracted or repelled by a variety of influences that are not well understood. Some larvae are gregareous. Others avoid their kind. Practically all react to a more or less complex combination of physical conditions. Most larvae seem to be indifferent to the mineralogic or inorganic chemical nature of the bottom. The coarseness or fineness of the bottom sediment, however, is of great importance, and whether the bottom is stable or unstable, firm or soft commonly determines the kind of larvae that will settle upon it and become established (see Figures 74 and 75).

Firmness of the bottom is related more or less directly to the size of sedimentary particles and the amount of interstitial water present. Sand is likely to be firm but unstable because wave and current action commonly keeps it in more or less constant motion. In general most silty and calcareous mud bottoms, regardless of the finer sediment that may be present, are likely to be reasonably firm. Silt-free and richly organic muds, on the other hand, provide soft bottoms into which most organisms sink. The latter kind of sediment may be no more than a colloidal slime incapable of supporting anything larger than microscopic size.

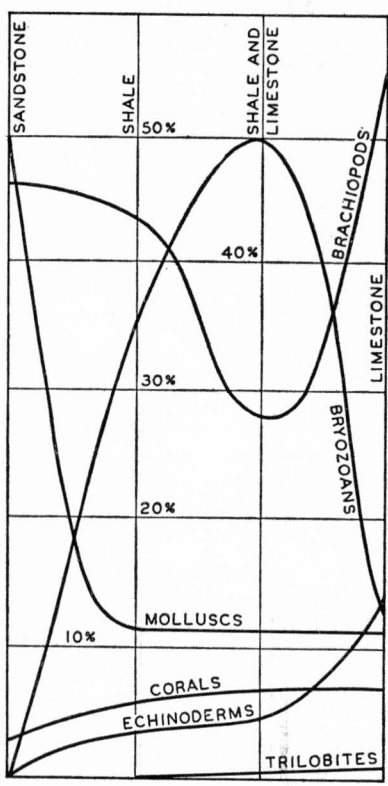

Figure 75. Diagram showing the general relative composition of early Mississippian faunas in the Mississippi Valley in different kinds of sedimentary rock. The percentages refer to numbers of species occurring in similar kinds of rock. Data compiled from the analysis of published faunal lists and lithologic classification of the rocks containing them. (Data from Sloss, 1958, J. Paleon., vol. 32, p. 721, fig. 4.)

Instability of the bottom may result from the stirring action of waves and currents on unconsolidated material or from continued sedimentary deposition that is rapid in terms of the life spans of benthonic organisms. In either case the bottom is unfavorable for the existence of most sedentary forms, and the presence of corals, bryozoans, and non-pedunculate brachiopods is unlikely. Vagrant animals such as molluscs are not so restricted. Many can creep about on shifting or accumulating sediments, and others burrow in the more or less soft bottom. Some organisms are adapted to almost every sort of bottom conditions, and the restriction of benthonic faunas or their absence generally is occasioned by other unfavorable features of the environment.

The nature of the bottom influences the proportions of benthonic organisms that comprise the infauna and the epifauna. Local conditions are likely to favor one group over the other. The infaunal environment is the most stable and uniform environment of the sea, and infaunas are less variable in both kinds of organisms and numbers of individuals than are epifaunas. The surface of the sea bottom differs greatly from place to place, ranging from soft unstable sediments to hard and rocky. It is exposed, also, to many other environmental variables that are less directly felt by infaunal creatures. Therefore, local epifaunal communities are more diverse in both composition and abundance of individuals. The diversity is most pronounced in very shallow water and in tropical regions.

Food Supply

A proper and adequate food supply is of the utmost importance to every organism at all stages of its existence. The food requirements of different organisms are extremely varied, and the kind of food available is one of the most important elements of an environment. In general a rather definite food chain links most components of a marine organic community. It begins with the microscopic plants of the plankton which create organic matter with the aid of sunlight. These plants are eaten by tiny planktonic animals and larvae, which in turn are consumed by larger creatures. Each link in the chain consists of larger animals that occur in smaller numbers.

Another group of organisms exists more or less outside the direct food chain. Its members are not predominantly predatory but they may become the prey of other animals. These are the scavengers, carrion eaters, and detrital feeders that subsist mainly upon dead organic matter. Here bacteria are important, and many different kinds of animals also consume the remains of organisms in various stages of decay. Other animals occupy a somewhat intermediate position, devouring both living and dead organic matter; detrital feeders particularly are unselective with respect to food suspended in the water or mixed with sediment of the sea bottom.

According to their methods of obtaining food and their dietary preferences, organisms can be classified as follows:

1. *Pigmented plants.* These are the primary producers of organic matter which provide the base supporting almost all other forms of marine life. Most important are diatoms and other microscopic planktonic plants.

2. *Herbivores.* These include a wide variety of animals belonging to most of the non-sessile phyla. They, and particularly the smaller species, provide the connecting link between plants and most other animals. Protozoans and

arthropods are of greatest importance among the plankton. Among benthonic animals commonly preserved as fossils are many gastropods and some echinoids.

3. *Carnivores.* Most carnivores are active animals that move about in search of prey. They also include members belonging to most of the non-sessile phyla. They are well represented in the plankton by arthropods. Most nektonic animals are carnivores, and fish and cephalopods are good examples. Although exclusively carnivorous benthonic animals are not abundant, starfish and some snails and worms are representatives of this group.

4. *Mixed feeders.* Many members of the plankton subsist on both plants and animals smaller than themselves.

5. *Sweepers and sifters.* These are mainly sedentary animals that feed upon minute organisms and particles of dead organic matter suspended in the sea water. This food is brought to them by both natural and artificially induced currents. Most of these animals are benthonic and they include sponges, corals, crinoids, bryozoans, brachiopods, pelecypods, and many worms.

6. *Scavengers.* Scavengers live mainly upon dead and decaying organic matter lying upon the sea bottom. Many of them are more or less omnivorous and upon occasion they will attack or capture other living organisms. Included here are many arthropods and some echinoids.

7. *Mud eaters.* These are a special type of scavengers that extract nourishment from the bottom sediment which they ingest. Their food consists mainly of decaying organic matter and bacteria. Examples are holothurians and some worms, echinoids, and arthropods.

8. *Bacteria.* These are the agents of decay. Most organic matter that is not consumed by animals is decomposed by them and the elements are returned in simplified form to circulation in the sea.

This classification is imperfect because distinctions are not sharp and the different groups overlap. Also the examples listed are not exhaustive.

Under optimum conditions all organic matter produced by plants is successively reused several times by animals until it is all consumed or destroyed by bacterial decay. In every stage of this process organic matter is used as a source of energy. Only a portion of it persists and is converted into the bodies of other creatures. In each stage of this recycling process, it has been estimated, about three-fourths of the organic matter is destroyed and thus removed from the system of interdependent life.

Organic Associations

The relations between organisms and the biologic elements of their environments are fully as numerous and complex as the relations between them and the physical elements. Those concerned with food supply have been reviewed. They are fairly obvious. Most other features of organic association are related to competition and the struggle for existence. The results of competition can be seen in the great variety of more or less well-stabilized biologic communities. These are so numerous, however, and differ in so many ways that they are difficult to interpret. Different organisms react upon each other either favorably or unfavorably in various degrees. Their influences may be very subtle, and probably they are not the same under all circumstances.

All organisms compete for living space and food. Reproduction is so efficient and the potentiality of multiplication is so great that only a small proportion of the new individuals produced can possibly survive. To do so a new individual must either (1) find a favorable spot that is unoccupied or (2) enter an established community and make a place for itself by crowding out an individual that is already there. The chances of finding vacant favorable spots are very small except for early members of a population that is seasonally renewed. Consequently, the efforts of most individuals to become established involve competition with other individuals of the same kind, whose requirements are identical, or with organisms of other kinds, whose needs are somewhat different. The abundance of organisms living in an area is a good index to the food supply unless physical conditions are particularly restrictive in some respect. This cannot be judged accurately for a fossil community, however, because soft-bodied creatures generally are not preserved.

Intraspecific and interspecific competition operate somewhat differently. If competition is mainly between individuals of the same species, all with essentially the same potentialities, pressures are likely to build up and become progressively more severe as the individuals and population grow. In this type of community, therefore, weak or less favorably situated individuals succumb at all stages of development, and a fossil assemblage probably would consist of abundant specimens of all sizes and ages. Such competition apparently is reduced among some animals by subtle influences that discourage larvae from settling among established individuals of their own kind. The result may be the occurrence of fossil assemblages consisting of mature specimens unaccompanied by juveniles. If, on the other hand, competition is mainly between individuals of different species with somewhat different potentialities, any advantage possessed by a very young individual is more decisive and is likely to increase with growth. If such an individual is successful in gaining a good start it has a much better chance of surviving until maturity. Therefore, a fossil assemblage consisting of abundant fully grown specimens not accompanied by many young ones likewise may indicate competition with species that have not been fossilized. These are only two possibilities, however, because such assemblages also can be explained in other ways.

Before biologic communities become relatively stable by the attainment of interspecific equilibrium, they are likely to pass through a succession of evolutionary stages. In evolution of this kind some species become estab-

lished before others and by their presence alter biologic environments and
the possibilities for successful competition by other species. Thus some organisms prepare the way for others until at last a so-called *climax community*
appears that persists with relatively little change as long as physical conditions remain the same. This is a principle well known particularly to bota-
nists and it also holds true with respect to terrestrial animals. Although it is

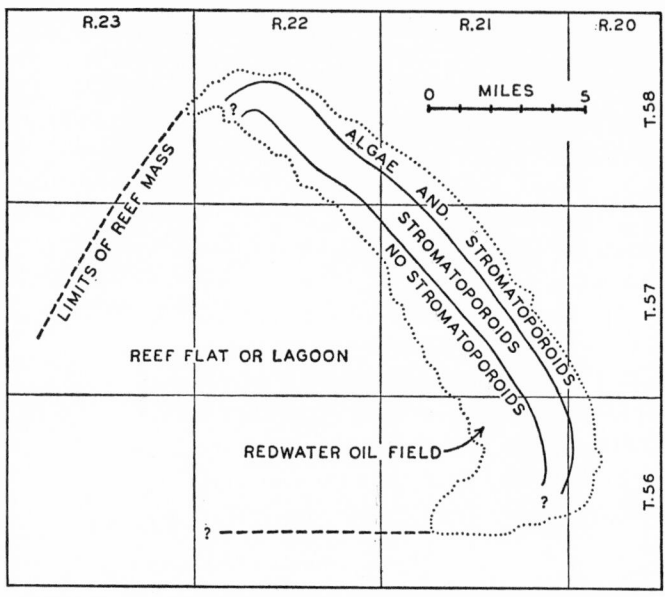

Figure 76.   Map of the Redwater area in Alberta, Canada, showing
the organic nature of the Leduc Limestone (Dev.) in the upper 100
feet of a reef mass. The concentration of algae and other reef builders
along the northeast side resembles the pattern evident in modern organic reefs. The conclusion is drawn that the growth of this reef was
strongly influenced by prevailing winds and currents that came from
the northeast. (After Andrichuk, 1958, *Bull. Am. Assoc. Petroleum Geol.*,
vol. 42, p. 78, fig. 33.)

not applicable to all phases of marine ecology, one of the clearest examples
that can be cited is the development of an organic reef community.

Organic reefs start with the appearance and local establishment of colonial
corals, or other organisms of similar habit, in the midst of a typical benthonic
community. They form the beginning of a hard substratum and also serve to
trap between them whatever sediment is available. By both of these processes
they build up an area that rises slightly above the surrounding sea bottom.
This platform provides a base for the establishment of organisms, chiefly
corals and calcareous algae, that require a hard substratum. Other organisms
discover a favorable environment in sheltered niches in the framework so

provided. Calcareous debris derived from them fills in the space between the frame builders and is bound in place by algae and other encrusting organisms. In this way the reef platform rises until it comes into the zone of wave turbulence. Here physical conditions change. An environment is provided for organisms that require more light and better-aerated water, and the older reef community is replaced. Species closely related to those inhabiting the quiet lower levels give way to others that are unsuited to existence on the bottom. Further upward growth into rough water of the surface zone results in other biologic changes. Lateral differentiation also begins: A community adapted to the exposed situation on the outer edge of the reef grades into others that occupy the less disturbed area of the reef summit and perhaps the relatively quiet water of an interreef lagoon (see Figure 76).

In contrast, many marine benthonic communities apparently never achieve stability. Some organisms may prepare the way for others, but no climax community develops and change gradually follows change in a never ending sequence. The differences between communities of this type and stable communities of the land probably are consequences of (1) the common failure of some marine benthonic animals to reproduce themselves locally and (2) the dominant role played by terrestrial plants in creating environments favorable for certain animals and the general lack of any similar ecologic control in large areas of the sea.

Pelagic Environment

Planktonic organisms are the most abundant inhabitants of the sea. Most of them are of microscopic size, many fall prey to larger animals, and very few are well suited to preservation in sediment if they sink to the bottom after death. Most nektonic creatures leave little more than fragmentary evidence of their existence. Consequently the fossil record yields only scanty information concerning environments above the bottom of the sea. Pelagic environments throughout large areas are much more uniform than benthonic ones, varying mainly in temperature and salinity. Fossils derived from upper zones, such as planktonic foraminifera, graptolites, and some cephalopods and fish, are not very useful in indicating differences in these conditions.

Fresh-Water Environment

All of the factors discussed in connection with marine environments also are important in fresh water. Organisms inhabiting fresh water, however, are much fewer in kind than those of the sea and their fossils provide much less information regarding environmental variations. The physical characters of sediments generally are more serviceable than fossils as indicators of depositional conditions.

Terrestrial Environment

Most terrestrial fossils are the remains of organisms that did not inhabit the environment in which they were preserved. Therefore, the correlation of sediments and fossils generally is not so significant as it is in the case of marine environments. Much can be learned about terrestrial conditions from the structures of both plants and animals, particularly vertebrates, but mostly these conditions were characteristic of places that are unknown even though they probably occurred near the localities where fossils have been found. The principal exception is the swamp environment, but swamp conditions commonly are more clearly indicated by the nature of the sediments than by the remains of the plants they contain.

INFLUENCE OF ORGANISMS ON SEDIMENTS

The influence of sediments on marine organisms and their ecology has been considered in the foregoing sections devoted to turbidity and bottom conditions. Conversely, organisms exert an important influence on sedimentation. They have been instrumental in determining some of the most prominent characters of many deposits now preserved as sedimentary rocks. Organisms have been important geologic agents in connection with (1) the production of sediments, (2) the accumulation of sediments, and (3) the alteration of sediments after deposition. Their relations to these processes have ecologic implications that are of considerable interest if they can be recognized.

Production of Sediment

On land, plants play an important role because they both accelerate and retard the production of sediments. Carbon dioxide and so-called humic acids resulting from the decay of vegetation circulate in ground water and aid in the decomposition of unstable rocks and minerals. Plant roots exchange hydrogen for metallic ions, required for plant metabolism, and create acid conditions that alter minerals in the soil. Such chemical action certainly is important but its relative contribution to weathering processes can rarely be determined. On the other hand, vegetation forms an effective protective covering on most land surfaces outside of desert and arctic regions and on all but the steepest slopes. This cover blankets and binds the soil and prevents erosion and the production of transient sediment. Plants have been more or less effective in this way since at least late Paleozoic time and probably their efficiency has steadily increased.

The actual production of organic sediments, rather than the alteration of minerals by organic action, is a much more obvious and important result of the activities of organisms. Many rocks consist predominantly of organic products or include such abundant organically derived material that their whole character and appearance are affected. Carbonaceous shales and other carbonaceous rocks particularly record the existence of abundant life even though none of the organisms that contributed to the sediment is well enough preserved to be identified. Thus Precambrian carbonaceous rocks are evidence of life long before the beginning of the fossil record. Carbonaceous rocks also indicate the existence of an environment in which an important amount of organic matter was not utilized as food or destroyed by bacterial decay. Such evidence, however, is not sufficient to characterize an environment with desirable precision. Therefore, other sedimentary features and relations must be called upon where possible to aid in determining whether the organic material was derived from plants or animals, whether it accumulated in place or was transported, and whether it was deposited under marine, fresh-water, marsh, or terrestrial conditions.

Calcareous material occurs in rocks mixed in all proportions with detrital sediments of inorganic origin. Much of the coarser calcareous material obviously is organic because the structures of fossils in various stages of fragmentation can be recognized. Fine calcareous sediment, however, is of somewhat doubtful derivation. Some of it certainly is of fossil origin but an unknown amount was precipitated from sea water as the result of biologic activity without having been part of any organic structure. Depending upon how such material is regarded, it might be classified as either organic or chemical sediment. Because custom has not been uniform in this point, estimates of the proportions of calcareous sediment considered to be organic have varied widely. Agreement is general, however, that very little calcium carbonate is precipitated totally without relation to biologic activity except in a few specialized environments. The principal exception is limestone associated with evaporite deposits, and oolitic limestone is another possible example.

Organisms, therefore, account for the production of most calcareous sediment, and the calcareous content of most rocks, except that present as secondary cement, is a rough index to the relative importance of biologic activity in many marine environments. Judgments based on this factor, however, must take into account the greater solubility of lime in cold water where shallow benthonic communities include a larger proportion of naked and thin-shelled species. Throughout all geologic time, organisms appear to have caused the deposition of calcium carbonate just about as rapidly as it was carried to the sea in solution from the land. During all of this time most of the lime has accumulated in relatively shallow water where warm climatic conditions prevailed and lime-secreting organisms were most plentiful.

Calcium carbonate is much less abundant in fresh-water deposits than in marine sediments, but some fresh-water limestones do occur. They also are largely the result of biologic activity and require no special comments except that plants probably played a greater part in their development than in the formation of many marine limestones.

Accumulation of Sediment

Most organic sediments accumulate close to the places where they originate. This is particularly true of much calcium carbonate and is in strong contrast to the great distances that some fine-grained, detrital, land-derived sediments are transported. Consequently organisms are mainly responsible for determining the general areas in which calcareous sediments accumulate.

Organisms also influence the deposition of detrital sediment. Seaweeds, particularly where they grow abundantly on the bottom, interfere with currents and reduce the turbulence of waves. Their presence creates a more tranquil environment than would otherwise occur and at many places provides a favorable situation for the settling of fine suspended sediment. Some animals, such as colonial corals, bryozoans, hydroids, and stalked crinoids that grow upward from the sea bottom, have a similar effect but probably they produce somewhat less efficient traps for sediment. In addition, the binding action of encrusting organisms and some tube-inhabiting worms serves to prevent the scattering of sediment by waves and currents. This is especially important in the building of organic reefs.

Alteration of Sediment

Land plants draw sustenance from the earth, and the action of their roots results in some alteration of its upper layers. Although this process has contributed to the formation of soils, probably it is greatly subordinate to the leaching and chemical activity of downward-percolating ground water. Old soils have been preserved in terrestrial sedimentary deposits of various ages extending back at least into the late Paleozoic. Many underclays that occur beneath Carboniferous coal beds and the interglacial soils of Pleistocene age are good examples.

The growth of seaweeds does not have comparable effects because these plants are equipped with holdfasts that do not function the same way roots do, and no layer akin to soil develops on the sea bottom. Organisms of the marine epifauna have little or no direct effect upon the sediments except for the surface mud eaters. These creatures remove organic matter, their stomach juices may alter some unstable minerals, and they break some of the sedimentary particles down to smaller sizes. The results of their activities, however, are not conspicuous and are likely to pass unrecognized. Bacteria are very abundant in most bottom sediment where they consume much organic matter and their waste products may alter unstable minerals, but without special study they and the results that they accomplish are not likely to be noticed. Burrowing animals of the infauna plow through the bottom and, if

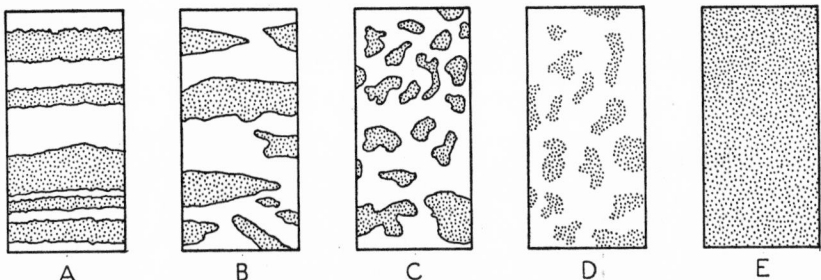

Figure 77. Burrowing or crawling benthonic animals can either destroy or create various kinds of minor structures in sediments. The results depend upon (1) type of sediment, (2) kind and number of animals, (3) their activity, and (4) rate of sedimentary deposition. For example, sediment consisting of more or less regularly bedded layers can be disturbed and mixed so that alteration progresses from A to B, C, D, and E, in the last of which the sediment has been thoroughly mixed. On the other hand, homogeneous sediment consisting of a mixture of different grain sizes or materials as in E can be worked over to produce structures similar to those in D, C, or B. (After Moore and Scruton, 1957, *Bull. Am. Assoc. Petroleum Geol.*, vol. 41, p. 2743, fig. 12.)

they are abundant, may quickly destroy all evidence of bedding (see Figure 77). Therefore, the occurrence in any sediment of well-marked lamination that is not the result of compaction or some other secondary process is excellent evidence of the absence of most creatures of this kind.

BIBLIOGRAPHY

Allee, W. C., Emerson, A. E., Park, Orlando, Park, Thomas, and Schmidt, K. P. (1949), *Principles of animal ecology*, Philadelphia, Saunders.
  This book contains a wealth of information. See especially Chapters 4 to 15 and 25, pp. 73–215 and 436–461, for data on environmental factors and community relationships.
Allee, W. C., and Schmidt, K. P. (1951), *Ecological animal geography*, 2nd ed., based on Richard Hesse, *Tiergeographie auf oekologischer Grundlage*, New York, Wiley.
  In this important reference see Part 2, pp. 179–344, for broad consideration of the distribution of animals and their relations to environments.
Axelrod, D. I. (1957), Late Tertiary floras and the Sierra Nevadan uplift, *Bull. Geol. Soc. Amer.*, vol. 68, pp. 19–46.
  Ecologic interpretation of Tertiary floras is given with respect to temperature, altitude, topography, and rainfall.
Beerstecher, Ernest, Jr. (1954), *Petroleum microbiology*, Houston, Elsevier.
  See Chapter 2, pp. 23–71, for consideration of the role of microorganisms in geologic processes.
Craig, G. Y. (1955), The palaeoecology of the Top Hosie shale (Lower Carboniferous) at a locality near Kilsyth, *Quart. J. Geol. Soc. London*, vol. 110, pp. 103–118.

Interpretations of benthonic conditions are made from associations, size distributions, orientation, and preservation of fossils.

Dapples, E. C. (1942), The effects of macro-organisms upon near-shore marine sediments, *J. Sediment. Petrol.*, vol. 12, pp. 118–126.
The destruction of sedimentary structures and textures resulting from activities of benthonic organisms is discussed.

Denison, R. H. (1956), A review of the habitat of the earliest vertebrates, *Fieldiana, Geol.*, vol. 11, pp. 357–457.
Environmental relations of early Paleozoic fishes are considered with reference to fresh and salt water as inferred from enclosing sediments and associated organisms, see pp. 362–367 and 430–441.

Dorf, Erling (1959), Climatic changes of the past and present, Univ. Mich. Contrib. Museum Paleon., vol. 13, pp. 181–210.
Cenozoic climates of North America are reconstructed on the evidence of fossil plants.

Ekman, Sven (1953), *Zoogeography of the sea*, London, Sidgwick and Jackson.
Shelf faunas of the world and factors controlling their distribution are comprehensively treated.

Ellison, S. P., Jr. (1951), Microfossils as environment indicators in marine shales, *J. Sediment. Petrol.*, vol. 21, pp. 214–225.
Distinction must be made between indigenous and introduced specimens when fossils are compared with modern environmental associations.

Fenton, C. L., and Fenton, M. A. (1958), *The fossil book*, Garden City, Doubleday.
Popularly written, this generally authentic consideration of all the important fossil groups includes accounts of where and how the organisms lived.

George, T. N. (1958), The ecology of fossil animals: I, Organism and environment, *Sci. Progress*, vol. 46, no. 184, pp. 677–690.
Preservation and accumulation of fossils are considered mainly in relation to life habits and physical environments.

George, T. N. (1959), The ecology of fossil animals: II, Faunal facies, *Sci. Progress*, vol. 46, no. 185, pp. 86–106.
Relations of organisms and fossils to environmental changes in both space and time are discussed.

Ginsburg, R. N., and Lowenstam, H. A. (1958), The influence of marine bottom communities on the depositional environment of sediments, *J. Geol.*, vol. 66, pp. 310–318.
Organisms trap and bind sediment and build submarine barriers that modify water circulation.

Grabau, A. W. (1913), *Principles of stratigraphy*, New York, Seiler, reprinted 1924.
Chapters 27 to 29, pp. 991–1072, discuss environmental and geographic distribution of organisms with emphasis on fossils.

Hedgpeth, J. W. (ed.) (1957), *Treatise on marine ecology and paleoecology*, vol. 1, *Ecology*, Geol. Soc. Amer., Mem. 67.
The 29 chapters, by many authors, are devoted to phases of oceanography, marine ecology, and related subjects of interest to paleoecologists; besides

bibliographies accompanying chapters there are 215 pages of annotated bibliographies arranged biologically.

Hunt, O. D. (1925), The food of the bottom fauna of the Plymouth fishing grounds, *J. Marine Biol. Assoc.*, vol. 13, pp. 560–599.

Benthonic animals are classified according to their food habits.

Imbrie, John (1955), Quantitative lithofacies and biofacies study of the Florena Shale (Permian) of Kansas, *Bull. Am. Assoc. Petroleum Geol.*, vol. 39, pp. 649–670.

The author reports fossil abundances in successive stratigraphic zones and their relations to lithologic variation.

Jones, N. S. (1950), Marine bottom communities, *Biol. Reviews*, vol. 25, pp. 283–313.

This is concerned with benthonic communities especially in the North Atlantic and North Sea areas.

Ladd, H. S. (ed.) (1957), *Treatise on marine ecology and paleoecology*, vol. 2, *Paleoecology*, Geol. Soc. Amer., Mem. 67.

The 24 chapters, by different authors, are mostly devoted to selected areas in the United States where strata ranging from Precambrian to Recent are interpreted paleogeographically and paleoecologically; besides bibliographies accompanying chapters there are 340 pages of annotated bibliographies arranged biologically.

Ladd, H. S. (1959), Ecology, paleontology, and stratigraphy, *Science*, vol. 129, pp. 69–78.

This popular account traces developments and accomplishments particularly of marine paleoecology.

Lowenstam, H. A. (1957), Niagaran reefs in the Great Lakes area, Geol. Soc. Amer., Mem. 67, vol. 2, pp. 215–48.

In this excellent account of reef paleoecology see particularly pp. 230–239.

MacGinitie, G. E. (1939), Littoral marine communities, *Am. Midland Natur.*, vol. 21, pp. 28–55.

Marine communities and their relations to ecology are considered.

MacGinitie, G. E., and MacGinitie, Nettie (1949), *Natural history of marine animals*, New York, McGraw-Hill.

Observations of shallow-water marine organisms, mainly of the California coast, are described.

Moore, H. B. (1958), *Marine ecology*, New York, Wiley.

Ecologic factors, habitats, organisms, and communities of the sea are discussed.

Shrock, R. R., and Twenhofel, W. H. (1953), *Principles of invertebrate paleontology*, 2nd ed., New York, McGraw-Hill.

This standard textbook includes brief accounts of the ecology and paleoecology of many groups of invertebrate animals.

Sloss, L. L. (1958), Paleontologic and lithologic associations, *J. Paleo.*, vol. 32, pp. 715–729.

The author relates biologic characters of marine faunas to lithology from Upper Ordovician to Cretaceous and draws generalized conclusions regarding relations to physical environments.

Sverdrup, H. U., Johnson, M. W., and Fleming, R. H. (1942) *The oceans, their physics, chemistry and general biology*, New York, Prentice-Hall.

In this standard work on oceanography Chapters 8 and 9, pp. 267–330, and 16 to 18, pp. 762–924, discuss marine environments and modern marine populations.

Symposium on General Petroleum Geochemistry (1959), Preprints of papers to be presented at the Fifth World Congress, June 4, 1959, Pt. 1, *Fundamentals of organic chemistry*, New York, Dept. of Chemistry, Fordham Univ.

Twelve short papers discuss formation, nature, and alteration of organic matter and calcium carbonate in sediments.

Thorson, Gunnar (1950), Reproductive and larval ecology of marine bottom invertebrates, *Biol. Reviews*, vol. 25, pp. 1–45.

This is an important review of a subject having many paleoecologic implications.

Twenhofel, W. H. (1950), *Principles of sedimentation*, 2nd ed., New York, McGraw-Hill.

Chapter 5, pp. 167–198, discusses the interrelations of organisms and sediments.

Twenhofel, W. H., and collaborators (1932), *Treatise on sedimentation*, 2nd ed., Baltimore, Williams and Wilkins.

Chapter 4, pp. 148–186, discusses the interrelations of organisms and sediments.

Yonge, C. M. (1948), Bottom fauna of the sea, *Research*, vol. 1, pp. 589–595.

Nature and composition of bottom faunas are described.

ZoBell, C. E. (1946), *Marine microbiology, a monograph on hydrobacteriology*, Waltham, Chronica Botanica.

This is a standard reference. Chapters 6 to 8 and 10, pp. 90–128 and 136–149, deal with benthonic bacteria and the destruction of organic matter.

8

Tectonics

Most sediments and sedimentary rocks owe their existence to tectonic activity. Were it not for upland areas no detrital sediments would be produced, and without rejuvenation uplands would be worn down by erosion and disappear beneath a universal ocean. In much the same way, if there were no basins close to upland areas, sediments would be swept away and lost in the deep sea, and if basins did not subside, they would soon be filled and deposition within them could not continue.

The main episodes in the tectonic history of depositional areas are recorded by the structural relations of successive strata. A similar register is not preserved in upland regions where the erosion of one epoch destroyed the evidence of its predecessor. The record is not completely lost, however, because something can be learned about a region by observing the sediment it has produced. Thus the nature and extent of sediments provide a record of the tectonic activity of both the areas where they occur and those from which they came. The structures, such as folds and faults in sediments and rocks, also may provide some indication of the forces responsible for the uplifting of certain regions and the depression of others.

The patterns of sediment-producing lands and basins of deposition have varied greatly in the past. They have been influenced and at times profoundly changed by tectonic activity. So far as is known, however, these changes have been relatively minor with respect to the structure of the whole earth since at least the beginning of the Paleozoic Era. Some geologists believe that the geographic distribution of continents and ocean basins has changed importantly, but most are agreed that, throughout this time, areas approximately equivalent to the present continents have always stood higher than the ocean basins. In any consideration of the structure of the earth, attention must be directed to features at two levels: (1) the major features—the great continental and oceanic blocks—and (2) the minor features that characterize portions of these blocks.

CONTINENTS AND OCEAN BASINS

The earth's surface, both land and submarine, has an extreme relief of more than twelve miles. Although this is very great by human standards, it amounts to only 0.15 percent of the earth's diameter. The mean topographic elevation of the earth's surface is about 1.5 miles below sea level. There are, however, two preferred levels, an upper one whose average elevation is about 0.5 miles above sea level and a lower one at an average elevation of about 2.5 miles below. Altogether the earth's surface is apportioned topographically about as follows (see Figure 78):

Higher	10%	
Upper level	20%	Continental area
Intermediate	10%	
Lower level	55%	Oceanic area
Lower	5%	

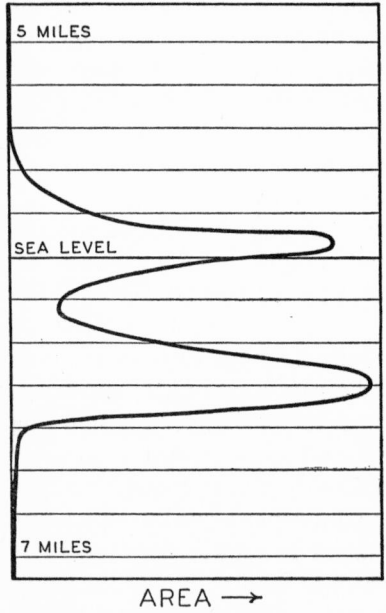

Figure 78. Generalized curve showing the relative areal extent of the lithosphere surface at different elevations above and below sea level.

The average three-mile differential between the elevations of the continental and oceanic regions is very striking. It is one of the reasons leading to the theory that the outer part of the earth is composed of at least two layers differing in chemical composition and relative density. The upper layer is believed to consist of material of acid or granitic composition and specific density of about 2.7. This material is termed *sial*, a contraction of silica and alumina. The lower layer is believed to consist of material of basic or basaltic composition and specific density of about 3.0. It is designated *sima*, a contraction of silica and magnesia. Ideas regarding the mutual relations of these two layers, or a larger number, vary considerably, but in general the lighter sial layer is visualized as floating on a lower denser one. The sial layer is believed to be thick beneath

the continents but thin or absent beneath the ocean basins and for this reason the continents stand higher, as shown in Figure 79. This floating balance
of blocks of different thickness and density is termed *isostatic equilibrium*.

The theory of isostasy appears to be confirmed by measurements of terrestrial gravity. These reveal differences that in general show systematic relations to elevation if local inequalities of topography are ignored. Attraction
varies inversely as the square of the distance so that gravity measurements are
influenced much more by near-surface mass than by deeper material. There-

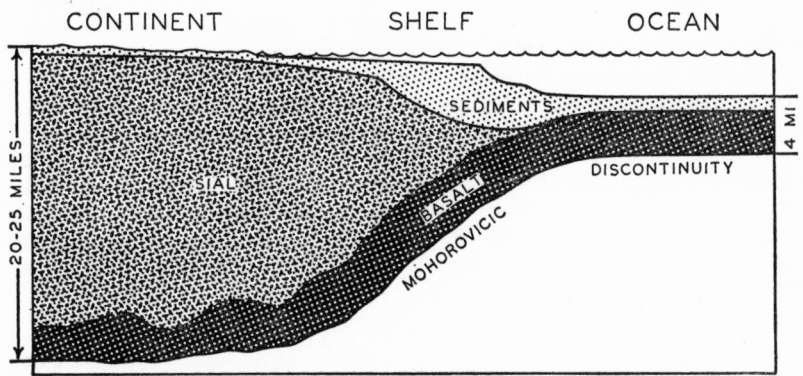

Figure 79. Schematic diagram illustrating the most common simple concept of the
layered composition and gross structure of the earth's crust at the margin of a
continent. (After Wilson, 1954, *The earth as a planet,* p. 148, fig. 2, by permission of
the University of Chicago Press and G. P. Kuiper.)

fore, gravitational attraction should be less over a thick layer of sial than over
a thinner one. Calculations based on many gravity measurements indicate
that the level of isostatic compensation, perhaps the contact between the
sial and sima layers, occurs at a depth of not more than about twenty-five or
thirty miles beneath the continents.

Layering of the outer portion of the earth is substantiated by seismic records. These show that the speed of earthquake waves is different at different
depths (see Figure 80). The sharpness of transitions indicates at least one
more or less abrupt discontinuity, at a depth of twenty to twenty-five miles
below the continents, that rises beneath the ocean basins as shown in Figure 81. The speed of waves varies inversely with density of rock and temperature and directly with pressure, but at the depth of this discontinuity these
all have unknown values. If an assumption is made with respect to one, however, limits are set upon the others and, among the various possible combinations, one may appear most probable. Thus conditions below the discontinuity seem to be met most satisfactorily if the rock there is dunite, which is
mainly composed of olivine and is more basic than basalt. Rocks at much

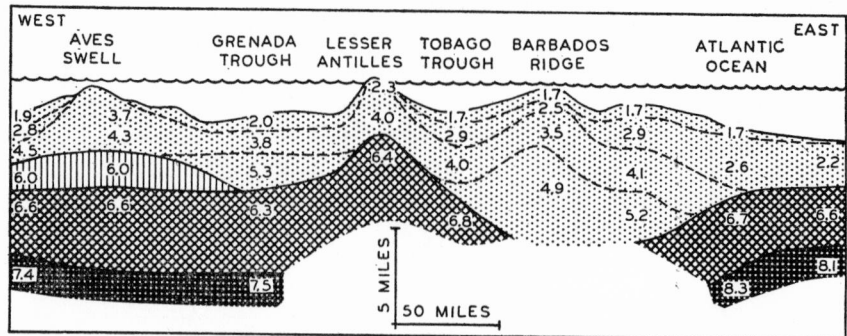

Figure 80.   Generalized section of the earth's crust in the Caribbean region as indicated by seismic observations. Figures show the velocities of compressional waves in kilometers per second. Speeds of about 6.0 are believed to identify granitic rocks, and slower waves are those that pass through sediments in various stages of compaction. Basalt transmits waves at about 6.5 kilometers per second and speeds of about 8.0 characterize ultrabasic rocks below the Mohorovicic discontinuity. (After Ewing and others, 1957, *Bull. Geol. Soc. Amer.*, vol. 68, p. 905, fig. 6.) The Lesser Antilles constitute a volcanic island arc. Barbados occupies a position corresponding to an outer exclusively sedimentary arc.

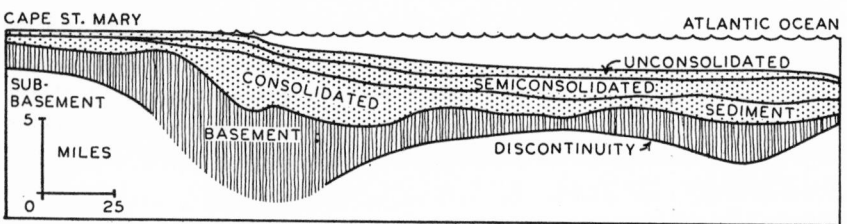

Figure 81.   Interpretation of a seismic section of the continental border and adjacent Atlantic Ocean bed at Cape May, New Jersey. The subbasement indicated to the left beneath the continental margin occurs above the Mohorovicic discontinuity. Compare with Figure 79. (After Bentley and Worzel, 1956, *Bull. Geol. Soc. Amer.*, vol. 67, p. 16, fig. 8.)

shallower depth, immediately beneath the cover of overlying sediments, have the properties and probably the composition of granite. Waves that pass through an intermediate zone, however, are very uncertainly interpreted. They indicate the possibility that this zone may be occupied by basalt. For this reason, therefore, the contact between sial and sima may be transitional and it generally is believed to occur some distance above the evident discontinuity.

A thin layer of sial may or may not occur in the Atlantic and Indian Ocean blocks. The Pacific, whose main part averages about 1000 feet deeper than the other oceans, seems to lack this layer. Lava erupted from the central Pacific volcanoes is invariably basic, and this region differs from all other parts of the world, where basic lavas are likely to be associated with more acidic types.

Various theories have been offered to account for the differences between continents and ocean basins and their distribution. They range from those that emphasise original magmatic segregation in a molten earth to those that call upon expulsion of the moon from the Pacific Ocean basin or the extensive displacement of floating continents. Many of these theories have elements that are interesting and attractive, but serious objections can be raised to each of them. All of the theories are so highly speculative that they need no consideration here. Perhaps problems are involved that can never be solved to the satisfaction of most scientists.

Ocean Basins

The ocean basins occupy about two-thirds of the surface area of the earth. They have been explored extensively in recent years by sonic sounding and a wealth of information has been gathered concerning the topography of some parts of the ocean bottom. These vast regions, formerly thought to be characterized by general featureless regularity, have been found to resemble emergent portions of the earth in many important respects. There are mountain ranges, plateaus, volcanic cones, and fault scarps whose duplicates are visible on the land. Submarine topography, however, generally lacks one element that pervades most landscapes: evidence of much erosion. Some erosion has occurred, as shown by submarine canyons cut in the edge of the continental shelf and by the truncation of submerged seamounts, but certainly erosion has not been widespread. Much submarine topography has been modified, however, by the deposition of a considerable thickness of fine-grained sediment.

A very rough idea of the average thickness of sediment deposited in the deep sea can be obtained. Comparison of the estimated proportions of shale, sandstone, and limestone produced by the weathering of average igneous rock and the estimated proportions present in sedimentary formations on the continents (see Table 9) shows a loss from the land of about 60 percent if all limestone is assumed to have remained on the continental blocks (see Figure 82). Some lime, however, was certainly lost to the deep sea and for simple calculation this figure may be raised to 66⅔ percent. As the ocean basins have about twice the area of the continents, the average thickness of sediment in the sea is thus nearly the same as the average on the land. The latter has been estimated at 1.4 miles or approximately 7500 feet. Of course this sediment has not been distributed evenly over the deep-sea bottom; it is much thicker in some areas than in others. Almost everywhere, however, sediment probably is thick enough to obscure some of the details of deep-sea topography.

The geology of the oceanic blocks never can be known in as great detail as

TABLE 9.   Calculation of the Proportions of Sediments Lost to the Deep Sea

	From Igneous Rock, Average of 3 Estimates	Continental Sediments, Average of 5 Estimates	Continental Sediments Recalculated	Percentage Lost to Deep Sea
Shale	77.3%	49.4%	19.9%	57.4%
Sandstone	14.3%	29.0%	11.7%	2.6%
Limestone	8.4%	21.6%	8.4%	0.0%
Total				60.0%

that of the land. Probably these blocks do not differ materially from the continents in their main structural features. The transfer of large volumes of sediment from higher submerged areas to lower depositional basins, however, has not occurred beneath the sea. Therefore, tectonic activity related to the isostatic readjustment of unloaded and loaded areas probably has been relatively unimportant in the structural development of the oceanic blocks. Almost certainly the continents have been more mobile.

Most submarine stratigraphy probably is exceedingly monotonous. Deposition has been continuous and in most areas recent sediments blanket the surface and hide all older strata. There are no unconformities comparable to those which interrupt exposed strata on the land, and lateral variation in both lithologic character and thickness probably is very gradual. Fossils are rare except for the remains of pelagic organisms. Inclination of strata conforms to a more or less irregular surface of deposition and does not provide as reliable a record of structural warping as it does upon the land. Probably the only important stratigraphic irregularities are related to mud flows and turbidity currents, displacement along faults, and submarine lava flows.

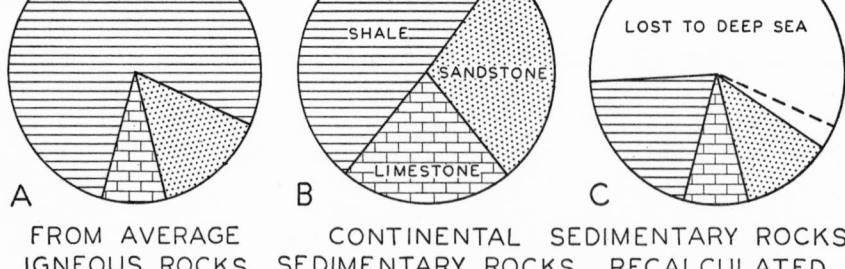

FROM AVERAGE   CONTINENTAL   SEDIMENTARY   ROCKS
IGNEOUS ROCKS   SEDIMENTARY   ROCKS   RECALCULATED

Figure 82.   Diagram showing estimates of A, the proportions of the three principal kinds of sedimentary rocks produced by the weathering of average igneous rock, B, the proportions of the sedimentary rocks occurring on the continents, and C, the proportions of shale and sandstone lost from the continents by the transportation and deposition of sediments in the deep sea.

Studies of deep-sea cores reveal some details of submarine stratigraphy. Unconsolidated sediments have been recovered dating back to late Tertiary time as shown by their contained foraminifera and radioactive nature. These cores are of principal interest because they record temperature fluctuations and dates that can be correlated with the Pleistocene glacial cycles (see Figure 213, p. 551). Temperatures are calculated from oxygen isotope ratios and dates from carbon 14 determinations, radium content, and relative thicknesses of sedimentary layers.

Much of the subject matter treated in textbooks on submarine geology concerns submerged portions of the continental blocks and is not properly attributable to the geology of the true oceanic regions.

Relations of Continents and Ocean Basins

All geologists recognize that the modern continents are submerged about their margins and that in the past much greater submergence has been common. Generally the continents are considered to terminate at the outer edge of the continental shelf. This is a submerged, gently inclined terrace ending at most places at a depth of from 400 to 600 feet, where a steeper continental slope begins and carries the sea bottom down to abyssal depths. The origin and significance of the continental shelf are not certainly understood. It must be related to sea level as this has been maintained during fairly recent geologic time. Some geologists consider the shelf to be a plane of marine erosion that has been moderately warped. Hard rocks including granite constitute its surface at a number of places. On the other hand, extensive parts along some coasts are great wedges of unconsolidated material that thicken seaward and the shelf also has been interpreted as a depositional terrace. Large areas, particularly near the outer edge, however, do not appear to be receiving sediment at the present time.

The continental slope has an average inclination of 2 to 4 degrees but in

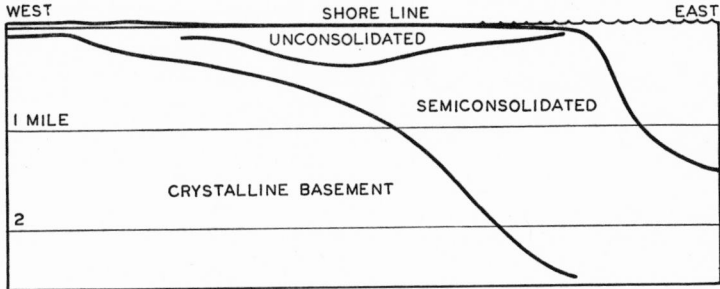

Figure 83. Interpretation of the structure of the continental margin at Cape Henry, Virginia, based upon the records of deep wells and a seismic traverse; vertical scale exaggerated 25 times. (After Ewing and others, 1937, Bull. Geol. Soc. Amer., vol. 48, p. 790, fig. 32.)

certain places it is much steeper. It has been considered by some geologists to be the scarp of a system of great faults separating the continental and oceanic blocks. Others believe that these blocks are not offset by faults but are connected by great flexures. Deep wells and seismic investigations carried from the coastal plain to beyond the edge of the continental shelf along the eastern coast of North America show that crystalline basement rocks descend outward at a rate of 100 feet or more per mile, as shown in Figures 83 and 84. Much of this basement surface has been interpreted as a peneplane. It is overlain by semi-consolidated and unconsolidated sediments whose lithologic characters, fossils, and coal beds prove that they are shallow-water deposits. This surface has been downwarped into a trough reaching a depth of 17,000 feet. Outside of the continental shelf and under the continental slope the basement surface rises to within 5000 feet of the present sedimentary surface and then plunges downward into a second trough containing 30,000 feet of sediment (see Figure 85). Somewhat similar relations are believed to occur in other parts of the world.

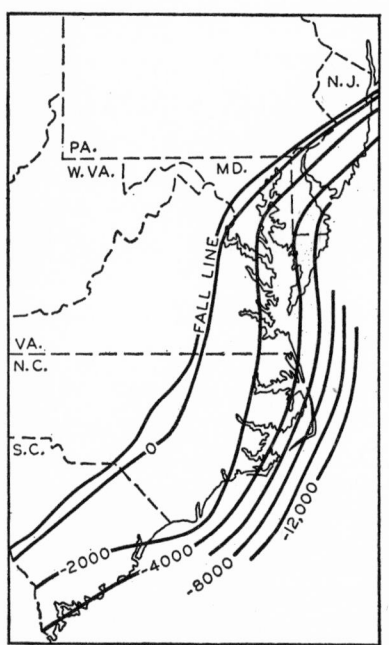

Figure 84. Map showing slope of crystalline basement floor beneath the Atlantic coastal plain as interpreted from well records and seismic observations. (After Eardley, 1951, *Structural geology of North America*, p. 132, fig. 71, by permission of Harper & Brothers.)

South of Cape Hatteras in North Carolina and extending to the Bahama Islands, the Blake Plateau appears to be related to the North American continental block. This submarine plateau is more than 150 miles wide. Its surface lies at depths of from 2000 to 4000 feet below sea level. It is bounded on one side by an abrupt rise leading to the continental shelf and on the other by a steep descent which may be a fault scarp ending at a depth of 10,000 or more feet. The Gulf Stream flows across this surface and appears to have prevented the lodgment of much sediment upon it since at least mid-Tertiary time.

The Pacific border of North America is much different from the Atlantic. The continental shelf is less well developed and, even where clearly recognized, is generally very narrow. Deep water occurs close to the west coasts of both North and South America at many places. Off the southern California coast, beyond a narrow continental shelf, a zone of basins and ridges extends for 150 miles, ending at a slope

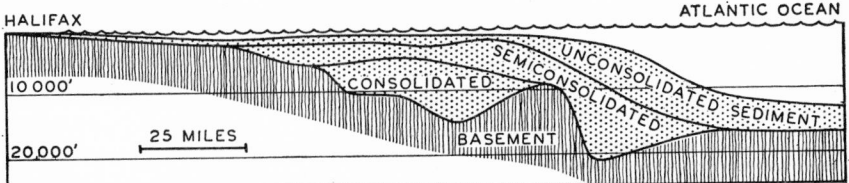

Figure 85. Geologic interpretation of a seismic section of the Atlantic Ocean bed off-shore from Halifax, Nova Scotia. The structure of the basement surface here is generally similar to that determined farther south off the coast of the United States. (After Officer and Ewing, 1954, *Bull. Geol. Soc. Amer.*, vol. 65, p. 659, fig. 2.)

that descends steeply below depths of from 4000 to 5000 feet (see Figure 86). The topography of this zone suggests that the geology, and particularly the structure, is similar to that of the adjacent mainland. There seem to be good reasons to conclude that the zone is a down faulted and submerged part of the continental block.

The western Pacific region is characterized by festoons of volcanic islands

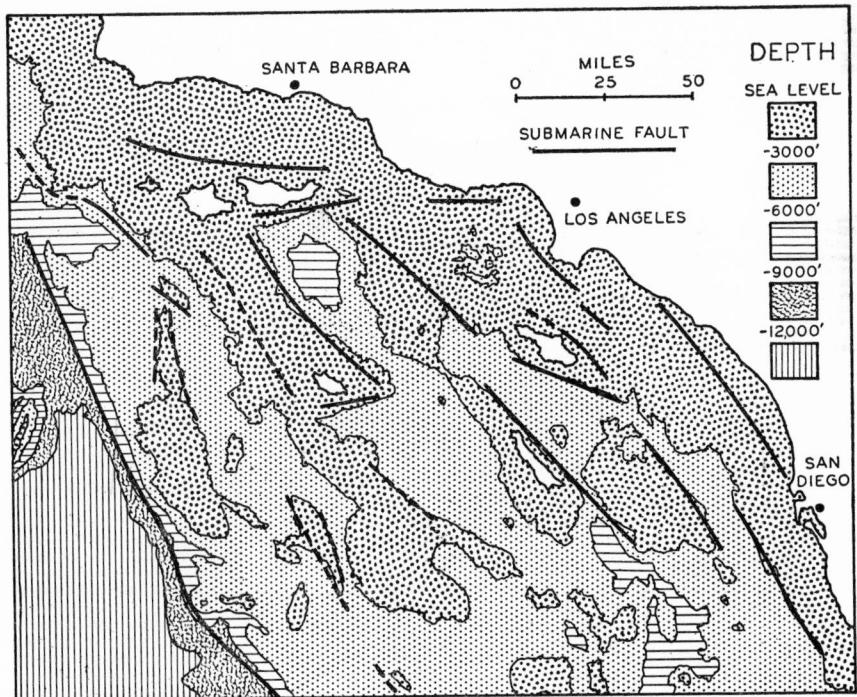

Figure 86. Map of the Pacific Ocean bottom off the coast of southern California showing major topographic features and the locations of presumed important faults. (After Shepard and Emery, 1941, Geol. Soc. Amer., Spec. Paper 31, p. 47, fig. 18 and pls. 1 and 2.)

rising from curving submarine ridges, several of which are paralleled on the outside by deep narrow submarine trenches (see Figure 87). These island arcs are convex toward the Pacific. They are separated from each other and from the Asiatic mainland by basins of various depths. The principal ones, such as the South China Sea, Sea of Japan, and Sea of Okhotsk, descend to more than 10,000 feet, but there also is much very shallow water, particularly in the Yellow Sea, along the China coast, and in the region extending from Indo-China and Malaya through Indonesia to Australia. Some of these shallow sea bottoms undoubtedly are parts of the continental block. The submarine topography between Borneo and adjacent islands is believed to show a system of river valleys that drained the area when it was emergent in the fairly recent past. Some of the deeper basins also may be portions of the continent that have been downwarped but not filled with sediment.

The features of the western Pacific are duplicated on a smaller scale in the Caribbean region of the Western Hemisphere. Here a volcanic island arc, particularly well developed in the Lesser Antilles, curves from northeastern Venezuela to Jamaica. Branching from it is a nonvolcanic arc extending from Haiti through Cuba to the Yucatan peninsula of Mexico. The Caribbean Sea is a deep basin comparable to those of the western Pacific. The Gulf of Mexico is another deep basin but it lies outside the island arc. Its general region is bordered on the northwest, however, by the ancient Ouachita-Marathon orogenic belt. This is largely buried beneath post-Paleozoic sediments but may at one time have been an island arc.

Many important earthquakes have their origins along or near the island arcs, which undoubtedly are zones of structural instability. Those islands that are not exclusively of volcanic or reef origin are geologically complex. Their strata are much disturbed and they give evidence of considerable relatively recent elevation. Deep-focus earthquakes that appear to be related to these zones are displaced inward from the arcs and suggest the existence of shear planes dipping backward from the arcs beneath the edge of the continent.

From the scanty evidence available, it does not seem possible to locate the structural contacts of the continents and ocean basins with great accuracy. Perhaps these contacts are not permanent. The structures recognized in different regions make it seem unlikely that all continental margins are similar. Three types appear to be distinguishable: (1) flexure margins as along the Atlantic coast of the United States north of Cape Hatteras, (2) downfaulted margins as along the Pacific coast of California, and (3) upthrust margins as along at least some of the island arcs. Consideration of these types suggests that marginal portions of the continents may be lost by downfolding and downfaulting and sinking perhaps permanently beneath the sea. On the other hand, additions to the continents might be made by the elevation of parts of the ocean basins. These processes are speculative in the extreme, but both of them have been called upon to explain certain features of geosynclinal development.

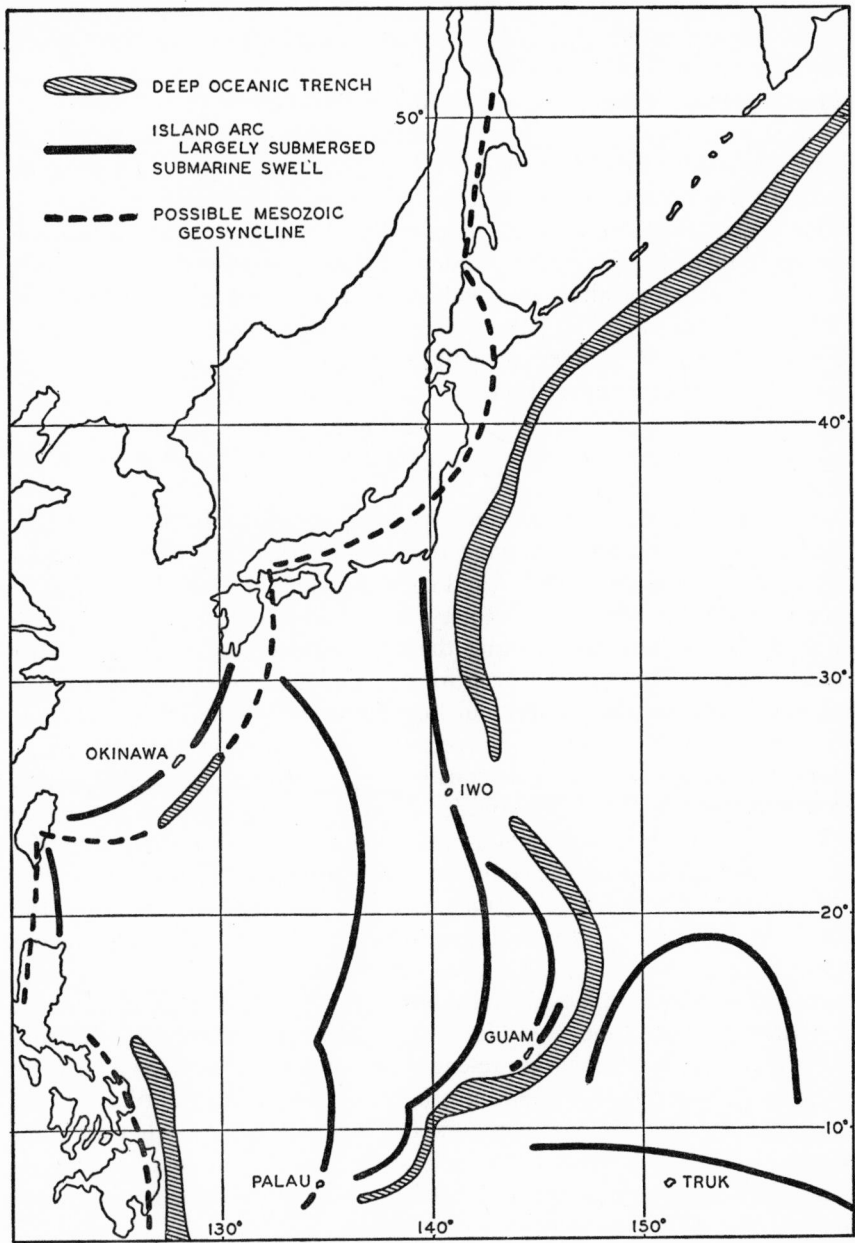

Figure 87. Map of the major topographic and structural features of the western Pacific Ocean. (After Dietz, 1954, *Bull. Geol. Soc. Amer.*, vol. 65, p. 1221, fig. 5, and Hess, 1948, *ibid.*, vol. 59, p. 417, pl. 1.)

If such alteration of the continental margins has occurred, it is necessary to conclude that either (1) deep-seated lateral transfer of material in the sial and sima layers must have taken place to permit subsidence or uplift or (2) a deep-seated phase change involving important volume and density alteration is indicated. Three types of phase change that might accomplish these results have been suggested: (1) alternate melting and crystallizing, involving differential volume relations of about 10 percent, (2) alternate hydration and dehydration as in the alteration of olivine to serpentine and vice versa, involving differential volume relations of about 25 percent, and (3) other mineralogic alterations that do not require any change in chemical composition, probably involving differential volume relations of about 10 percent. All of these changes are considered to be reversible depending upon temperature and pressure relations.

CONTINENTS

Sedimentary rocks of the emergent portions of the continents exhibit an extreme range in structure varying from undisturbed horizontal strata in some areas to intensely deformed and metamorphosed rocks in others. There is equal contrast between areas possessing thick and comparatively complete stratigraphic sections, representing the deposition of sediments for many millions of years, and others where, for equally long intervals of time, there was little or no sedimentary accumulation. Somewhat similarly, certain areas, commonly with thick stratigraphic sections, have had long histories of subsidence, whereas others have had equally long histories of uplift and erosion. Although all gradations in complexity of structure, degree of subsidence or elevation, and stratigraphic section can be found, these features serve to subdivide the continents into regions of two different general types. These are (1) geosynclines and attendant upland areas, which together constitute the mobile regions, and (2) the main continental platforms or relatively more stable regions.

Each rock stratum as it exists today preserves a record of all tectonic action in its area since the time it was formed. It does not, however, indicate any earlier event. Because the rocks present at the surface of the earth vary greatly in age from place to place, their histories go back to different points in geologic time. Young rocks have witnessed few tectonic changes. They are comparatively easy to interpret but they give evidence only of recent happenings. Old rocks may have been affected by so many tectonic episodes that their histories are practically indecipherable.

Tectonic action has been neither constant in intensity nor unchanging in its pattern. Certain trends of action have persisted in certain areas for more or less long intervals of time and then have changed importantly or have been reversed. Older patterns cannot be determined if older rocks do not occur or if they are buried beneath younger rocks and are not known. Many Precambrian rocks already were so disturbed and altered before the beginning of the Paleozoic Era that any later changes affecting them cannot be recognized.

The differentiation of tectonic regions depends upon the ages of the rocks that can be studied and their condition. Thus a Paleozoic geosyncline can be traced in the Appalachian region where little subsequent disturbance has occurred and no younger rocks hide the old formations. A similar geosyncline adjacent to the Gulf coast is very imperfectly known because it is buried deeply below the surface. A Paleozoic geosyncline somewhere near the Pacific coast is obscure because conditions there have been greatly altered and complicated by several more recent strong tectonic episodes. Almost nothing is known about pre-Paleozoic tectonics except where Precambrian rocks are now exposed.

All geologic structures that occur today developed more or less gradually during longer or shorter intervals of time. Some sequences of tectonic episodes have run their course and were completed long ago. Others are still in progress. The tectonic map of a modern continent is restricted to showing structures dating variably back into the geologic past. It does not represent conditions or happenings of the more distant past or indicate what is happening at present.

Geosynclines

The name *geosyncline* was originally introduced for a large elongated area that (1) subsided more or less continuously for a very long period of time and (2) was filled with sediments almost as fast as it subsided so that a thick succession of sedimentary rocks accumulated. Most geosynclines have been compressed and folded into mountains. The Appalachian Mountain region, with a stratigraphic section 30,000 to 40,000 feet thick, is the typical geosyncline. All geologists recognize geosynclines but there is much disagreement over the definition of the term and the origin and development of what it stands for.

The word *geosyncline* has been (1) used for an area, (2) defined as a structure, or (3) identified by the strata present in a region. It has been applied to a great variety of synclinal situations. To some geologists it obviously has meant little more than a large syncline generally filled with sediment. The shape, the kind of sediment filling, and the possible subsequent deformation of a geosyncline have been considered unimportant by some persons. The variety of structural and stratigraphic concepts identified by this name has been most confusing. From time to time attempts have been made to clarify the situation by classifying so-called geosynclines, and new names have been coined to designate different types. Distinction generally has been based on (1) shape, (2) location, (3) structural relations, (4) kind of sediment, and (5) source of sediment. None of these classifications has won general approval and none appears to be particularly useful.

Geosynclinal Characteristics

The concept of geosynclines has become so confused and the nomenclature applied to them is so cumbersome that reaction has set in. Comparisons of so-called geosynclines show that their differences probably outweigh their similarities. A growing tendency is evident to revert to the original concept or something close to it. The noncommittal term *basin* is available for synclinal situations that do not warrant recognition as geosynclines.

One of the best ways to assess the geosynclinal concept is to reëxamine the Appalachian Mountain belt and attempt to distinguish its more characteristic and significant features. Then by comparison with similar regions of the world, those features that they have in common can be recognized and perhaps a more generally useful definition can be framed. The Appalachian geosyncline has the following characteristics:

1. It is long and relatively narrow. Its known length is more than 2000 miles and it extends without interruption from Newfoundland to Alabama. At one end it plunges beneath the sea and at the other its continuation is concealed by younger rocks. Its original width cannot be determined accurately because of lateral compression, overthrusting, metamorphism, and uncertainty concerning boundaries. The present folded mountain belt south of New York is about 100 miles wide at most places. The entire geosyncline, depending upon how it is defined, of course, may have been 500 or more miles wide in some parts although at others it may have been much narrower.

2. It closely adjoins and parallels the present eastern coast of North America.

3. It had a very long history possibly beginning in the late Precambrian. Sediments accumulated in it throughout most of the Paleozoic Era.

4. The stratigraphic section is extremely thick. An accurate estimate of maximum and minimum thicknesses is not possible because of post-Paleozoic erosion and the fact that rates of deposition varied greatly from place to place and from time to time. All parts of the stratigraphic section, however, appear to be much thicker and less interrupted by unconformities than corresponding strata present in the interior of the continent.

5. Many kinds of sedimentary rocks occur in it. Detrital sediments predominate, particularly along the southeastern side of the mountain belt. Graywacke is one of the most characteristic types where the sediments are thickest. Most of the sediments were deposited in a shallow marine environment.

6. Detrital sediment was derived mainly from the southeast as shown by coarsening and other lithologic changes in that direction. Coarse material in-

cluding conglomerates, unweathered minerals, evidence of rapid deposition, and quantity of sediment all indicate the existence of land that, from time to time and from place to place, was probably high, certainly subject to rapid erosion, and possibly extensive in area.

7. Volcanism occurred particularly in the northeastern part at various times. Both intrusive and extrusive igneous rocks are present ranging from basic to acidic. Metabentonite beds are widespread in the Ordovician.

8. After long subsidence and sedimentary accumulation, the geosyncline was folded, uplifted, and deeply eroded. It has since become a stable region. Structural disturbances were noteworthy in the late Ordovician, during the Devonian Period, and near the end of the Paleozoic Era.

9. The strata were much compressed, thrown into large folds, and overthrust in a pattern consisting of long, gently curving arcs that are convex toward the northwest. Thrusting forces seem to have come from the southeast.

10. Immediately to the southeast of the present mountain belt from New York southwestward is the Piedmont Plateau, consisting of crystalline metamorphic and plutonic rocks resembling the Precambrian. These rocks have been peneplaned, and their surface dips beneath the coastal plain and continues out under the Atlantic Ocean.

A definite relationship seems to exist between a thick succession of sedimentary rocks and folding. Both are outstanding features of the Appalachian region and comparison can be made with other folded mountain systems. The following similarities and differences appear:

1. Except for the western cordillera of North and South America few mountain systems are as long or as straight as the Appalachians. The best examples in the Eastern Hemisphere are the Urals and to a less extent the Himalayas.

2. Outside of the Western Hemisphere, folded mountains do not so generally parallel modern coastlines.

3. A thick stratigraphic section seems to be more important than a long depositional history. A section which is much thicker than those in neighboring areas also seems to be characteristic.

4. Other areas have had depositional histories as long as the Appalachian but not all of them have been comparably deformed.

5. Sediments of some folded mountains are less coarsely detrital, and some of them are interpreted as having accumulated in deeper water than in the Appalachian region.

6. Volcanism has not been important in all folded mountain regions.

7. Most detrital sediment came from one direction. The source generally appears to have been on the concave side of the mountain arcs if these occur.

8. The degree and type of folding and overthrusting vary considerably.

9. A region similar to the Piedmont is not invariably present.

10. The general sequence of events—subsidence and thick sedimentary

accumulation, folding, uplift, deep erosion, and attainment of relative stability—seems to be characteristic.

Several features of possible geosynclines may be expected to differ more or less importantly. For example, an old geosyncline that has passed through all stages of development and a younger one that has not, certainly will exhibit different structural characters. Perhaps a region like the American Gulf coast, where sediment is now accumulating, may not be certainly identifiable as a geosyncline. Also the type of deformation in a geosyncline would be influenced strongly if not determined by the constitution of its stratigraphic section. Thus it has been suggested that, if thick competent lower strata are present, folding will predominate, but, if the lower strata are weak, overthrusting is more likely to develop. Finally, the depth of erosion is important because the rocks and structures encountered at different levels may be expected to show many dissimilarities.

In consideration of the foregoing, the original concept of geosynclines seems to require supplementing in only a few respects: (1) Detrital sediments were derived largely from one direction. (2) Geosynclinal development was concluded by strong structural deformation and uplift. (3) overthrust faulting may be as important as or even more important than folding. And (4) the compressive force seems to have acted from the same side that produced the sediment. The last feature, however, might be a consequence of the form of the geosynclinal trough. If the slope on one side were much steeper than on the other, the folds probably would lean toward the gentle side and overthrusting would occur in that direction.

Geosynclinal Theories

Two general theories are current that seek to explain the development of geosynclines. The older one is the theory of borderlands, and the other, which is relatively recent, is the theory of structural arcs. Each finds its support in certain facts but each demands the acceptance of certain apparently improbable suppositions. A critical evaluation reveals that both are beset by serious difficulties and certainly neither is entirely satisfactory. Several other theories have gained much less acceptance. There can be no denying the existence of geosynclines, but the problem they present is so great and knowledge of the composition of the earth, and the forces which have shaped it, is so imperfect that, like other grand theories of the earth, a solution meeting all objections is not likely to be formulated soon.

Borderlands

The theory of borderlands is almost as old as the concept of geosynclines. It holds that the geosyncline is the negative element of a mechanical couple whose complement was a rising adjacent region (see Figure 88). Thus the

Appalachian geosyncline is supposed to have been paralleled on the southeast by a borderland named Appalachia. As the geosyncline sank, the borderland rose, was eroded, and produced the sediment that filled the geosyncline. Because this reciprocal action was in operation very early in Paleozoic time, the borderland must have consisted almost exclusively of Precambrian rocks. The Piedmont Plateau is identified as the deeply eroded western part of Appalachia.

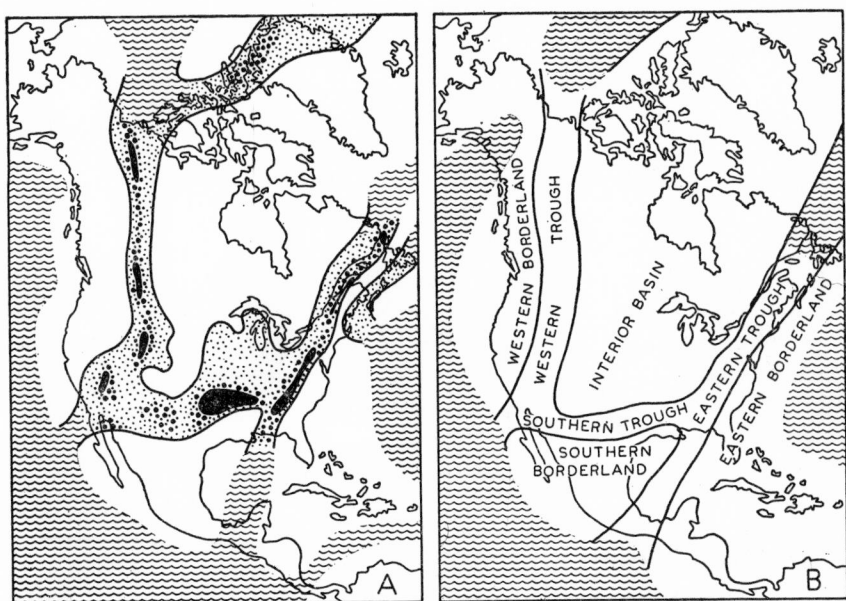

Figure 88. Tectonic maps of North America. These illustrate the concept of geosynclines and borderlands that formerly was the common belief of most American geologists. In A the areas of deepest downwarping and thickest sedimentary accumulation are indicated in black and by heavier stippling. (A after Schuchert, 1923, *Bull. Geol. Soc. Amer.*, vol. 34, p. 217, fig. 5; B after Snider, 1932, *Earth history*, p. 91, fig. 46, by permission of Appleton-Century-Crofts, Inc.)

As sediment accumulated and was warped downward in the sinking geosyncline, lateral pressure developed and the upper sedimentary layers were thrown into folds. Continued depression of the geosyncline and thickening sediment gradually produced a weak zone in the earth's crust. At last this zone could no longer withstand pressure resulting from shrinking of the earth. Failure occurred, the borderland was thrust against the geosyncline, and the weak strata were compressed, further folded, and faulted. Then the borderland sank and much of it disappeared beneath the water of the Atlantic Ocean.

Disagreement has marked the identification of cause and effect in the development of geosynclines according to this theory. It has been argued, on one side, that sedimentary loading resulted in subsidence and, on the other, that sinking provided a depression where sediment accumulated. In either case it is obvious that readjustment of underlying material is required, and deep flowage of material from beneath the geosyncline to the borderland was postulated. The requirements of isostatic balance have been explained in various ways. Evidently loading alone is not a sufficient mechanism because the addition of porous sediment above, compensated by the outflowing of solid material below or volume change related to a heat and pressure gradient, involves the exchange of different densities. If no other force were active, the sedimentary surface in a geosyncline would gradually rise and, after a brief initial stage, further sedimentary accumulation would be impossible.

The borderland theory was widely accepted by American geologists probably because the Appalachian Mountains and Piedmont Plateau are such prominent and well-known geologic and structural features of the continent. It seems to explain successfully the relations of this geosyncline to the Piedmont belt, the source of sediments, and Appalachian structures. The application of the theory to other regions, however, requires much more imagination. It fails to explain how geosynclinal development began, what kept it in operation for long periods of time, and why it ended. It fails particularly to explain the final complete reversal of movement when the geosyncline was uplifted and the borderland sank. It also ignores happenings on the outer side of the borderland where presumably an equal quantity of sediment was deposited.

An explanation for the origin of geosynclinal depressions is provided by a thermal hypothesis of an alternately expanding and contracting earth. Upon expansion, the earth's crust failed along a series of zones radiating from the Pamir Mountains of southwestern Asia, which extend to an antipodal circle ringing the Pacific Ocean. The subcrust beneath these zones was tensionally thinned by flowage, the surface was depressed, and geosynclinal troughs were initiated. Subsequent contraction of the earth resulted in compression and folding of geosynclinal sediments. This cycle was repeated producing different patterns that are apparent in the locations of geosynclines of different ages.

Orogens

Alpine geologists in Europe generally have not been impressed by the borderland theory because the Alps and their extensions neither parallel one of the major ocean coastlines nor are associated with a zone comparable to the American Piedmont. Also geologists noticed that mountain ranges can be joined into long sinuous belts of deformation. Two such belts can be constructed in the Mediterranean region and continued well across southern

Asia, as shown in Figure 89. These are overthrust outwardly to the north and south respectively. They have been interpreted as the opposite sides of a single great structural zone termed an *orogen*. As it now exists, the Mediterranean orogen has a maximum width of about 500 miles but the two sides come very close together in northern Italy and Switzerland.

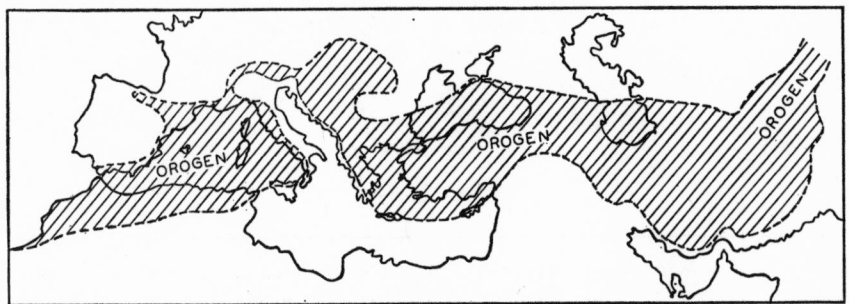

Figure 89. Map of the Mediterranean region showing form and extent of the great orogen as interpreted by Kober. The two boundaries are supposedly continuous mountainous belts characterized by outward overthrusting in opposite directions. (Adapted from Longwell, 1923, *Bull. Geol. Soc. Amer.*, vol. 34, p. 233, fig. 1.)

The orogen is considered to be a geosyncline that subsided beneath accumulating sediment. When the earth contracted, its contents were squeezed between the adjacent rigid crustal blocks and overthrust onto the forelands along its margins in both directions. As the mountains rose, they formed the rims of topographic basins. The western Mediterranean is one such basin, the plains of Hungary and northern Yugoslavia are another, and the Black Sea and Turkey are a third. If the orogen and its forelands lay beneath the sea, marginal mountains might or might not reach the surface to form island arcs.

This theory may be questioned in many ways. It is seriously deficient in not providing a hinterland in the midst of the orogen, which is required as a source of the sediments present in the marginal deformed mountain belts.

Magma Blisters

The same mountain ranges that have been joined to mark the edges of an orogen can be arranged to form closed or nearly closed oval figures margining the topographic basins already mentioned. The western Mediterranean is one of the best examples (see Figure 90). Another of similar size and form is outlined by the West Indian islands and the northern coast of South America. The outward folding and thrusting of the mountains and the inward origin of the sediment are explained by the presence of a great magma blister that formerly raised the central region. Eventual cooling and solidification of the magma reduced its volume, caused the central area to subside, and produced the present basin form.

Accumulated radioactive heat produced the magma blister. Melting increased rock volume nearly 10 percent and raised the central area. Erosion began and, as the central mass became lighter, isostatic equilibrium was dis-

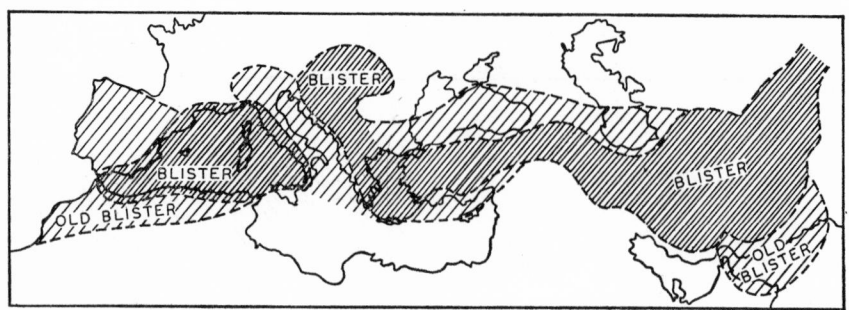

Figure 90. Map of the Mediterranean region showing the positions of magma blisters according to interpretations by Rich. The margins of the blisters are marked by mountainous belts characterized by outward thrusting. Compare with Figure 89. (After Rich, 1951, *Bull. Geol. Soc. Amer.*, vol. 62, p. 1198, pl. 1.)

turbed and further uplift followed (see Figure 91). Subcrustal matter flowed inward from beneath the marginal zone and geosynclinal sinking started. As the blister rose, sedimentary layers, under the force of gravity, slid down its outer slopes and compressed newly deposited sediments of the geosyncline. Backfaulting occurred along the inner edge of the geosyncline, magma ascended through these fractures, and volcanoes developed. The stretched surface over the top of the blister was tension-faulted and lava erupted in great flows. The blister cooled, solidified, and contracted. The central area, from which much of the light surface rock had been eroded, sank deeply and became a basin characterized by positive gravity anomalies. Isostatic adjustment caused reversal of deep flowage and the geosyncline, which had been anomalously light, was elevated.

This is a remarkably ingenious explanation for arcuate geosynclinal mountains enclosing central depressed areas. It does not, however, seem to fit the situation presented by long, nearly straight ranges like the Appalachians, Andes, and Urals. The Piedmont Plateau is identified as the inner backfaulted zone where metamorphosed geosynclinal sediments and rocks from the magma cover are intimately intermixed and have been intruded by the magma. The main part of the old blister should lie beneath the Atlantic Ocean, and its other side should be marked by another great mountain range. Because it would be submerged, this range should not have been worn down by erosion like the Appalachians. There is no such range.

If a blister formed beneath the sea and remained submerged, erosion would not occur. Therefore a downwarped marginal geosynclinal trough would not be filled and a deep trench might develop. This explanation does not seem to fit the unclosed Pacific island arcs that are more or less concentric and all face outward toward the open sea. Also sliding of the surface layers off a submerged blister probably could not raise an island arc or a great

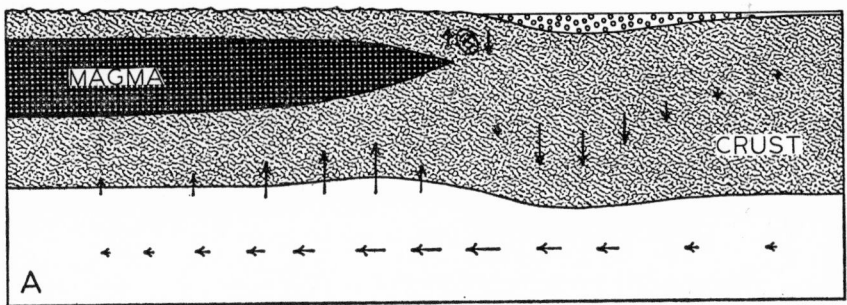

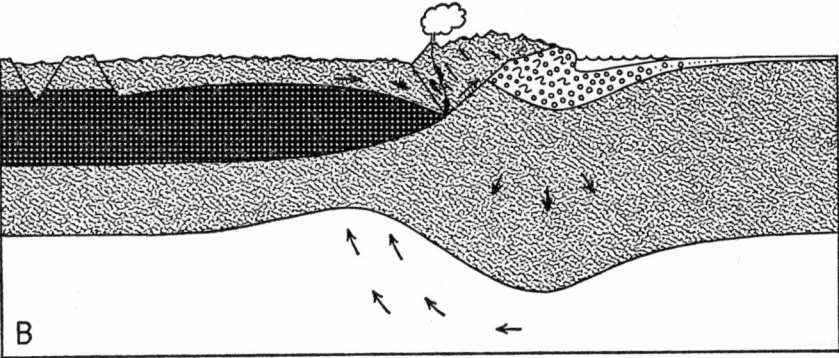

Figure 91. Diagrams illustrating the development of a magma blister and adjacent geosyncline. In A the blister has formed as the result of accumulating radioactive heat that melted a portion of the crust. Expansion raises the overlying area, which is attacked by erosion. Sediment is deposited in an adjacent trough, which sinks isostatically. In B the crust overlying the margin of the blister slides laterally and downward under the force of gravity and compresses sediments in the geosyncline. Later the blister cools, solidifies, and shrinks and its surface sinks beneath the sea. (After Rich, 1951, *Bull. Geol. Soc. Amer.*, vol. 62, p. 1182, figs. 1 and 2.)

submarine ridge in advance of what is now a fairly deep sea basin. Certainly a deep trench could not be preserved in front of an arc if sliding had occurred.

Tectogenes

For many years the East Indian island arcs have provided a challenging subject for geologic speculation (see Figure 92). Numerous different ideas have been presented to account for their origin, development, and structural patterns, but extensive geologic, oceanographic, and gravitational studies in the former Dutch Indies have refuted most of them. Nevertheless the obvious connection of these arcs with the mountain ranges of Burma and Malaya, that turn abruptly south from the Himalayas, continues to focus attention upon the East Indies as a region offering unusual opportunities for the investigation of some of the more fundamental large-scale features of earth structure.

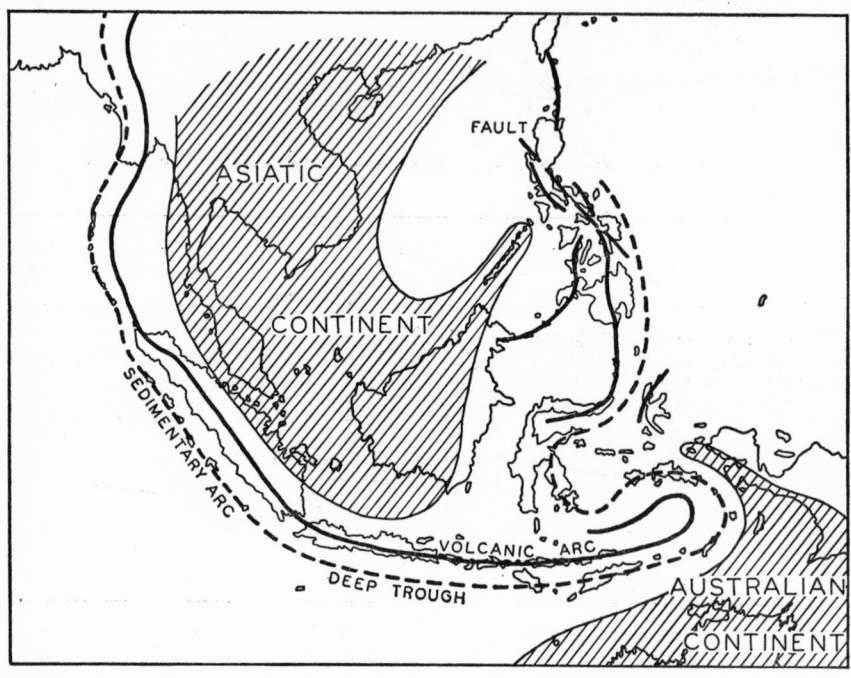

Figure 92. Map showing the tectonic arcs of the East Indies. Volcanic arcs are indicated by solid lines and the axis of the tectogene is marked by dashes. Both can be extended to connect with the mountains of Burma. The tectogene is characterized by very high negative gravity anomalies and it is expressed topographically by either an upsqueezed ridge that may emerge as sedimentary islands or a deep oceanic trench. (Compiled from various sources including Bemmelen, 1949, The geology of Indonesia.)

Structures in the central and eastern parts of the Indies are so complex that their consideration would add needless confusion to a discussion of geosynclinal problems. The relations of Sumatra and Java to adjacent regions on both sides, however, are relatively simple. In passing from south to north the following zones are clearly distinguishable (see Figure 93):

1. Sea floor at a depth of about 15,000 feet, characterized by moderate positive gravity anomalies.

2. A deep elongated trench whose axis lies about 150 miles offshore from the main islands. This trench is less than 100 miles wide and appears to oc-

cupy a position intermediate between the positive anomalies of the general ocean bottom and the negative anomalies of the next zone.

3. A narrow ridge whose crest is about 100 miles from the coast of the main islands. It emerges as a series of small islands southwest of Sumatra and is characterized by very large negative anomalies.

4. A second trough less than 100 miles wide and generally less than 10,000 feet deep characterized by moderate positive anomalies that increase toward the main islands.

5. A mountainous and volcanic belt about 100 miles wide that constitutes the outer or southern parts of Sumatra and Java. Gravity has not been measured here, but this may be a zone of somewhat greater positive anomalies than those on either side of it.

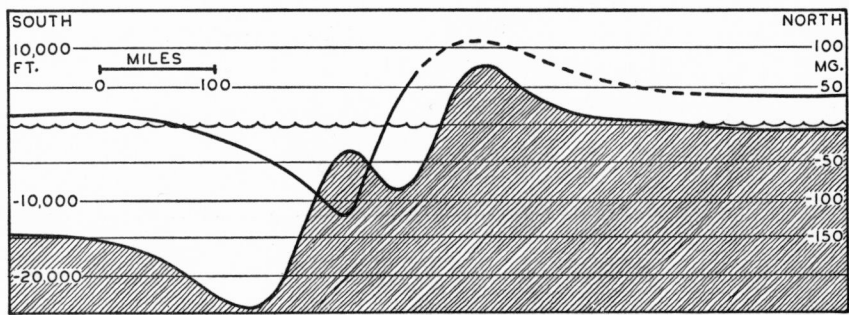

Figure 93. Curves showing the relations of gravity measurements in milligals to topography across the main tectonic arcs of the East Indies. The deep oceanic trench lies just outside of the zone of greatest negative anomalies. Inside the trench occurs a submarine ridge that here and there bears islands. Inside of these is a shallower trench and then a chain of volcanic islands. (Data from Kuenen, 1950, Marine geology, pls. A and B.)

6. A lowland area that dips gently beneath the Strait of Malacca, the southern tip of the South China Sea, and the Java Sea with water nowhere much more than 500 feet deep. This zone both emergent and submerged has a minimum width of 150 miles and is characterized by moderate positive anomalies.

The features of this region that have attracted the most attention are the deep-sea trench (2), the high negative gravity anomalies (3), and the volcanic zone (5). These are all unusual but they are more or less closely duplicated by similar relations in the other Pacific and in the West Indian island arcs. Their association appears to be significant. The deep trench has been likened to an unfilled geosynclinal trough and the volcanic islands seem to provide a potential source for geosynclinal sediments.

The high negative anomalies indicate that important isostatic maladjustment occurs close in front of the island arc and suggest that the gravitationally deficient zone is underlain by a thickening of the sial layer. Calculations indicate that displacement of 250 to 400 cubic miles of sima by overlying sial

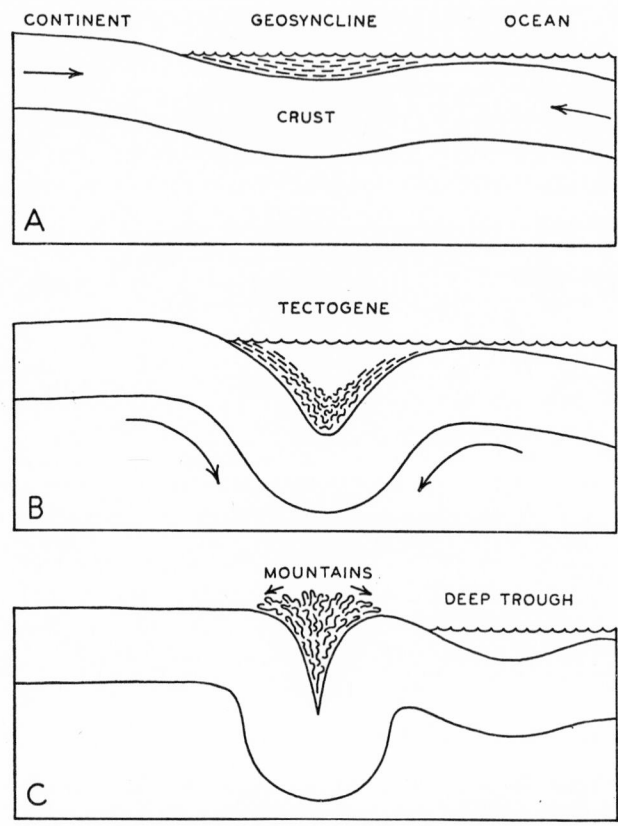

Figure 94. Development of a tectogent. A. Geosynclinal downwarping begins as a result of tangential pressure. Sediments accumulate in the geosyncline. B. Increased tangential pressure reinforced perhaps by converging convection currents in the earth's mantle causes the crust to buckle downward. Deformation of geosynclinal sediments begins. The trough developed at this stage has been considered by some persons to correspond with the foredeeps adjacent to some continental margins and island arcs. C. Downbuckling continues. Greatly deformed sediments are squeezed upward out of the central part of the tectogene. Overthrusting occurs in both directions. A deep marginal trench develops outside of the tectogene.

per linear mile would produce anomalies of the order of magnitude that have been observed. This could be accomplished by symmetrical downbending of the sial-sima contact to a depth of about fifteen miles and would involve slightly greater crustal shortening. Such a postulated downfolding of the sial is termed a *tectogene* (see Figure 94).

In a shrinking earth the sial layer would bend downward more readily than upward. If it were accomplished slowly, displacement of the slightly heavier sima by the sial would require far less force than equal upward bulging into much less dense air. The occurrence of very slowly circulating convection currents within the earth which converge below the surface and return downward has been suggested as an additional mechanism to aid in the development of tectogenes. Although the tectogene is pulled downward in some

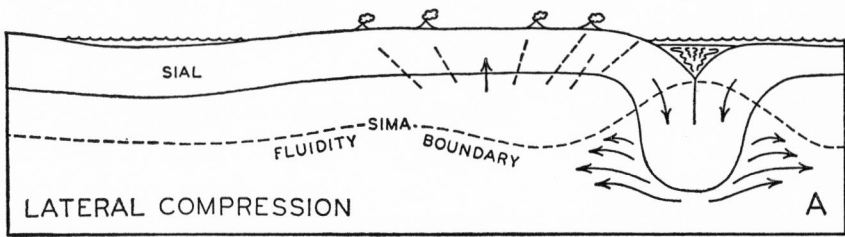

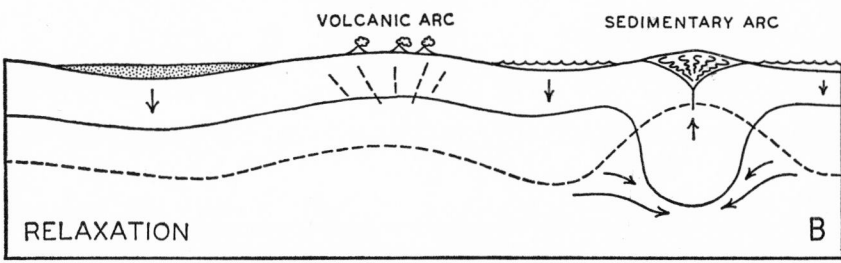

Figure 95. Development of a double island arc as explained by Umbgrove. A. Tangential pressure produces a tectogene and throws the crust to the left in the diagram into a broad gentle wave. Volcanism breaks out on the uplifted part of the wave and the depressed part becomes a sedimentary basin. B. Relaxation of pressure permits the tectogene to rise because the downbuckled light sialic material is not in isostatic equilibrium. Subcrustal flowage results in subsidence of adjacent zones creating a trough between the newly uplifted deformed sediments of the outer arc and the inner volcanic arc, which has been reduced in width. At the same time and in the same way an outer trough subsides. (After Umbgrove, 1947, *The pulse of the earth*, p. 186, fig. 123, by permission of Martinus Nijhoff.)

unknown way, the lower density of material in it should tend to buoy up adjacent areas on both sides, where possibly the sial layer was thinned by stretching and the sima thickened by lateral movement from beneath the tectogene. Consequently the negative zone should lie between positive anomalies. When growth of the tectogene ceased, isostasy would reassert itself, the central zone would rise, and the border zones would sink as shown in Figure 95.

The tectogene hypothesis has been adapted to explain the origin and development of the Appalachian and other geosynclines. Initial downbending in a tectogene along the continental margin produced a submerged trough that was filled at first by sediment derived from the emergent continental platform. As downwarping continued, the sedimentary strata were pinched between the converging sides of the tectogene and squeezed upward and outward. At the same time, volcanic activity began and islands emerged consisting partly of upthrust sediment but more largely of extrusive volcanic material. From this time on, such islands, rapidly eroded but repeatedly uplifted or replaced by others, provided most of the sediment received by the growing geosyncline. This great structure was now divisible into two parts, a *eugeosynclinal zone*, in which the volcanic islands were located and whose very thick sediments later were extensively metamorphosed, and a parallel subsiding *miogeosynclinal zone*, without volcanoes, whose thick accumulating sediments thinned toward and lapped upon the continental platform. Although no reference has been made to it, a second miogeosynclinal zone presumably should occur upon the outer side of the volcanic islands. The volcanoes brought mainly basic or intermediate lavas to the surface but from time to time the eugeosynclinal zone may have been intruded by acid plutonic rocks. Geosynclinal development was concluded by a final squeezing of the tectogene which folded and faulted the miogeosynclinal sediments. According to this theory the Appalachian Mountains mark an inner miogeosyncline and the Piedmont Plateau is the deeply eroded eugeosyncline.

This theory is attractive because it provides some analogy to the structure of modern island arcs. The volcanic islands suggest comparison with the volcanism that occurred in some ancient geosynclines, and the outer miogeosyncline might correspond to the deep-sea trench. More importantly, it is in harmony with some facts that contradict the old theory of borderlands. Thus radioactive dating of some minerals from the Piedmont region reveals Paleozoic ages ranging from about late Ordovician to Carboniferous for rocks formerly identified by their general characters as Precambrian. Some poorly preserved Paleozoic fossils have been discovered in associated metamorphosed sediments. Deep wells in Florida have found unmetamorphosed sedimentary rocks with Paleozoic fossils that have been interpreted as coming from an outer miogeosyncline. Thus the Piedmont does not consist entirely of very ancient rocks and it appears to be the central part of a great symmetrical structure. The suggestion has been made that the continents grew intermittently throughout geologic time by the addition of stabilized geosynclinal zones of these types along their margins.

On the other hand, when the Appalachian region is considered, serious objections to this theory can be raised:

1. Similarities drawn between the demands of this theory and modern island arcs appear to be fortuitous. The elements of the two systems face in

opposite directions. The structural arcs of the Appalachians face toward the continent but the island arcs invariably face toward the open deep sea.

2. The two systems are out of proportion, the Appalachian zones being wider than those of modern island arcs.

3. If the Appalachian volcanoes were located above the deepest part of the geosyncline, as postulated (see Figure 96), they cannot correspond to those of the island arcs, which are 100 miles in from the center of the tectogene and mark an uplifted zone with positive gravity anomalies.

4. The miogeosynclines occupy positions that should be marginal to the tectogene and, according to this theory, these are zones that should rise slightly rather than subside deeply.

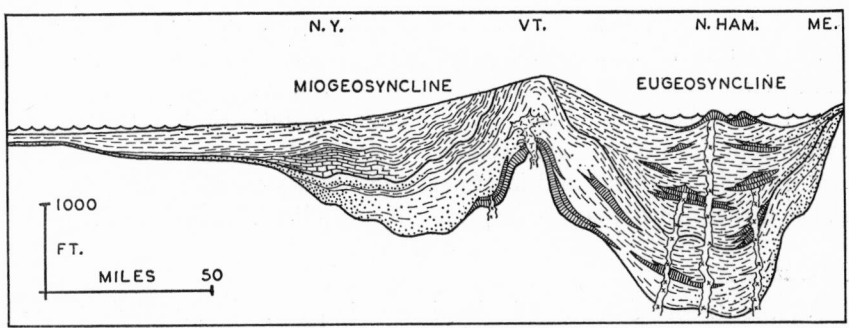

Figure 96. Reconstruction of the Appalachian geosyncline in New England at the end of the Ordovician Period as interpreted by Kay. The eugeosyncline and miogeosyncline are separated by a great uplifted welt that later was overthrust westward. (After Kay, 1951, Geol. Soc. Amer., Mem. 48, p. 26, pl. 9.)

5. Most of the continental coasts of the world are not bordered now and have not been bordered since late Cretaceous time by volcanic island arcs. Modern arcs are concentrated on the western side of the Pacific Ocean with only minor representatives elsewhere. This suggests that they are related to some localized peculiarity of structure. There is no present positive evidence that island arcs comparable to modern ones ever existed at other places.

These and similar objections have been recognized by various geologists, and certain modifications of the tectogene theory have been suggested in an effort to meet them. Nevertheless they seem to eliminate the possibility of drawing a close parallel between the postulated island arcs of ancient geosynclines and modern island arcs. The following objections are directed against the prevailing concept of eugeosynclines:

1. It does not seem likely that the deepest part of the geosyncline could have both been filled with sediment of local derivation and contributed additional enormous volumes of sediment to adjacent regions. This could have been accomplished only by stupendous volcanic activity which, in the Ap-

palachian geosyncline, must have been equivalent at the very minimum to fifty times the volume of the Columbia Plateau basalts but probably much more.

2. It does not seem likely that basic volcanism should break out and be confined to the zone where sediments were thickest, where they were subjected to lateral pressure because of downbending in the geosyncline, and where subsidence probably displaced the isotherms downward. The volcanoes of modern island arcs appear to be located along an upbowed zone inside the axis of the tectogene and they may be fed by lava rising along the shear planes indicated by deep-seated earthquakes (see Figure 97).

3. It does not seem likely that mainly extrusive basic and intermediate volcanics could have produced the quantities of quartz sand and silt that were deposited in the miogeosyncline and at times spread over the continental platform. For the Pennsylvanian Period alone this may have amounted to more than 50,000 cubic miles in eastern North America.

4. It does not seem likely that extensive granitization requiring large amounts of silica could have occurred in sediments squeezed in a tectogene and derived from basic and intermediate volcanics overlying only the thin sial layer that may or may not be present beneath the Atlantic Ocean.

Mountain Arcs

Another theory also draws its inspiration in part from the modern island arcs but it overcomes some of the more serious difficulties that beset the tectogene theory. The island arcs are in effect mountain ranges rising from the sea floor. Some of them pass laterally into terrestrial mountain chains to which they presumably are fundamentally similar (see Figure 92, p. 258). Examples are the large Indonesian islands of Sumatra and Java (extensions of the southward trending mountains of Burma) and the Aleutian Islands, that continue the mountains of the Alaska Peninsula (see Figure 98).

Both island arcs and mountain arcs may be single or double. Where single, it is the inner arc that is developed; where double, this arc generally is more prominent than the other one. Both islands and mountains of the inner arcs commonly bear volcanoes, as in the western Pacific islands and the Cascade Range of Washington and Oregon. These mountains, if worn down deeply enough by erosion, may expose granitic batholiths as in the Sierra Nevada. If there is no outer arc, its position may be marked by a deep linear oceanic trench, as along the south coast of Java and the coast of northern Chile. Where an outer arc is developed, the islands or mountains consist of upthrust deposits that had accumulated in such a trench. Examples are a chain of small islands paralleling the south coast of Sumatra, the Kodiak islands adjacent to the Alaska Peninsula, and the Coast Ranges of Washington, Oregon, and California.

The sedimentary rocks exposed in the island and mountain arcs consist mainly of graywackes, and associated basic extrusive igneous rocks are common. These rocks are characteristic of the suite that is generally considered to occupy and to identify eugeosynclines. The arcs also may include intermediate to acid intrusives.

All modern primary arcs are convex outward from the continents and many of them face the open sea. They are active seismic zones with epicenters concentrated along and behind them. The earthquake foci occur at greater and greater depths inward from the arcs and seem to identify planes of shearing that extend back toward or beneath the continents (see Figure 97). At shallow depths these planes dip at angles of 30 to 35 degrees but

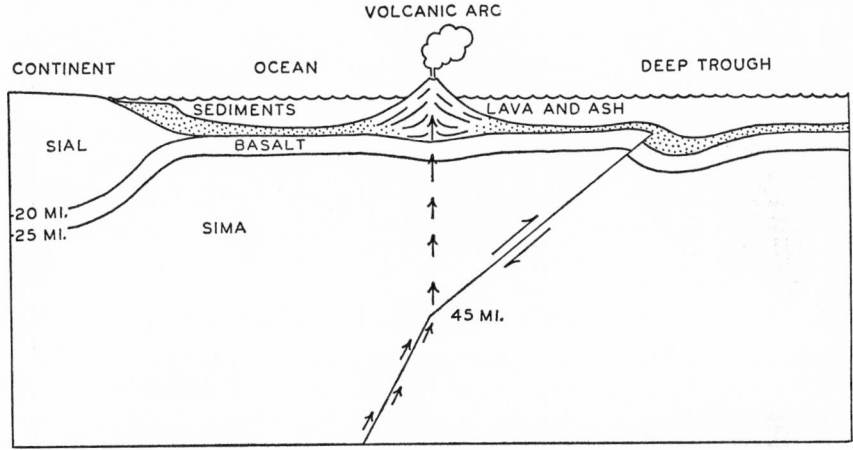

Figure 97.   Schematic structural section showing the relations of a concentric volcanic arc to the continental border as interpreted by Wilson. The position and inclination of the zone of thrust faulting is determined on the basis of earthquake foci. (Modified from Wilson, 1954, *The earth as a planet*, p. 156, fig. 4, by permission of the University of Chicago Press and G. P. Kuiper.)

they steepen abruptly to about 60 degrees some forty to forty-five miles below the surface. The foci show that these planes continue to a depth of about 400 miles.

The pattern of shear planes indicated by earthquakes suggests overthrusting along intersecting conical surfaces. In the island arcs, these surfaces seem to emerge beneath the sea at the oceanic trenches which may become the sites of outer arcs. The inner arcs approximately overlie junctions of the gentler and steeper shear planes. Volcanoes are fed by magma that rises along the shear planes and overlying fractures.

Secondary arcs may occur behind the primary arcs and opposite their points of angular deflection. These face in the other direction and are convex toward the continents. They consist of sedimentary rocks of the types

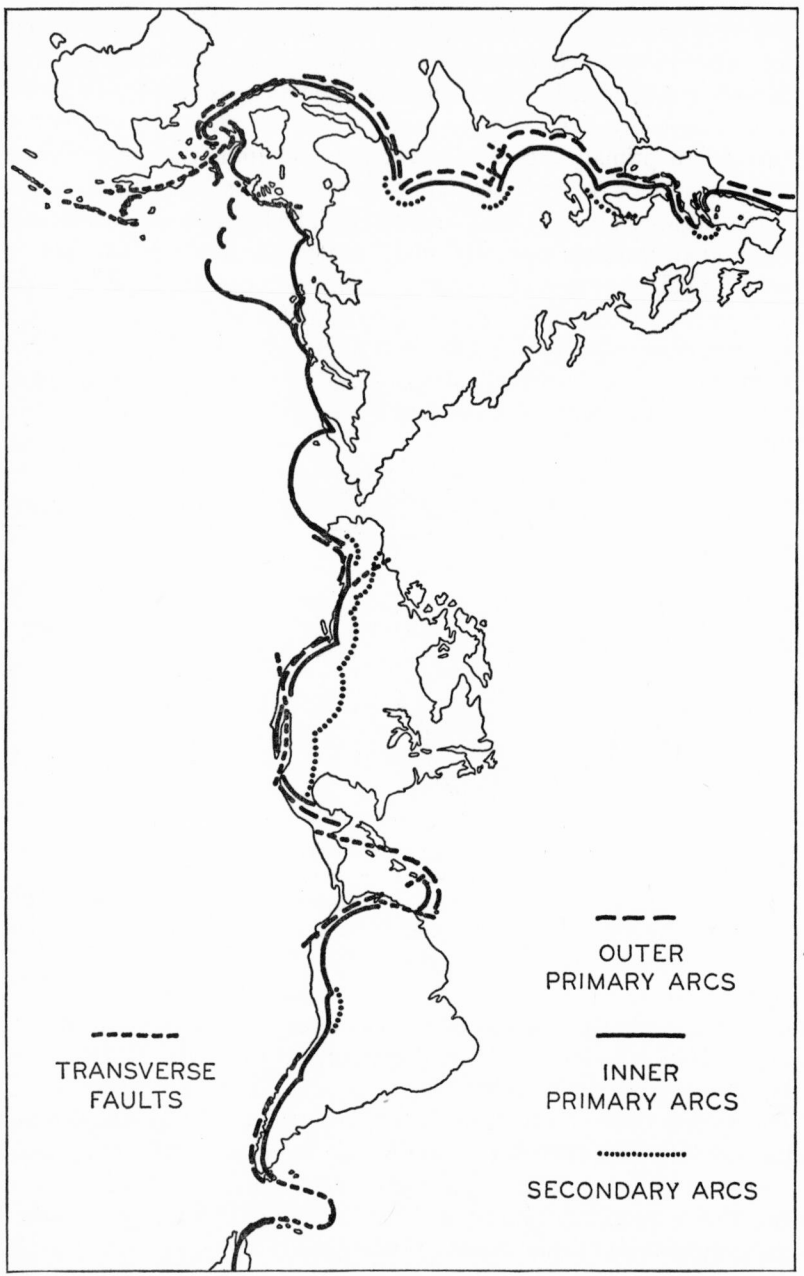

OUTER
PRIMARY ARCS

TRANSVERSE
FAULTS

INNER
PRIMARY ARCS

SECONDARY ARCS

Figure 98. Map of the world laid out to emphasize the continuity of the two great zones of relatively recent and modern tectonic arcs that follow great circles. (Structural interpretations after Wilson, 1954, *The earth as a planet*, p. 153, fig. 3 and others, by permission of the University of Chicago Press and G. P. Kuiper.)

commonly considered to occupy and to identify miogeosynclines and are largely nonvolcanic. Earthquakes originating in or near these arcs are all of the shallow type.

This pattern of primary and secondary arcs is most apparent in the mountains and islands that have been elevated during Cenozoic time. The arcs are arranged in two systems approximating great circles, as shown in Figure 98. One rings the Pacific Ocean and the other extends along the Mediterranean, crosses southern Asia, and meets the first in the East Indies. Other systems of mountain arcs, of greater age, in part follow other courses. They are less easy to identify and trace because they have been worn down deeply by erosion, their volcanoes have been long extinct, and important parts of them are now covered by younger sediments. According to this theory, the Appalachian Mountains are secondary arcs convex northwestward (see Figure 99). They are best developed opposite deflections of the primary

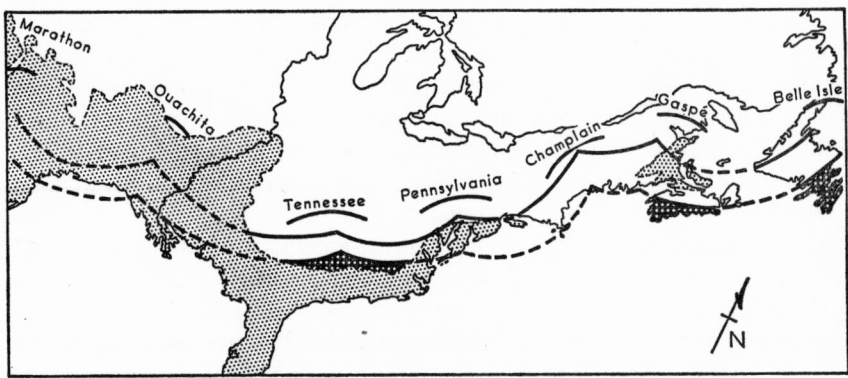

Figure 99.   Map of eastern North America showing the Appalachian system of tectonic arcs as interpreted by Wilson. The volcanic parts of the primary arcs, shown in darker pattern, are largely covered by coastal plain deposits except in some of the Peidmont plateau, Nova Scotia, and Newfoundland. Structures in Paleozoic rocks of the Appalachian and adjacent region mark the secondary arcs. (After Wilson, 1954, The earth as a planet, p. 176, fig. 14, by permission of the University of Chicago Press and G. P. Kuiper.)

arcs that are convex toward the Atlantic Ocean. The inner primary arcs are evident in the metamorphic and intrusive igneous rocks of the Piedmont region. Outer arcs, if they existed, are largely concealed beneath the coastal plain deposits or have subsided beneath the ocean.

This theory postulates an evolutionary sequence in the development of island arcs and mountain ranges as follows:

1. Fracturing and overthrusting along part of a conical surface initiated formation of an arc. This resulted from lateral compression in the outer shell, about forty miles thick, of a slowly cooling earth although tension may have prevailed in an underlying shell. Such surfaces of structural failure seem to

curve around the centers of thick deltaic accumulations of sediment derived from the erosion of a continent. The shear surfaces generally emerge from the lithosphere beneath the sea some distance beyond the sedimentary area and they are convex toward the sea.

2. A submarine trench began to form where the shear surface emerged and compression resulted in downbending of the crust. The nature of any subsiding trench, however, depended upon the rate at which sediment was deposited in it. The trench may have received little sediment and become progressively deeper or it may have been completely filled as fast as it subsided. Deficient gravity anomalies reflect the presence of thick sediments and not downbending of a sial layer which probably does not extend beneath the ocean. The so-called tectogenes are related primarily to compression and sedimentary loading and not to convection currents within the body of the earth.

3. At or a little after the time trenches began to form volcanism commenced along the line of the inner arc. Heat produced by friction along shear planes caused melting, and magma escaped through fractures extending upward from a depth of about forty miles, where the angle of shear planes changes. Extrusive lavas generally were basic but, as this process continued, differentiation occurred progressively and more and more acid magma rose, perhaps from deeper and deeper zones, until granite batholiths were intruded or the rocks were granitized metasomatically.

4. As soon as volcanic islands of the inner arc appeared above the surface of the sea, erosion began. Sediments were delivered to the trench and to a basin inside the arc. These sediments were derived from basic volcanics and became quartz-free graywackes. Granitization beneath the inner arc disturbed isostatic equilibrium, and the same compression that deepened the trench resulted in deformation and uplifting of the islands. Erosion cut down into quartz-bearing metamorphic and igneous rocks, and sediments were produced that became typical quartz graywackes.

5. As this process progressed and compression continued, the islands of the inner arc were increasingly deformed and further uplifted. They grew in size and became connected. Islands also may have appeared along the outer arc, squeezed up from the sediments of the trench. Further compression raised the entire double arc and a borderland was formed. Erosion of this more extensive land area produced sediments of varied origin that were more completely weathered. After deposition, they became subgraywackes. These sediments were transported in both directions. Depending upon conditions, the basins inside the arcs were shallowly marine or they became filled and the sediments accumulated in terrestrial deposits.

6. Continued compression resulted in folding and faulting behind the primary arcs, especially opposite the angles of their junction, and secondary arcs developed at these places. The secondary arcs consist of sediments de-

posited in basins behind the primary arcs. If they had not been raised earlier, the basins were elevated above sea level and the continental margin was extended beyond the site of the primary arcs. In this way continents grew by accretion along their margins.

7. Uplift and compression of both primary and secondary arcs continued more or less spasmodically but the new marginal portion of the continent gradually became stabilized. The mountains of the arcs were worn down, producing sediments that were deposited offshore in thick accumulations. Thus the stage was set for crustal failure along a new system of shear planes and the initiation of a new cycle of arc development.

Arcs that join to form a single system generally exhibit different developmental stages. Either a system began to form in one or more areas and progressed laterally by the addition of successively younger arcs, or certain arcs evolved more rapidly than others. The modern Pacific border system appears to consist of elements of somewhat different ages. Thus the arcs of North America began to form in middle or late Mesozoic time and are now mature, whereas most of those adjacent to the Asiatic coast are of Tertiary age and are still youthful. Some parts of a system, even if mature, may never have developed outer arcs, as in the coastal zone of South America.

This theory is particularly interesting for several reasons. (1) It relates mountain arcs and island arcs exhibiting close similarities in geometric form and geographic continuity. (2) It transfers emphasis from the geosynclines themselves to the tectonic and sedimentologic processes that resulted in the production and accumulation of thick sedimentary deposits of different kinds. (3) It provides an explanation for the development of borderlands of the type that could have furnished the variety of sediments observed in geosynclinal deposits.

Although in outline this theory is attractive in many ways, various difficulties and objections become apparent on close examination. Among the objections and unexplained features are the following:

1. The mountains of the world cannot be arranged as neatly into outer and inner primary arcs and secondary arcs as this theory requires. Particularly at junctions of many mountain arcs and in such great ranges as the Himalayas, Alps, and Rocky Mountains, complexities defy classification of this kind.

2. Some important mountains find no place in this arrangement—for example, the Carpathians and Pyrenees and the mountains of the Isthmus of Panama and other parts of Central America south of Mexico.

3. Pre-Cenozoic mountains do not seem to be arranged in great-circle systems. Older structures undoubtedly influenced later structural developments. Parts of the present arcs began to form in Mesozoic time, and, if the relations that this theory proposes actually exist, correspondence between present and ancient arcs should be more evident.

4. If arcs are related to preceding centers of thick sedimentary accumulation, the Marianas arc, on which Guam is located (see Figure 87, p. 247), and some other less prominent ones in the western Pacific Ocean are anomalous. These lie far from any continent, are distant from thick and extensive sedimentary accumulations, and are situated outside of other arcs that have not completed their structural development.

5. Some islands of the arcs, such as the Philippines, contain Tertiary formations with much quartz sand for which there is, at present, no obvious source. These young formations, now raised above the sea, indicate that in fairly recent geologic time an important land area existed closer than the continent of Asia. The conclusion seems justified that this land has subsided deeply beneath the adjacent sea. If so, arc development has not necessarily resulted in enlargement of the continents.

6. The occurrence of some great intrusive bodies like the Idaho batholith, as well as other smaller ones, appears to be out of place. Such bodies were emplaced at a late stage of development in some structural elements that are identified as inner arcs. This theory provides no explanation, however, for such occurrences in secondary or outer arcs, or in the regions intervening between primary and secondary arcs.

7. It does not seem likely that the Pacific ranges and the Rocky Mountains of North America can be related as the primary and secondary parts of a single tectonic system such as this theory postulates. Rocks certainly are too weak to transmit compressive forces across the great distances that separate these ranges.

Comparison of Theories

None of the foregoing theories provides an entirely satisfactory explanation for the origin, development, and stabilization of geosynclines as structural features or for the sedimentary deposits that accumulated in them. On the whole and in spite of its imperfections, the mountain arc theory comes closest to being adequate. This theory is a good example of the many that have been suggested or strongly influenced by generalizations and the doubtful significance of more or less fanciful patterns recognized in geographic, topographic, or structural relationships. Thus it is closely akin to the orogen and magma blister theories, which attempt to explain different generalizations of exactly the same features (see Figure 100 and Figures 89 and 90, pp. 255, 256). Even if it succeeds in part, the mountain arc theory, like any other based on generalizations, is likely to be too simple and incomplete because generalization suppresses complicating details, some of which may be of great importance.

An effort can be made to test these geosynclinal theories by considering their implications with respect to the mutual relations of ocean basins and continents and their effects on sea-level changes.

Sea level is determined by the capacity of the ocean basins and the volume of water they contain. These relations are altered mainly by (1) gradual filling of the basins by land-derived sediments, (2) additions of juvenile magmatic water to the sea, and (3) structural readjustments between the ocean basins and the continents. The first two cause sea level to rise gradually. The last must involve enlargement or deepening of the basins or rise of continents; otherwise the continents could not persist as land. Other causes of fluctuating sea level, such as expansion and contraction of continental glaciers, are minor by comparison and can account for variations of no more than a few hundred feet.

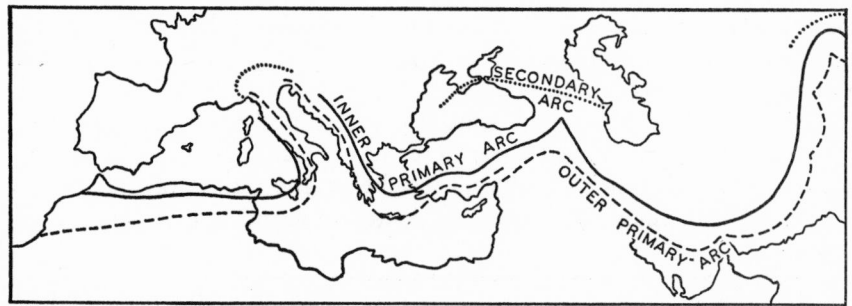

Figure 100.   Map of the Mediterranean region showing Wilson's identification of the outer and inner primary arcs and the best-developed secondary arcs. (After Wilson, 1954, *The earth as a planet*, p. 165, fig. 11, by permission of the University of Chicago Press and G. P. Kuiper.)

Some theories postulate the growth of continents by marginal geosynclinal accretion. This process would decrease the area of ocean basins, and sea level would rise. In order to be maintained as land the entire continents would have to rise even more rapidly because they were constantly subject to the destructive action of erosion. In contrast, other theories postulate foundering of former portions of the continents that furnished sediments to geosynclines. This would increase basin areas, and sea level would fall unless the basins were concurrently filled with sediment.

Evidence of long-term sea-level variation is more or less contradictory. No certainly identified deep-sea sediment is known in any land area of the world today except perhaps on a very few islands of outer arcs such as Timor in the East Indies and Barbados in the West Indies. Red clay of possible abyssal origin has been reported on both of these islands. On the other hand, areas along all three types of coast (see p. 246) appear to have subsided beneath the sea. The peneplane below sediments of the North American Atlantic coast has been traced by seismograph to depths of more than 15,000 feet (see Figure 84, p. 244). A considerable area off the southern California coast almost certainly has been downfaulted 4000 feet or more (see Figure

86, p. 245). Also some sediments on islands of the arcs seem to record the presence of important land areas where now there is moderately deep sea.

The possible foundering of continental regions has been denied repeatedly because seismic and gravitational evidence does not indicate the occurrence of a thick continental sial layer anywhere beneath the ocean. Uplift or depression of any large part of the earth's surface presumably demands the transfer of sialic material in order that isostasy may be maintained. The presence of marine sediments and fossils many thousands of feet above sea level and particularly the elevation of extensive regions like the Colorado plateaus and the great Tibetan uplands demonstrate that such transfer probably has taken place. The addition of sial to the crust beneath such regions has been considered possible but its abstraction below others that have subsided correspondingly has been regarded as unlikely. This reasoning does not seem to be well founded.

Flat-topped Pacific seamounts are believed to be former volcanic islands whose summits were planed down to sea level by erosion. Their various elevations, ranging from 3000 to 6000 feet below the surface of the sea (see Figure 101), therefore, have been considered to record former stands of sea

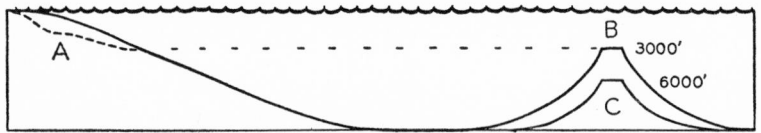

Figure 101.   Schematic section illustrating the relations of submarine canyons and flat-topped seamounts of the Pacific Ocean. A shows Monterey canyon off the California coast. B and C represent the general depth limits of the seamounts. Some submarine canyons are reported to have been traced to depths much greater than 3000 feet.

level. The opinion has been expressed that they date from very ancient times, probably Precambrian, when the seas held much less water than at present and before reef-forming organisms had evolved. Otherwise they would have been built up slowly as sea level rose and they would now be atolls. Shallow-water Cretaceous fossils have been dredged from some seamounts, however —apparently good evidence that these submerged islands do not date back to much earlier times. In contrast, submarine canyons that incise the continental shelf and continue to depths comparable to summits of the seamounts have been interpreted as dating only from the Pleistocene Epoch. A plausible explanation for their erosion by turbidity currents without the necessity of greatly lowered sea level has been presented.

Relative sea level has not been constant but has fluctuated within moderate limits throughout all geologic time. Withdrawal and return of sea water occasioned by the cycle of Pleistocene continental glaciation are well established. In earlier times extensive marine flooding of the continents occurred as during the Ordovician and Cretaceous periods but involved no great rise of sea level and was temporary. At present sea level may be slightly lower than its average throughout the past. On the whole no large change in the capacity of the ocean basins has been demonstrated with any reasonable degree of certainty. Therefore, the extensive growth of continents by marginal accretion since at least Precambrian time can be doubted.

Conclusions

Most of the sediment in the Appalachian geosyncline seems to have been derived from some kind of borderland more extensive than volcanic islands like those of modern island arcs and differently constituted. The borderland, however, probably was not such an ancient and persistent land mass as was formerly believed and it may not have extended along the entire Atlantic coastline simultaneously. Possibly its position changed from time to time.

Late Precambrian and early Cambrian sediments seem to have been carried outward from the continent. They formed very thick deposits in the early stages of Appalachian geosynclinal development. These contributed to the depression of a subsiding trough. Basic submarine lava flows broke out along its outer margin and interfingered with the sediments. A ridge began to rise in this position. Part of it became emergent and bore volcanoes. At the same time the continental platform sank shallowly beneath the sea. Subsequently the ridge was greatly elevated first in one area and then in another in several main pulses of activity. It was deformed, its rocks were metamorphosed, and its core was granitized. It grew unevenly in width. The sediments on its flanks were progressively involved in its deformation. This borderland occupied the position of the present Piedmont, and its erosion provided sediments derived from older sedimentary formations, metamorphosed strata, and plutonic rocks. An important part of the sediments was deposited in the subsiding geosynclinal trough immediately to the northwest. The thick and coarsely detrital formations of different ages identify those parts of the borderland that were currently most active. Presumably an equal quantity of sediment was carried eastward into the Atlantic basin.

Toward the close of the Paleozoic Era the geosyncline was compressed and its strata were folded and faulted. Thereafter activity in the borderland rapidly declined. In Triassic time mountainous ridges were elevated by faulting and some lava was erupted but soon this region was worn down by erosion. By mid-Mesozoic time the borderland had achieved relative stability. It was nearly peneplaned, and subsidence began that has continued intermittently in its outer part until the present. At the same time the deformed geosyncline was moderately elevated.

The mechanism responsible for earth movements in and near the Appalachian geosyncline is unexplained. Phase change at depth does not seem to provide the answer because it appears exceedingly unlikely that such changes acting in opposite ways would simultaneously characterize the sinking geosyncline and the closely adjacent borderland for a very long period of time. More probably the mechanism involved the lateral movement of large volumes of material by subcrustal flow that, for some unknown reason, began, continued throughout much of the Paleozoic Era, then ceased, and finally was reversed.

Conditions and the sequence of events in the Paleozoic geosyncline along the Pacific coast of North America may have been considerably different (see Figure 102). Unfortunately this region is too incompletely known to permit comparison in any detail. There are some indications that the western geosyncline was much wider and that sediments were delivered to it both from the continental platform on one side and from an archipelago of volcanic islands on the other.

Geosynclines are very important in stratigraphy. Since the beginning of

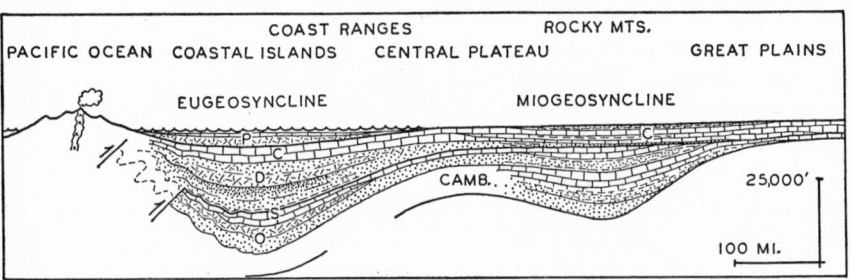

Figure 102. Reconstruction of the Cordilleran geosyncline of western Canada near the end of Permian time. Relations to modern geography are indicated above. The eugeosyncline is filled largely with volcanic deposits and graywacke derived from islands that later sank beneath the Pacific Ocean. The miogeosyncline was the depositional site of limestone and detrital sediments eroded from the continental region to the east. (After Eardley, 1947, J. Geol., vol. 55, p. 342, fig. 9.)

the Cambrian Period, much of the detrital sediment now constituting the stratified rocks of the continents originated in or adjacent to geosynclines. These sediments cannot be interpreted completely unless their origin is understood. Many times the geosynclines or parts of them also acted as great sediment traps lying between the sedimentary sources and the continental platforms. The nature, form, and tectonic activity of the geosynclines exercised a dominating control over the kind, quantity, and distribution of detrital sediments that reached the platforms. If the geosynclines were depressed, all coarse material may have lodged within them. If they were filled, widespread distribution of sands and silts was possible. Consequently the characters of sediments on the continental platforms and in the continental basins reflect both local and geosynclinal activity.

Although geosynclines undoubtedly are real, they are not well enough understood to permit the framing of a definition satisfactory to all geologists. Therefore the geosyncline remains a concept whose essential features are not agreed upon. Geosynclines might be better understood if it were possible to recognize and study present-day examples. Unfortunately a geosyncline does not seem to be identifiable with certainty until it has reached its final orogenic stage. Thick successions of sediments of geosynclinal magnitude are accumulating now in some regions, as along the American Gulf coast (see Figure 103), but mostly they appear to lack some of the essentials.

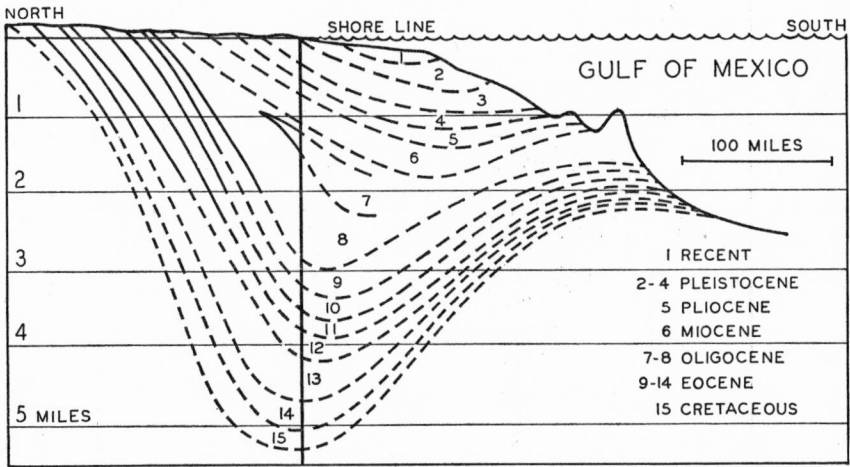

Figure 103.   Cross section showing the presumed form of post-Cretaceous sediments in the Gulf coast region. Southward dips and sedimentary thickening have been established by drilling, but details beneath the Gulf of Mexico are largely conjectural. (After Storm, 1945, Bull. Am. Assoc. Petroleum Geol., vol. 29, p. 1329, fig. 8.)

The Gulf coast lacks an adjacent highland area or island arc. Perhaps the Indo-Gangetic alluvial plain at the foot of the Himalayas is an example of a modern geosyncline. If the continents were not now so abnormally high and if this region were flooded by the sea, it might seem more typical. Mesopotamia and the Persian Gulf provide another possible example (see Figures 104 and 105). Perhaps the best of all is the lowland and shallow-water belt north of the volcanic mountains of Sumatra and Java (zone 6, see p. 259). A rather close parallel might be drawn between this region and the Appalachian geosyncline. If the possible similarities are significant, the relations of geosynclines to tectogenes or comparable structures are quite different from those that have been suggested. Finally, the possibility should not be neglected that geosynclines are not all the same and that similar structural and stratigraphic situations do not surely indicate exactly similar origins and development.

The stratigraphy of geosynclinal regions is unusually difficult to study. The sedimentary succession is very thick and commonly important parts of it are monotonously similar. Profound lateral changes in lithology and scar-

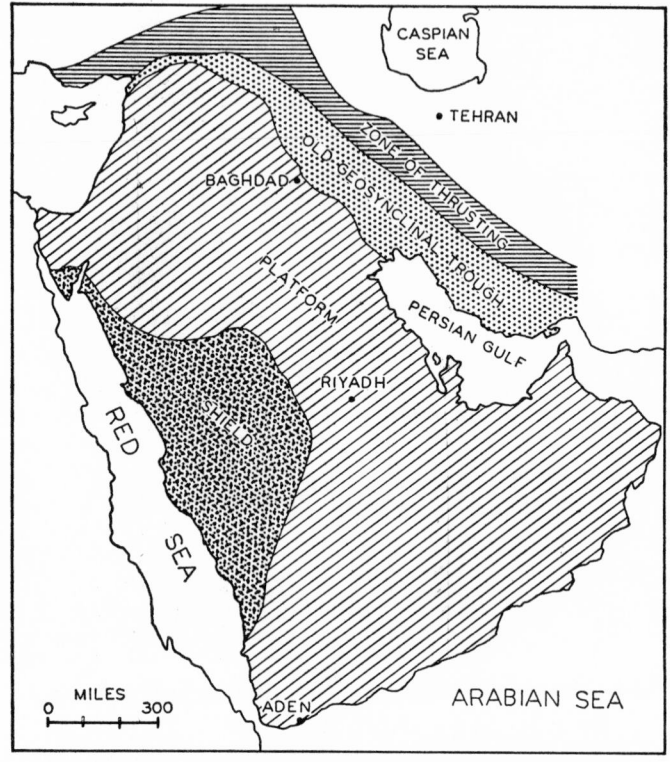

Figure 104.   Generalized map showing the main geologic features of the Persian Gulf region. The oil produced here comes from the transitional zone between the old geosyncline and the sedimentary platform. (After Law, 1957, *Bull. Am. Assoc. Petroleum Geol.*, vol. 41, p. 54, fig. 2.)

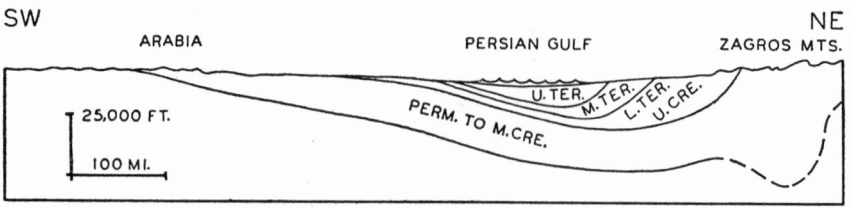

Figure 105.   Greatly generalized geologic cross section of the Persian Gulf region which does not show post-Pliocene folding. Since Cretaceous time the trough of thickest sedimentary accumulation appears to have migrated gradually southwestward. (Modified from Law, 1957, *Bull. Am. Assoc. Petroleum Geol.*, vol. 41, p. 55, fig. 3.)

city of fossils in some parts are likely to contribute to uncertain correlations. Structure is complex and involves both folding and extensive overthrusting. Metamorphism may be severe and add a further obstacle in the deeply eroded central parts of geosynclines. Altogether geosynclinal stratigraphy provides a rigorous test of the abilities of the most competent geologist.

Continental Platforms

Those portions of the continents that lie between or beyond the geosynclines are the continental platforms. Division between these two types of differently characterized tectonic regions, however, is not immutable. Geosynclines have a span of active existence—they originate, develop, and expire.

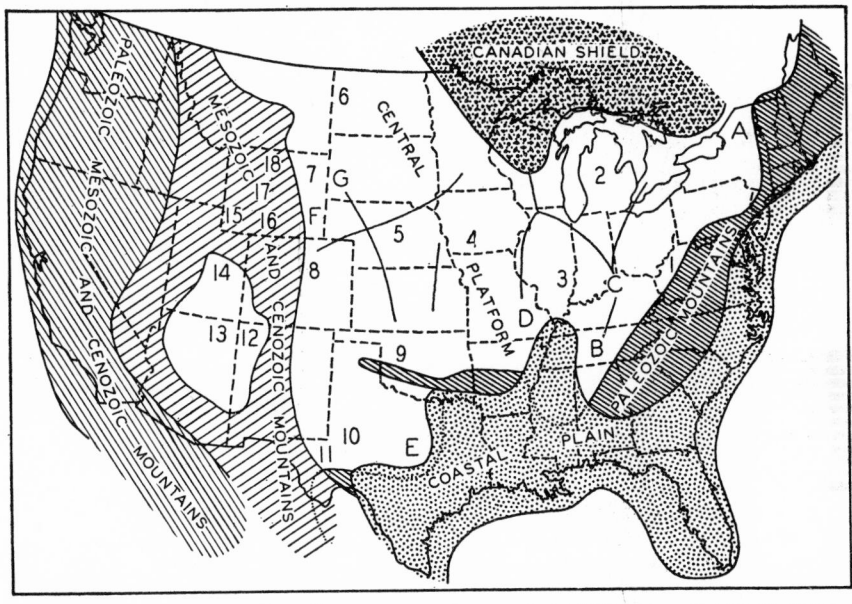

DOMES	F-HARTVILLE	3-ILLINOIS	9-ANADARKO	15-GREEN RIVER
A-ADIRONDACK	G-BLACK HILLS	4-FOREST CITY	10-MIDLAND	16-WASHAKIE
B-NASHVILLE		5-SALINA	11-DELAWARE	17-WIND RIVER
C-LEXINGTON	BASINS	6-WILLISTON	12-SAN JUAN	18-BIG HORN
D-OZARK	1-APPALACHIAN	7-POWDER RIVER	13-BLACK MESA	
E-LLANO	2-MICHIGAN	8-DENVER	14-UINTA	

Figure 106. Map showing the major structural features of the United States. Arches are shown in the central platform region by lines but their names are not indicated. The structures were variously active at different times. Most of those of the central platform region are of Paleozoic age, and the western ones are hidden beneath post-Paleozoic sediments. The Black Hills dome (G), the Hartville uplift (F), and the Powder River basin (7) are younger and are related to Rocky Mountain structures. The western basins also are younger and mostly they are margined by uplifts that are mountainous at present. (Compiled from various sources including King, 1944, *Tectonic map of the United States.*)

Divisions of a continent, therefore, at different times have not been the same. Precambrian geosynclines ran their course, tectonic patterns changed, and these old mobile zones became stabilized and have since behaved as parts of a stable continental platform. The Appalachian geosyncline had a similar but later history. It now is apparently part of a stable platform region. New geosynclines may follow old geosynclinal trends or diverge widely from them. Geosynclines and platforms, therefore, must be dated. Divisions of the modern continents, however, generally are not classified in accordance with present tectonic activity but with reference to the rocks and structures now occurring at the surface. Thus the divisions that are recognized throughout much of central and eastern North America are Paleozoic divisions.

The continental platforms are not homogeneous regions. Although they possess far greater stability than do geosynclines, they are not uniformly stable. On the basis of more or less local tectonic activity that finds expression in the development of basins, arches, and large domes, or the lack of it, they may be separated into stable and unstable platform areas (see Figure 106).

Stable Platform Areas

The Canadian shield in North America and somewhat comparable regions in other continents commonly have been looked upon as stable nuclei that remained unchanged throughout very long ages of geologic history. They are the great regions of Precambrian rocks, and the opinion has been widely held that they have never been submerged beneath the sea or covered by younger strata. The complex Precambrian structures are ample evidence that these regions have had a long and varied tectonic history and suffered deep erosion. Many difficulties and uncertainties of correlation, however, make the reading of their records nearly impossible except in broadest outline.

Except along its southern border, much of the Canadian shield is poorly known or unexplored geologically but, so far as information is available, it has been a relatively stable region since the beginning of Paleozoic time. Its surface, which is generally considered to be a late Precambrian peneplane little altered by subsequent erosion, rises as a gentle dome of vast dimensions indented by the sag of Hudson Bay. So far as knowledge goes, this surface has not been warped into depressions or elevations comparable to the basins and arches that characterize the Paleozoic terrain of the central and eastern United States but it has not survived half a billion years totally unchanged. Faulting has produced some long scarps, beautifully shown in aerial photographs. Also a few remnants of fossiliferous Paleozoic rocks are preserved well in from the present margin in downfaulted blocks. The latter are evidence of marine submergence that may have extended over the whole shield. Perhaps a comparatively thin cover, now stripped away by erosion, was an important factor in the preservation of the peneplane. Submergence in itself does not imply instability, however, because sea level undoubtedly has fluctuated to some extent eustatically. Moderate elevation and depression of the shield as well as some gentle warping probably also has occurred.

Unstable Platform Areas

This Precambrian surface dips beneath younger strata southward and westward and within a comparatively short distance reaches depths rarely attained in drilling. In many areas the position of the Precambrian surface is uncertain and very little is known about the details of its configuration. Broad structures in Paleozoic strata demonstrate, however, that this surface has been strongly warped. In the Michigan basin, for example, it subsided nearly 15,000 feet, as shown by Figure 107. This and similar warping in other basins was accomplished slowly during almost the entire Paleozoic Era. It was accompanied by the deposition of a comparably thick and dominantly marine stratigraphic section. These movements ended at or shortly after the close of the Paleozoic Era and the region probably was peneplaned by mid-Cretaceous time. At about the beginning of the Mesozoic Era, therefore, the tectonic nature of the region was completely altered. An unstable portion of the continental platform became stabilized. It has since maintained a position above sea level, and little or no further subsidence in the basins has occurred.

This transformation of an unstable platform region to a stable one and the consequent enlargement of an older stable region is striking and remarkable. Perhaps the peripheral growth in stability might be considered evidence favorable to the theory of peripherally growing continents.

An unstable platform region is characterized by the slow growth of large structural features that eventually may attain considerable proportions. Generally there appears to be relationship between marine submergence, sedimentary deposition, and this type of instability. Thus the Canadian shield, which probably was emergent during much of the Paleozoic Era and did not support a thick sedimentary cover, has been stable whereas the adjoining region to the south, submerged repeatedly and deeply buried, was unstable. In post-Paleozoic time when the southern region became emergent it also achieved stability.

The structures of an unstable platform region consist of (1) arches and large domes that are commonly considered to be positive structural areas, and (2) basins that are negative (see Figure 106).

Arches and Domes

The condition of the North American continental platform south of the Canadian shield at the beginning of the Paleozoic Era is not known. A thick succession of pre-Upper Cambrian detrital strata from which no fossils

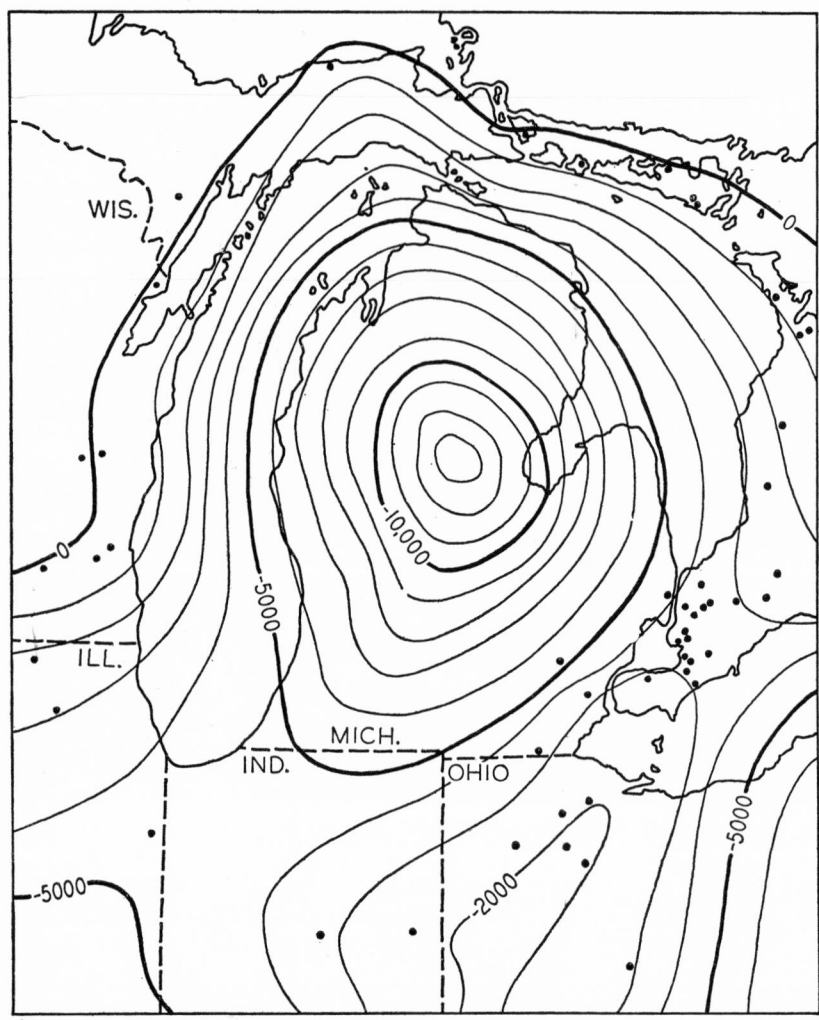

Figure 107. Structural contour map of the Michigan basin and neighboring areas showing the position of the top of the Precambrian rocks. Subsurface control is shown by dots. Contours in the central basin area are based on isopach studies. (After Cohee, 1945, U.S. Geol. Surv., Oil and Gas Invest., Prelim. Chart 9.)

have been recovered is present deep below the surface in the Michigan basin and in the northern part of the Illinois basin. Although these strata may be either earlier Cambrian or late Precambrian, they are evidence that at least one sedimentary basin existed at that time. Its extent and the nature and position of its boundaries have not been determined but one of them probably was a ridge that extended along its western side southward from Wisconsin to the Ozark area.

The Ozark and Adirondack domes and the Llano region of central Texas may be inheritances from Precambrian structure. They generally have been referred to as positive areas although their principal role was resistance to subsidence. While neighboring areas sank intermittently, they approximately maintained their original positions and in this respect closely resemble the Canadian shield.

It is not known whether the arches now dividing the unstable platform region into a number of large basins correspond to Precambrian structural trends. Perhaps they do not because little evidence of warping along their axes has been recognized in early Paleozoic strata whereas movement became progressively more important later. At the beginning of the Paleozoic Era the platform may have been relatively featureless. To the east, west, and possibly south, however, it dipped gradually beneath developing geosynclines.

From late Cambrian time to the end of the Paleozoic Era, the unstable portion of the platform was alternately shallowly submerged and slightly emergent. Sediments of many kinds accumulated on it. It experienced progressive subsidence as a whole but the basins sank most deeply. Thus the arches are not actually positive in the sense that they were elevated. They are only less negative than the basins.

The term *geanticline* was introduced originally as the antithesis of geosyncline. It has been used extensively for arches like the large broad Cincinnati anticline. It has also been applied to such theoretical structures as an uparched borderland or a geosynclinal welt supposedly separating a miogeosyncline from a eugeosyncline. On the whole this word has been employed so indiscriminately that it has no specific useful meaning.

Basins

Large basins are the identifying features of an unstable continental platform region. They are evidence of important localized inequalities of subsidence in a generally subsiding region. Such subsidence was maintained for long periods of time and probably was accompanied by the displacement of large volumes of material in the underlying crust. The Michigan basin, for example, indicates displacement of this kind in the order of about 60,000 cubic miles. If evenly apportioned throughout the Paleozoic Era, this amounts to about a million cubic yards per year. Displacement of this magnitude is very great but it is relatively minor in comparison with geosynclines, where, in an equivalent segment, probably five to ten times as much subsidence and displacement occurred.

General parallelism in the histories of the Paleozoic unstable platform in the central and eastern United States and the Appalachian geosyncline indicates that they were closely bound by some relationship. If isostatic equilibrium was approximately maintained, material displaced from beneath the basins did not simply flow to the areas of the arches because these were sub-siding also. The conclusion seems inescapable that, if transfer by deep flow-age did occur, it extended outward toward the zone where upward move-ment, whether this was upbowing of a borderland or the rise of lava in a eugeosyncline, raised sediment-producing uplands. The differential forces acting on stable and unstable regions, areas, and zones may have been relatively small. Sedimentary loading of the submerged portion of the plat-form may have accentuated subsidence and expedited outward flowage there. Perhaps this was all that was required to maintain the process, which did not occur in the generally emergent region of the shield, where similar sedimentary loading was not effective. Such an explanation, however, does not account for the origin and continuance of subsidence in individual ba-sins.

If the Paleozoic basins were not filled with sediment, their topographic form would rival that of many oceanic basins behind island arcs and many mountain-rimmed terrestrial basins. Comparison, however, is not exact be-cause the origins of these basins probably were very different. The Paleozoic platform basins perhaps never would have subsided greatly if the subterra-nean forces acting on them had not been supplemented by the weight of sediments accumulating in them. If this is true, the water in the basins never could have been deep and such a conclusion seems to be substantiated by the nature of the rocks and fossils they contain.

Stratigraphic sections show that the growth of basins was not uniform. At some times they sank and filled with sediment more rapidly than at oth-ers (see Figure 180, p. 486). Also subsidence may have ceased entirely dur-ing some intervals of time and the basins were temporarily stabilized.

The structural history of a basin is recorded by the strata that it contains. A structural contour map of any horizon approximating a stratigraphic time plane is a reasonably close representation of the amount of subsidence that has occurred since the underlying stratum was deposited. This is not exact because the contoured horizon was not originally horizontal. The deposi-tional surface corresponding to a time plane lay at different elevations be-neath different depths of water, but a discrepancy of this kind, ordinarily amounting to no more than a few hundred feet in a basin 200 miles or more in diameter, introduces an error that is negligible for all practical purposes. Further error results because sediments later were compacted beneath the weight of overburden, but in most large areas such errors probably are not great.

In a similar way an isopach map shows, with the same types of error, how much subsidence occurred within the time limits represented by the strata from the base of the measured unit to the base of the overlying one. Sim-ilar errors apply to each isopached stratigraphic interval. Errors resulting from the non-horizontality of strata as originally deposited mostly cancel each other and are not cumulative. Those introduced by compaction, however, accumulate and if thick stratigraphic sections are involved they may become appreciable. The information furnished by isopachs does not indicate exactly when the subsidence occurred. If the isopached stratigraphic interval is large, representing perhaps one or more geologic systems, it may be desirable to date the subsidence more closely if that is possible. In this connection three different types of structural relations require consideration (see Figure 108):

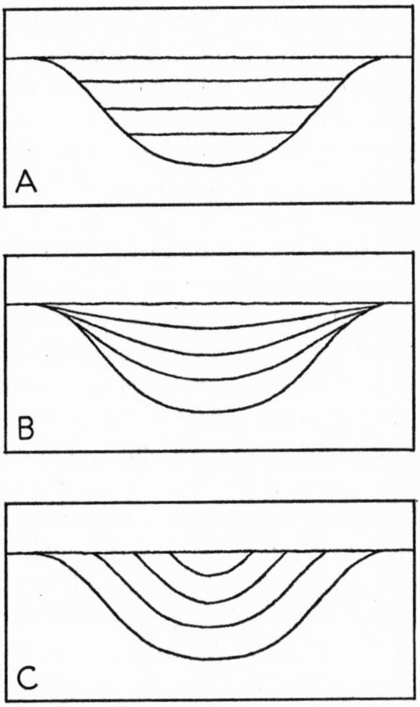

1. Subsidence occurred before deposition of the isopached strata. In this case the strata were deposited in a depression and they should overstep each other and each stratigraphic subdivision should extend farther outward toward the basin margins.

2. Subsidence occurred concurrently with deposition of the isopached strata. In this case there would be no overstepping and all stratigraphic subdivisions would thin systematically toward the margins of the basin.

3. Subsidence occurred after deposition of the isopached strata but before deposition of the overlying unit. In this case stratigraphic subdivisions would neither overstep nor thin outward in the basin. They would all rise uniformly toward the basin margins and be cut off above by an unconformity at the base of the overlying unit.

In an actual situation any one, two,

Figure 108. Diagrammatic sections illustrating the structural relations of strata occurring in a depressed basin. A. Deposition followed subsidence. B. Deposition was concurrent with subsidence. C. Deposition preceded subsidence. Isopach data do not distinguish between these possibilities.

or all three of these relationships might occur in different subdivisions of the isopached unit. Also the relations might be dissimilar on different sides of the same basin. In subsurface studies the assessment of these possibilities is likely to be difficult and uncertain.

TECTONIC INTERPRETATIONS

No sharp structural demarcation can be made between basins and the arches that bound and separate them. Insofar, however, as these structures were reflected by topographic inequalities at any time, they may have influenced contemporary deposition. Thus if the arches or domes rose above the level of the basins, they may have formed islands in a shallow sea. Even if they did not project above sea level, differences in water depth might affect the type of sediment that accumulated.

The oceans of today do not provide many parallels to conditions as they existed in most of the epicontinental seas that flooded North America. Hudson Bay and the Baltic Sea are the only water bodies closely comparable to these ancient more or less landlocked seas. Most parts of the present continental shelf are subject to tides, currents, and great storms of the open ocean that certainly affect the transportation and deposition of sediment. The ancient epicontinental seas generally were more placid than present open coasts and this should make the interpretation of their more uniform sediments much easier.

The identification of various types of depositional environments, as these are indicated by sediments and fossils, has been discussed in previous chapters. Mostly the effects of local environments such as those determined by depth of water and distance from the shore have been emphasized. These are the types of environments whose variations commonly were related to local tectonic activity expressed most clearly in the subsidence of geosynclines and platform basins and in more general gentle tilting of the platform.

In much work devoted to sedimentary facies analysis, this facet of interpretation, and particularly the influence of local tectonic tendencies, appears to be overemphasized. For example, it has been held that graywacke is characteristic of geosynclines, subgraywacke of basins (termed unstable shelf areas), and limestone of arches (considered stable areas). The implication likewise seems to be that these sedimentary types do not occur in other situations. These generalizations are not entirely justified.

Obviously, no sediment can be deposited anywhere unless sediment is provided. The occurrence of limestone indicates that detrital sediment was not abundant and that lime-secreting organisms were fairly plentiful. Limestone can form in shallow moderately warm seas wherever these conditions prevail. Limestone could be and was deposited in geosynclines, where it records an environment of this kind. Limestone constitutes much of the stratigraphic section in the Paleozoic basins. At some times of limestone and other nondetrital deposition the basins were as tectonically active as they were when detrital material accumulated in them. The Michigan basin during late Silurian time is an outstanding example (see Figure 180, p. 486).

Relating sediments to the local tectonic environment can furnish no more than half of the explanation for their occurrence and it may be the less important half. The same sediment actually is related within a much larger frame of reference extending all the way back to its source wherever that may have been. Its characters and distribution also furnish information regarding the larger tectonic features of the continent. Moreover, characters and distribution are the only remaining record of such features. If geologic history is to be reconstructed with any degree of completeness, this aspect of sedimentary interpretation cannot be neglected.

For example, much of the Paleozoic detrital sediment deposited within what is now the eastern half of the United States originated in a highland adjacent to, or islands rising in, the Appalachian geosyncline and its possible extension as the Ouachita geosyncline to the southwest. During much of early and middle Paleozoic time most of the detrital material accumulated in the geosynclines. Little was carried far inward and distributed over the interior platform region. The geosyncline acted as an efficient sediment trap and limestone or dolomite characterizes the interior. Where these strata are interrupted by detrital sediments, the latter consist mostly of material carried southward from the Canadian shield. At a few times, however, the geosynclines subsided less rapidly than they were filled. Their effectiveness as traps then decreased, and fine detritus was transported across them in suspension to settle on the platform as extensive formations like the Maquoketa-Sylvan Shale (Ord.).

In the latter half of the Devonian Period conditions began to change. The Appalachian geosyncline sank more slowly and the borderland probably grew in size. The trough was completely filled. Detrital sediment built the Catskill delta out onto and over the edge of the continental platform. During the Mississippian, filling of the trough continued, extending southward, and detrital material reached farther across the platform. At the beginning of the Pennsylvanian Period no open trough remained. Some subsidence continued but it did not keep pace with deposition of greater quantities of sediment derived from a larger and more extensive borderland. Most of the continental platform south of Canada at least was blanketed with sandy and silty sediment different from any that had reached this region previously. The geosyncline had nearly completed its tectonic evolution. The final stage of its history is somewhat doubtful because no adequate sedimentary record has been preserved.

BIBLIOGRAPHY

Bemmelen, R. W. van (1949), *The geology of Indonesia*, vol. 1, The Hague, Government Printing office.
    Chapter 4, pp. 257–297, discusses geophysical problems in relation to island arcs.
Bentley, C. R., and Worzel, J. L. (1956), Geophysical investigations in the emerged and submerged Atlantic coastal plain, pt. 10, Continental slope and continental rise south of the Grand Banks, *Bull. Geol. Soc. Amer.*, vol. 67, pp. 1–18.

The authors report on the results of seismic studies and interpret crustal structure.

Bucher, W. H. (1933), *The deformation of the earth's crust*, Princeton Univ. Press. (Reprinted 1957, New York, Hafner.)

This book describes broad-scale structures of the earth and develops a theory for their formation based on alternate expansion and contraction.

Bullard, Sir Edward (1954), The interior of the earth, in *The earth as a planet*, G. P. Kuiper (ed.), Univ. of Chicago Press, pp. 57–137.

See pp. 61–75 for a consideration of the relations of seismic waves to layering in the outer part of the earth.

Dietz, R. S. (1954), Marine geology of northwestern Pacific; description of Japanese bathymetric chart 6901, *Bull. Geol. Soc. Amer.*, vol. 65, pp. 1199–1224.

The geomorphology and geology of about one-sixth of the Pacific Ocean floor are described and interpreted.

Eardley, A. J. (1951), *Structural geology of North America*, New York, Harper.

This book is largely descriptive of structure and structural development of mountainous regions and the continental borders.

Eardley, A. J. (1957), The cause of mountain building—an enigma, *Amer. Scientist*, vol. 45, pp. 189–217.

In an excellent semipopular account mountain structure is discussed and theories are presented to explain it.

Ewing, J. I., Officer, C. B., Johnson, H. R., and Edwards, R. S. (1957), Geophysical investigations in the eastern Caribbean: Trinidad shelf, Tobago trough, Barbados ridge, Atlantic Ocean, *Bull. Geol. Soc. Amer.*, vol. 68, pp. 897–912.

The results of seismic studies in the West Indies are reported and geologic interpretations are suggested.

Gilluly, James (1955), Geologic contrasts between continents and ocean basins, Geol. Soc. Amer., Spec. Paper 62, pp. 7–18.

Deep transfer of material within the earth's crust and mantle is necessary to account for uplift or depression of large areas and changes in the relations of continents and oceans.

Glaessner, M. F., and Teichert, C. (1947), Geosynclines: a fundamental concept in geology, *Am. J. Sci.*, vol. 245, pp. 465–482 and 571–591.

An account is given of the origin and subsequent development of geosynclinal concepts.

Guilcher, André (1958), *Coastal and submarine morphology*, London, Methuen.

See pp. 195–259 for description and explanation of submarine topographic features.

Heezen, B. C., and Tharp, M. (1957), Physiographic diagram, Atlantic Ocean (sheet 1), Columbia Univ., Lamont Geol. Observatory; reprinted 1957, *Bell Syst. Tech. Jour.*, 1958, Geol. Soc. Amer., vol. 36, no. 5.

Submarine topography as revealed by soundings is sketched in considerable detail.

Heezen, B. C., Tharp, M., and Ewing, M. W. (1959), The floors of the oceans. I: The North Atlantic, Geol. Soc. Amer., Spec. Paper 65.

This report is a descriptive account to accompany the physiographic diagram of the North Atlantic, sheet 1.

Howell, B. F., Jr. (1959), Introduction to geophysics, New York, McGraw-Hill. See particularly Chapters 4, Geochronology; 15, Isostasy; 17, Origin of continents; and 21, Cause of mountain building.

Kay, Marshall (1951), North American geosynclines, Geol. Soc. Amer., Mem. 48. The many types of so-called geosynclines occurring in North America are classified and described.

King, P. B. (1944), Tectonic map of the United States, prepared under the direction of the Committee on Tectonics, Division of Geology and Geography, National Research Council, material compiled by committee members, C. R. Longwell, chairman, arranged for printing by P. B. King, Tulsa, Am. Assoc. Petroleum Geol.; scale 1:2,500,000, 2 sheets in color.

King, P. B. (1951) *The tectonics of middle North America*, Princeton Univ. Press.
This is a condensed but comprehensive description of structure east of the Rocky Mountains.

King, P. B. (1959), The evolution of North America, Princeton Univ. Press.
This book discusses structure with special reference to theories of continental growth.

Kuenen, P. H. (1950), *Marine geology*, New York, Wiley.
Submarine canyons are described and their erosion is attributed to turbidity currents in Chapter 7, pp. 480–526.

Longwell, C. R. (1923), Kober's theory of orogeny, *Bull. Geol. Soc. Amer.*, vol. 34, pp. 231–241.
A theory of orogens based mainly on the form and continuity of mountains in the Mediterranean region is explained.

Reitan, P. H. (1959), Hypothesis accounting for a two-phase orogenic cycle, *J. Geol.*, vol. 67, pp. 129–134.
Alternate tension and compression in geosynclines result from reversal of movement in convection cells.

Rich, J. L. (1951), Origin of compressional mountains and associated phenomena, *Bull. Geol. Soc. Amer.*, vol. 62, pp. 1179–1222.
A theory relating geosynclines to the development of great magma blisters is presented.

Scheidegger, A. E. (1958), *Principles of geodynamics*, Berlin, Springer.
Chapters 5 and 6, pp. 134–220, analyze mathematically the physical implications of theories explaining the formation of continents and mountains. All theories appear to be inadequate.

Schuchert, Charles (1923), Sites and nature of the North American geosynclines, *Bull. Geol. Soc. Amer.*, vol. 34, pp. 151–230.
The relations of borderlands and geosynclines are described; included is an atlas of 17 paleogeographic maps.

Sitter, L. U. de (1956), *Structural geology*, New York, McGraw-Hill.
Part 3, pp. 323–518, is devoted to descriptive and theoretical consideration of geotectonics.

Umbgrove, J. H. F. (1947), *The pulse of the earth*, 2nd ed., The Hague, Martinus Nijhoff.

Chapters 2 to 8, pp. 26–256, discuss problems and theories of earth structure.

Weeks, L. G. (1952), Factors of sedimentary basin development that control oil occurrence, *Bull. Am. Assoc. Petroleum Geol.*, vol. 36, pp. 2071–2124.
This article summarizes in a broad way the structure and presumed development of geosynclines and large basins.

Weeks, L. G. (1959), Geologic architecture of circum-Pacific, *Bull. Amer. Assoc. Petrol. Geol.*, vol. 43, pp. 350–380.
This article traces evolution of geosynclines with examples in various stages of development drawn from the Pacific borders.

Wilson, J. T. (1954), The development and structure of the crust, in *The earth as a planet*, G. P. Kuiper (ed.), Univ. of Chicago Press, pp. 138–214.
A lucid account is given of the theory that continents have grown by the accretion of peripheral arcuate mountains.

Woodward, H. P. (1957), Chronology of Appalachian folding, *Bull. Am. Assoc. Petroleum Geol.*, vol. 41, pp. 2312–2327.
Four episodes of mountain building are distinguished; Precambrian, pre-Silurian (Taconian), Devonian (Acadian), and terminal Paleozoic (Alleghenian).

9

Interpretation of Sedimentary Rocks

INTERPRETATION of the origin and history of a sedimentary rock is dependent upon the careful assessment of all its physical and biologic characters considered within the tectonic and local environmental framework of its time.

THE SEDIMENTARY CYCLE

Most sediments have been produced by the weathering and erosion of igneous rocks. The constituents of some sedimentary rocks were derived directly from igneous rocks and have passed through only one cycle of weathering, erosion, transportation, deposition, and diagenesis. Many, however, contain material derived from older sedimentary rocks which has passed through two or more such cycles. The older sedimentary rocks may or may not have been altered importantly by metamorphism (see Figure 109).

During its passage from igneous to present sedimentary rock, mineral matter has been subjected to the action of a succession of different processes one or more times. These may be grouped into four stages as follows:

1. Destruction
   a. Mechanical disintegration. This produced multigranular fragments of the parent rock and discrete mineral grains, mostly quartz and feldspar.
   b. Chemical weathering. This resulted in the partial or complete decomposi-

tion of the less stable minerals of the parent rock and the development of alteration products, of which the clay minerals are most important.

  c. Solution. This removed some of the original constituents of the parent rock and some of the alteration products resulting from chemical decomposition.

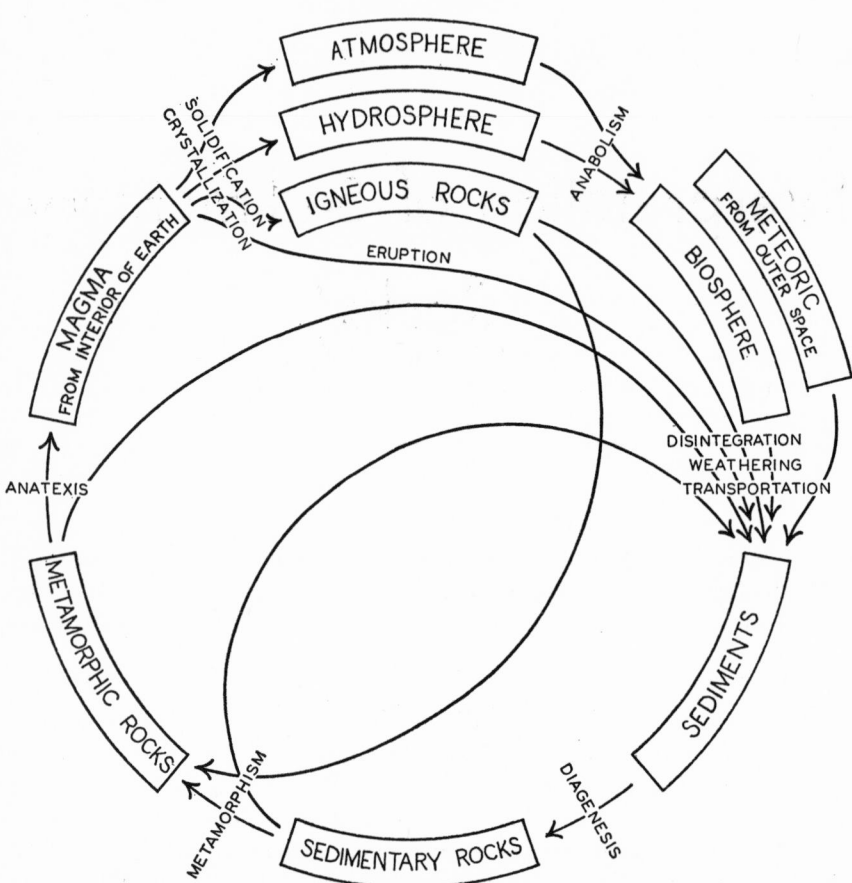

Figure 109. The petrologic cycle showing the relations of all rocks, the materials of which they are composed, and their derivatives. (Suggested by "The geochemical cycle," Mason, 1954, *The earth as a planet*, p. 296, fig. 2.)

2. Transportation

  d. Disintegrated and weathered material and dissolved substances were removed from the site of the parent rock and carried to the site of deposition. During transportation solid material suffered more or less mechanical wear, unstable minerals were further decomposed, and soluble substances passed into solution.

3. Deposition
   e. Mechanically transported material finally settled and remained in place and dissolved material was removed from solution to produce sedimentary deposits.
4. Reconstruction
   f. Compaction. As new sediment was deposited upon old, compaction resulted, volume and porosity were reduced, and density was increased.
   g. Cementation. Sedimentary particles were bound together by the deposition of cementing material of either indigenous or foreign origin.
   h. Recrystallization. This involved such mineralogic changes as the alteration of aragonite to calcite, the growth of some crystal grains at the expense of others, and some chemical rearrangements that produced new minerals.
   i. Replacement. The transfer and substitution of one mineral or mineral constituent for another involved either the rearrangement of indigenous material or the introduction of one substance and the removal of another. Replacement ordinarily has resulted in volume for volume exchange as in the formation of many chert nodules and the silicification of fossils. A related but somewhat different process resulted in gradual chemical and mineralogic change as in the substitution of magnesium for calcium in progressive dolomitization.

Most sedimentary rocks are complex accumulations of materials derived from one or more sources and altered from the original materials of the parent rocks. Many of them contain organic matter in addition to their mineral constituents, and this is not accounted for in the preceding outline. Generally the locations of the source areas and the nature of the parent rocks are imperfectly known. Except for deposits of most recent origin, the source areas and parent rocks have been destroyed or are buried so that they are not available for observation. With few exceptions, therefore, the sedimentary rocks and their enclosed fossils constitute the only evidence recording past geologic and geographic conditions and past physiographic processes. Only by observing the present rocks and their organic remains and attempting to trace each rock backward through its history and by recognizing and evaluating the successive changes that have been effected is it possible to reconstruct the geologic past.

With the foregoing processes in mind, every sedimentary rock should be examined from the standpoint of the following questions:
   1. What was the nature of the sediment before diagenesis?
   2. What was the environment of deposition?
   3. How was the sediment transported?
   4. Where was the source area?
   5. What were the topographic and climatic characters of the source area?
   6. What kinds of rock furnished the sediments?
A careful study of most sedimentary rocks will provide partial answers to

these questions. Because the rocks are known but their origins are not, their histories must be reconstructed in an order reversing that of their actual development.

DIAGENESIS

Processes chiefly involved in the diagenesis of sediments or the reconstruction of consolidated rock from its sedimentary components are (1) compaction, (2) cementation, (3) recrystallization, and (4) replacement as indicated in the preceding outline. These processes have been variously important in the diagenesis of different kinds of sediment. Ordinarily their results as shown by consolidated rocks have not greatly disguised the original characters of the sediments. Further metamorphism, however, can alter sedimentary rocks so profoundly that the original nature and previous history of the sediments cannot be determined. If a metamorphic stage occurs in the lineage of a sedimentary rock, it generally forms a barrier that cannot be surmounted. Consequently the discernible history of a sediment may be completely traceable to its igneous source or it may begin at some intermediate metamorphic stage.

Sandstone

Sandy sediments are comparatively little altered in their diagenetic transformation into sandstone. Their mineral composition generally is changed little or not at all. The two processes primarily responsible for consolidation are compaction and cementation.

Compaction

Clean sands newly deposited in water generally have porosity of about 45 percent, but a small amount of easily accomplished rearrangement, such as that resulting from the washing back and forth by waves, reduces porosity to about 37 percent. In considering compaction the higher figure can be disregarded because only a very thin surface layer of a sedimentary deposit is likely to possess so much porosity. Therefore, 37 percent can be accepted as the approximate porosity of common types of firmly settled loose sand and the initial porosity of uncompacted sand. Very poorly sorted or very angular sand may be somewhat more porous.

If small amounts of silt or clay are present, the porosity may be a little less because some of this material can be accommodated in the interstices between the sand grains. If the amount is appreciable, however, porosity is higher because more adsorbed water is held within the sediment and its density is reduced. With further increase of fine material, particularly of clay size, the sediment gradually passes into mud or clay that may be compacted to produce shale. Probably no rock that might be identified as sandstone consists of sediment whose original porosity was much greater than 50 percent.

The original porosity range of sandy sediments indicates that very few sandstones can represent original deposits of more than twice their present thicknesses. Compaction to this extent would produce nonporous quartzite (see Figure 111B). Many sandstones that have been studied, including some sampled from cores taken at a depth of more than 20,000 feet, retain intergranular space averaging about 25 percent. This suggests that compaction of sand occurring during its lithification commonly is about 15 percent and rarely exceeds 25 percent. These volume relations are important when comparisons are made between the diagenesis of sands and muds (see Figure 110).

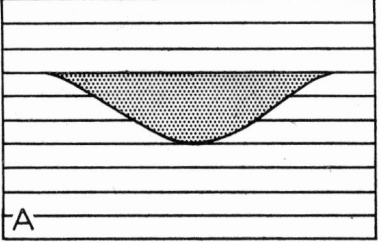

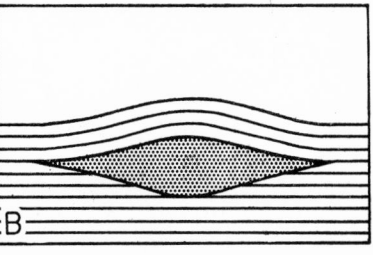

Sand subjected to pressure in laboratory tests shows little compaction under loads as great as 8000 pounds per square inch. This corresponds in most situations to the weight of more than a mile of sedimentary overburden. Beyond this pressure, crushing of the grains occurs. Crushing, however, does not appear to have been important in the compaction of most sandstones, probably because pressure resulting from the deposition of thickening overburden increased slowly. Readjustment by solution at grain boundaries and structural strengthening by cementation produced larger areas of grain contact and generally kept pace with loading. Solution at grain boundaries may be indicated by sutured contacts resembling microscopic stylolites. No

Figure 110. Diagrams illustrating alteration in the form of a sand body enclosed in muddy sediment resulting from compaction. A. Uncompacted sediment. B. After 50 percent compaction of shale and 10 percent compaction of sandstone. In nature, of course, compaction would occur gradually as the deposition of sediment progressed. Compare with Figure 212, p. 545.

close relationship exists between the compaction of sandstone and load or depth of burial as it does in shale.

It is important to recognize that intergranular volume and not the porosity of sandstone is a measure of its compaction. Equally compacted sandstones vary greatly in porosity depending upon the amount of cement that has been deposited between the grains. Intergranular volume is difficult to determine, however, and few measurements of it have been made except in thin sections. Therefore little is known about the actual amount of compaction that has occurred in many sandstones.

Cementation

The sand grains of most sandstones are bound together either by a matrix of clayey minerals or by intergranular cement (see Figure 111A). Clay if present is a primary constituent of the sediment although its mineralogic character may have been altered by diagenesis. Cement is clearly post-depositional, however, and is evidence of either solution along grain boundaries and deposition of mineral matter in nearby pores, or the introduction and deposition of mineral matter derived from some external source, or both. The presence of an appreciable amount of clay seems to inhibit the deposition of quartz cement particularly in the finer-grained sandy sediments. Calcite, however, may occur as the cement in sediments of this kind.

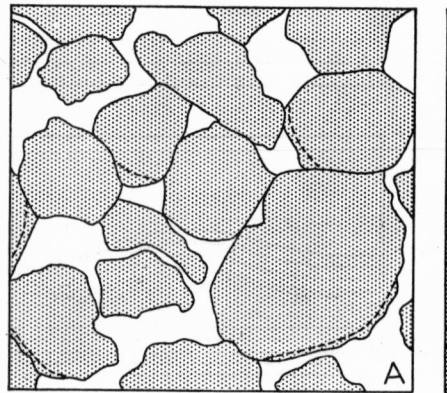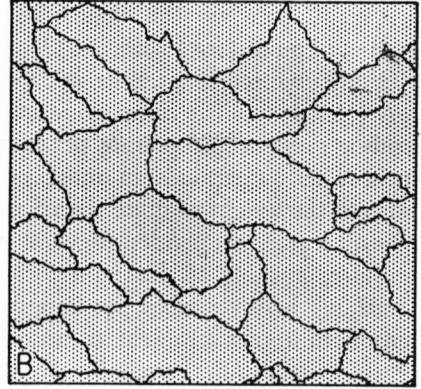

Figure 111. Thin sections of St. Peter Sandstone (Ord.) from St. Charles County, Missouri, x55. The grains in A show evidence of only slight solution at their margins and little compaction has occurred. They are cemented by secondary quartz. Some of these grains possess rims resulting from secondary enlargement in a previous sedimentary cycle. The sandstone in B is completely compacted as the result of intergranular solution. All of the grains show sutured contacts and no cement is present. These specimens from the same quarry demonstrate that sandstone compaction is not necessarily related to depth of burial. (Drawn from photographs by Heald, 1956, J. Geol., vol. 64, p. 20, pl. 1, figs. C and D.)

Both quartz and calcite, or dolomite, either separately or together are the common cementing minerals of sandstone. Other minerals are comparatively rare. If both of the common cementing minerals are present, quartz generally was the first to be deposited although reverse relations have been reported. The most common relations show quartz deposited directly on detrital grains and enlarging them, with carbonate more or less filling the remaining pore space. Some rocks show evidence of partial replacement of quartz by carbonate.

The solubilities of quartz and calcite are determined by the pH values of solutions, acidity favoring the solution of calcite and alkalinity favoring that of quartz. Sea water, and presumably original connate water, generally is not saturated with calcium carbonate. Its slight alkalinity is within the range where silica may be either dissolved or deposited. Consequently it is possible that pressure at grain contacts during the earlier stages of consolidation may result in solution and almost immediate redeposition of silica in nearby pores. This has been accomplished in the laboratory in alkaline solutions under the influence of heat and pressure. At this early stage of diagenesis calcium carbonate probably remained in solution. Later, as water was expelled from adjacent shale and drained away through the more permeable sandstone, the chemical quality of the water may have changed with the result that deposition of quartz ceased and that of calcite began. If this should be the proper explanation, at least part of the quartz cement was derived from the sediment very near the place where it now occurs.

Calcium carbonate deposited with the sand could have been removed in solution during an early stage of consolidation. If this occurred, the later calcite cement is of foreign origin and may have been contributed by solutions draining from compacting shale. The study of some sandstones suggests that part of their quartz cement also was introduced. This is probable if the amount of quartz cement exceeds the amount of quartz that was dissolved at grain boundaries while compaction was in progress (see Figure 27, p. 94).

Cementation of sandstone with chalcedony or chert appears to be a process occurring in the zone of weathering related to the activity of meteoric water. This cement probably was not derived from the materials of the original sediment.

Cement may be removed from sandstone by solution but silica is very rarely eliminated in this way. If calcite cement has been removed, there generally is nothing to indicate its former presence. Some strata, however, that outcrop as friable sandstone can be traced into more or less tightly cemented beds in the subsurface. Their alteration appears to have resulted from the solvent action of circulating meteoric water.

Recrystallization and Replacement

Alterations involving recrystallization or replacement have been unimportant in most sandstones that have not been subjected to metamorphism by more heat and pressure than ordinarily accompanies diagenesis. The enlargement of quartz and more rarely other kinds of sand grains by the deposition of cement in optical continuity with crystal grains and the development of crystal faces, however, is fairly common. This generally begins as a part of the cementing process, but the crystals may continue to grow by replacement of surrounding minerals. Ragged contacts also may develop as the result of irregular marginal replacement. This may involve either the chemical and mineralogic rearrangement of material present in the sediment or the introduction of new material from some external source. Well-marked replacement is most likely to occur in dirty sandstones of the graywacke type.

Shale

Diagenetic changes that occur in mud, shale, and related rocks involve principally (1) compaction and (2) mineralogic alteration of the clays. Both of these processes are conditioned by the colloidal properties that characterize sediments of this kind.

Colloidal Nature of Clay

Most muddy sediments are complex mixtures of fine-grained minerals whose compositions vary between wide extremes. Besides fineness of grain their most characteristic properties are plasticity and cohesiveness, which are closely related to their constituent clay minerals. These minerals commonly occur as very tiny mica-like crystals, noteworthy because of relatively great adsorptive powers attracting and more or less tenaciously holding water and other substances in surrounding films. Any sedimentary mixture that includes an appreciable quantity of clay minerals possesses a large internal surface area. Before consolidation it is capable of containing a much larger amount of water than could be accommodated in the interstices of a coarser sediment (see Figure 112). Consequently it is more porous and less dense.

Because the adsorptive properties of clays are influenced by electrolytes, their behavior in salt and fresh water is not the same. Differences are revealed by inequalities in flocculation, adsorptive powers, and thicknesses of water films. Some clay minerals dissociate in water so that their crystal structure and physical properties are not the same in suspension and in consolidated sediment.

As clayey sediment flocculates and is deposited, an orderly arrangement of the clay particles begins. In a relatively short time a gel-like structure generally develops that in most clays possesses an appreciable amount of strength and resistance to shearing and compression. This structure is destroyed, however, when the sediment is disturbed. A sudden shock may be sufficient to transform a mass of comparatively solid sediment into a muddy liquid almost instantly.

Some of the most important properties of a clay mixture are indicated by its water content (1) when this is at a maximum immediately after deposition and material has settled from suspension in a turbid liquid to form a plastic solid, and (2) when drying or compaction has served to transform a plastic mass into a relatively rigid one. Standardized mechanical tests have been devised to measure the water content at approximately these transition points. The values so determined are known respectively as the *liquid* and *plastic limits.* Between these limits the mixture contains enough water to lubricate the mineral grains, and the mass is plastic and yields readily in response to minor stresses. The liquid limits of clayey sediments vary greatly depending upon the quantity and kind of clay minerals present, but plastic

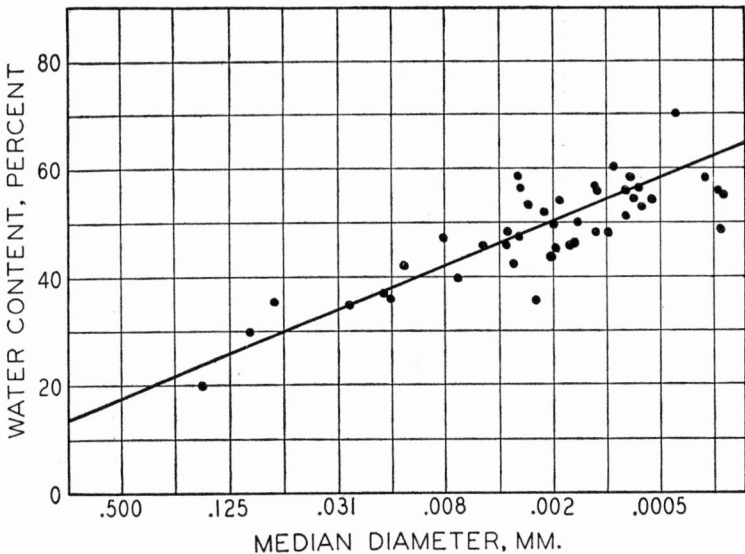

Figure 112.   Diagram showing relations between median diameter of recent Gulf of Mexico sediments and water content figured as percent of volume. Water content calculated in this way is the same as porosity. Compare with Figure 28, p. 97. (After Shepard and Moore, 1955, *Bull. Am. Assoc. Petroleum Geol.*, vol. 39, p. 1584, fig. 73B.)

limits are much more uniform. These limits, however, are not equally good indices to the properties of clayey material under all conditions. For geologic interpretation they cannot be accepted as more than relatively gross approximations.

Compaction

Water-laid argillaceous sediments are deposited with porosities that probably range from about 5 to 10 percent higher than those indicated by their liquid limits. Measurements of natural sediments show that initial porosities vary from about 55 percent for very silty or sandy material to more than 80 percent for fine-grained marine clays. The latter contain more than three times as much water in proportion to solid sedimentary material as do the former. Compaction is accomplished by the gradual elimination of the water and the closer packing of sedimentary particles resulting mainly from the pressure exerted by accumulating overburden (see Figure 113).

Compaction of mud and shale probably is accomplished in several stages that progress in the following order:

1. In newly deposited sediment, adsorbed water films completely surround all mineral particles. Pressure squeezes these films out from between the grains until they come is contact with each other, but there is little rearrangement and packing is not efficient. This stage appears to end at a porosity of about 45 percent in common muddy sediment, which corresponds to the porosity of loose but uncompacted sand and to the average plastic limit of numerous sediments that have been tested. At this point mineral grains begin to adhere to each other, plasticity is lost, and the original volume of sediment has been reduced by 18 to more than 60 percent.

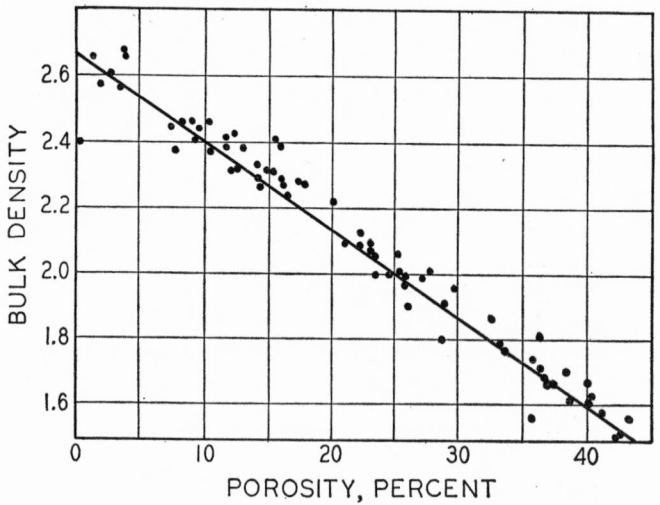

Figure 113. Diagram showing the relations of porosity to bulk, or dry, density. As packing of sedimentary particles improves, density increases. (After Davis, 1954, J. Geol., vol. 62, p. 105, fig. 2.)

2. Next, rearrangement of the grains takes place, resulting in more efficient, closer packing. The end of this stage probably is reached at a porosity of about 37 percent, which corresponds to that of loose but compacted sand, and the original volume has been reduced by about 28 to 68 percent.

3. Further compaction can be accomplished only by the distortion of mineral grains. During this stage the soft clay minerals are believed to be squeezed into the interstices between the harder grains of quartz and other resistant minerals and the harder minerals come into contact with each other. In common fine-grained argillaceous sediments this seems to occur at a porosity of about 10 percent when original volume has been reduced by about 50 to 78 percent.

4. In the final stage of compaction the harder grains must be deformed or crushed. When all porosity has been eliminated in this way, the completely compacted sediment occupies only 45 to 20 percent of its original volume.

Relations to Pressure and Depth

Data that can be used to calibrate compaction of mud and shale against pressure or depth of burial are scanty and not entirely satisfactory. If certain assumptions are made, laboratory compression tests and measurements of the porosity or density of oil well cores (see Figure 114) are serviceable as

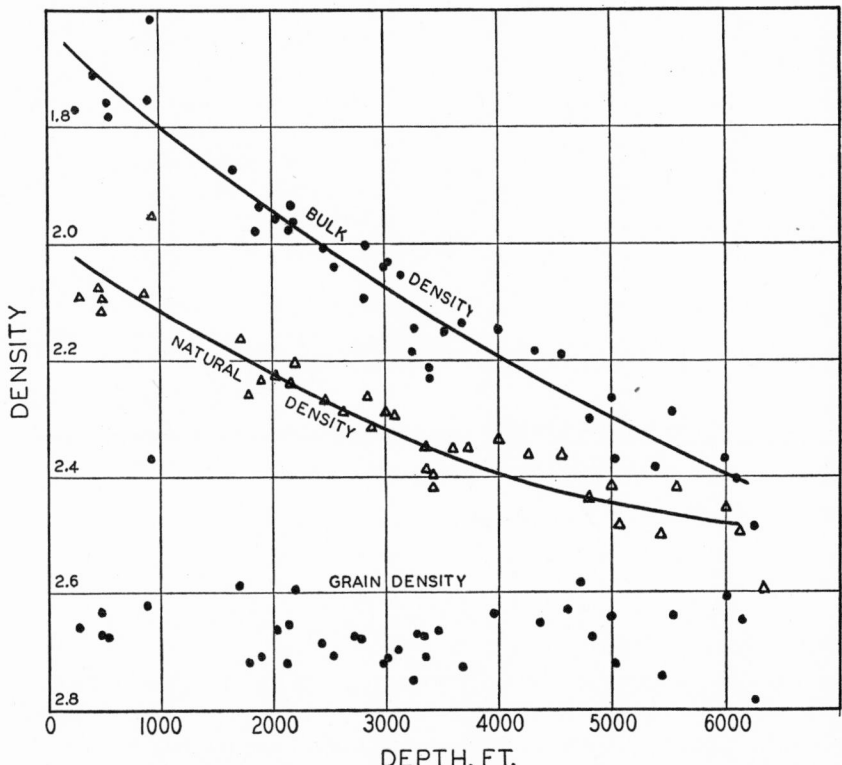

Figure 114. Diagram showing the relations of bulk, or dry, natural, or wet, and grain density to depth as determined from Tertiary shale cores recovered from Venezuelan oil wells. Compaction has increased both bulk and natural density, but grain density is unchanged. (After Hedberg, 1936, Am. J. Sci., ser. 5, vol. 31, p. 255, fig. 1.)

guides for calculation. Laboratory tests may not give results closely comparable to natural compaction, however, because sedimentary structure is destroyed in samples, and compaction may proceed more readily in the laboratory than in nature. Also the porosities of cores taken from deep wells can be related to depth, but this is present depth and the probability that considerable thicknesses of formerly occurring overburden have been removed by erosion cannot be neglected.

Figure 115 is a curve showing the approximate relations of porosity to depth of burial in a hypothetical homogeneous column of slightly silty sediment deposited with an initial porosity of 80 percent. Its calculation was guided by the relations indicated in laboratory tests and deep well cores and

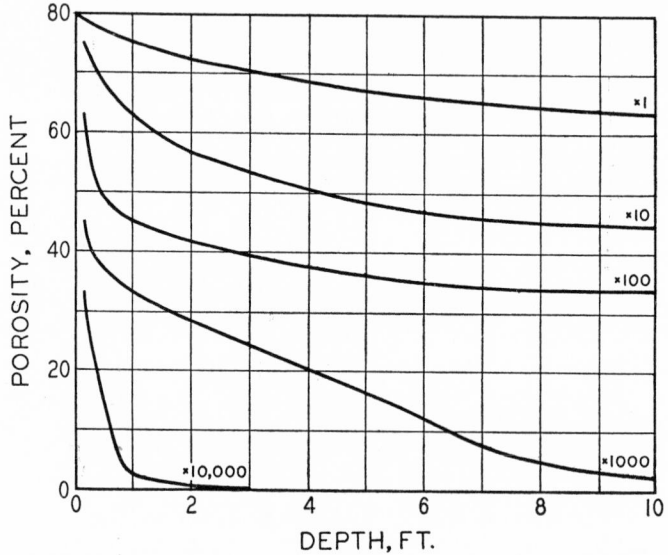

Figure 115. Graph showing calculated relations of porosity to depth or thickness of overburden in homogeneous mud or shale of original 80 percent porosity. The curve is drawn to several horizontal scales in which the depth values are increased successively by a factor of 10. Data adapted from observations by Terzaghi, Hedberg, and Athy. (After Weller, 1959, Bull. Am. Assoc. Petroleum Geol., vol. 43, p. 276, fig. 1.)

the assumption that all porosity is eliminated by overburden pressure at a depth of 30,000 feet. The 80 percent initial porosity is a reasonable figure for recently deposited fine-grained marine sediment. The depth estimate is arbitrary but porosity is very low in deeply buried argillaceous sediment and this does not influence calculations importantly. If this curve is satisfactory, numerous other relations of interest in stratigraphy can be determined. Figure 116 is a graph showing the compaction that results in similar sediment buried beneath different thicknesses of overlying strata.

Other curves can be calculated for sediments of less initial porosity to which the curves presented here do not apply. Initial porosity of 80 percent is selected as a limiting case because much greater porosity and much greater compaction are not likely to occur in any natural stratigraphic section. The other limiting case is completely nonporous material which would accomplish the greatest compaction of porous underlying strata at the least depth. Figure 117 shows the relations of maximum and minimum thicknesses of overburden to porosity. The differences are great for stratigraphic sections of small and intermediate thicknesses but they decrease with depth.

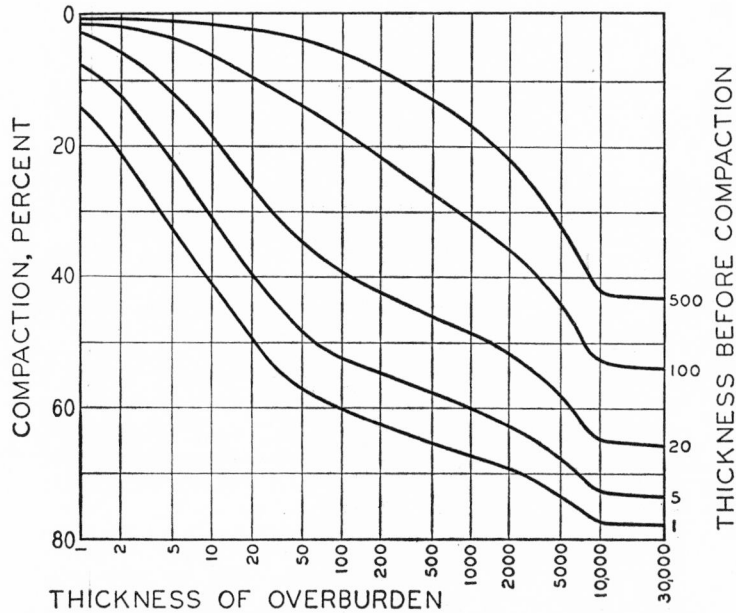

Figure 116. Semilogarithmic graph showing percent compaction of different thicknesses of originally 80 percent porous mud after burial beneath increasingly thick overburden. To use this graph, consider the case of 100 feet of sediment that is gradually buried to a depth of 1000 feet. Follow the curve marked 100 on the right to its intersection with the line rising from 1000 on the lower scale and read the answer, or 30 plus, at the left. Other values can be estimated by interpolation. (After Weller, 1959, Bull. Am. Assoc. Petroleum Geol., vol. 43, p. 290, fig. 7.)

Estimates of the maximum depth of burial of shale, and of stratigraphic thicknesses at different stages of geologic development, can be made by testing, estimating, and comparing the sediments of a stratigraphic section and employing appropriate curves constructed from data and calculations of this kind. For example, measurements of a Pennsylvanian clay outcropping in Indiana suggest that this bed once lay nearly a mile below the surface.

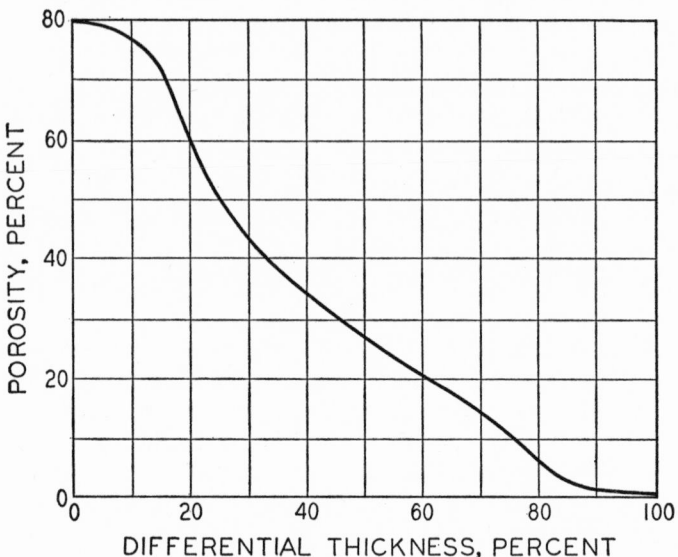

Figure 117. Graph showing thickness of nonporous overburden, expressed as a percentage of the thickness of originally 80 percent porous mud, required to compact similar sediment. For example, a nonporous layer only 20 percent as thick will reduce porosity from 80 to 60 percent, but a layer 60 percent as thick is needed to reduce porosity to 20 percent. Nonporous and porous layers in these proportions provide equal overburden loads.

Evidence of Concretions

Some calcareous and sideritic concretions that occur in shale developed very early in the history of the sediment as shown by the bending of thin laminae around them (see Figure 41, p. 117). These relations are most apparent in some highly carbonaceous black shales. Although it is not possible from field inspection to determine at what stage in the compaction process such concretions formed, measurements reveal approximately the minimum compaction that has occurred. On the other hand, concretions in some very silty argillaceous beds have laminae that pass laterally into shale without noteworthy decrease in thickness. Because the enclosing shale certainly has been compacted, these concretions are shown to have developed much later after most compaction had been accomplished.

Evidence of Fossils

The bending of shale laminae is rarely observed around objects as small as fossils. The compaction of some shales is shown, however, by the presence of crushed fossils, and certain very fissile and highly carbonaceous strata contain completely flattened specimens. The fossils of other shales reveal remarkably little damage. As with concretions, relations of the fossils indicate minimum compaction but, unlike concretions, most fossils are original constituents of the sediment.

The occurrence of uncrushed fossils in beds of shale, and particularly specimens whose interiors are filled with shaly matrix, demonstrates that considerable flowage of argillaceous material accompanies compaction. During the first stage of consolidation, sediment is highly plastic and pressure is essentially hydrostatic. Adjustments under these conditions might be accomplished without damage to the fossils. Further compaction of stiffer material, however, would be more likely to result in crushing particularly of the weaker, thinner shelled, more convex or hollow specimens.

The crushing and flattening of fossils in some beds indicates much greater compaction than occurs in the later stages of consolidation. In contrast to these, the distortion of specimens in other beds is much less than might be expected. Such variability in preservation demonstrates that plastic flowage in compacting mud and shale has not been uniform. Probably the condition of fossils in argillaceous strata is a general index to the rapidity with which compaction was accomplished. Thus if compaction was very rapid, fossils would be flattened even during the early, nearly hydrostatic stage. On the other hand, clayey material undoubtedly retains some plasticity even at low porosity. If compaction was slow enough, flowage around fossils appears to have been sufficient to preserve them from much breakage or distortion.

Compaction Structures

Differential compaction of sediment deposited upon an irregular resistant surface and of unevenly interbedded strata differing in initial porosity or compactability may result in the development of structures resembling those produced by gentle folding. Depending upon the original stratigraphic relations, anticlines may form over buried hills or reefs, initial dips may become steeper, and sand bodies enclosed in shale may be deformed. Figures 118 and 119 illustrate diagrammatically some of the relationships that may develop (see also Figures 29, p. 98; 110, p. 293; and 127, p. 316). Compaction

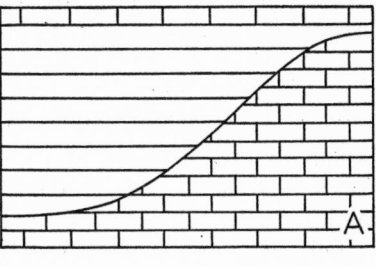

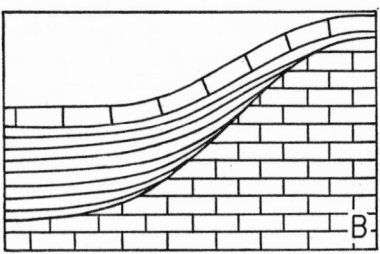

Figure 118. Diagrams illustrating the development of structure above an uneven unconformity resulting from compaction.

structures generally die out upward, but the influence of buried reefs or hills may persist for very long intervals of time, as shown in Figure 120.

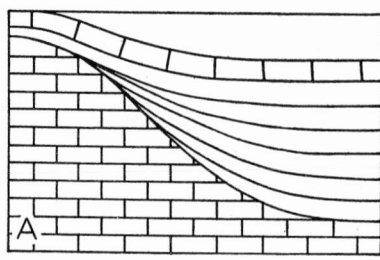

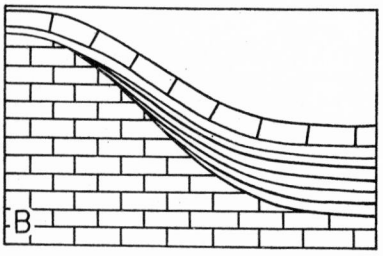

Figure 119. Diagrams illustrating the accentuation of initial dips produced by compaction in strata deposited upon an uneven unconformable surface. The results are not greatly different from those shown in Figure 118.

Development of Fissility

Shales are characterized by their thinly laminated structure and more of less well-marked fissility. These features are variably developed in different strata. All gradations occur from massive mudstone, in which they are wholly lacking, to shale that splits easily into uniform thin layers. They are in part inheritances from original sedimentary structures and in part secondary features resulting from diagenetic changes.

Some argillaceous sediments are deposited in layers that differ from each other in color, texture, or composition in such a way that lamination is obvious and splitting may occur parallel to the bedding because of discontinuities in the type of sediment. Such strata are formed in places where the supply of sediment varies, or changes in local conditions prevent uniform deposition. Generally they are characteristic of relatively shallow and nearshore situations rather than of deep water at more remote localities. Unless sediments are disturbed and mixed by organisms after deposition, layering of this kind persists. It may even be accentuated by compaction because the laminae become thinner and more closely crowded.

Thick beds of fine-grained sediment without conspicuous layering may ac-

Figure 120 (opposite). Maps of the Patoka area in south-central Illinois showing the influence of Silurian organic reefs on the subsequently deposited stratigraphic section.

A is an isopach map showing the thickness of strata included between the top of the Kimmswick Limestone (Ord.) and the base of the New Albany Shale (Dev.-Miss.). The three restricted areas of thicker strata, indicated by hachured contours, two in the northeastern township and the other in the southwestern one, reflect the presence of prominent Silurian reefs which stand as resistant masses in the midst of more compactable strata.

B shows the thickness of rocks between the base of the New Albany shale and the top of the Ste. Genevieve Limestone (Miss.). Thinning is evident over the reefs. This probably indicates that the underlying non-reef beds continued to compact as new sediment was deposited above them.

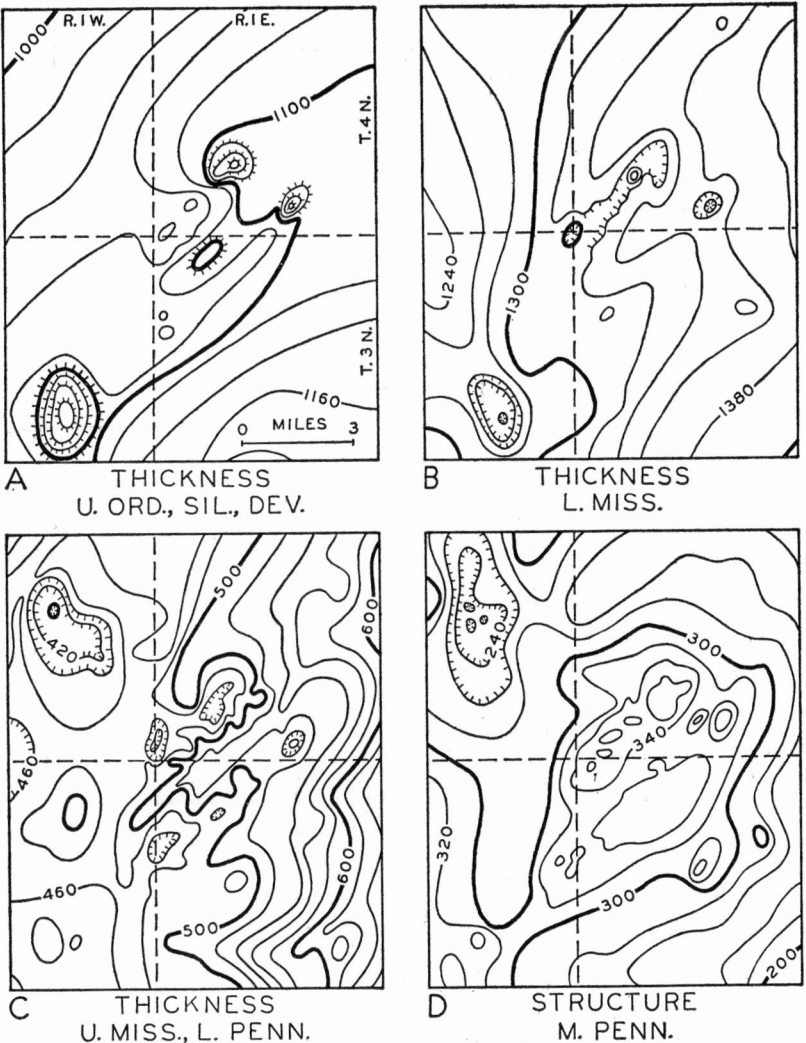

A THICKNESS
U. ORD., SIL., DEV.

B THICKNESS
L. MISS.

C THICKNESS
U. MISS., L. PENN.

D STRUCTURE
M. PENN.

C similarly shows the thickness of strata between the base of the Glen Dean Limestone (Miss.) and Coal No. 2 (Penn.). Thinning continues over the two northeastern reefs, and the development of northeast-southwest structural trends, suggested also in the two previous maps, is more evident.

D shows the structure of the Shoal Creek Limestone (Penn.). Highs mark the positions of the reefs. These structures probably are related in part at least to compaction resulting from the deposition of still younger sediments.

All of these relations strongly suggest that two low northeast-southwest reef ridges bore three high and perhaps several other less prominent reef knolls. Their resistance to compaction appears to have influenced sedimentary deposition throughout all later Paleozoic time. (After Smoot, 1958, Ill. Geol. Surv., Circ. 258, pp. 7, 9, 12, and 15, figs. 3, 4, 6, and 8.)

cumulate in quiet situations where deposition is uniform and continuous. Similar strata, however, may result from the activity of organisms that mix the sediment and prevent the development of layering or destroy it. Distinction between these two types of deposits is likely to be difficult and doubtful. In either case the sedimentary particles at first are randomly disposed, and little or no tendency exists for parting or splitting parallel to the sedimentary surface. As compaction progresses, the tiny mica-like crystals of the clay minerals are rotated. Many of them become roughly oriented at right angles to the direction of incident vertical pressure. When such secondarily induced orientation has progressed far enough to effect splitting in a preferred direction, the development of shale has started.

Laboratory experiments show that the rapid compaction of mud even under great pressure does not produce a shale. The development of well-marked fissility requires more than the partial orientation of clay minerals. Apparently recrystallization and perhaps some chemical reorganization also are necessary. These processes involve very slow changes. Evidence is provided by the prevalence of well-developed shales in most Paleozoic formations and the general lack of good shaly structure in most argillaceous beds of Tertiary age.

Relative abundance of the clay minerals is different in the older and younger rocks, most conspicuously with respect to kaolinite and montmorillonite, which are dominant in some post-Paleozoic strata but are comparatively unimportant in older beds. Kaolinite is almost unknown in pre-Carboniferous rocks. These minerals appear to have altered slowly after deposition and changed to illite and chlorite. Kaolinite probably is unstable in an alkaline environment and in the presence of calcium. Pressure may be a factor in the alteration of montmorillonite as this would tend to squeeze out the water layers characteristic of this mineral.

Illite is predominant in most laminated shales (see Figure 130, p. 319). It also generally is the prevalent clay mineral in calcareous strata and marine deposits. In contrast, kaolinitic beds are rarely laminated and this mineral is not likely to occur importantly in calcareous shale or in association with limestone or dolomite. The diagenetic alteration of kaolinite, which lacks micaceous structure, to illite or possibly chlorite, which are micaceous, may be one of the most important factors in the development of fissility in shale. This alteration, and also the alteration of montmorillonite and the possible recrystallization of other clay minerals without noteworthy chemical change, may modify argillaceous deposits so greatly that their original qualities, such as composition and texture, may not be determinable.

Cementation

Shales rarely are cemented in a way that is comparable to the cementation of coarser-textured rocks. Clay mineral particles may have grown during diagenesis but mostly they are less than two microns in diameter (see Figure 9, p. 54) and their sizes, shapes, and mutual relations are very difficult to determine. Few other mineral grains are smaller than 1 micron, and most of them are much larger, ranging up to sand. Many shales contain more silt-sized particles than clay.

Porosity of mud and shale is reduced almost entirely by compaction and the closer crowding of sedimentary particles. Generally there seems to be little filling of the pores by cementing material. When compaction has forced the non-clay grains into close contact they may develop an interlocking mosaic structure producing hard tough shale that does not split readily except when weathered. This type of structure has been observed in calcareous shales whose calcium carbonate is present in silt-sized grains. It also may occur in noncalcareous shales and in the much less common highly siliceous shales.

Limestone

Limestones are the sedimentary rocks whose origins and diagenesis are least well understood. They have been formed by the consolidation of a great variety of lime muds and sands whose original characters resembled those of the whole range of clayey and sandy sediments. It seems logical to compare the diagenesis of fine-grained or coarse calcareous deposits to that of shale or sandstone, and similarities undoubtedly do exist. The chemical and physical properties of calcium carbonate, however, are such that there is not close parallelism.

The consolidation of calcareous sediments is accomplished mainly by (1) cementation and pore filling. Other diagenetic processes of variable importance are (2) conversion of aragonite to calcite, (3) compaction, (4) recrystallization, and (5) dolomitization.

Porosity

Most calcareous sediments are of organic origin. This is obvious for the coarser particles, which generally can be identified as whole or broken shells or other structures built by animals and plants. The coarser calcareous sediments are likely to be considerably more porous than ordinary sand because many of the particles are not solid mineral grains but consist of hollow shells such as those of foraminifera or of open-structured material like echinoderm plates and fragments of bryozoans and corals. The porosity of firmly settled modern calcareous sand has been observed to range between 50 and 60 or more percent as compared to about 37 percent for quartz sand.

In contrast to unconsolidated calcareous sediments, few limestones retain more than 10 percent porosity and many are practically nonporous. In fact, noteworthy porosity in limestones, which are important oil reservoirs at many places, is commonly considered to be of secondary origin resulting from the solvent action of circulating ground water. This undoubtedly is the correct explanation of porosity in many limestones as shown by the form and distribution of the openings that occur (see Figure 121). It is not true of all, however, and the type of porosity present in many limestones has not been determined. Much attention has been devoted by geologists to the development of secondary porosity because it is of great economic importance. Remarkably little study has been devoted to the common elimination of

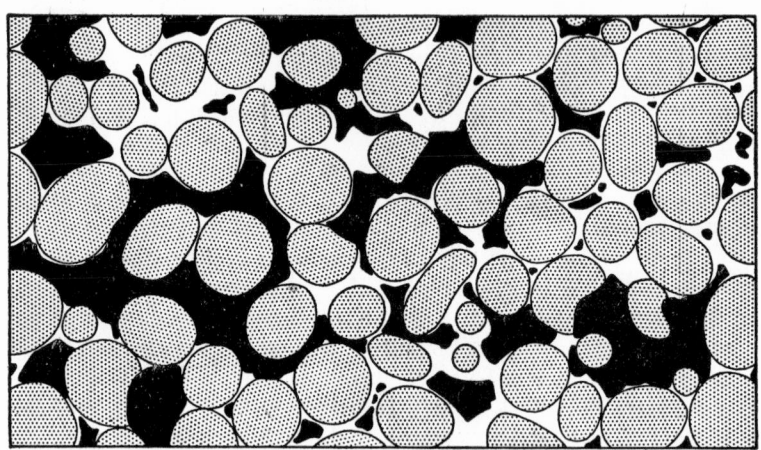

Figure 121. Oolitic limestone with secondary porosity x20. Intergranular calcite cement has been partially and irregularly dissolved, and a few of the oolites also have been attacked by solution and partly destroyed. Pore openings are indicated in black. Fredonia Member of the Ste. Genevieve Limestone (Miss.) from southern Illinois. (Drawn from photograph of a smoothed surface after Graf and Lamar, 1950, Bull. Am. Assoc. Petroleum Geol., vol. 34, p. 2328, fig. 9.)

most original porosity that is characteristic of calcareous sediments.

Most secondary porosity probably can be identified because solution attacks both the original sedimentary particles and the cement that binds them. It is likely, also, to be selective in enlarging some openings more than others and it develops irregular, relatively coarse interconnecting openings. In contrast, some of the original porosity of calcareous sediment may remain because of incomplete cementation (see Figure 122). In limestone of this type, the pores are small, more regularly distributed, and surrounded by thin coatings of cement that encrust the surfaces of all sedimentary particles. Secondary porosity is most likely to develop in coarse or irregularly textured limestones whereas most beds that retain original porosity are fine grained and even textured. Porosity of the Salem Limestone (Miss.), which is the widely used building stone of Indiana, varies up to more than 20 percent and probably is primary. That of the Miami Oolite (Tert.) of Florida is greater than 75 percent at some places and much of it is secondary.

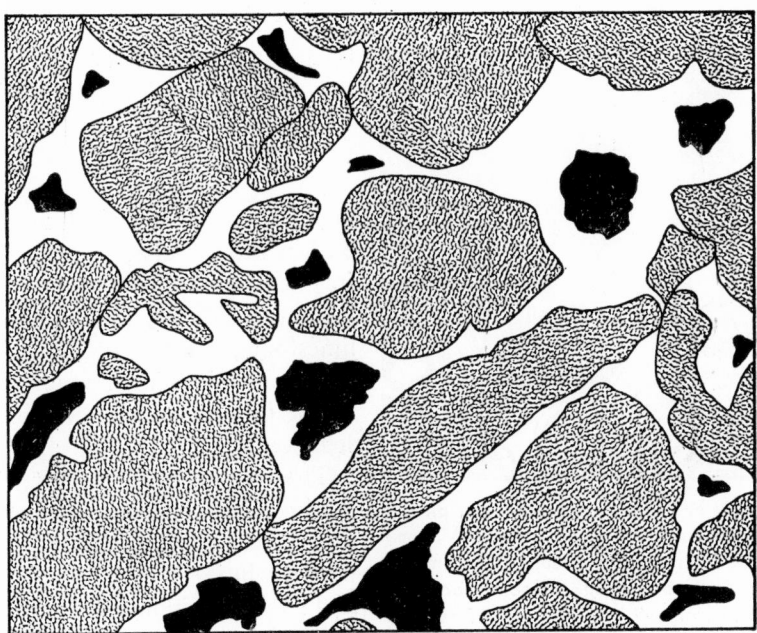

Figure 122. Thin section of Recent Florida beachrock showing original porosity x47. Fragments of shells and other calcareous debris are incompletely cemented with calcium carbonate. The remaining openings, shown in black, are lined with tiny needle-like crystals of aragonite. Compare with Figure 121. (Drawn from photograph by Ginsburg, 1953, *J. Sediment. Petrol.*, vol. 23, p. 90, fig. 5.)

Cementation

The conversion of calcareous sediment to almost nonporous limestone might be accomplished either by compaction or by deposition of calcium carbonate in the pores or both (see Figure 123). The coarser grains of most fragmental limestones, however, generally show little or no evidence of tighter packing or of solution along their boundaries where these are in contact as shown in Figure 124. Also empty shells and porous organic structures ordinarily are not crushed; very little actual compaction has occurred. Moreover, consolidation of most limestone apparently was accomplished early, before the sediment was subjected to the pressure of much overburden.

Fine-grained limestones are poorly understood because their origin is not obvious and lime muds have been little studied. Some lime mud was deposited with very high porosity. Its reaction to compression has not been adequately investigated. Reports of laboratory tests are contradictory. Fossils preserved in fine-grained limestone, however, rarely show much evidence of crushing. On the whole such beds reveal no more indication of compaction than do coarser strata.

Figure 123. Thin section of completely cemented oolitic limestone showing evidence of some intergranular solution and compaction x20. Several chains of oolites occur in which one or both neighboring oolites have been partially dissolved. At several places solution has attacked only one oolite so that the other partly penetrates it. Fredonia Member of Ste. Genevieve Limestone (Miss.) from southern Illinois. (Drawn from photograph by Graf and Lamar, 1950, Bull. Am. Assoc. Petroleum Geol., vol. 34, p. 2332, fig. 15.)

There are exceptions to all of the foregoing observations but they are not common. A few oolitic limestones clearly show that intergranular solution and compaction have occurred, and calcareous debris of organic origin in some beds has been broken without displacement of the fragments probably as the result of loading. The consolidation of most limestones, however, evidently was accomplished mainly by the cementation of originally highly porous sediment.

The macadam effect that binds crushed limestone proceeds rapidly by alternate wetting and drying, the partial solution of calcium carbonate and its redeposition as intergranular cement. A process of this type is responsible for the development of beachrock in the intertidal zone where cementing calcium carbonate is furnished by evaporating sea water. Some elevated late Tertiary limestones in the tropics are case-hardened and cemented near their surfaces but remain porous and resemble marl at a little distance inward from the outcrops. This action depends upon evaporation and cannot occur below a permanent water cover. No consolidation of calcareous sediment on or close below the sea floor involving cementation similar to that which has produced most limestone is known to be occurring at the present time.

Some sedimentologists and geologists have suggested that the consolidation of all calcareous sediment into dense limestone followed its uplift into the subaerial zone. This does not seem likely. Borings on modern coral reefs show variable amounts of cementation in sediments that probably never were exposed to atmospheric influences. Thin limestone layers enclosed in shale are thoroughly consolidated but, even if they had been elevated, their impervious surroundings would have protected them from surface conditions. Essentially unconsolidated calcareous strata occur in Cretaceous chalk deposits that have been altered very little in spite of having stood above sea level for much of the time since the end of the Mesozoic Era.

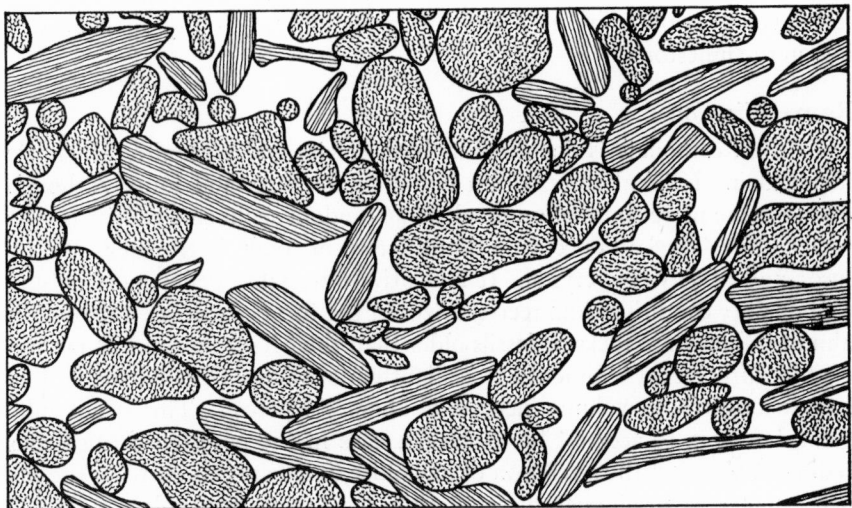

Figure 124. Thin section of Salem Limestone (Miss.) from Ste. Genevieve County, Missouri. This rock consists mainly of fragmental fossil debris and foraminifera cemented by clear calcite. The lack of interpenetration or suturing at grain contacts is evidence that little or no intergranular solution or compaction of the original sediment has occurred. The relations shown here are common in many limestones. Enlargement not recorded. (Drawn from photograph by Moore, 1957, Soc. Econ. Paleon. and Miner., Spec. Publ. 5, p. 117, fig. 7a.)

Origin of Cement

However and wherever consolidation of lime sediments occurred, the problem of the source of the calcareous cement remains unsolved. Because the original sediments were so porous, a very large amount of calcium carbonate was required, an amount perhaps greater than that contained in the original sediment. This calcium carbonate probably was not derived from the solution of overlying strata at any time because the results of such extensive solution have nowhere been recognized. It probably was not contributed by solutions squeezed from adjacent shale because vast quantities of such water would be required and some thick limestone sequences of low porosity are associated with very little shale. Solution along stylolitic surfaces might have been the source of much calcium carbonate cement, and some limestones certainly were greatly reduced in thickness in this way, but stylolites are rare or absent in many dense limestones. Also stylolites at some places can be proved to have developed after the complete consolidation of the rock.

Although little positive evidence can be presented, the cementation of most calcareous sediment seems to have begun soon after its deposition and while it was still submerged beneath the sea. Thereafter it may have continued slowly for long periods of time. Possibly an important part of the cement was provided by much unrecognized solution along planes that did not develop stylolites and now are marked by fairly even clay or shale partings in the limestone.

Recrystallization

Calcium carbonate is deposited as both calcite and aragonite, which are identical in chemical composition but different in crystal form. Although calcite is the more common mineral, some modern sediments consist mostly of aragonite. The latter occurs in the skeletons of corals, in the shells of molluscs, and as very tiny crystals. It is relatively unstable under most natural sedimentary conditions and recrystallizes in the form of calcite. Aragonite is almost unknown in rocks or fossils older than the Mesozoic and it is rare except in fairly recent sediments. It is slightly more dense than calcite, and its conversion involves volume increase of about 7.5 percent. This is not sufficient, however, to account for much decrease in the porosity of calcareous sediment. At most the alteration of aragonite to calcite can decrease the porosity of 60 percent porous sediment only about 3 percentage points.

Recrystallization of calcium carbonate is common in many limestones. It seems to occur most generally in the finest-grained portions of the rock. Whether this indicates the original presence of aragonite in the sediment cannot be determined. The process results in coarser textures, and some original features of the sediment or sedimentary particles may be obscured or totally destroyed.

Dolomitization

The mineral dolomite is rare in sediments of the modern sea floor but many limestones are more or less richly dolomitic. Their magnesium is contained in small disseminated dolomite crystals of variable abundance. These rocks are divisible into two classes: (1) dolomitic limestones with less than 20 percent of the mineral dolomite and (2) true dolomite rock with less than 20 percent calcite, as shown in Figure 125. Intermediate mixtures are uncommon. Dolomite is the major constituent of many thick and extensive formations particularly in the pre-Devonian systems (see Figure 14, p. 62). It also occurs concentrated in beds, lenses, or other restricted bodies enclosed between or within essentially non-dolomitic strata.

No one surely knows how dolomite was formed although most geologists agree that its development in sedimentary deposits involved a replacement process. A few small dolomite rhombs have been observed in modern sea-bottom sediments but they are too rare to be considered evidence for the beginning of dolomite development. Dolomite is not known to be accumulating anywhere on the sea bottom at the present time. Probably it never did, except possibly in some supersaline environments where it was associated with evaporites.

In most respects, dolomites are identical to limestones in appearance and stratigraphic associations. Their fossils are similar, although preservation commonly is poorer, and indicate no important differences in depositional environments. Dolomites, however, are inclined to be brownish from the

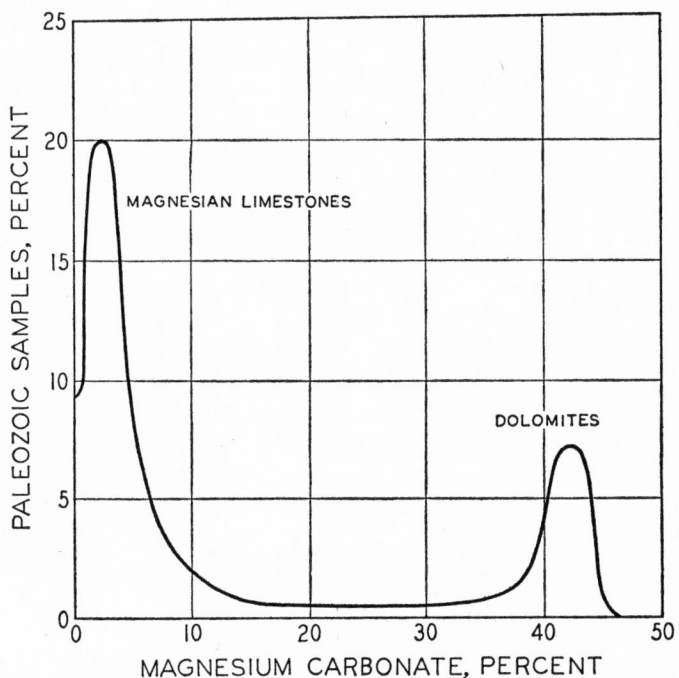

Figure 125. Curve showing the prevalence of magnesium in analyzed samples of Paleozoic limestones. Two distinct peaks occur. The first peak, below 10 percent, represents limestones in which most of the magnesium replaces some of the calcium in calcite crystals. Dolomite crystals are rarely observed in limestone with less than 15 percent magnesium. The second peak represents fully dolomitized limestones. Remarkably few samples were found to contain intermediate amounts of magnesium. (After Fairbridge, 1957, Soc. Econ. Paleon. and Miner., Spec. Publ. 5, p. 128, fig. 1.)

presence of small amounts of oxidized ferrous iron that may have substituted for some of the magnesium in dolomite crystals. Also some dolomites have a sandy granular texture resulting from recrystallization. Many do not possess these characters, and some can be distinguished from limestones only by chemical tests.

Borings on modern coral reefs show downward transition of calcareous de-

posits to beds containing variable amounts of dolomite. Possibly dolomitization is occurring in them now. Some organic calcite contains about one-
third enough magnesium in solid solution to produce dolomite on recrystallization but such calcite is not likely to be abundant enough to be an important factor in dolomite development. The only adequate source of magne-

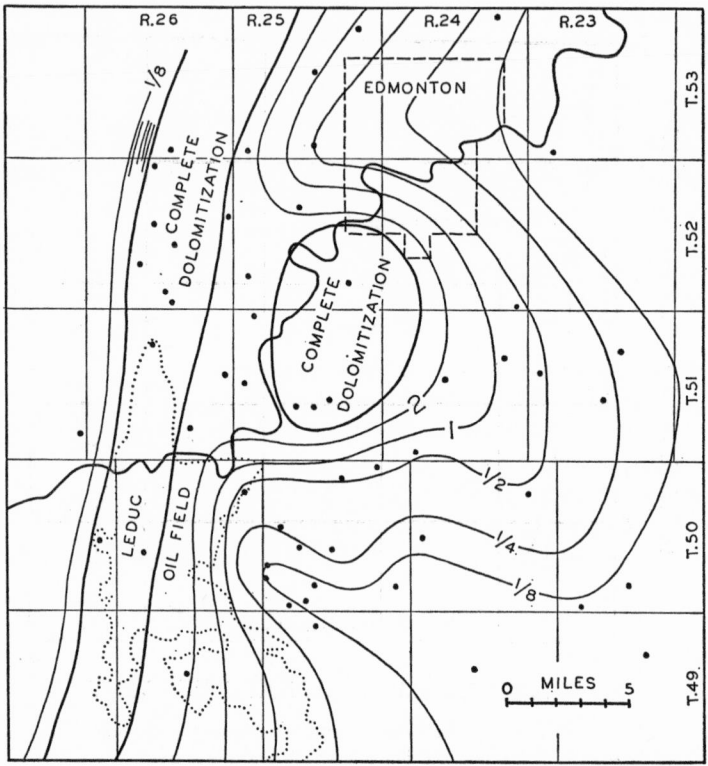

Figure 126. Map of the Leduc-Edmonton area of Alberta, Canada,
showing the ratio of dolomitization in the lower part of the Cooking Lake
Formation (Dev.). The abrupt decrease in dolomitization to the west corresponds with the edge of the shallow-water platform that extended eastward from the trend along which the great Leduc reef and others later
grew. Some of these reefs attain thicknesses of more than 1000 feet. Decrease in dolomitization to the east suggests that during Cooking Lake time
the sea deepened gradually in this direction. (After Andrichuk, 1958, Bull.
Am. Assoc. Petroleum Geol., vol. 42, p. 34, fig. 11.)

sium is mineral matter dissolved in sea water, which contains about six times
as many atoms of this element as of calcium. Nevertheless the complete alteration of calcite to dolomite would require the magnesium in about 275
volumes of sea water for one volume of resulting dolomite. Downward circu-

lation of sea water in compacting material at the bottom is exceedingly un-likely, but magnesium may have diffused into the sediment. Probably dolo-mitization is a very slow process. Chemical experiments suggest that replace-ment of calcium by magnesium is favored by increase in temperature and pressure. Therefore, the optimum conditions for the development of dolo-mite seem to occur at some distance below the sea floor in areas where the water is relatively warm and shallow and calcareous sediment is accumulating slowly. This conclusion is corroborated by some extensive carbonate forma-tions which show a tendency for dolomite to grade laterally into limestone in the direction of deeper water (see Figure 126).

Dolomite is a little more dense than calcite. Atom for atom substitution of magnesium for calcium would result in some reduction in volume and the possible development of increased porosity. Comparisons, however, do not indicate that dolomites generally are much more porous than limestones. Therefore, the replacement of calcite by dolomite is believed to involve es-sentially a volume-for-volume exchange.

Organic Sediment

Organic matter occurs in many sediments and is altered by diagenesis. The amount, however, is generally small. Even if enough is present to affect the appearance of a sediment or rock, as in black mud or shale, it commonly is so intimately admixed with mineral substances that its alteration is very dif-ficult to determine. Coal is an exception. Much that can be learned by study-ing it probably is applicable to most organic sediment.

Organic matter, as exemplified by coal, is altered diagenetically in two well-marked stages: (1) simple compaction resulting in the elimination of pore space, which occurs only in the first stage, and (2) decomposition in-volving the loss of substance principally in the form of water, carbon dioxide, and methane, which is accomplished biochemically in the first stage and dy-namochemically in the second.

Compaction

Few accurate measurements have been made of the porosity in peat. Even if they were available they would not have much meaning because porosity varies between wide extremes and no sharp divisions can be drawn between newly settled vegetable matter on the one hand and the beginning of lig-nite development on the other. New peat obviously is very porous. It is con-sidered to contain about 90 percent of water. In contrast, mature peat, such as occurs at the bottom of a well-developed bog, may include no more than 30 percent water by volume. If these figures are accepted tenta-tively, they account for reduction to about 14 percent of the original vol-ume.

Strictly speaking, this is an estimate of the compaction that occurs in peat. It is not a complete measure of volume reduction because compaction is accompanied by decay and the loss of organic substance. Decomposition accomplished by bacteria and fungi is an important process in the development of peat. It alters chemical composition and involves deoxidation, dehydration, and increase in carbon content. If loss of substance in peat development is estimated at 25 percent, volume is reduced altogether to about 12 percent (see Figure 127). Compaction and volume reduction appear to proceed naturally in this early stage without the necessity for the application of much overburden pressure.

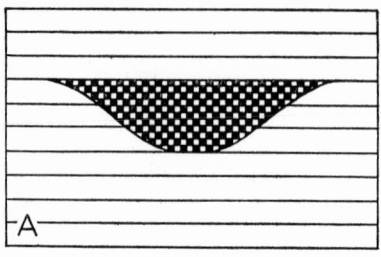

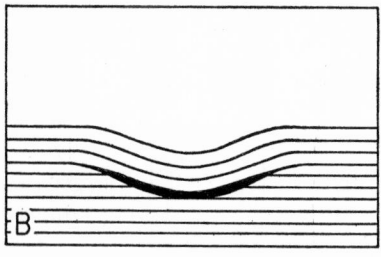

Figure 127. Diagrams showing the effects upon enclosing sediments of the transformation of peat to coal. A. Uncompacted muddy sediment and new peat. B. After 50 percent compaction of shale and 90 percent reduction in volume of peat. In nature these processes progress gradually as sediments accumulate and peat decays and is transformed to coal. In some areas several successive Pensylvanian coals are abnormally thick, suggesting that rapidly compacting peat produced surface depressions in which more than ordinarily thick accumulation of later peat occurred.

Consolidation

Actual consolidation of vegetable material does not occur until after the peat stage has been passed. This may be compared roughly to the transformation that marks the point where mud looses its plasticity and begins to convert to shale and where sandy and limy sediments become cemented. In the coal series water plays a most important role in the transformation of spongy peat to solid lignite.

Among the decomposition products formed during the development of peat are water-soluble so-called humic compounds. Some of these are lost as peat becomes less porous, but concentration increases in the pore water that remains. Finally a concentration is reached at which the solutions gel. At this point almost all remaining porosity is eliminated without additional appreciable compaction. Lignite is the resulting product.

Rank Increase

Rank increase from lignite to coal of higher and higher carbon content is accomplished by further dehydration and deoxidation, as shown in Figure 128. Such chemical change beyond the peat stage is a function of pressure, heat, and time, but overburden pressure appears to be the predominating influence. Many observations show that carbon content generally increases progressively with depth in any vertical succession of coal beds although some exceptions have been noted that probably are related to differences in original composition. Nevertheless the relative rank of coals of similar ages seems to have been determined mainly by depth of burial. Attempts have been made to work out these relations. Evidently they are not straight-line functions and the details have not been determined. Time also is an important factor, however, because most Carboniferous coals have attained full bituminous or higher rank whereas few Tertiary coals have done so except where they have been affected by severe structural deformation (see Figure 16, p. 66) or nearby volcanism.

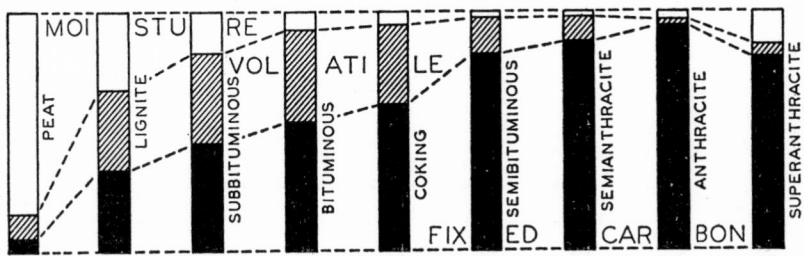

Figure 128. Diagram showing the proportions of constituents in ash-free coal as determined by proximate analysis. Moisture content decreases rapidly in the early stages. Decrease in volatile matter is much more gradual. Fixed carbon attains its peak in anthracite. Peculiarly, the moisture content generally increases beyond the semianthracite stage. (After Campbell, 1930, Econ. Geol., vol. 25, p. 688, fig. 4.)

Chemical alteration and increase in the rank of coal is accompanied by increase in density from about 1.15 for average lignite to 1.40 for anthracite. Volume decrease beyond the peat stage, therefore, is related to loss of substance by dynamochemical decomposition and increase in density, and not to decrease in porosity or compaction in the ordinary sense (see Figure 129).

Two Organic Series

The foregoing discussion is concerned with the process of coalification, which involves the driving off and loss of decomposition products. The coal is a remaining residue whose molecules become progressively larger and denser until the graphite stage is almost reached. Coal molecules contain hundreds of atoms that appear to be arranged in very complex carbon rings. This process, therefore, can be likened to polymerization.

The alteration of organic matter that produces petroleum and natural gas follows a similar but somewhat different path. Here larger organic molecules are broken down to smaller and simpler ones. This is indicated by the general decrease in gravity and increase in paraffinic quality of petroleum associated with older, deeper, and more deformed rocks. These results may be compared to cracking.

In a way, the alterations that produce coal and petroleum might be considered the two halves of a single process but there are important differences. The decomposition products lost during coalification are not similar to those constituting petroleum, and probably the residues left after the development of petroleum are not similar to coal. Also it is well known that much coal occurs in strata unaccompanied by petroleum and that much petroleum is

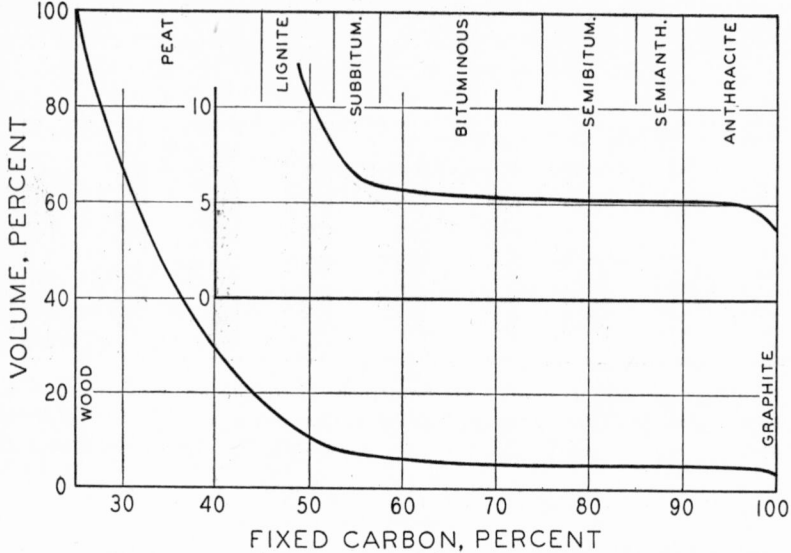

Figure 129. Curve representing volume decrease from new peat to graphite calculated on the basis of certain assumptions regarding the decay of peat and the elimination of moisture and volatile matter in the development of progressively higher-rank coals. (After Weller, 1959, *Bull. Am. Assoc. Petroleum Geol.*, vol. 43, p. 302, fig. 15.)

present in beds older than those containing coal. Probably the differences in organic degradation leading to coal or petroleum were determined by early environmental factors, and the patterns were set by different types of bacterial decay occurring under fresh and salt-water conditions respectively.

DEPOSITION

The depositional environment of a sediment is indicated by (1) its mineralogic and chemical composition, (2) its physical characters, and (3) its fossils. These criteria are variously significant with respect to different kinds of sediment. Individual criteria are variously useful, also, in the recognition of different features of the environment.

Mineralogic and Chemical Composition

The common sedimentary minerals are divisible into two classes, (1) silica and silicates and (2) carbonates. Their occurrences and distributions are particularly important in indicating the relations of depositional areas and sediment-producing lands.

Detrital Minerals

Detrital minerals are transported by water, wind, and ice. They are deposited in a great variety of environments. With few and relatively unimportant exceptions they are the only minerals deposited from flowing water on the land and they are the constituents of all fluvial deposits. Limestone pebbles, the principal exception, may occur with detrital minerals. Detrital minerals also are deposited in standing water of the sea and lakes. In these situations they accumulate mainly in areas reached by appreciable currents, and thick deposits generally identify shallow-water or near-shore locations. The thicknesses of detrital deposits are closely controlled by water depth, surface gradient, and tectonism. After sedimentation has built up to wave base in a stable basin or to grade on a stable land surface, deposition is halted. Additional sediment is carried on to farther areas. Enormous thicknesses, however, can accumulate in subsiding regions.

Clay Minerals

Although clay minerals respond to environmental conditions, their reactions are slow, and clay mineralogists do not agree regarding alterations that may indicate differences in depositional environments. Montmorillonite has been reported to change to illite under marine conditions, and illite generally dominates in marine strata, particularly in Paleozoic rocks (see Figure 130). Montmorillonite is abundant in some modern marine sediments, however. It is the principal clay mineral in some post-Paleozoic marine deposits such as the Pierre Shale (Cret.) and Porters Creek Formation (Eoc.). Perhaps the alteration of montmorillonite is mainly a result of later diagenesis than that which occurs in newly deposited sediments on the sea floor. Kaolinite may provide a better index. It is reported to be unimportant and commonly lacking in open-sea marine strata but may

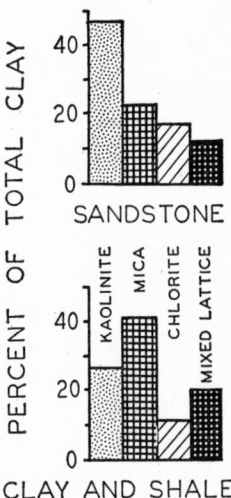

Figure 130. Histograms showing proportions of the principal clay minerals present in Pennsylvanian sandstones and shales of Illinois. The large amount of kaolinite in sandstones suggests that these strata are largely nonmarine whereas the preponderance of "mica" or illite in shales is consistent with the deposition of many of these beds in a marine environment. (After Glass and others, 1956, *Bull. Am. Assoc. Petroleum Geol.*, vol. 40, p. 753, fig. 3.) See also Figure 230, p. 607.

constitute up to nearly 30 percent of lagoonal deposits. Its presence probably indicates near-shore situations and generally rapid deposition. On the other hand, kaolinite dominates in many lacustrine sediments, and illite is likely to constitute less than 30 percent of the clay minerals unless the deposit is calcareous.

Carbonates

Carbonates are much better indices of broad differences in depositional environment. With few and unimportant exceptions, such as calcareous tufa, cave onyx, and some dolomitic sand, they identify deposition in standing water. If the deposits are thick and extensive, marine conditions are indicated because lakes are comparatively small and impermanent.

Most carbonate sediment is produced by the activity of organisms. It is formed most abundantly in water considerably less than 600 feet deep where light penetrates to the bottom and conditions are most favorable for life. Very little calcium carbonate is known to have accumulated in deep water before the appearance of pelagic foraminifera in late Cretaceous time. Since then, however, the shells of these and some other pelagic animals have settled over large areas of the deep-sea floor. Their rate of deposition is very slow.

Calcium carbonate deposition is influenced by temperature. Consequently it is most important in regions where the water is temperate or warm. Where carbonate sediment predominates, a situation far from land is indicated or nearby land is low and it provides only small quantities of detrital sediment. Little difference in significance can be recognized between limestone and dolomite except that dolomite may indicate very shallow-water situations and is unlikely to occur in fresh-water deposits anywhere.

Evaporites

Gypsum, anhydrite, and rock salt are deposits characteristic of a highly restrictive environment that cannot be mistaken. Most of them identify shallow basins in relatively arid regions that were imperfectly or intermittently connected with the sea.

Trace Elements

Some evidence is accumulating that certain metals present in sediments in minute amounts occur in proportions varying according to differences in depositional environments. Thus boron and rubidium are reported to be more abundant in marine than in fresh-water deposits, but the reverse is true of gallium. Nickel and vanadium appear to be associated particularly with organic material in marine strata, but copper, zinc, and tin occur in greater concentrations in similar fresh-water deposits. The thorium-to-uranium ratio has been found to be high in non-marine sediments, intermediate in ordinary marine shales, and low in marine black shale, coal, limestone, and evaporites.

Physical Characters

The textures, structures, and colors of sedimentary rocks were considered in Chapter 5. Some of these and also larger physical characters, such as the form and extent of sedimentary bodies, are particularly useful in relating deposition to physical forces. The influences of currents and waves that transport sediments and constitute important elements of their environments, and the depth of water in which sediments were deposited, are more or less clearly indicated by some sedimentary structures.

Coarseness

The coarseness of sediment is a measure of the transporting power of the medium in which it was deposited. In fluvial sediments it indicates the maximum current velocity. In sediments of standing water it reflects the combined action of waves and currents. Detrital sediments include the coarsest particles that can be moved no farther, but a calcareous deposit that was formed essentially in place consists of those particles too large to have been moved away.

Pebbles and large rock fragments are moved more or less easily by many

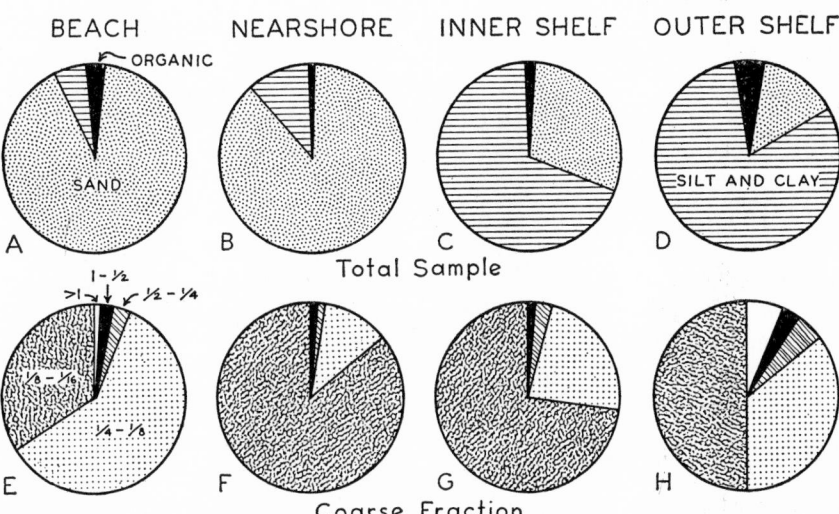

Figure 131. Analyses of sediments from the central Texas Gulf coast. The beach and near-shore sediments are strikingly different—compare A and B with C and D. Beach sand, however, is considerably coarser than near-shore sand—compare E and F (see also Figure 56, p. 164). The plus 1 mm. fraction consists of shells which are rare in the near-shore and inner-shelf sediments. The increasing proportions of the ¼–⅛ mm. fractions from the near-shore outward appear anomalous but result mainly from a great increase in the number of foraminifera occurring in this size range. (Data fom Shepard and Moore, 1955, *Bull. Am. Assoc. Petroleum Geol.*, vol. 39, p. 1503, fig. 28.)

streams and are deposited where currents slacken. In bodies of standing water they ordinarily are confined to a very narrow zone of strong wave action along the beach and decrease in size with distance from their source. Wave action is not strong enough along most coasts to move sand appreciably beyond a depth of about thirty or forty feet. Sand may be carried farther at some places by strong offshore currents, but mainly it moves parallel to the coasts. In normal offshore deposits the grain size of detrital sediment may be expected to decrease regularly and gradually outward from the shore (see Figure 131), but many irregularities occur. Mud is trapped in protected bays and in the shallow water of mangrove swamps. Sand and even gravel in deep water may result from peculiar topographic conditions, the action of density currents, or be inheritances from former lower stands of sea level. Muds are spread far and wide in deeper water. Calcareous material may occur in patches surrounded by other sediments where local conditions permit abundant lime-secreting organisms to exist (see Figure 220, p. 581).

Sorting

The size sorting of sediment is a measure of the selective action of the transporting medium. Its degree of perfection may aid in the identification of the medium. Glacial ice is wholly unselective, and till is a mixture of particles ranging from the finest to the coarsest. Mud flows produce similar deposits. Sediments deposited by rivers and smaller streams, including all but the finest layers in flood-plain and deltaic areas, are likely to be poorly sorted because of local and variable current action. The detrital sediments of large bodies of standing water, particularly the sea, generally are much better sorted because wave agitation keeps fine material suspended in shallow water and eventually carries it out to sea while currents move coarse particles along the bottom. Most widespread marine sands are well sorted. The best appear to have been deposited in transgressing seas. The most perfect sorting is accomplished by the wind. Eolian sands also commonly consist of rounded, frosted grains and possess pronounced and irregular cross-bedding. Many limestones are less well sorted than other marine deposits.

Sediments whose sizes and sorting have been studied are commonly described in terms of their median dimensions and a sorting index that is a measure of their spread in sizes or the perfection of their sorting. These might characterize the sediments of a deposit adequately if all material were transported in a similar way. Many sediments, however, are mixtures consisting of one fraction that was moved along the bottom and another that was carried in suspension. The proportions of the fractions and the relations of their sizes vary considerably depending upon the circumstances of their transportation and deposition. These differences become apparent if comparisons are made between median size and the size of the coarsest fraction. The plotting of such measurements in graphic form shows that different distribution patterns are characteristic of different kinds of sediment, as shown in Figure 132.

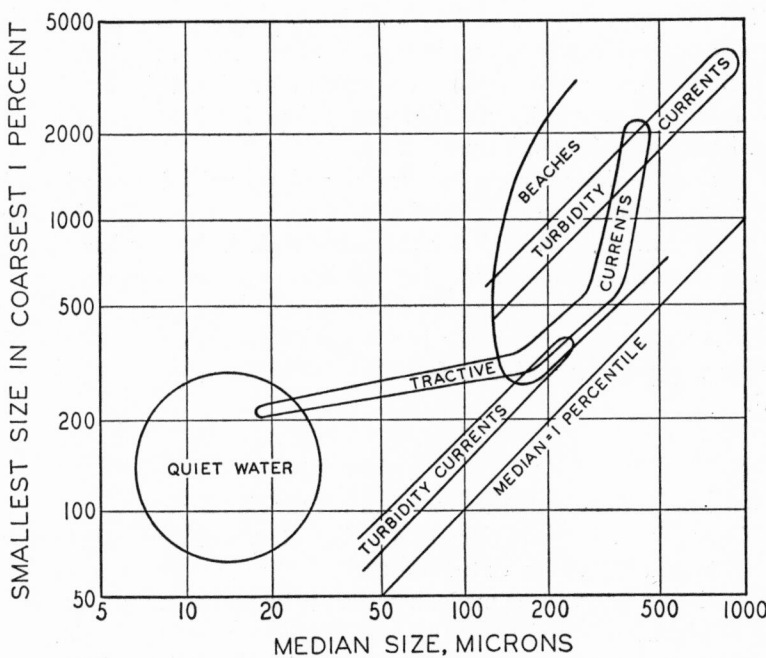

Figure 132. Diagram showing that the relations between the coarsest fraction of a sediment and its median diameter provide evidence that can aid in
the determination of its means of transportation and environment of deposition.
The outlined areas show the distribution of points on a series of scatter diagrams. (After Passega, 1957, *Bull. Am. Assoc. Petroleum Geol.*, vol. 41, p. 1973,
fig. 12.)

Sedimentary Structures

Sedimentary structures, mostly of small scale, and markings preserved on sedimentary surfaces are variously serviceable in identifying some features of sedimentary environments, particularly depth of water. Thus mud cracks, tracks of land animals, rain prints, and impressions of salt and ice crystals all indicate surfaces that became temporarily emergent as on the flood plains of streams or adjacent to a shore. These are not common, and all are restricted to fine-grained detrital material except mud cracks, which may occur in limestone. Also the more or less local presence of thin layers of limestone conglomerate in a limestone matrix generally records similar emergence.

Shallow-water sediments are marked at many places by cross-bedding, ripples, load casts, and minor erosion features. If they are abundant, a shallow-
water environment is strongly indicated which may have been fluvial, lacus-

trine, or marine. None of these features, however, is exclusively restricted to shallow-water situations. Cross-bedding may be eolian, ripples have been discovered at great depths beneath the sea, load casts probably are at best indications of rapid deposition, and some erosion can occur wherever sufficiently strong currents flow. All of these features require moderately coarse sediment for their development and preservation, but this may be either detrital or calcareous. Many shallow-water deposits, however, are not distinguished by any of these features.

Deep-water sediments are more regular and generally finer grained. The only feature definitely suggestive of this environment is graded bedding of the type produced by turbidity currents, but such beds may have been deposited in moderately shallow water.

Slump and flow structures, such as contorted bedding and boudinage, generally identify sediments deposited on sloping surfaces. The inclination may have been very gentle and no information regarding depth of water is provided.

Colors

Colors, more than any other rock feature, provide information about the oxidizing or reducing conditions of a sedimentary environment. Dark gray or black commonly indicates the presence of organic matter and reduction. Careful distinction must be made, however, between rocks that are carbonaceous or bituminous, and those that are dark because of their mineral constituents such as many graywackes and volcanic sands. If in addition pyrite or marcasite occurs, strongly reducing conditions probably prevailed. Organic-rich sediments and iron sulfides do not necessarily record an environment that was anaerobic. Strong red colors are sure signs of oxidation and are most likely to identify terrestrial deposits. Green colors in sediments most commonly result from the presence of glauconite which is believed to have developed on relatively shallow sea bottoms where deposition was slow and conditions were mildly reducing. Most other rock colors are indeterminate as far as the depositional environment is concerned, and other evidence must be sought.

Fossils

Fossils are by far the most important potential means of differentiating and identifying depositional environments because the existence of organisms at any place and their distribution within any region are so closely controlled by environmental conditions (see Figure 133). The complexities of ecology, however, and the more or less unknown requirements of most organisms occurring only in the fossil state make all interpretation difficult and much of it unsure. Fossils have long been used to distinguish marine and non-marine strata but beyond this their potentialities have not been fully realized. The entire subject of interpretative paleoecology has not received the attention it deserves.

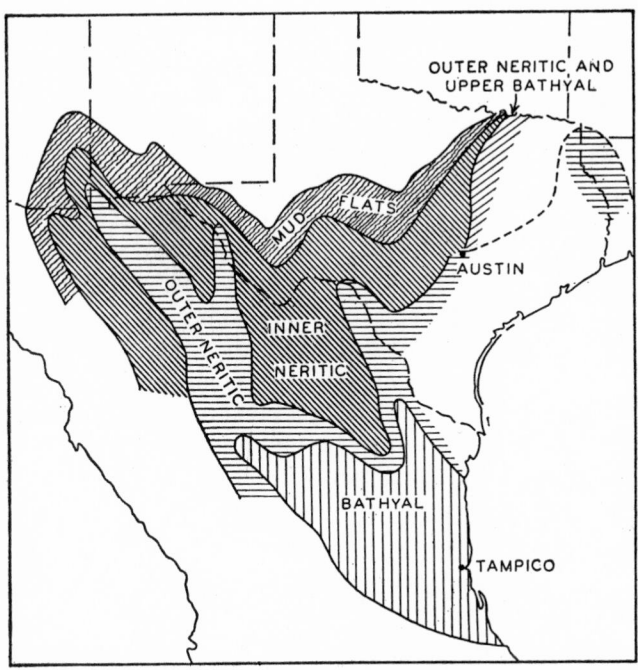

Figure 133. Map of the Texas-Mexican region indicating the probable relative depth of the sea during Albian time (Cret.) represented by the Trinity, Fredericksburg, and Washita formations. This interpretation is based mainly upon the distributions of the various types of ammonites shown in Figure 71, p. 218. (After Scott, 1940, *J. Paleon.*, vol. 14, p. 318, fig. 9.)

Occurrence

The first feature of paleontologic significance that is noted by any observer is the occurrence of fossils within a stratum. The absence of fossils is not similarly noted because absence can be established only by a very careful search. Many geologists are not particularly interested in fossils and little or no search may be made for them. Even rather obvious specimens may be overlooked in any casual inspection. It is exceedingly important to recognize, therefore, that any environmental conclusions based on the apparent absence of fossils falls into a different class from conclusions based upon their presence. The absence of fossils provides only negative evidence which never is conclusive. No amount of searching can ever prove that an organism was really absent when sediment was deposited. It cannot even prove that fossils do not now exist because there is always a chance that the next piece of rock broken or turned over will reveal a specimen.

Almost every modern fauna includes numerous members that are unlikely to be fossilized, and most plants are ill suited for preservation in recognizable form. There is no reason to conclude that ancient faunas or floras were different in this respect. Consequently even the most prolifically fossiliferous rock is practically certain to contain a notably incomplete representation of the organisms that constituted a community of the past. An excellent example of almost totally unknown kinds of extinct creatures is provided by the Burgess Shale (M. Camb.) of British Columbia in Canada. The unique fauna of this formation is famous because of the variety of strange soft-bodied animals it contains. They are preserved as thin carbonaceous films that somehow escaped destruction. Even under the very exceptional conditions of preservation at this locality, however, the plants that must have existed at this time and place are unrepresented among the fossils.

The remains of all organisms are subject to complete destruction. Even the sturdiest shells can be worn away before burial or dissolved afterwards. Failure to find fossils, therefore, may be indication that (1) careful enough search has not been made, (2) all recognizable traces of organisms have been destroyed, or (3) organisms actually were very scarce or absent when the sediment was deposited.

Efforts should be made to learn, if possible, how the remains of organisms were destroyed or why an area was uninhabited. This is as important as an effort to determine differences in the environment as indicated by the occurrence of one type of fauna or flora rather than another in certain strata. If answers can be found, they are sure to have meanings of some importance in the reconstruction of depositional conditions.

Abundance

The second paleontologic observation likely to be made by any geologist concerns the relative abundance of fossils, particularly the larger and more conspicuous kinds. Abundance of specimens bears no necessary relationship to the number of organisms that actually lived together in any area because (1) an unknown proportion of the total fauna and flora has not been preserved, (2) the fossils are an accumulation of specimens representing a longer or shorter undetermined interval of time, and (3) the remains of some organisms may have been removed from the area of observation or some may have been brought into it from another area or another environment.

The number of fossil specimens present commonly varies considerably from bed to bed or from zone to zone within a single bed. This variability reflects the changing relations of the factors mentioned and also changes in the local population density with time. The relationships are complicated and probably unstable, but careful studies may provide some indication of their relative importance. The presence of abundant perfect specimens at a bedding plane may have resulted from the very rapid burial of a living population whose remains, if not protected in this way, would have been much damaged or destroyed. Concentrations of abundant fossils in thin layers most probably record either the intermittent transportation and accumulation of specimens in a particular small area or relatively brief intervals of time when local conditions were especially favorable for life. The comparative scarcity of specimens in other layers on the contrary is more likely to indicate the action of destructive processes or rapid sedimentary deposition.

Few areas on the sea bottom today, except in anaerobic situations, are totally uninhabited by animals (see Figure 134). Over the course of many years required for the deposition of slowly accumulating sediment, even a very sparse population should be indicated by many fossils unless destruction was effective and continuous. If destruction of certain kinds of organisms was incomplete, specimens in all stages of disintegration might remain. Observations reveal that many strata, and particularly limestones, contain a much smaller number of fossil specimens than might be expected considering the slowness of deposition of many marine sediments. Commonly the fossils that do occur are well preserved and unaccompanied by many damaged specimens. The reasons for such a seemingly inadequate representation of a probably continuously existing fauna and the excellent preservation of the specimens are not immediately apparent.

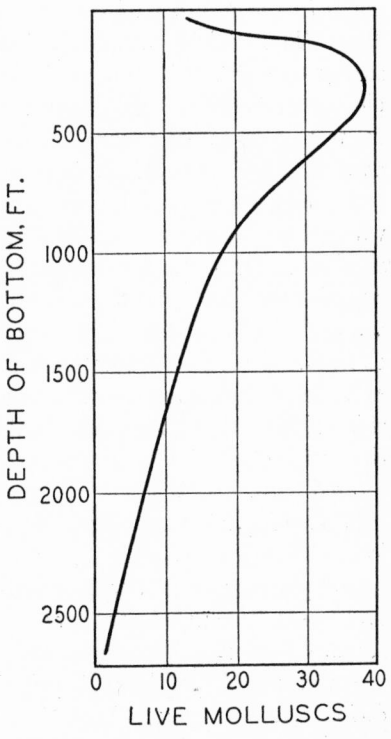

Figure 134. Curve showing the number of living molluscan specimens per sample dredged from various depths in the San Pedro basin between Santa Catalina Island and the California mainland (see Figure 86, p. 245). The densest molluscan populations occur at depths corresponding to the outer neritic zone (see Figure 55, p. 163). The greatest variety of species occurs at somewhat shallower depths. (Generalized from Bandy, 1958, *J. Paleon.*, vol. 32, p. 710, fig. 2.)

Variety

After abundance, the variety of fossils present in a stratum is next noticed. Regardless of the abundance of specimens, however, there are great differences in the number of species represented in individual fossil faunas and floras. The variety commonly increases with greater abundance but at a slower rate. This is not particularly significant because there is a better chance that unusual or rare species will be found among the abundant specimens of a large collection. On the other hand, specimens, although abundant, may be very restricted in variety.

Modern faunal communities of the level sea bottoms, similar to those where most fossiliferous strata accumulated, generally consist of a rather small number of species possessing preservable hard parts. No definite number of such species can be specified because it varies from place to place and probably has varied in the past from time to time. Perhaps a dozen fairly common species, excluding microfossils, is a reasonable figure not likely to be exceeded within the restricted area represented by many outcrops. Any considerable deviation from this number requires explanation in terms of factors that caused restriction in variety or possibly permitted the existence of a more diverse association. Many reported fossil faunas include a much greater number of species, but lists of this type generally are not serviceable for ecologic analysis because the specimens were found in different beds and at different places, and inadequate distinction was made between common and rare forms. The number of species that is significant is only the number that actually lived together and constituted a single local community.

A well-established biologic principle is that life is most diverse where conditions are most favorable for its existence—in other words, where the fewest adverse conditions must be overcome. As life is organized on earth, an optimum is reached where temperature is warm, and moisture and sunlight are abundant. This environment requires the least adaptation and specialization for successful living. Such conditions are most perfectly met in shallow tropical seas and it is there that intimately related biologic communities are most diverse.

Insofar as any factor of the environment deviates from the ideal, living becomes more difficult and some organisms are unable to compete with others that have succeeded in adapting themselves to less favorable conditions. This does not mean that life is less abundant but only that communities are less diverse. As deviation from the optimum in any or all ways becomes more and more pronounced, the number of species that can survive decreases.

This principle can be applied to the interpretation of variety in the number of associated fossil organisms limited only by the fact that fossil faunas are incomplete records of the former communities. It seems reasonable in general to assume that decrease in the number of fossil species below what is considered normal for a favorably situated community is indication of corresponding decrease in the total number of associated species. Therefore inquiry can be made in an effort to discover how and to what extent the local environment deviated from the optimum. Also if the number of fossil species is too great, the fossils may be suspected of being representative of members of more than a single integrated community.

Association

Characteristic associations of both (1) certain fossils and certain kinds of rock and (2) different kinds of fossils commonly occurring together have been recognized by many paleontologists although these relations are rarely remarked upon and are likely to escape notice by other persons. Both types of association have environmental implications. The first type apparently is determined mainly by physical factors of the environment. The second probably reflects both physical and biologic features. As far as stratigraphy is concerned the strictly biologic factors, such as food relationships, all organic competition, and several types of mutually beneficial association or mutual repulsion, are unimportant except where a noteworthy fraction of the sediment is of biologic origin.

Because biologic factors play a significant part in all biologic associations, faunas, and to a somewhat less extent floras, may vary considerably from place to place within a region where the physical environmental factors are practically identical. Consequently the physical variability within a depositional area may be much less than conspicuous differences in fossil associations might suggest. On the other hand, if any notable physical differences occur, they are almost certain to be reflected by differences in the fossils. Therefore, the first problem, as far as stratigraphic interpretation is concerned, is to distinguish between the results of biologic and physical factors in the local environment.

There is no easy solution to this problem. Perhaps the best way to approach it is through close attention to the association of individual fossil species with lithologic characters. Some species are almost nowhere found except in a certain particular kind of rock. Others occur more or less indiscriminately in many kinds. Obviously, distribution of the former kind of fossils was controlled by factors closely connected with the depositional environment whereas the latter kind may not have been similarly restricted. Neither of these types of fossils is likely to be very useful in interpretation. Some other fossils, however, occurring in rocks with a limited range of lithologic variability, may prove to be more serviceable. Next, the biologic associations of the second type of fossils should be noted with respect to other individual species and also the abundance and variability of all species particularly in vertical and lateral sequences where lithologic characters gradually change. These changes probably indicate such things as greater or less water depth or distance from the shore, more or less aeration, or variation in salinity. Corresponding and gradual consistent changes in fossil associations and other similar comparisons may reveal some features permitting the recognition of a sort of biologic spectrum that parallels variation in the physical environment.

Preservation

The remains of organisms vary greatly in the perfection of their preservation. Fossils range all the way from specimens apparently unchanged in any way, even retaining the color markings of living individuals, through those that are more or less bleached, crushed, recrystallized, replaced, dissolved, worn, fragmented, and decayed; finally they grade into calcium carbonate or organic material that certainly was derived from organisms but cannot otherwise be identified. All changes of these types reflect the action of physical, chemical, and biologic processes that affected organisms and their remains from the time they were living to the present. Undoubtedly most organisms have disappeared so completely that no tangible trace of them remains.

The features of fossil preservation that are significant in the interpretation of depositional environments are those that affected the remains of organisms without completely destroying them or eliminating all evidence of their existence as they lay on the sea bottom or were shallowly buried in the sediment.

Two classes of fossils differed with respect to the nature of their preservation: (1) those lacking mineralized hard parts, like graptolites, whose remains were very delicate and subject to rapid decay, and (2) those with shells or mineralized supporting skeletons. The first kind could not have survived much agitation or transportation by waves or bottom currents, and the fossils generally owe their preservation to prompt burial or the protection of an anaerobic environment.

Calcareous and other mineralized structures of organic origin are much more resistant to destructive processes. When buried and removed from the realm of physical forces active on the sea bottom they are mainly altered chemically or by solution. Carbon dioxide and hydrogen sulfide produced by the bacterial decay of sedimentary organic matter results in increased acidity, and calcareous shells may be dissolved completely or replaced by iron sulfide. In some black shales fossils consist of no more than impressions where the shells once lay. Aragonite is more soluble than calcite and in some limestones the aragonitic shells of molluscs have been removed whereas calcitic brachiopods and crinoids, for example, are well preserved. Shells that were originally aragonitic fared differently in some muds and shales whose low permeability prevented water movement and solution although the shells generally have been replaced by calcite. The removal of calcareous fossils from sandstone and the formation of empty molds commonly occurred only after strata were uplifted and entered the zone of actively circulating ground water.

Shells and other mineralized organic structures that are not promptly buried deteriorate as they lie upon or are moved along the sea bottom. Remains that have suffered in this way may be classed as different types (shown in Figure 135). If these can be distinguished from each other information is provided regarding some features of the depositional environment. Fossils of Type A were not removed from the place where the organisms lived and were not exposed long enough before burial to have been much damaged. Fossils of Type B lay on the surface for a protracted period of time without being moved away because deposition was very slow and currents were weak. They may have been partly dissolved, broken by scavengers, bored by sponges, scoured by drifting sand, or covered by the encrusting growths of other organisms. Fos-

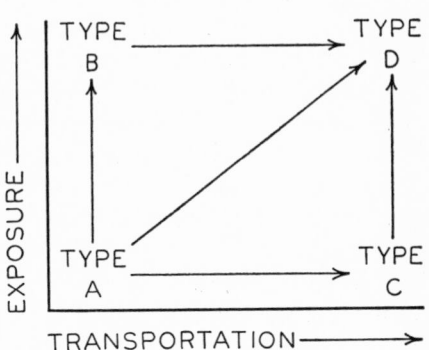

Figure 135. Diagram showing the relations of four types of marine organic accumulations that differ according to the comparative amounts of damage resulting from exposure and transportation on the sea bottom. (Suggested by R. G. Johnson.)

sils of Type C were picked up and transported by bottom currents. They may have been broken and much abraded. Fossils of Type D were transported after long exposure, were exposed after being moved, or suffered the effects of these processes alternately. Either exposure or transportation, if continued long enough, results in the complete destruction of the remains of organisms.

Sorting and Orientation

Currents in the sea are capable of sorting the remains of organisms just as they sort mineral particles. Therefore an accumulation of fossils of approximately equal size generally indicates current action. In this process shape as well as size and weight influences the results. The opposite valves of many brachiopods and some pelecypods differ considerably in convexity, size, and thickness. Among transported fossils it is not uncommon for the valves to be separated and carried to different places. Convex shells are less stable in a current if they lie on the bottom with their convex sides down because in this position they are easily overturned. Consequently, an accumulation of shells consisting mostly of one valve, rather than both in nearly equal numbers, and lying convex side upwards is evidence of current transportation. Because the valves of brachiopods are weakly hinged and easily separated, the presence of complete specimens suggests that little movement has occurred. The valves of pelecypods are held more securely by a ligament, but these also are not likely to be carried far without separation. If the ligament decays before the shells are buried, the valves will fall apart even in the most tranquil situation.

Shells and similar objects offer more resistance to a current and are more likely to be moved if they lie broadside to it. Also moving objects are most likely to come to rest with their long axis parallel to the current. If ripple marks occur, however, elongated objects such as fragmentary plant stems may lodge between them and be oriented transversely to the current. The most stable position of an unequally convex shell is that in which the slope is more gentle on the upstream side. High-spired gastropods and orthoceratoid cephalopods are most stable if the pointed end is directed upcurrent. Some rocks contain fossils that are oriented and these relations serve to identify current action and may indicate the direction in which the current moved. The absence of obvious orientation, however, is not equally good evidence for the lack of currents.

Non-marine Fossils

In the foregoing discussions marine fossils have received primary if not exclusive consideration. Although some conclusions may be drawn from the occurrence and nature of terrestrial fossils, these are relatively unimportant in interpretation because they are comparatively rare. The physical and chemical features of non-marine sediments generally are more useful indicators of depositional environments.

Rates of Deposition

Mention was made in Chapter 2 of an early method used for estimating the duration of geologic time by dividing the thickness of observed strata by an assumed rate of deposition. Radioactive dating now demonstrates that many of these estimates were almost ridiculously deficient. Two sources of error contributed to these results: (1) underestimation of the greatest thicknesses of strata representing various geologic time intervals and (2) over estimation of the sustained rate of deposition.

Estimates of the rate of deposition employed in these calculations were little better than guesses. They were to some extent based on observations of present-day deposition. This is known to be rapid at some favored places but it varies greatly, and at other places within depositional regions no sediment at all is now accumulating. There is little reason to believe that deposition at the present rates is likely to continue without much change in the same area for very long periods of time. In making comparisons between the present and the past, therefore, it is necessary to distinguish between transitory rates, which prevail for comparatively brief intervals, and sustained rates, which are rough measures of average deposition for long periods.

The foregoing method of calculation can be reversed. The duration of geologic time intervals, estimated on the basis of radioactive age determinations, and measured thicknesses of strata can be compared to produce ratios indicating either the average number of years per unit thickness of strata or the average thickness of strata per selected unit of time. Both are measures of the sustained rate of deposition. Calculations of this kind provide a figure of about seven inches of Tertiary strata per thousand years in that part of the Gulf coast region where the stratigraphic section is the thickest. In contrast, Paleozoic strata in the Michigan and Illinois basins represent deposition at an average rate of about one-half inch per thousand years. Of course, in some parts of these basins and at some times deposition undoubtedly was much more rapid.

Insofar as modern or near modern and ancient rates of deposition are measured in terms of stratigraphic thickness, two corrections are required to make them comparable. The first corrective factor is a variable dependent on relative compaction. As a very rough approximation and an average for all types of rock, 50 percent reduction in thickness is convenient for application to an example. Thus it may be assumed that the average rates of deposition of new sediment, before this was subjected to the compacting weight of overburden, were twice those that have been mentioned for ancient sediments.

The second factor is much more difficult to assess. It concerns an allowance that should be made to compensate for the erosion and removal of formerly existing strata at unconformities. Tertiary strata in the Gulf coast region probably are not interrupted by many or important erosional unconformities, and as far as they are concerned no correction of this kind seems necessary. Many unconformities, however, separate formations on the margins of the Michigan and Illinois basins. Mostly the intervals of time that they represent and the amount of erosion that was accomplished are not known. The extent to which many of these unconformities continue into the central basin areas where strata are the thickest also has not been determined. Therefore, this factor cannot be estimated for these basins with any accuracy. It does not seem probable, however, that a factor of more than two is required. This would only double the foregoing estimated rate or quadruple it if the compaction factor also is considered. Even so, the average rate of deposition in these basins evidently was very slow.

Recent and Pleistocene sediments recovered in deep-sea cores and dated by the carbon 14 method show rates of deposition ranging from less than one to rarely more than two inches per thousand years. These are very fine-grained sediments and for comparative purposes a larger compaction factor must be used. If assumptions are made that the average rate has been one inch per thousand years and that compaction would reduce volume 75 percent, average Paleozoic deposition in Michigan and Illinois appears to have been about eight times, and average Tertiary deposition in the Mississippi delta area about fifty-six times, as rapid.

Considering that the ancient examples compared to fairly recent ones concern areas much closer to the land, where presumably much more generous amounts of sediment were available, the smallness of the differences between the estimated rates of deposition is surprising. The conclusion to be drawn seems to be that deposition even in very favorable areas is far less continuous than has been generally realized and that most stratigraphic sections are interrupted by numerous unrecognized diastems. Important also is tectonic control of deposition in sedimentary basins. There, by-passing of sediment probably occurs on a large scale when and where the bottom has been built up to wave base, and further accumulation is not possible until subsidence or rising sea level displaces the bottom below this critical position.

In stratigraphic studies, rates of deposition applied to units of the magnitude of formations and members would be most useful if they could be determined. Unfortunately, acceptably accurate estimates of this kind are not possible at present because the margin of error with respect to time intervals is too great. The best results attainable seem to be no more than rough and relative estimates of "rapid" or "slow" sedimentary deposition based upon whatever useful kinds of internal physical and biologic evidence individual strata may afford.

No criterion is infallible as a guide to the relative rate of deposition. In general, a rapid rate is indicated by coarse grain, poor sorting, uneven stratification, thick bedding, lateral variation, and paucity of animal fossils whereas the opposite qualities suggest slowness. These apply to both detrital and calcareous sediments although calcareous material at many places is commonly believed to have accumulated considerably more slowly than detrital. This is not necessarily true everywhere. Cross-bedding is a more than ordinarily good indication of rapid deposition, and abundant fossils of sessile animals almost equally indicate slow accumulation. Numerous plant fossils, except in highly carbonaceous beds, indicate rapid deposition, but abundant root markings suggest relatively static conditions. Burrowing animals and mud-eating scavengers may obscure or destroy some of the distinguishing characters of slow accumulation, particularly the thin and even stratification of fine-grained sediments.

TRANSPORTATION

The physical features of sediments and sedimentary rocks provide some information regarding (1) the medium of sediment transportation, (2) the distance sediment was transported or the duration of the transportational episode in the history of a sediment, and (3) the direction of transportation.

Medium

The great majority of all sediments are transported by and deposited in water. This is so generally true that water transport and deposition can be assumed unless there is evidence to the contrary. Glacial till deposited directly from melting ice commonly is considered to be so characteristic that it has been identified even in partly metamorphosed rocks. There is chance for confusion, however, with mud-flow deposits, and some so-called tillites are of questionable origin. Till ordinarily is an unsorted mixture of material ranging from very fine to very coarse. It has been derived from many kinds of rock in all stages of freshness or decomposition and commonly includes more or less numerous faceted pebbles and boulders. Mud flows may consist of somewhat similar mixtures, but rock fragments are likely to exhibit less variety and be angular rather than faceted and the occurrence of striated fragments is most unusual. Also mud-flow deposits generally are restricted in areal extent, and their composition ordinarily is similar to that of associated stratified deposits. Eolian sediments are less easily differentiated from deposits laid down in shallow water. They are well sorted, however, and sands are likely to be conspicuously and irregularly cross-bedded and consist of rounded and frosted grains. Finer silty sediment like loess commonly is unstratified and homogeneous.

Much of the transportation of detrital sediment is accomplished by running water. This may move sediments longer or shorter distances but more essentially they travel from higher to lower altitudes. Fluvial deposits consist of relatively poorly sorted material and may show many irregularities such as local erosion features, interlensing of sediments differing in coarseness, cross-bedding, and other evidences of current action like ripple marks.

Most detrital sediment deposited in standing water is delivered to a sea or lake by streams. Thereafter its further transportation is largely horizontal. Sands are almost immediately deposited in deltas or they are moved laterally along the shore in very shallow water. As wave action removes fine material, sands become better sorted. Cross-bedding may be developed and current ripple marks are common. Most extensive marine sandstones consist of material that was moved and deposited in shifting zones along advancing or retreating shorelines. They vary somewhat in age from place to place. Silts and clays are much more extensively spread in progressively deeper water, and the deposits are generally characterized by more even and continuous bedding. Coarser layers may bear oscillation ripples.

Turbidity current transportation is indicated by evenly distributed graded beds which include detrital sediment of the finest sizes. Strata of this kind are likely to grade imperceptibly into deposits produced by submarine slumping and mud flows.

Calcium carbonate and other soluble substances are transported in solution. As sediments they have no fluvial history. Lime extracted from sea water largely by organisms may then be moved by wave and current action. This transportation is mostly horizontal although downslope movement is important on the flanks of reefs. The extent of most limestones, however, was controlled much more by the pattern of original calcareous deposition than by subsequent transportation of this kind of sediment.

Many sediments have had complex histories. Some have passed repeatedly from the realm of one transporting medium to that of another. After each transfer a sediment may retain some features indicative of its former state although these commonly are somewhat masked and may soon be lost. Coarse outwash material derived from melting glaciers is easily identified by its varied assortment of erratic pebbles. As textures become finer, these sediments are more difficult to identify. The St. Peter Sandstone (Ord.) appears to be a good example of a sediment with a complex but decipherable history. This sand probably was first transported by streams, delivered to a shrinking sea, and spread out along the coast. Then it was moved by wind and heaped in dunes. Finally, when the sea readvanced, the dune sand was reworked and redistributed along the coast. Many sediments, however, reveal little of their possibly varied pasts.

Distance and Duration

A general knowledge of paleogeography and areal geology may eliminate large regions as possible source areas of detrital sediments and thus furnish some idea as to the distance they were transported to their present resting places. More rarely, some peculiarity of mineral or lithologic composition may point directly to the rocks of a restricted area as the source of sediments and thereby indicate the path they have traveled. For example, igneous and metamorphic pebbles in the glacial drift of the Mississippi Valley can be matched with rocks of the Lake Superior district or places farther north in Canada. Pebbles of vein quartz and quartzite, abundant at some places in the lower Pennsylvanian sandstones of southern Illinois, could not have come from any place closer than Canada on the north or the Appalachian region on the east. These pebbles do not indicate a definite source area, but evidence is provided that they and the sands with which they are associated must have been transported for a distance of 500 miles or more.

Rounding of sand results from wear either during transportation or by backward and forward movement of grains as on a beach, where little actual transportation is accomplished. Although rounding does not prove that sand has traveled a long distance, sharp angularity is indication that extensive transportation has not occurred. Rounding may record a long sedimentary history rather than much transport. Quartz grains become rounded relatively slowly, and most well-rounded sand probably has experienced more than one cycle of erosion, transportation, and deposition. Silt-sized particles of quartz retain their angularity almost indefinitely.

Direction

If the source of sediment is known, the direction of its movement is also known; otherwise different evidence must be sought, for example in such sedimentary structures as cross-bedding (see Figure 136) and current ripple

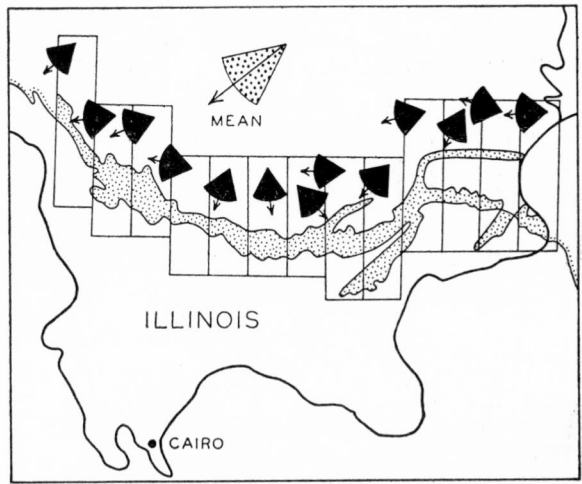

Figure 136. Map showing the outcropping band of Caseyville Conglomerate (Penn.) in southern Illinois and observations on the orientation of cross-bedding. Arrows show the mean directions of cross-bedding sampled in six-mile-wide areas, and the circle segments indicate the statistical limits of 90 percent confidence in these means. These measurements show that the mean direction of currents from which the sand was deposited in this whole region was approximately southwest, suggesting a northeastern source for the sediments. (After Potter and Olson, 1954, *J. Geol.,* vol. 62, p. 65, fig. 7.)

marks. These actually indicate only direction of the currents from which sediment was deposited and they are likely to show much irregularity. Regional studies and many observations serve to reveal general trends (see Figure 137), but the direction of movement may have been much different in more sourceward areas where no information of this kind is now available because strata have been eroded or are buried. Directional structures ordinarily occur only in sandy strata and they are not likely to be abundant enough to be useful or have the same significance except in fluvial sediments. Observations need not be limited to a single stratum so long as the material in all beds was derived from the same source.

Similar information probably can be obtained from any kind of detrital sediment by determining grain size. Coarsening indicates source direction

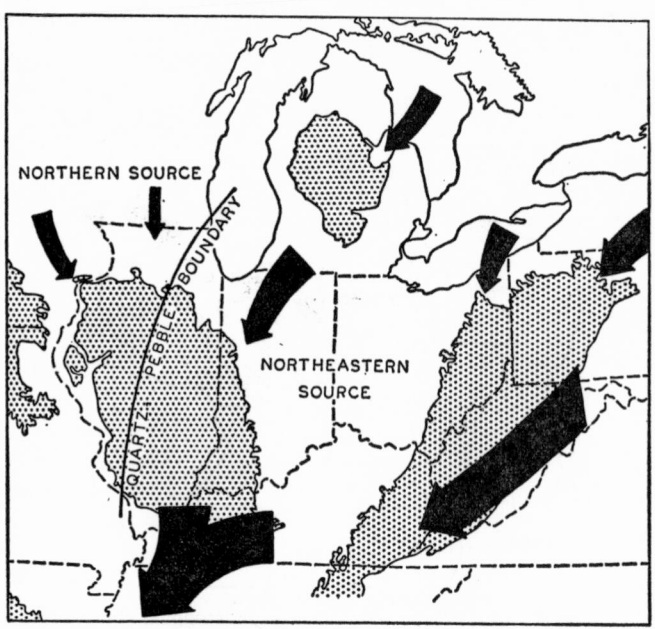

Figure 137.   Arrows indicate the presumed direction of Pennsylvanian sediment transport in the northeastern United States. Sizes of arrows suggest relative importance of the paths of transport. These conclusions were based on cross-bedding observations and mineralogic studies. The quartz pebble boundary corresponds to the limits of coarse sediment probably derived from Appalachian highlands to the northeast. Beyond this, similar material probably came from the Canadian shield to the north. The sands derived from these two regions differ in the amounts of metamorphic quartz and feldspars present and the degree of tourmaline roundness. Mixing of these sands occurred in some areas. (After Siever and Potter, 1956, J. Geol., vol. 64, p. 329, fig. 4.)

(see Figure 138). Laboratory analyses are required, however, and they might not be successful unless all samples were obtained from a single stratum whose age is the same everywhere. Fabric studies of coarser sediments also may reveal imbrication indicating direction of current flow, but such studies are laborious and slow. Probably their results would not be superior to more rapid and more easily made observations if these are possible.

The study of calcareous sediments is not likely to yield results of much significance because most sediments of this kind have not had a comparable history of transportation.

In some situations, thickening of strata may indicate the source of sediments. Thickness, however, is controlled by other factors, particularly by

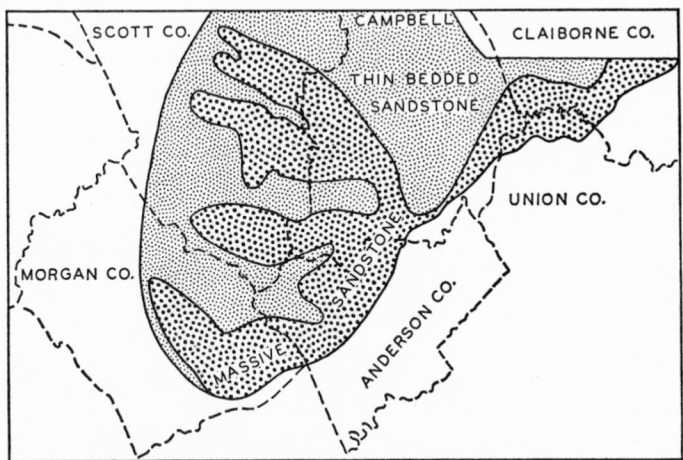

Figure 138.   Map of part of the eastern Tennessee coal fields showing the differential development of the Petros Sandstone (Penn.) in thick, coarse, and massive or thinner, finer-grained, and more thinly bedded facies. Distribution of the massive sandstone bodies indicates that the sand probably was derived from the southeast. Observations made on fourteen other Pennsylvanian sandstones in this same region suggest a similar origin for eight of them and a northern or northeastern source for two. The lithologic variations in the remaining four sandstones are indecisive. (After Wilson and others, 1956, Pennsylvanian geology of the Cumberland Plateau, Tenn. Geol. Surv. folio, pl. 11 L.)

local tectonism, and conclusions are unreliable unless they can be substantiated by progressive sedimentary grain size changes. Sediments commonly thicken, for example, inward in all directions toward the central deeper basin areas even though much the greater part of the detrital material was delivered from a single source. Thus the Paleozoic sediments of the Appalachian region coarsen as they thicken eastward whereas Gulf coast Tertiary strata become finer as they thicken toward the south. The reason for this difference is that the sediments available to observation in these two basins lie on the far and near sides, respectively, of the basin axes as these are viewed from the regions that produced the sediments.

SOURCE

The last step in tracing the history of a sediment backwards is the search for its place of origin and the attempt to reconstruct the nature of the source area. This brings into consideration (1) the identification of the kinds of rock from which the sediment was derived, (2) their location, (3) the climate that controlled their weathering, and (4) the topography that determined their erosion. Although something generally can be learned about most of these matters, results are likely to lack desirable clarity because of the mixing of sediments from different sources and the vicissitudes attendant upon an extended subsequent history during which sediments came under the influence of various chemical and physical conditions.

Source Rocks

The ancestry of a sediment may be evidenced by the minerals that have remained unchanged throughout its history. Mostly these are resistant minerals that are not altered or alter but slowly during weathering. The maturity of a sediment can be rated in terms of these minerals and others that are subject to comparatively rapid decomposition as shown in Figure 139. The sediments most easily interpreted are the least mature ones. The original detrital minerals are conveniently divisible into four groups: (1) quartz, (2) stable heavy minerals, (3) feldspars, and (4) ferromagnesian minerals.

Quartz is by far the commonest original mineral contained in sediments. It occurs in many varieties, and the differentiation of its kinds is important. Crystal grains derived from igneous and metamorphic rocks generally differ with respect to mineral and liquid or gaseous inclusions and evidence of strain. Both kinds may have passed through one or more cycles of erosion and deposition before becoming part of the sediment under observation. These grains may not be distinguishable from others derived directly from crystalline rocks. Secondarily enlarged grains that have been subsequently rounded, however, are indisputably of sedimentary origin (see Figure 111A, p. 294). Other well-rounded quartz grains probably have passed through at least one previous sedimentary episode.

The stable heavy minerals are almost indestructible although the older sedimentary rocks are reported generally to contain a smaller variety of them (see Figure 10, p. 56). Perhaps this indicates that some of them can be lost by very slow solution after deposition. The heavy minerals can be divided roughly into two groups: (1) those occurring most commonly in igneous rocks such as rutile and zircon and (2) those that generally develop as metamorphic minerals, such as tourmaline and garnet. Some similar or related minerals may be formed secondarily within the sediments, and confusion with these must be avoided. Detrital heavy minerals serve not only to suggest igneous or metamorphic origins but also to indicate subordinate varieties of the parent rocks.

Feldspar is more or less abundant in most submature sediments. It was chiefly derived from igneous rocks. The type of feldspar varies in a general way with the amount of silica in igneous rocks. Thus orthoclase or microcline

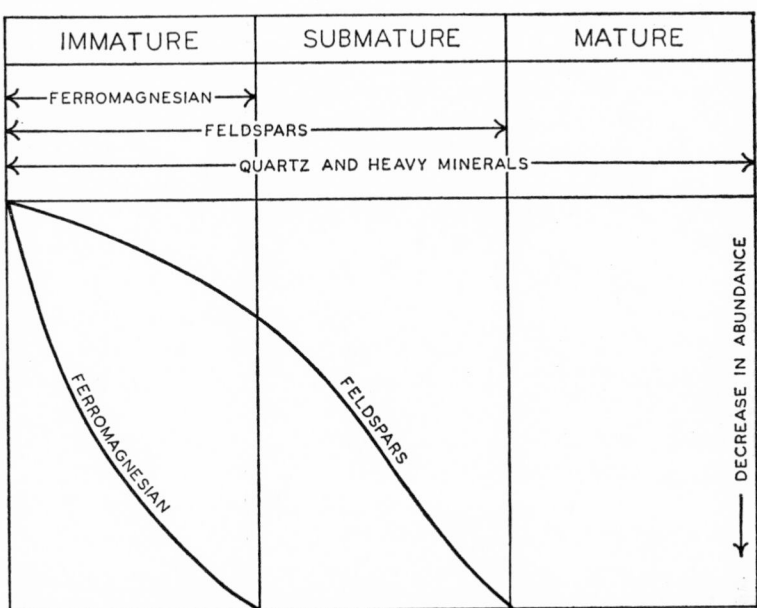

Figure 139. Relative mineralogic maturity of sediments is indicated by the amounts of ferromagnesian minerals and feldspars present in them. These minerals, which occur in most igneous and metamorphic rocks, are decomposed during weathering and sediment formation but are not likely to be much affected by transportation or deposition. Mineralogic maturity, therefore, provides evidence regarding the rapidity of erosion and topographic condition of the region from which the sediments were derived. See also Figure 26, p. 91.

predominates in acid rocks like granite, sodic plagioclase in intermediate rocks like diorite, and calcic plagioclase in basic rocks like gabbro as shown in Figure 140.

Ferromagnesian minerals are important constituents only of immature sediments. They may be abundant in detritus derived from basic igneous rocks, and the types present, somewhat like feldspar, provide information about the kinds of rock that produced these sediments.

Direct evidence of the origin of sediments is furnished by rock fragments. Except in conglomerates, which may contain pebbles of almost any kind of indurated rock, these are only very fine-grained aggregates or such tough and resistant material as schist and quartzite.

The original undecomposed minerals and rock fragments provide more or less clear evidence of the derivation of sediments. They may point toward particular kinds of rock or naturally occurring rock associations. More commonly, however, mixed sediments introduce confusion. The greatest difficul-

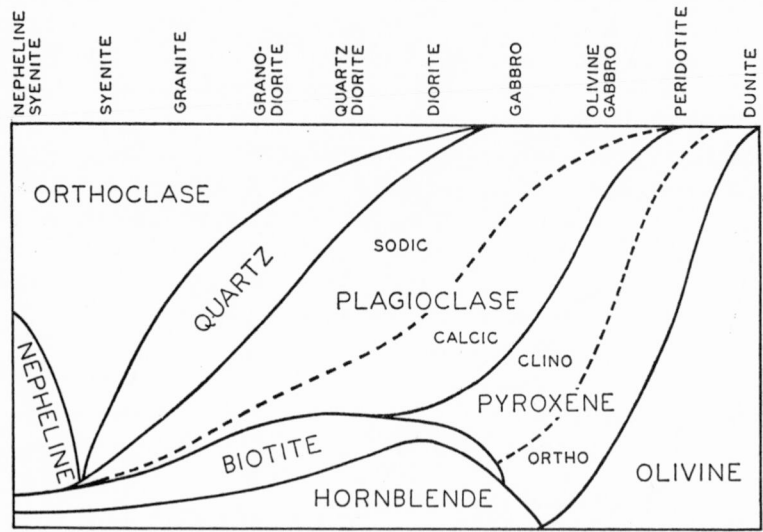

Figure 140.   Diagram showing the approximate relative abundances of the principal minerals occurring in igneous rocks. Ferromagnesian minerals do not occur commonly in sediments except in graywackes. Feldspars, however, which are more resistant to weathering, are present in many. If these minerals are found in sediments, their kinds provide evidence concerning the parent rocks ranging from acidic granite to progressively more basic varieties. (After Washington and Adams, 1951, from *The internal constitution of the earth,* Beno Gutenberg (ed.), p. 84, fig. 3, reprinted by permission of Dover Publications, Inc., New York 14, N.Y. [$2.45])

ties of interpretation are presented by the older and more mature sediments which contain few original minerals other than quartz. The possibility that much of the sediment has passed through previous depositional stages also is a common uncertainty, and minor contributions from different sources may escape detection.

Location

If composition serves to identify sediment with definite types of igneous or metamorphic rock, certain possible source areas may be eliminated and others may be favored as probabilities. The difficulty of establishing apparently satisfactory connections increases considerably with the older sedimentary rocks because the paleogeographic details of the more ancient stages of the earth's history are less surely known. This is especially the case for

Paleozoic and older rocks. Many possible old source areas have been destroyed or are buried beneath younger sediments and the nature of their rocks is not determinable. On the other hand, some of the source areas of more recent strata are now observable and are still producing detrital sediments. Positive identification with these may be possible as, for example, with many Tertiary formations.

The occurrence of an antecedent sedimentary stage in the history of a sediment commonly introduces uncertainties concerning the immediate source of reworked material even though the more ancient history of the sediment may be reasonably assured. Some notable exceptions, however, do occur. For example, in southern Illinois and the neighboring part of Missouri, two relatively local formations, the Dutch Creek and Beauvais sandstones (Dev.), consist of beautifully rounded quartz grains which almost certainly are reworked St. Peter (Ord.) sand. They are evidence that at least part of the Ozark region was land during mid-Devonian time, where erosion attacked uplifted Ordovician strata.

There is nothing in the character of calcareous deposits to identify their sources except for the essentially contemporaneous material that was derived from reefs and deposited close to them.

Climate and Weathering

Weathering alters and eventually destroys all rocks. The end product is residual soil, which cloaks the earth's surface almost everywhere and consists largely of insoluble material, mainly mineral grains singly or in aggregates, and clay. It develops most rapidly in regions where chemical action and solution are most effective. The two chief factors in its production are (1) the kind of rock present at the surface and (2) climate. Geologists generally have had little interest in soils except for those developed during interglacial times or those which are a source of valuable mineral products such as bauxite and some high-grade clays or manganese and a few other unusual metallic ores. Mostly soil has been regarded as a nuisance because it obscures outcrops. Residual soils, however, are important to stratigraphy because they are one of the principal sources of sedimentary material.

Residual soils developed by chemical weathering from igneous rocks are clayey but contain more or less abundant mineral grains whose kinds depend upon the nature of the parent rock. If quartz occurs, it is likely to be an abundant constituent, and other stable minerals of the heavy-mineral type accumulate. Most silicate minerals decompose to clay but, depending upon their kinds, the climate, and the completeness of weathering, some of these also may remain.

Sedimentary rocks react differently because their constituent minerals have already passed through at least one cycle of weathering and mostly they are stable. Many detrital sediments derived from them are little changed. Sandstones and shales are disaggregated largely by physical processes and produce sandy or clayey soils. The soil developed from limestone, however, is vastly different from its parent rock because calcium carbonate passes back into solution and only the insoluble residue remains. Residual soil derived from limestone is likely to contain weathered chert, and in well-drained warm-temperate and warm regions it is commonly red.

Soils produced by the weathering of metamorphic rocks are variable and resemble all kinds derived from both igneous and sedimentary rocks. The actual type developed in any instance depends to some extent upon the mineral character of the parent rock, but practically all contain identifying metamorphic minerals.

Climate is important in the formation of residual soils because moisture is necessary for chemical weathering and this action proceeds more rapidly at higher temperatures. Freezing inhibits chemical weathering. Consequently soil is produced most rapidly in moist tropical regions. Drainage also is important because percolating water carries carbon dioxide, oxygen, and organic acids downward to act upon unaltered rock and remove soluble substances. Under favorable circumstances in the tropics, soils more than 100 feet deep may develop whereas in arid and frigid regions chemical weathering is so slow that little residual soil may form.

The minerals of soils are transported and become sediments. The unaltered minerals furnish information concerning the nature of parent rocks whereas minerals produced by weathering, chiefly clays, give some indication of climatic conditions. The development of montmorillonite is favored by relative dryness in regions where little leaching can occur. It is especially a product of weathered volcanic ash. Perhaps illite is formed under somewhat similar conditions but much of it is a diagenetic mineral. Chlorite, which contains ferrous iron, may require reducing conditions for its development. All of these minerals are converted to kaolinite by thorough leaching. Kaolinite probably is rarely formed in any other way, and its occurrence in sediment is believed to indicate prolonged weathering in a humid climate. After deposition both montmorillonite and kaolinite appear to be transformed very slowly to illite or less commonly to chlorite. Consequently their absence is not as significant in older rocks as in younger ones.

Topography and Erosion

Weathering and erosion combine to produce sediments. Erosion removes material prepared by weathering but it also attacks fresh unaltered rocks and produces sediments directly without the intervention of weathering. Chemically unweathered sediments consist of the original minerals of the parent rocks. Consequently the proportions of unaltered silicate minerals and clay would be a measure of the relative importance of physical and chemical processes responsible for the destruction of igneous and some kinds of metamorphic rock if these proportions could be determined. Because of differences in the size of particles, however, these products are more or less separated during transportation and deposition. Also sediments derived from preëxisting sedimentary rocks and some types of metamorphics give little or no evidence of chemical weathering regardless of the actual conditions that produced them.

The feldspars decompose under chemical attack relatively slowly. Their presence and condition in sediments is a better index than clay ratios to conditions prevailing in source regions. The absence of feldspars from coarse detrital sediments suggests derivation from older sediments or thoroughly weathered crystalline rocks. Partially decomposed to fresh feldspar grains indicate various stages in the relative prevalence of chemical and physical processes in the production of sediment. Fresh feldspar and an appreciable association of undecomposed ferromagnesian minerals is evidence of predominant physical erosion.

The balance between chemical and physical destruction of rocks is determined by both climate and topography. Warm moist climate favors chemical decomposition. High topographic relief and heavy rainfall encourage mechanical erosion. The most rapid erosion occurs where these conditions coincide in rugged tropical regions. The resulting sediment consists of a mixture of decomposed and fresh material. Deficiency in moisture, temperature, or relief inhibits weathering and erosion more or less. If moisture or temperature is deficient, chemical weathering declines in importance and less mature sediments are produced. If topographic relief is low, erosion is slow and sediments are more mature.

At the present time climate influences erosion in another way. Abundant moisture and mild temperature favor plant growth. A dense cover of vegetation protects soil from erosion and reduces washing, gullying, and landsliding to a minimum. Thus plentiful rainfall is an important factor both in accelerating erosion by greater runoff and in retarding it by favoring the development of a protective cover. The balance depends upon local conditions and is determined by many other interacting factors such as seasonal distribution of rainfall, steepness of slopes, and the types of both soil and vegetation.

Conditions as they exist today are not representative of all past geologic time. The differences have been important and they were related to progress in the evolutionary development of plants. The earliest plants reproduced by cell division, and few of them could exist outside of water for any length of time. From these the spore-bearing plants developed. They could live on land but were restricted to damp situations because water was necessary for their reproduction. At first they had no true roots or stems and could survive only in permanently damp situations. Plants of this type are first adequately known as fossils in Devonian strata although they probably originated much earlier. Later, roots and stems became differentiated. These structures made adaptation possible to situations that may have been dry during certain seasons of the year. Finally seed-bearing plants evolved and their fossils are present in Upper Devonian strata. The development of seeds freed plants from their intimate dependence on water and made conquest of the land by them possible.

The history of plant evolution indicates that before Devonian time the lands may have been naked except for permanently damp lowland areas. Thereafter, plants increased their range. The speed with which they became adapted to drier and drier environments and spread over the land is not known because upland areas were destroyed by erosion and no Paleozoic upland floras have been discovered. Upland regions probably were not protected by vegetation before the latter part of the Paleozoic Era. Consequently erosion must have been more severe and rapid in ancient times, and no certain comparison can be made between conditions as they existed then and as they are at present.

BIBLIOGRAPHY

Adams, J. A. S., and Weaver, C. E. (1958), Thorium-to-uranium ratios as indicators of sedimentary processes: Example of concept of geochemical facies, *Bull. Am. Assoc. Petroleum Geol.*, vol. 42, pp. 387–430.
     Thorium tends to remain in non-marine sediments whereas uranium is concentrated in some marine deposits.
Campbell, M. R. (1930), Coal as a recorder of incipient metamorphism, *Econ. Geol.*, vol. 25, pp. 675–696.
     Progressive reduction in volatile matter of coal parallels increased lithification of other sedimentary rocks.
Cox, B. B. (1946), Transformation of organic material into petroleum under geological conditions ("The geological fence"), *Bull. Am. Assoc. Petroleum Geol.*, vol. 30, pp. 645–659.
     The origin of petroleum and the parts that physical and biologic conditions play in it are considered.
Degens, E. T., Williams, E. G., and Keith, M. L. (1957), Environmental studies of Carboniferous sediments, Part I: Geochemical criteria for differentiating marine from fresh-water shales, *Bull. Am. Assoc. Petroleum Geol.*, vol. 41, pp. 2427–2455.
     Trace amounts of several metals commonly occur in different abundances in marine and non-marine shales.
Dott, R. E., Jr. (1958), Cyclic patterns in mechanically deposited Pennsylvanian limestones of northeastern Nevada, *J. Sediment. Petrol.*, vol. 28, pp. 3–14.
     The source and varied depositional environments of a dominantly calcareous stratigraphic section are described and interpreted.

Dunbar, C. O., and Rodgers, John (1957) *Principles of stratigraphy*, New York, Wiley.
>Chapters 9 to 14, pp. 168–256, are devoted to the various major types of sedimentary rock, their occurrence and origin.

Ellias, M. K. (1937), Depth of deposition of Big Blue Series, Kansas, *Bull. Geol. Soc. Amer.*, vol. 48, pp. 403–432.
>This article attempts to estimate depth of water mainly on the basis of paleobiologic evidence.

Emery, K. O., and Rittenberg, S. C. (1952), Early diagenesis of California basin sediments in relation to origin of oil, *Bull. Am. Assoc. Petroleum Geol.*, vol. 36, pp. 735–806.
>Diagenetic changes in near-surface sediments cored from sea floor off the California coast are described.

Fairbridge, R. W. (1957), The dolomite question, Soc. Econ. Paleon. and Miner., Spec. Publ. 5, pp. 125–178.
>Dolomitization begins early in diagenesis and continues below the surface of newly deposited calcareous sediment.

Farrington, W. B. (1954), Relation of coal rank to original depth of burial in West Virginia, *Am. J. Sci.*, vol. 252, pp. 627–633.
>Variations in carbon ratio are consistent with interpretation of overburden thickness increasing toward center of basin.

Ginsburg, R. N. (1957), Early diagenesis and lithification of shallow-water carbonate sediments in south Florida, Soc. Econ. Paleon. and Miner., Spec. Publ. 5, pp. 80–99.
>The author describes modern calcareous sediment and observes that it is not known to become lithified on or below the sea floor.

Glass, H. D. (1958), Clay mineralogy of Pennsylvanian sediments in southern Illinois, Proc. 5th Nat. Conf. Clays and Clay Minerals, Nat. Acad. Sci.-Nat. Research Council, Publ. 566, pp. 227–241.
>Evaluation is made of clay mineralogy and its possible changes in response to environmental conditions in source area and depositional basin, diagenesis and weathering.

Graf, D. L., and Lamar, J. E. (1950), Petrology of Fredonia Oolite in southern Illinois, *Bull. Am. Assoc. Petroleum Geol.*, vol. 34, pp. 2318–2336.
>Intergranular relations in limestone are described, with particular respect to cement and porosity.

Grim, R. E., Dietz, R. S., and Bradley, W. F. (1949), Clay mineral composition of some sediments from the Pacific Ocean off the California coast and the Gulf of California, *Bull. Geol. Soc. Amer.*, vol. 60, pp. 1785–1808.
>Detrital clay minerals are slowly altered after deposition in the sea.

Hamblin, W. K. (1958), The Cambrian sandstones of northern Michigan, Mich. Geol. Surv., Publ. 51.
>Sedimentary composition and structures indicate a shifting source area and important differences in depositional environments.

Heald, M. T. (1956), Cementation of Simpson and St. Peter sandstones in parts of Oklahoma, Arkansas, and Missouri, *J. Geol.*, vol. 64, pp. 16–30.

Great variability in the amount of intergranular porosity and quartz cement is reported.

Hedberg, H. D. (1936), Gravitational compaction of clays and shales, *Am. J. Sci.*, ser. 5, vol. 31, pp. 241–287.

The author records close correlation between porosity and depth and analyzes mechanics of the compaction process.

Hohlt, R. B. (1948), The nature and origin of limestone porosity, *Quart. Colo. School Mines*, vol. 43, no. 4.

Primary concern is with the nature and development of secondary porosity in limestone.

Ireland, H. A. (ed.) (1959), Silica in sediments, a symposium, Soc. Econ. Paleon. and Miner., Spec. Publ. 7.

Ten papers are devoted mainly to the occurrence of non-detrital silica and its role in the diagenesis of sediments.

Jones, O. T. (1939), The consolidation of muddy sediments, *Quart. J. Geol. Soc. London*, vol. 100, pp. 137–160.

The problem of mud and shale compaction resulting from the weight of overburden is considered.

Miller, R. L., and Olson, E. C. (1955), The statistical stability of quantitative properties as a fundamental criterion for the study of environments, *J. Geol.*, vol. 63, pp. 376–387.

Properties of sediments that cannot be measured in rocks, those that are changed by diagenesis, and those that persist unaltered are distinguished.

Milner, H. B. (1940), *Sedimentary petrography with special reference to petrographic methods of correlation of strata, petroleum technology and other economic applications of geology*, 3rd ed., London, Thomas Murby, reprinted 1952.

Chapter 13, pp. 490–514, notes usefulness of minerals as indicators of source areas and climate.

Passega, R. (1957), Texture as characteristic of clastic deposition, *Bull. Am. Assoc. Petroleum Geol.*, vol. 41, pp. 1952–1984.

A method of distinguishing different depositional environments on the basis of the relations of sorting parameters is developed.

Payne, T. G. (1942), Stratigraphical analysis and environmental reconstruction, *Bull. Am. Assoc. Petroleum Geol.*, vol. 26, pp. 1697–1770.

This is a comprehensive theoretical analysis of the production, transportation, and deposition of sediments and their alteration to sedimentary rocks.

Pelletier, B. R. (1958), Pocono paleocurrents in Pennsylvania and Maryland, *Bull. Geol. Soc. Amer.*, vol. 69, pp. 1033–1064.

Interpretations of depositional environments and source area are based on cross-bedding and coarseness of conglomerates.

Pettijohn, F. J. (1957), *Sedimentary rocks*, 2nd ed., New York, Harper.

Chapters 14 and 15, pp. 648–690, deal with the diagenesis, lithification, and historical geology of sediments.

Potter, P. E., and Glass, H. D. (1958), Petrology and sedimentation of the

Pennsylvanian sediments in southern Illinois: A vertical profile, Ill. Geol. Surv., Rept. Invest. 204.

This detailed study of sedimentary structures, petrography, and clay mineralogy provides evidence regarding provenance of sediments and depositional environments.

Potter, P. E., Nosow, E., Smith, N. M., Swann, D. H., and Walker, F. H. (1958), Chester cross-bedding and sandstone trends in Illinois basin, *Bull. Am. Assoc. Petroleum Geol.*, vol. 42, pp. 1013–1046.

This study establishes southwestern regional slope and sediment transport during late Mississippian time.

Rubey, W. W. (1930), Lithologic studies of fine grained Upper Cretaceous sedimentary rocks of the Black Hills region, U.S. Geol. Surv., Prof. Paper 165 A.

Compaction is influenced by pressure developed during structural folding.

Siever, Raymond (1957), The silica budget in the sedimentary cycle, *Am. Mineralogist*, vol. 42, pp. 821–841.

The source, transportation, and precipitation of silica in solution and its relations to the geochemical environment at the surface of the earth are discussed.

Skempton, A. W. (1953), Soil mechanics in relation to geology, *Proc. Yorkshire Geol. Soc.*, vol. 29, pp. 33–62.

Porosity and the plastic qualities of clay are related in a way that has application to compaction and other geologic processes.

Sugden, W. (1950), The influence of water films adsorbed by mineral grains upon compaction of natural sediments and notes on allied phenomena, *Geol. Mag.*, vol. 87, pp. 26–40.

Emphasis is laid on the importance of water to the properties of clay and its reaction to pressure.

Sujkowski, Z. L. (1958), Diagenesis, *Bull. Am. Assoc. Petroleum Geol.*, vol. 42, pp. 2692–2717.

Most sediments are unstable chemical mixtures, and diagenesis tends to produce purer rocks by the concentration of particular components in separate beds.

Symposium on clay mineralogy (1958), *Bull. Am. Assoc. Petroleum Geol.*, vol. 42, pp. 233–338.

Papers are by W. D. Keller, R. E. Grim, C. E. Weaver, J. F. Burst and I. H. Milne, and J. W. Eardley with particular reference to the relations of mineralogy to source and depositional environments.

Taylor, J. M. (1950), Pore space reduction in sandstones, *Bull. Am. Assoc. Petroleum Geol.*, vol. 34, pp. 701–716.

Thin-section studies show that porosity is reduced by cementation, solution at grain boundaries, and distortion or crushing of grains.

Taylor, J. H. (1952), Clay minerals and the evolution of sedimentary rocks, *Clay Minerals Bull.*, vol. 1, pp. 238–242.

The effects of parent material, weathering, depositional environment, and diagenesis on the development of clay minerals are briefly reviewed.

Terzaghi, R. D. (1940), Compaction of lime mud as a cause of secondary struc-
ture, *J. Sediment. Petrol.*, vol. 10, pp. 78–90.
  Results of compression tests on fine-grained calcareous mud from the
  Bahamas are reported.
Waldschmidt, W. A. (1941), Cementing materials in sandstones and their
probable influence on migration and accumulation of oil and gas, *Bull. Am.
Assoc. Petroleum Geol.*, vol. 25, pp. 1839–1879.
  Characters of sandstones of the Rocky Mountains region are described,
  with special attention to their consolidation and cementation.
Weller, J. M. (1959), Compaction of sediments, *Bull. Am. Assoc. Petroleum
Geol.*, vol. 43, pp. 273–310.
  This is a general consideration of compaction and its problems in all the
  common kinds of sediments and sedimentary rocks.
White, W. A., and Pichler, E. (1959), Water-sorption characteristics of clay
minerals, Ill. Geol. Surv., Circ. 266.
  The relations of water to clay minerals are explained.

Part III

STRATIGRAPHIC BODIES
AND RELATIONS

Strata and stratigraphic units are the bodies of stratigraphy. Their relations within the frames of space and time provide the essence of stratigraphic study. This necessarily involves consideration both of vertical and of horizontal physical continuity and lithologic variability in space and of the discontinuities that interrupt stratigraphic sequence. Stratigraphic classification and nomenclature are practical developments designed to achieve some order amidst complexities in the relations of stratigraphic bodies and to facilitate communication among geologists.

Correlation seeks to relate stratigraphic bodies in the frame of time. It constitutes a subjective extension of stratigraphy of paramount importance. Correlation permits the synthesis of all geologic knowledge and establishes stratigraphy as the central area of geologic science. Synthesis culminates in geologic history or the unified organization of all that has been learned about the materials of the earth and the forces and processes that have controlled its development to the present time.

10

Stratification and Vertical Sequence

STRATIFICATION is such a characteristic and conspicuous feature of most natural accumulations of sediment and sedimentary rocks that these can equally appropriately be termed stratified deposits. Few exposures five feet thick fail to reveal stratification subdividing formations and members into beds more or less distinctly set off from each other. Bedding is clear evidence that deposition and lithogenesis have not been static but have altered repeatedly with the passage of time. This variability of sediments in vertical sequence is more abrupt but otherwise comparable to lateral variability. One involves facies change in time, the other facies change in space.

Bedding results from the segregation of differently sized or differently constituted sediments in layers extending more or less parallel to the surface of deposition. The changes in sediments may be gradational upward in a zone, or from one zone to the next, or transition may be abrupt. Both produce stratification but the latter is more conspicuous and is responsible for the gross type of bedding at most outcrops. The kind and degree of change from one bed to another and the arrangement of differently constituted beds produce vertical sequences of several types.

STRATIFICATION

Although well-marked stratification has been observed by every geologist who has been concerned with sedimentary rocks, it has been remarkably little studied. Attention has been directed almost exclusively to relatively unusual types such as cross-bedding, whereas the more prevalent type characterized by more or less parallel beds appears to have been accepted as normal and, probably for that reason, given little consideration. Few efforts have been made to relate stratification in sedimentary rocks to the processes responsible for bedding in modern sediments. Consequently bedding generally has been explained more on the basis of casual observations and speculation than on any real understanding. Stratification commonly is more a puzzle than an aid in stratigraphic interpretation.

Stratification is produced in a great many different ways. The conditions or processes may be (1) physical, (2) chemical, or (3) biological. These can be outlined and analyzed to some extent but their application to actual examples of bedding in stratified rocks and the interpretation of stratification in relation to them are uncertain. Much attention needs to be devoted to this subject before the relative importance of the various possibilities can be determined and an adequate understanding of stratification can be attained.

Physically Controlled Stratification

The physical control of stratification cannot be wholly divorced from chemical and biologic controls because these interact with one another in complex ways. For convenience, however, the physical controls can be considered to be concerned mainly with (1) the nonuniform deposition of sediments, (2) most types of disturbance of sediments after deposition, and (3) the possible development of stratification by the compaction of fine-grained sediments.

Nonuniform Deposition

Stratification may result from (1) changes in the type of material deposited or (2) changes in the rate of deposition. Either of these might be an independent variable but commonly they are associated, and a change of one kind is likely to be accompanied by some related change in the other. Intermittently interrupted deposition probably is an especially important type of irregularity in rate and deserves separate recognition.

Factors affecting the kind of sediment deposited in a basin are numerous. Several of them are more or less intimately interrelated. Because they have been considered in previous chapters, further discussion of them is not necessary here. They can be classified in several different ways but it is convenient to differentiate three groups: (1) factors affecting the amount and kind of sediment produced, (2) factors affecting the transportation of sediment, and (3) local factors determining whether or not sediment accumulates in any area.

The quality and quantity of detrital sediment produced is determined mainly by (1) the kinds of rock outcropping in the source area, (2) the climatic conditions prevailing in the source area, and (3) its elevation and topographic condition. These are not subject to rapid or repeated changes, and sedimentary variation from bed to bed is not likely to reflect important changes of these kinds unless relatively long time intervals are involved. If, however, a considerable hiatus separates adjacent strata, changes in any or all of these respects may find expression in the sediments. Thus prolonged erosion may strip away an old sedimentary cover from a source area and bring metamorphic and igneous rocks to the surface; change in climate may be reflected in the degree of weathering and the resulting maturity of sediment; and change in elevation may alter importantly the effectiveness of erosion and the quantity of sediment produced.

Variability of transportation may be related to changes in (1) the kind of transporting medium, (2) the transportational effectiveness of the medium, and (3) the path or direction of transportation. Thus Pleistocene glacial deposits are stratified because of the alternation of ice-borne till and wind-borne loess. Changes in the power of streams may result in the interlayering of coarse and fine sediments in flood-plain and deltaic areas. Changes in the size of waves and depth of water may drastically alter the depositional patterns in shallow water of the sea and lakes. Changes in the direction of streams or currents may control the amount of sediment delivered to a particular area. Any two or all three of these types of changes may act in concert to produce more complex variations in the amount of sediment and its kind derived from one or many sources. Unlike the other variables that have been mentioned, the efficiency of transportation by streams, currents, or waves may change greatly in short intervals of time, and much nonuniformity of deposition in very shallow-water sediments is likely to be related to such changes. The ebb and flow of tides result in important depth variations in shallow water at many places. Tides, however, probably were insignificant in most of the landlocked seas of the geologic past just as they are today in the Mediterranean and the Baltic.

No sharp distinction can be made between factors affecting transportation and deposition because when transportation ceases deposition immediately begins. Depth of water has been mentioned but is best considered a local factor to be evaluated positively in connection with its effect on deposition rather than negatively with transportation. As related to wave action, it is the principal factor that determines deposition in the sea and other bodies of standing water. Thus wave base, or the depth at which waves cease to stir the bottom, is a critical level with respect to sedimentary deposition. Wave base, however, does not correspond to any particular depth because wave turbulence, as it declines downward, becomes progressively less effective in moving smaller and smaller sedimentary particles. Also wave base is far from constant. It varies greatly from day to day and from season to season as periods of calm and stormy weather alternate.

The depths at which variably strong waves move variously sized sediment are not known accurately. Nevertheless, if sediment is not supplied too rapidly and other conditions do not change, a sedimentary surface cannot be built permanently at any place above a certain level. When the bottom attains this level, which is the effective wave base at that place and time, equilibrium is established and additional sediment is swept across the area and finds a farther resting place. Much sediment moves slowly across the shallow land-margining sea bottom in a discontinuous manner. When waves are small it settles temporarily but with every storm it is stirred up and moved onward and outward. Final deposition occurs at a depth that is beyond the reach of the greatest waves—probably not much more than about 300 feet on open coasts.

Equilibrium may be disturbed by change in depth of water resulting from either tectonism in the basin or shift in sea level. If water shoals, erosion of the bottom is likely to occur. If it deepens, deposition may build up the bottom to its previous position. If sediment is supplied rapidly, however, and more is deposited during fine weather than can be moved away by storms, conditions are changed and the bottom rises. Smaller waves are then generated in the shallower water, and a new state of equilibrium is established.

Nonuniformity of supply, transportation, and deposition of sediment certainly are important in the development of stratification in sedimentary rocks. A considerable variety of factors is involved and their combinations introduce a bewildering array of possibilities. The predominant importance of variable currents and wave action and depth of water, as these affect transportation and deposition, however, is fairly obvious. Most variability in sedimentary deposits resulting from physical changes appears to be closely related to these factors with more or less modification by the others. Much stratification probably is related directly to intermittent deposition, and most stratigraphic sections probably are interrupted by many more diastems than are generally recognized.

The deposition of sediment in most areas, or its by-passing, is controlled in a broad way by tectonism. If sedimentary basins did not intermittently or continuously subside, they would soon be filled and all sediment would be carried on to other depressions elsewhere.

Disturbance of Sediments

Physical disturbances of sediment after deposition that may produce bedding are of two types: (1) roiling of bottom material followed by settling at essentially the same place and (2) erosion, by which deposited sediment is picked up and removed to another locality. Both wave and current action are likely to be associated in the disturbance of unconsolidated sediment, but waves predominate in roiling and currents in erosion.

The degree to which bottom sediment is disturbed by waves depends upon (1) the size of waves, which is determined by the strength, persistence, and sweep of wind, (2) the depth of water, and (3) the coarseness of sediment. Wave-stirring returns sediment to suspension and acts mainly on sediment below sand size. If agitation is protracted, fine material is prevented from re-settling. This may be removed by currents, and thus sorting of the sediment is accomplished. If agitation is temporary, resuspended sediment settles according to size and density and graded bedding may result.

Above wave base, stirring affects sedimentary particles according to their size, density, and shape. As depth decreases, the sorting of sediment becomes more and more efficient. Bottoms at a depth of about 100 feet or less are likely to be subject to more or less continuous agitation and here most sedimentary sorting is accomplished. Between this depth and about 300 feet, therefore, where wave action is intermittent and related to stormy conditions, the best opportunity for the development of graded bedding is provided.

Erosion may accomplish the destruction and removal of sediment at any stage of its transition from newly deposited material to consolidated rock. Recognizable unconformities generally record the erosion of consolidated sediment but they are not common enough to play an important part in the development of bedding. Discussion of them is reserved for the next chapter. Minor erosional episodes that affected unconsolidated sediment in relatively small areas may have produced many bedding planes particularly in fluvial deposits. These are invariably related to current action. They are recognizable if they resulted in the truncation of older beds and bedding planes as in various types of cut-and-fill structure. The combined action of waves and currents may accomplish erosion in bodies of standing water at shallow depth. Bedding planes so produced may be difficult to distinguish from those caused by only interrupted deposition, and there is complete gradation between these types.

The action of turbidity currents provides a special case of subaqueous sedimentary disturbance. Deposits resulting from them provide excellent examples of stratigraphic nonuniformity related to intermittent deposition. Sediment moved by experimentally produced turbidity currents in the laboratory settles in characteristic graded beds. Turbidity currents have won wide popularity as a mechanism explaining the textures and bedding of some ancient sediments and the nature and distribution of some fairly recent deep-sea deposits. The uncritical linking of graded bedding with turbidity currents, however, opens the way for serious misinterpretations.

Graded bedding certainly can be produced in other ways. It results, for example, from differential settling in calm water of intermittently supplied sediment no matter what its source. The sediment may be delivered in the ordinary manner by streams, as was the sediment of glacial varves, or it may be stirred from the sea bottom by waves. Furthermore, laboratory experiments suggest that grading of fine-grained material may be caused by the differential settling of larger and heavier particles within a mass of newly deposited sediment. Perhaps this process continues during the early stages of compaction. Deposition from currents of decreasing competence also produces graded bedding. Such bedding is common in many fluvial deposits; it may likewise result from slackening currents in standing water. Turbidity currents probably have been more or less important in the transportation and deposition of sediment in deep water but their prevalence has not been established, and the possibility of other causes for graded bedding, particularly in shallow-water sediments, should be carefully investigated.

Compaction Bedding

Compaction in argillaceous sediments that were originally highly porous has been responsible for at least part of the apparent bedding of many shales. Compaction probably is accomplished partly by the rearrangement and re-crystallization of clay minerals—a very slow process. It may be difficult to distinguish between the fissility so developed and true original stratification.

Chemically Controlled Stratification

A variety of chemical conditions has been the cause both for the direct development of stratification and for the alteration of sediments and sedimentary rocks in such a way that stratification is accentuated.

Chemical Sediments

The evaporites are the most important chemically precipitated sediments. Their deposition was controlled by the composition and concentration of evaporating brine. The interbedding of rock salt, gypsum or anhydrite, and perhaps dolomite reflects changes in these factors. It records, on the one hand, increasing concentration of solutions and, on the other, dilution resulting from the inflow of fresh or normally saline sea water.

The occurrence of abundant oolites, glauconite, and phosphatic nodules, which characterize some strata and set them apart more or less sharply from others, records the action of certain chemical processes that were effective in restricted areas for limited periods of time. These were more complex than such a relatively simple process as concentration. Also they seem to have required the concurrence of certain physical conditions such as wave-agitated water for oolites and very slow detrital sedimentation for glauconite and phosphate. Change in either the chemical or the physical environment would inhibit the development of these deposits.

Oxidation-Reduction Products

The oxidizing or reducing qualities of environments and their changes are important chiefly in connection with the production, transportation, deposition, and alteration of organic sediments, which are considered later, and of iron compounds. The latter may be concentrated in beds of nearly pure siderite or hematite, which might be considered chemical sediments, or they may occur as more or less minor constituents producing color banding in other sediments.

The presence of banded or bedded sedimentary iron ores interlayered with other material suggests that reducing conditions permitting the transportation of ferrous iron compounds in solution may have alternated with oxidizing conditions inhibiting such transportation or that iron passed from one environment to the other. The iron may have been deposited in the form of siderite that remained unchanged or was later oxidized to hematite, or change to oxidizing conditions may have resulted in the direct deposition of hematite. In Precambrian time some alternation of chemical conditions that is not understood seems to be required to explain the banded hematite deposits occurring in widely separated regions of the world. Paleozoic and younger sedimentary iron ores, however, probably owe their existence to the local presence or absence of organic matter and an abundant supply of iron compounds derived from some unknown source.

Red marine strata are not common but their occurrence in some formations seems to indicate a deficiency of organic matter on the sea bottom capable of reducing their ferric pigments. Striking interbedding of red and grey strata as in some Silurian formations of western Tennessee suggests either abrupt fluctuations in the amount of organic matter deposited with the other sediments or an intertonguing of sediments derived from different sources. Color layering in terrestrial deposits may indicate variable amounts of iron pigment and its degree of hydration that was related to fluctuating climatic conditions.

Dolomite

Although dolomite and limestone resemble each other closely, some dolomite is characterized by granular texture and brownish color. These features, comparatively uncommon in limestone, aid in the recognition of dolomite. Partial dolomitization of limestone may be very irregular, and transition from one kind of rock to the other may not correspond to obvious bedding structure. Selective dolomitization, however, probably was influenced by some physical and chemical characters of the parent calcareous material. These are more likely to maintain lateral rather than vertical uniformity. Consequently dolomitization in most partially replaced strata tends to persist laterally, and attendant alteration of texture and color may serve to accentuate some originally obscure features of stratification.

Calcareous Concretions

Calcareous and more or less ferruginous concretions in argillaceous strata generally are disposed along parallel planes that correspond with bedding. In many shales they furnish more conspicuous evidence of stratification than the shaly laminations which may have been developed by compaction. Layers or zones of concretions commonly are continuous for considerable distances and provide easy and secure means of tracing stratigraphic horizons across large outcrops.

Chert

Chert nodules, which are abundant in many limestones, also generally lie along planes or in zones extending parallel with the bedding. Much chert is secondary and developed by replacement. Its presence probably indicates original textural or chemical peculiarities of the sediment. Therefore it may serve to accentuate some obscure stratigraphic features of the limestones. Some chert forms continuous beds or layers that contrast strongly with adjacent limestone. More rarely it constitutes entire well-stratified formations. Possibly some chert is an original sedimentary accumulation of silica. If so, such chert should be classed with the chemical sediments.

Interstratal Solution

Some stylolites are continuous for long distances and their development has produced a type of pseudostratification in otherwise rather massive limestones. The Salem Limestone (Miss.), for example, is divided by horizontal stylolitic surfaces that form convenient parting planes in the large building-stone quarries of southwestern Indiana. Insofar as stylolites developed along surfaces or in zones characterized by slight differences of texture or chemical composition, they accentuate features of original stratification. However, they may cut abruptly across the strata and so are not a sure guide to bedding.

Although a similar origin for thin partings of clay or shale in limestone has not been certainly established, it is probable that some partings of this kind have been developed by interstratal solution similar to that which produced stylolites except that interpenetrating stylolitic columns did not form. Many limestones consist of beds separated by such partings. Generally they have been explained as resulting from the periodic deposition of intermittently supplied or transported mud or from the differential settling of fine material stirred up from bottom sediments by waves. Many partings undoubtedly were produced in one or the other of these latter ways.

Biologically Controlled Stratification

Most calcareous sediment is of biologic origin, and biologic control has played an important part in both the amount and the kind of calcareous material deposited in different strata. Also organic matter derived from plants and animals occurs in variable amounts in most sediment. Color and other properties may be directly influenced by its presence, and its role in oxidation-reduction reactions likewise is important.

Stratification obviously has been affected by organic influences. The type and distribution of both plant and animal communities, however, have been controlled by physical and chemical conditions and these have ultimately determined the characters of all strata. Nevertheless the very sensitive reactions of organisms to all elements of their environments, and the consequent differences in floras and faunas, have produced much more striking differences in strata than would have occurred without their presence.

Abundance of Life

The composition and appearance of sediments and sedimentary rocks do not necessarily indicate the abundance of organisms that may have existed at the time and place of sedimentary deposition. The absence of calcium carbonate and organic matter is not evidence of a lifeless environment because the first may have been dissolved, the second may have decomposed completely, and either or both may have been physically removed. The presence of these substances and their quantities in sediments depend upon (1) the abundance of organisms of the proper kinds, (2) the destruction or removal of organic products, and (3) the rate of detrital deposition. Organic products are most likely to be preserved and to be abundant in fine-grained sediments. Shale is the most common highly carbonaceous kind of rock, and calcareous shale grades into limestone at many places. Coarse sediment, because of possibly more rapid deposition and the relatively unfavorable environment it provides for many organisms, is unlikely to contain large proportions of organic products. These are more subject, also, to subsequent destruction by both oxidation and solution because of the permeable nature of the sediment.

The interbedding of limestone and shale or the alternation of pure and impure limestone strata suggests either a fluctuating population of lime-secreting organisms or an intermittent supply of fine detrital sediment. The interbedding of gray and black shale may indicate variability in sedimentary deposition or organic population, or alternating intervals of greater or less destruction of organic material by bacterial decay or consumption by mud-eating scavengers. This destructive organic activity may have been related to the variability of available oxygen. Interbedding of limestone and sandstone is not common but does occur in various Paleozoic formations particularly in the west, as the lower part of the Tensleep Sandstone (Penn.) of Wyoming. This kind of interlayering probably resulted from the intermittent spreading of clean wave-washed sand far from its source of origin and may have been controlled by fluctuating sea level. The periodic introduction of mud into an area of calcareous deposition also may have occurred in response to temporary intervals of lowered water level.

In interbedded strata, textural gradation upward from sandstone to shale is common whereas the reverse transition is likely to be more abrupt. Both lower and upper contacts of limestone interbeds in shale, however, generally are sharp, perhaps because of environmental changes that were alternately favorable and unfavorable for lime-secreting organisms but did not necessarily involve any great change in physical conditions. Thus when turbidity decreased and mud was deposited more and more slowly, a threshold may have been reached when an area became habitable and it was rapidly colonized. The newly established organisms produced calcium carbonate in sufficient amounts to dilute and largely mask the fine detrital sediment that continued to accumulate. In a similar way, as local conditions became progressively less favorable for organisms, these may have disappeared suddenly, and in the absence of further lime production only argillaceous mud was deposited.

Kinds of Life

The kinds of organisms that contribute material to accumulating sediments are important in determining the type of deposit in proportion to the amounts of organic products and detrital minerals in the sedimentary mixture. The two extreme and outstanding examples of organically derived sediments are limestone and coal. The occurrence of organisms that produce such sediments is controlled by local environmental conditions.

Organic products may be altered both before they are permanently deposited and afterward. Changes in calcium carbonate are mainly physical and involve alteration of aragonite to calcite and modification of sedimentary particles in form and size. Large particles and structures may be fragmented before deposition and recrystallized subsequently. Organic matter is altered chemically first by bacterial and later by dynamic processes. Its composition changes and the change is accompanied by modification of its properties and appearance that may vary in different strata. As either kind of organic product suffers change, more generalized material results, however, and original differences may become progressively less clear.

Organic matter in much sediment is so greatly altered that little can be determined with respect to its origin. In stratigraphy it is important mainly in proportion to the amount present in any bed and the effect it has had on local oxidation-reduction conditions and the appearance of the stratum.

In contrast, calcareous sediments are more likely to preserve original textures and structures that vary from bed to bed, from zone to zone, and from formation to formation. Very fine-grained calcareous sediment produced by the action of algae or bacteria or resulting from the comminution of coarse material is a common constituent of much limestone. Recognition of its origin, however, is uncertain if not impossible. Coarse calcareous sediment generally provides evidence of its derivation. It consists of identifiable fossil fragments or whole specimens whose nature determines texture of the rock. Two of the most conspicuous and easily recognized types are crinoidal limestone, consisting largely of disarticulated plates, and coquinoid limestone, composed almost wholly of shells. These and other kinds are commonly interlayered. They may distinguish different beds or zones, some of which are continuous throughout more or less large areas. Each variety records some peculiar combination of environmental conditions. Another characteristic type of calcareous strata consists of chalk. Its difference from limestone may be related to post-depositional environment which has not fostered consolidation and firm cementation.

Destruction of Stratification

Most areas of modern sea bottom support a variety of burrowing and scavenging, or mud-eating, animals. Their activities stir and mix the bottom sediments and may destroy not only details of stratification in the form of thin layers of distinctive sediment (see Figure 77, p. 233) but also all evidence of these animals' existence. Some briefly stable sea-bottom surfaces of the past have been preserved by sudden burial beneath later sediment and have retained the U-shaped burrows of worms. Such burrows are known in rocks of many ages. They are most likely to persist in fine-grained marine sandstones but they also occur more rarely in limestone and in shale. Many fossil pelecypods with their shells closed in natural position are found in shale and less abundantly in limestone. Some of them appear to be burrowing forms that died and were entombed within the sediments where they lived. Aside from these fossils, evidence of burrowing and organic disturbance of sediment is rarely recognizable. Where thin and delicate stratification, with which compaction lamination should not be confused, occurs, sediment evidently was not disturbed in such a manner.

VERTICAL SUCCESSION

Different types of beds succeed each other in stratigraphic sections in a great variety of ways. As considered in greater or less detail, distinctions can be drawn between sections characterized by (1) lithologic uniformity, (2) lithologic heterogeneity, and (3) patterned successions. These can be viewed at a small scale that recognizes all lithologic variations from bed to bed, at an intermediate scale in which minor variations are ignored, or at large scales necessitating more or less important generalizations.

Lithologic Uniformity

Uniformity requires that a complex combination of conditions and processes extending all the way from the production of sediment through its transportation and to its deposition remained in balance practically unchanged. As the time interval represented by a deposit lengthens, the probability rapidly increases that some change will have occurred and will be recorded by a recognizable difference or discontinuity in the sediment. Some

changes have, however, left no indication in the sedimentary record. For example, Pleistocene loess deposits are accumulations resulting from a long succession of seasonal dust storms that occurred in winter when glacial melting
ceased and outwash channels were relatively dry and subject to attack by variable winds. The loess shows no stratification or other indication of the annual increments of which it probably is composed. Aqueous sedimentary deposits are much less likely to be uniform because of the less selective nature
of water transportation.

Actual lithologic uniformity is very rare in stratigraphic sections. Some
change is likely to be evident even within a single bed. Any degree of stratification is an indication of some nonuniformity. Very fine-grained sediments,
such as shales and certain limestones, are likely to be most uniform because
they were deposited either in deep water or far from land where the variability of factors related to sedimentary supply and transportation were reduced
to a minimum and depositional conditions were most constant. Also very
slowly accumulating materials are likely to show much uniformity because
temporary variations add little that is different to them and there is ample
opportunity for mixing. On the other hand, rapidly deposited sediment may
be relatively uniform because no important change occurs during the brief
time interval it represents.

Uniformity may occur within a single bed or, with only minor variations,
may characterize an entire formation. The most satisfactory formations are
defined and recognized on the basis of their lithologic unity. In some formations great uniformity is broken only by thin partings of different sedimentary material or other discontinuities that are responsible for bedding. Such
formations record remarkably stable conditions that persisted with only minor interruptions for appreciable intervals of time. Formations of this kind,
such as the Chattanooga Shale (Dev.-Miss.), that persist throughout wide
areas are not abundant. Considerably greater latitude in lithologic uniformity generally is tolerated in the definition of formations. Furthermore, if
variability within such major lithologic rock varieties as the commoner types
of limestone, shale, and sandstone is ignored, important thicknesses of strata
may present an appearance of noteworthy uniformity. Thus in parts of Illinois, the entire Silurian and Devonian systems form a continuous limestone
sequence that is difficult to subdivide or differentiate on the basis of subsurface records. In general, however, lithologic uniformity is likely to characterize only minor segments of the stratigraphic column.

Heterogeneous Successions

Close examination of almost any stratigraphic section bed by bed reveals
nonuniformity or irregularity in lithologic composition that has resulted from
the variable production, transportation, or deposition of sediment. Considering the many possibilities there are for change from time to time in any one

or all of these respects, a disorderly succession of somewhat differently constituted strata may seem normal.

These changes, however, are not likely to be entirely random. A natural order relates sediments with respect to grain size and mode of origin: from coarse to fine-grained material and then to calcareous sediment and vice versa. The variations exhibited in successively deposited strata tend to move gradually or by small steps backward and forward between related types of material. Thus shale commonly is associated with sandstone on the one hand and with limestone on the other, but the direct association of sandstone and limestone without intervening shale is by comparison unusual in most areas. The latter association requires much more pronounced changes in the factors responsible for the accumulation of different kinds of sediment than do the former. Such changes are much less common than are more moderate ones.

The direction of change at any horizon in a stratigraphic section whose constitution is intermediate in the lithologic series as just noted is ordinarily unpredictable. The general interrelation of factors governing production, transportation, and deposition determines the average type of sediment, and very minor shifts may throw the balance first one way and then the other. Thus silty shale may be succeeded by either sandstone or argillaceous shale, and calcareous shale may be followed by either argillaceous shale or limestone. General drift in one direction or the other, however, is not uncommon in zones of oscillating sedimentary influences. More abrupt changes, such as those that are employed to define many formation boundaries, are clear evidence of more rapid or more pronounced alterations in these influences. Abrupt change is more likely to occur from finer to coarser sediment than in the other direction.

Patterned Successions

Many stratigraphic sequences, or parts of them, show more or less distinctly various types of repetitions involving the successive orderly arrangement of different kinds of sediment. These range from very simple to remarkably complex. Each type of repetition seems to indicate the recurrence of similar sedimentary processes and conditions in a rhythmic or cyclic manner. The patterned sequences generally are not exact duplications of each other; distortions and irregularities occur in both the thicknesses and the detailed lithologic characters of their corresponding parts. The repetitions are likely to be most obvious in the simpler patterns because the more complex ones provide greater opportunity for variation and, as complexity increases, more and more generalization is required for their recognition.

Alternations

The commonest type of simple pattern is the repeated alternation of two kinds of strata. This is most conspicuous if the differences include hardness or resistance to weathering in addition to other alternating qualities. Inter-bedded sandstone and shale or limestone and shale are good, and fairly common, examples. All of them record unstabilized episodes during which more or less regular fluctuations in one or several of the sedimentary factors influenced local deposition. Some mark transitional zones between formations of contrasting lithologic characters.

In alternating successions members occur in couples that resemble each other closely. The relative thicknesses of members in different couples and in different successions, however, are likely to vary considerably. A comparatively uniformly bedded succession broken only by thin partings of different lithologic character is an extreme example of alternation. The time frequency of whatever oscillation caused alternation also may have varied greatly and thus produced inequalities of this type.

The members of a couple and adjacent couples in alternating successions may be transitional and grade into each other, or they may be sharply defined by abrupt contacts. Alternating detrital members are likely to be more or less transitional. They record deposition within a single sedimentary realm governed by sedimentary factors that are not necessarily subject to great or sudden change. In contrast, contacts between shale and limestone members are likely to be less gradational. Successions of such members exhibit the most conspicuous and unmistakable type of alternation. Shale and limestone record the dominance of different more or less mutually exclusive sedimentary factors that governed the deposition of detrital material and of organically derived calcium carbonate respectively.

Varves

Typical varves are annually deposited sedimentary layers that grade from coarser and lighter-colored lower parts into finer-grained and darker-colored upper parts. They accumulated in temporary lakes formed along the margins of melting late Pleistocene glaciers or in other quiet water. Thicknesses commonly range from a few tenths of an inch to an inch or more, but both thinner and much thicker varves have been observed. Most varves consist of silt and clay although some are sandy or even pebbly below. The coarser parts were deposited in summer when new sediment was contributed by meltwater. The finer parts settled in winter from very quiet water that may have been protected from disturbance by surface ice. Varves commonly occur in uninterrupted sequences some of which consist of a large number of comparable laminae.

Sedimentary layers physically very similar to glacial varves occur at various places in rocks of all ages from the Precambrian onward. These are not definitely known to be annual deposits. Although some may be annual, others probably represent much longer periods of time. Other successions of repeated graded bedding resemble varves in their general characters and relations. All such deposits can be grouped together for descriptive purposes because they constitute a single type of patterned succession. Certainly, however, they are not all genetically similar.

A varve or comparably constituted layer corresponds to a couple in an alternating sequence but its parts are not divisible. There is no doubt where a varve begins and ends. In an ordinary alternating succession one member might be combined equally well with either a preceding or a following member to form a couple. In varved sediments there is a definitely expressed direction of change repeated many times that is not present in all alternations. Ordinary alternating successions and varves might be considered to be the simplest types of sedimentary cycles. If so, the alternating successions consist of symmetrical cycles and the varved successions of asymmetrical ones.

Cycles

Sedimentary cycles are recurrent sequences of strata each consisting of several similar lithologically distinctive members arranged in the same order. A great variety of cycles is possible ranging from simple to quite complex but only a comparatively few types actually have been recognized. Cycles may be either symmetrical or asymmetrical depending upon the pattern presented by their members. They record the occurrence of a definite series of physical conditions, and resulting sedimentary environments, that were repeated in the same order with only minor variations.

Symmetrical Cycles

Symmetrical cycles consist of members arranged first in a progressive and then in a perfectly matching reverse order. The simplest clearly expressed type requires five members and includes three different kinds of sediment. Such a cycle, for example, is indicated in Figure 141A, by the succession of sandstone, shale, limestone, shale, and sandstone or equally by limestone, shale, sandstone, shale, and limestone, which is exactly the same sequence differently divided. This type of cycle may also consist of different sediments —conglomerate, sandstone, shale, sandstone, and conglomerate, or shale, gypsum, salt, gypsum, and shale, as well as many others. Greater complexity may be introduced by an increasing number of members of more kinds or by greater discrimination in lithologic characters as in the succession sandstone, silty shale, black shale, calcareous shale, limestone, calcareous shale, black shale, silty shale, and sandstone (see Figure 141B). This pattern can be expressed in a general way by the formula 1, 2, 3, 2, 1 or in more detail by 1, 2s (silty or sandy), 2b (black), 2c (calcareous), 3, 2c, 2b, 2s, 1.

A succession of symmetrical cycles represents a series of more or less perfect oscillations. The turning points occur within members 1 and 3 in the foregoing examples. No horizon within these members, however, provides a satisfactory stratigraphic boundary. For convenience, therefore, the divisions between cycles are made at member boundaries. Accordingly, a symmetrical succession of members might be written 1, 2, 3, 2–1, 2, 3, 2 or 3, 2, 1, 2–3, 2, 1, 2 or some other similar way, as shown in Figure 142.

Cycles are most likely to be developed in marine deposits. The sea provides greater stability than the other general environments, and, in spite of succes-

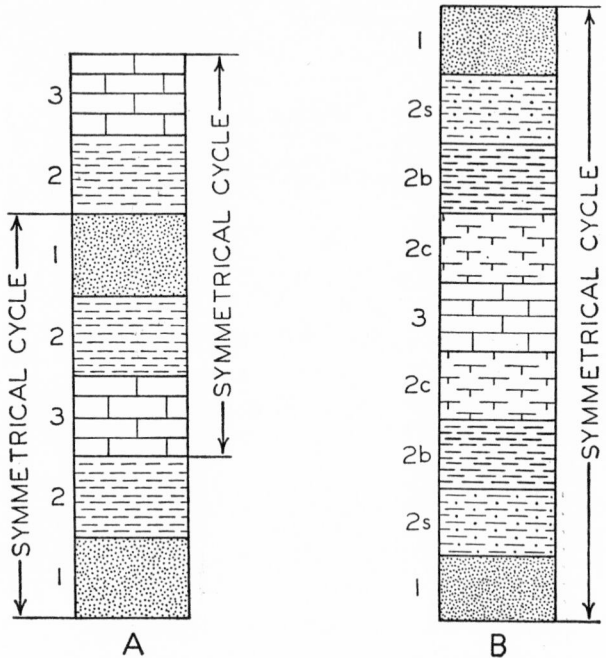

Figure 141. Stratigraphic columns illustrating symmetrical cycles. A shows the simplest cycle, as contrasted with alternation, consisting of five members. B shows a similar cycle in which a larger number of members can be recognized.

sive changes that result in the deposition of different lithologic members, freedom from interference by minor irregularities is required for the clear expression of sedimentary cycles. For perfect symmetry matching members should be equally thick as well as identically constituted. Some variability, however, is inevitable and for practical purposes differences in thickness and some differences in the lithologic development of corresponding members can be ignored.

Symmetrical marine cycles can be explained simply as resulting from rather regular fluctuations of depth of water in the depositional basin, or amount and kind of sediment supplied to it, although more complicated interactions of factors may have occurred. In such a succession as sandstone, shale, limestone, shale, and sandstone, for example, regular transgression and regression of the strand line is suggested with attendant deepening and shallowing of water in offshore areas. If, however, the strata under consideration were deposited within the zone that was alternately emergent and submergent, the cycle might be terminated by an unconformity or might include terrestrial as well as marine strata. An unconformity might produce a cycle that could be expressed by the formula U, 1, 2, 3, 2. Here the unconformity provides a logical intercyclical boundary (see Figure 143A).

Detrital non-marine strata are difficult to distinguish from similar beds deposited in deltas or other shallow marginal areas of the sea. Their presence may make little difference in the constitution of cycles unless they are accompanied by coal. If nonmarine strata are designated by bold symbols, the cycle might have some such form as 1, 2, 3, 2, or 1, 2, 2, 3, 2, 2.

Asymmetrical Cycles

Asymmetrical cycles consist of successions of members that do not match in their progressive and reverse orders. The asymmetry may stem from the absence of one member from one or more of the matching pairs or from the introduction of one or more single new unmatched members as indicated by such formulas as 1, 2s, 2b, 2c, 3, 2, or U, 1, 2, C (coal), 3, 2, as shown in Figures 143C and 144.

The number of possible irregularities of these types is very great and some cycles are much more asymmetrical than others. An otherwise symmetrical cycle from which one or more members have been lost through erosion at an unconformity should not, however, be considered asymmetrical (see Figure 143B).

Pennsylvanian Cyclothems

The foregoing discussion and analysis of symmetrical and asymmetrical cycles are largely theoretical. The actual sedimentary cycles that are best known and have been most carefully studied are characteristic of and constitute the Pennsylvanian Sys-

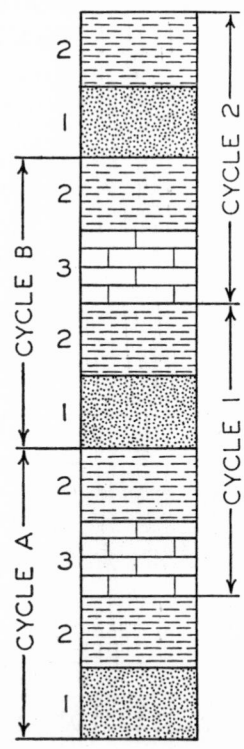

Figure 142. Columnar section composed of strata representing a succession of symmetrical sedimentary cycles. For practical reasons boundaries are placed at the contacts between members of different lithologic character rather than in the midst of members 1 or 3 as would be required if each cyclic sequence were to show perfect symmetry.

tem in the central and eastern United States. They are asymmetrical, and most of them are coal-bearing. They are termed *cyclothems.*

Pennsylvanian cyclothems are quite varied in their development and range from simple to complex. All of them, however, can be related to a single pat-

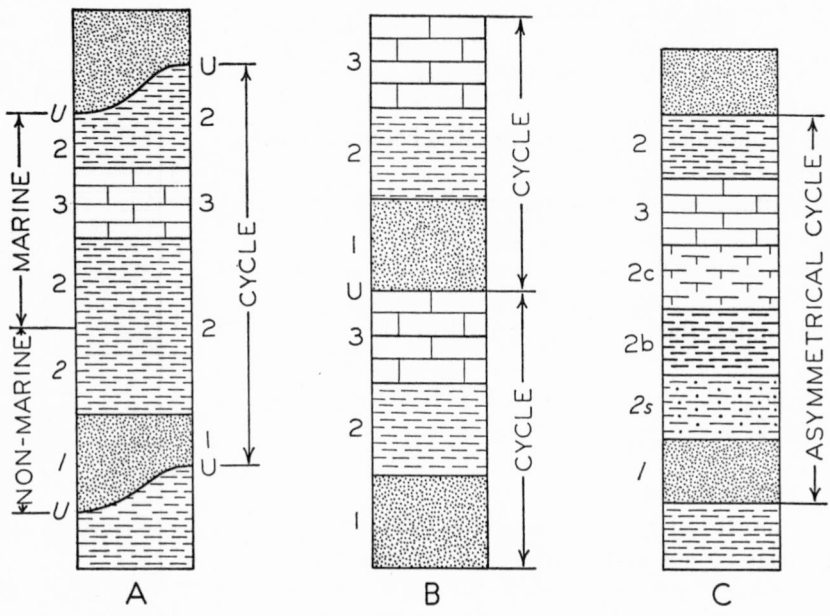

Figure 143.   A. Columnar section showing strata representing a sedimentary cycle limited above and below by unconformities which provide convenient boundaries. The strata of most cyclic sequences of the Pennsylvanian in Illinois and neighboring states can be divided into non-marine and marine parts.

B. Column showing strata representing a simple asymmetrical sedimentary cycle. In such an example, asymmetry results from the absence of one or more members from the sequence.

C. Column showing strata representing a more complex asymmetrical sedimentary cycle. In such an example, asymmetry results from the presence of one or more members that are not repeated in reverse order.

tern that corresponds with the most complex type. The others can be considered incomplete expressions of this pattern. The full succession of members identified by the numbers and symbols used in the foregoing formulas, and a few additional ones, is shown in Figure 145 and Table 10.

This is a composite idealized succession based on the observation of many cyclothems at many places. It is especially characteristic of their development in Illinois and immediately adjacent states. Few cyclothems attain this full development at any place and almost all cyclothems, as they are actually con-

TABLE 10.   Members of a Fully Developed Idealized Cyclothem
of the Type Occurring in Illinois Identified by Symbols as Used
in Text (see Figure 145)

Upper (Marine) Hemicyclothem	Lower (Non-Marine) Hemicyclothem
2s, Shale, silty	C, Coal
3, Limestone	2u, Underclay
2c, Shale, calcareous	L, Limestone
2b, Shale, black	2s, Shale, sandy
L, Limestone	1, Sandstone
2s, Shale, silty	U, Unconformity, local

stituted locally, are incomplete in some respect. Incompleteness varies from place to place in individual cyclothems as particular members are lacking throughout different areas. Many cyclothems, however, if they are considered broadly, possess all of these members. Also, though each member is somewhat variable in its lithologic development and thickness within a cyclothem or in different cyclothems, it possesses certain general features that characterize it and serve to identify it with the corresponding members of other cyclothems. On the other hand, few strata occur in the Pennsylvanian System in the central and eastern parts of the United States that do not fall into this pattern and do not correspond with one or another of these members. The complete cyclothem as outlined, therefore, is a rarely realized ideal represented by a great variety of more or less imperfect actual examples.

The Pennsylvanian cyclothem is very strongly asymmetrical. Of the eleven members indicated, the lower ten represent a progressive or transgressive phase and only the last, or the uppermost shale member, represents the reverse sequence or regressive phase. A more useful subdivision recognizes a lower or non-marine hemicyclothem and an upper or marine hemicyclothem. In Illinois and adjacent states these parts commonly are comparable in their development with respect to thickness and number of constituent members. In other regions these relations differ.

Most of the detrital sediment of the Pennsylvanian System in the central and eastern United States is believed to have been derived from highlands on the east and south. As stratigraphic sections developed in areas nearer

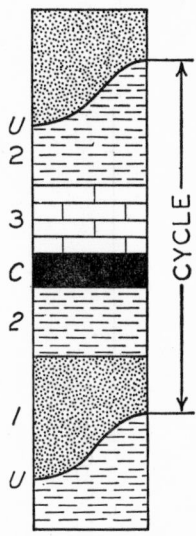

Figure 144. Stratigraphic column showing strata representing an asymmetrical sedimentary cycle consisting of non-marine and marine parts such as characterize some of the simplest Pennsylvanian cyclothems in Illinois and neighboring states.

to or farther from these source areas are compared, the relative importance of the two hemicyclothems varies with respect to thickness and differentiation into members. In the northern Appalachian region non-marine strata dominate. Only shale overlies the coal in many cyclothems and in some this member may not be marine. Such a cyclothem might be constituted **U, 1, 2s, L, 2u, C, 2s,** as shown in Figure 146A. In northeastern Kansas and Nebraska, on

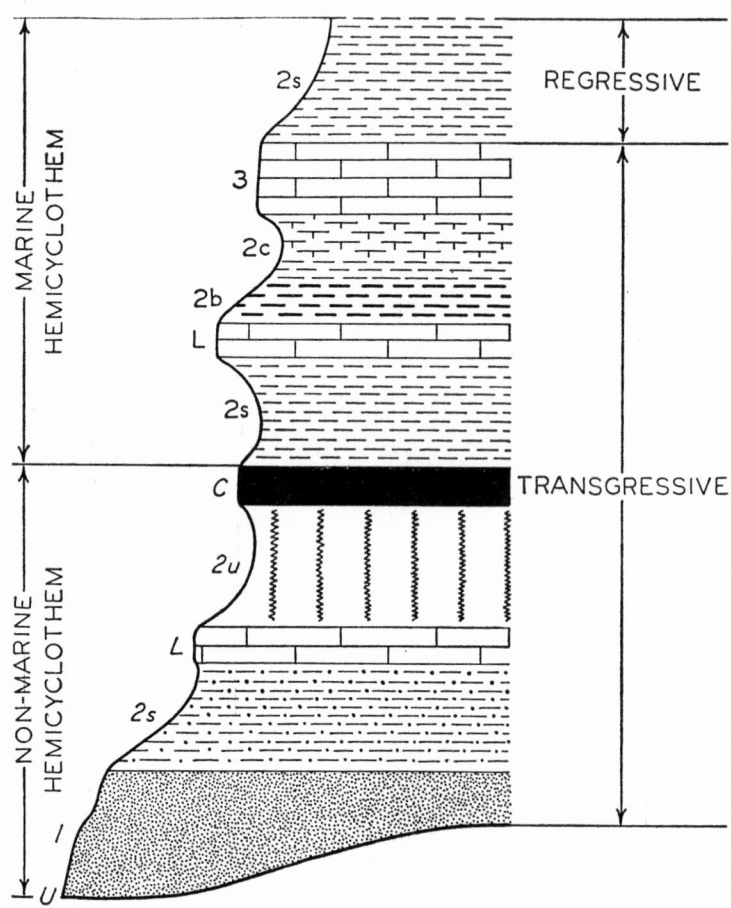

Figure 145. Stratigraphic section showing a completely developed Pennsylvanian cyclothem of the kind that occurs in Illinois and neighboring states. This column is generalized and idealized. Few actual cyclothems are so fully developed at any locality, and one or more of the members shown here commonly are absent. All of these members occur, however, at one place or another in many cyclothems. Few strata other than those shown here are present in any Illinois cyclothem. Where they do occur, they constitute very local irregularities of this sequence. (After Weller, 1957, Geol. Soc. Amer., Mem. 67, vol. 2, p. 331, fig. 2.)

the other hand, marine strata dominate. In many of the cyclothems of that region only shale underlies the horizon of the missing coal and in some this member also may be marine. Such a cyclothem might have the constitution 2s, L, 2b, 2c, 3, 2c, 2s, as shown in Figure 146B. In many respects the cyclothems of these two regions are so different that they could not be compared

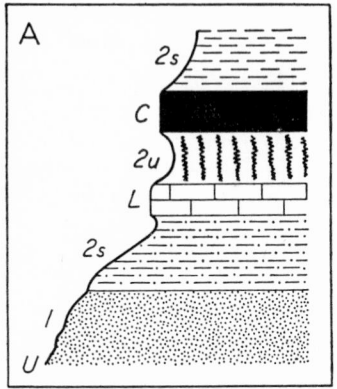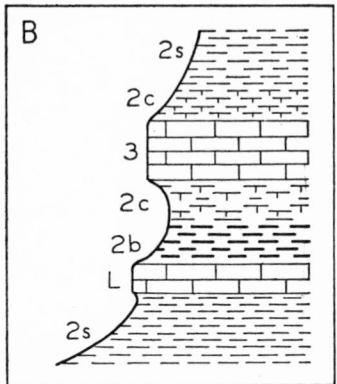

Figure 146.   A. Stratigraphic section showing a Pennsylvanian cyclothem of the type that is common in the northern Appalachian region. This is an incomplete development of the cyclothem represented in Figure 145. Beds of the upper hemicyclothem are undifferentiated, certainly identifiable marine strata are lacking, and the upper shale, 2s, may be non-marine.

B. Similar section showing a Pennsylvanian cyclothem of a type that is common in eastern Kansas. It also is an incomplete development of the cyclothem represented in Figure 145 characterized particularly by the absence of coal and underclay. Beds in the lower hemicyclothem generally are undifferentiated in the lower shale, 2s, which may include no non-marine strata.

if the intermediate type of cyclothem known in Illinois, which shares some of the characters of both, did not exist.

The general development of cyclothems changes with their positions in the stratigraphic section. The older ones are comparatively simple and incomplete. They are much the same in the three regions compared. Later ones become more complex and, particularly, exhibit greater differentiation of the marine members. This progress is more rapid and proceeds farther toward the ideal cyclothem as corresponding parts of the stratigraphic section are traced from east to west. The youngest Pennyslvanian cyclothems differ considerably in the three regions. In the northern Appalachian district they revert to simple types and include few certainly marine members. In Illinois some of them most closely approach the ideal cyclothem. In Kansas and Nebraska some may be exclusively marine.

The complexity and variability of Pennsylvanian cyclothems and their general changes, both geographic and stratigraphic, provide so many features requiring explanation that their interpretation is extraordinarily difficult. Among the many ideas that have been presented in attempts at explanation and interpretation of cyclothems and similar stratigraphic successions, some have been concerned with conditions of sedimentary deposition, some with transportation, and some with the origin of sediments both in source areas, which contributed detrital material, and within the basins where various organic products were created and preserved. Among the more important are the following:

1. Production of detrital sediment. Differences in the quantity of detrital sediment produced in and eroded from the source areas may have been determined by alternations of (a) uplift and subsequent peneplanation, (b) elevation and subsidence (c) glaciation and deglaciation, (d) relatively humid and more arid ages, and (e) episodes of greater and less growth of protective vegetation.

2. Transportation of sediment. The transportation of variable quantities of detrital sediment from the source areas and its delivery to the basins may have been determined by (a) climatic change that altered the amount of water flowing in the streams, (b) crustal warping that modified slopes and changed the transportational efficiency of running water, (c) the building up and breaking of sedimentary barriers and bars that served to direct the delivery of sediment first to one area and then to another, and (d) differential compaction of newly deposited sediment that resulted in unequal depression of the surface, thus determining where additional sediment would be delivered.

3. Quantity of sediment. The quantity of detrital sediment deposited in the basins may have been controlled by (a) intermittent subsidence in the basins, (b) alternate depression and uplift of the basin areas, (c) sea-level fluctuations, (d) amount of sediment delivered to the basins, and (e) filtering action of coal swamps that interfered with delivery of sediment to the basins.

4. Quality of sediment. The kind of sediment deposited in the basins may have depended upon (a) type of sediment delivered, (b) depth of water, (c) distance from shore, (d) salinity of water, (e) growth of seaweeds, (f) aeration of bottom water, (g) amount of detrital sediment deposited, (h) transgression or regression of sea, (i) slope of alluvial surfaces, (j) climate, (k) differential compaction of sediments, (l) existence of barriers or bars, and (m) occurrence of fresh-water lakes. Most of these possible factors may have influenced detrital sedimentation. Those which may have been specially important with respect to lime deposition are b, c, d, f, g, and m, and peat accumulation may have been especially responsive to b, g, h, i, j, k, and l.

No attempt is made here to evaluate in detail these suggested factors or to consider all the possibilities of their interactions. The very widespread occurrence, however, of many members which are believed to approximate time-rock units and the extensive continuity of individual cyclothems indicate that some of the most important factors were broadly influential. They therefore were probably related to controls operating principally outside of the basins of deposition. On the other hand, the characteristic variability of most cyclothems seems to provide evidence that other factors were only locally effective in controlling or modifying sedimentary deposition at different places. The strong asymmetry of the composite cyclothem is clearly shown by the general progressive decrease in coarseness of detrital sediment deposited first on one side and then continued on the other side of a transgressing shoreline and forming the members from the basal sandstone to the uppermost limestone. Thus the changing conditions and processes responsible for the development of cyclothems shifted gradually and more or less continuously in one direction and then were terminated by a relatively short and abrupt reversal that is recorded by only the final shale member.

About 100 successive cyclothems have been distinguished in the Pennsylvanian System of the United States. Similar or only slightly modified cyclothems continue in the lower Permian. The number of cyclothems present in comparable parts of the stratigraphic section varies somewhat from place to place.

Other Cyclothems

Coal-bearing cycles, which also have been termed cyclothems, occur in several post-Paleozoic systems. These are superficially similar to Pennsylvanian cyclothems, but detailed comparisons show that most of them are different in several important respects. For example, cyclic members are neither so numerous nor so distinctive, the relations of marine and non-marine strata are not the same, coal beds are not nearly so extensively developed, and typical underclays do not occur.

Upper Cretaceous cyclothems in Utah and Colorado consist of four members: (1) marine shale unconformable on underlying strata, (2) littoral marine sandstone, (3) lagoonal sandstone and shale, and (4) coal. They can be represented by the formula U, 2, 1, **2s, C,** as shown in Figure 147. The development of these cyclothems varies in a direction at right angles to the ancient shoreline. In a seaward direction the lagoonal deposits and coals disappear and the shales and sandstones form an intertongued succession (see Figure 191, p. 501). In the other direction the shale and sandstone members thin, and the succession consists mainly of lowland estuary, flood-plain, and swamp deposits with coal beds. Each cycle seems to represent rapid depression of the marine basin followed by a period of stability during which deposition built up the level of the sea bottom and the shoreline migrated seaward. Coal swamps generally were confined behind barrier bars or beach ridges as shown in Figure 59, p. 177. These relations are very different from those that prevailed during Pennsylvanian time, when subsidence of the marine basin was gradual, the sea slowly spread over an extensive coal swamp, and deposition in the sea was insufficient to compensate for deepening of the water. The Cretaceous cycles are dominantly regressive whereas those of the Pennsylvanian are dominantly transgressive.

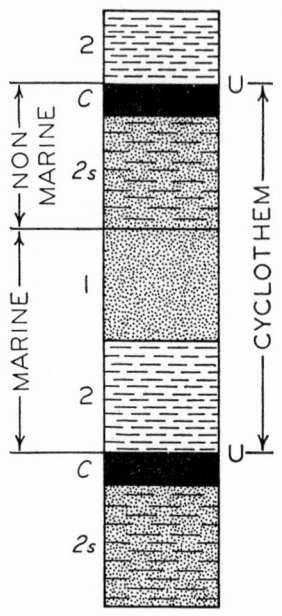

Figure 147. Stratigraphic column showing the members of a regressive cyclothem of the kind that occurs in the Mesa Verde Group (Cret.) in Utah and Colorado. This cyclothem is not closely comparable to that shown in Figure 145. The sandstone member is marine and it is not unconformable on underlying shale. If any stratigraphic break occurs it is at the top of the coal bed. This accounts for the different position of the boundary chosen to separate the Cretaceous cyclothems. (Data from Young, 1957, Bull. Am. Assoc. Petroleum Geol., vol. 41, p. 1766.)

Some of the coal-bearing middle to late Tertiary deposits of the Philippines appear to be arranged in nearly symmetrical cycles in which both transgressive and regressive hemicycles are well developed. Coal beds occur at rather regular intervals separated by argillaceous strata which alternately include sandstones and limestones (see Figure 148). All of the details of this succession have not been determined but at least some of the sandstones are marine and the limestones grade laterally into clay with abundant coral fragments. A single cycle appears to include two coals; perhaps it can be represented by the formula 1, 2, C, 2, 3, 2, C, 2.

Megacyclothems

A megacyclothem is a cycle of cyclothems. When megacyclothems were first described in Kansas, a recurring sequence of three to five limestone members, separated by shale, was believed to be equivalent to an equal number of cyclothems of the type described in Illinois. At that time cyclothems with more than one marine limestone had not been observed. Later when a second marine limestone was discovered to occur in many cyclothems, doubt developed regarding the nature of so-called megacyclothems. The possibility was considered that the non-marine limestone of the lower hemicyclothem in Illinois graded westward into a marine bed and thus accounted for a third limestone of the Kansas cycle. Therefore the so-called megacyclothem might be only a more complexly developed cyclothem characteristic of a region where marine conditions dominated.

More detailed comparisons have shown, however, that all but one of the shale members separating the limestones in a megacyclothem are very incomplete representatives of non-marine hemicyclothems and that the central and most characteristic part of a megacyclothem with its four limestones is composed of three cyclothems, as shown in Figure 149. The middle cyclothem has the general formula 2u, C, 2s, L, 2b, 2c, 3, 2c, 2s. The coal and under-clay generally are absent but the limestone-black shale-limestone sequence is characteristic and almost invariably present. Beneath this lies a second cyclothem with the general formula 1, 2s, 2c, 3, 2s. It is less uniformly developed than its neighbor. Its limestone may be lacking and it may include a thin coal. The uppermost cyclothem of the three has the general formula 2s, 2c, 3, 2c, 2s. It also is variably developed, it rarely includes coal, and its limestone may be missing. Successions of this type, generally with three or four marine limestones, are separated by imperfectly differentiated strata, mostly shale, that may include another limestone and one or two thin coals. These intervening sequences appear to correspond to one, two, or possibly more very incomplete cyclothems. Seventeen megacyclothems have been distinguished in Kansas.

The megacyclothem is conspicuous in Kansas because of the poor development or absence of non-marine strata in two successive cyclothems (the middle and upper ones that have been noted) and the close grouping of the marine limestones in these and a third underlying cyclothem. A comparable but differently constituted megacyclothem consisting of three to five cyclothems occurs in the uppermost Pennsylvanian strata of Illinois. Its principal parts are two well-developed cyclothems. The lower one is characterized by the limestone-black shale-limestone part of the sequence and the upper has an unusually thick marine limestone. These correspond to the middle and upper limestone-bearing cyclothems of Kansas. Both Illinois cyclothems, however, have well-developed non-marine hemicyclothems and their limestones are not closely grouped like those in Kansas. Above and below these cyclothems occur thinner but fairly well-developed cyclothems without marine limestones. The shales of their

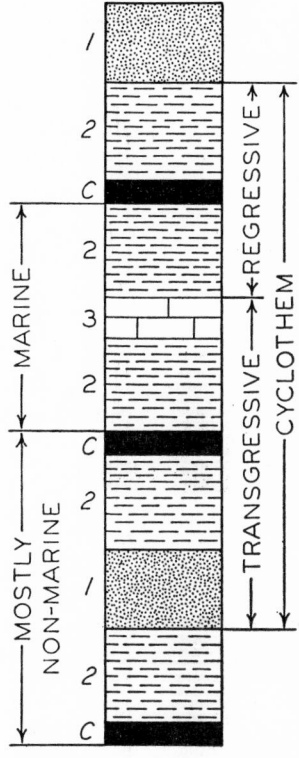

Figure 148. Generalized columnar section showing the approximate relations of recurring strata of Miocene age on Batan Island, Albay Province, Philippines. The succession here is suggestive of a symmetrical cyclothem that includes coal in both the transgressive and regressive parts. (Data from Crispin and others, 1955, Phil. Bur. Mines, Spec. Proj. Ser., Publ. 3, p. 15 and pl. 2.)

upper hemicyclothems contain fossils of brackish water rather than normally marine types. No megacyclothems have been recognized in the Appalachian region.

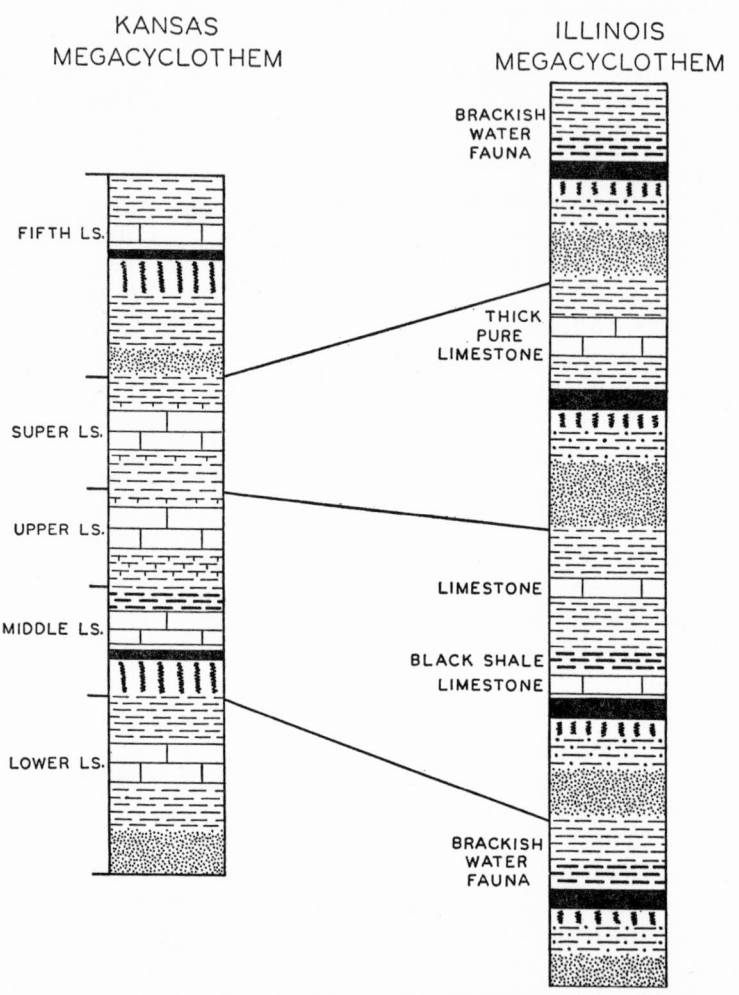

KANSAS
MEGACYCLOTHEM

ILLINOIS
MEGACYCLOTHEM

BRACKISH
WATER
FAUNA

FIFTH LS.

THICK
PURE
LIMESTONE

SUPER LS.

UPPER LS.

LIMESTONE

MIDDLE LS.

BLACK SHALE
LIMESTONE

LOWER LS.

BRACKISH
WATER
FAUNA

Figure 149.   Generalized correlation diagram showing the presumed equivalence of successive differently developed cyclothems in the upper Pennsylvanian of Illinois with parts of the megacyclothem recognized in eastern Kansas. (After Weller, 1958, *J. Geol.*, vol. 66, p. 202, fig. 3.)

A still larger Pennsylvanian cycle occurs in Kansas. It consists of four successive megacyclothems. Each group of this type is separated from adjacent similar ones by comparatively thick sequences of detrital strata probably arranged in several imperfectly differentiated cyclothems that include channel sandstones and generally one or more thin coals. They are termed *hyper-cyclothems* and there are four of them.

The origin of megacyclothems and hypercyclothems is not understood. Periodic variability of marine submergence and emergence undoubtedly determined, to some extent, both the thickness and the lithologic character of the marine and non-marine parts of individual cyclothems. The occurrence of larger cyclic sequences in basins adjacent to the stable Ozark region probably indicates, however, that the larger sequences were related to a longer period of rhythmicity in the subsidence of the basins. The particularly good development of large cyclic sequences in Kansas also suggests that intermittent episodes of important downwarping in the Ouachita geosyncline to the south may have played a part in the control of northward-spreading detrital sediment. Perhaps such movements produced a great sediment trap whose effectiveness varied from time to time. Periodic activity in the geosyncline, however, does not seem to have been related closely to whatever processes were responsible for the development of individual cyclothems.

Great Cycles

As cycles become larger, consist of greater thicknesses of strata, and represent increasingly longer intervals of time, the opportunities for variation multiply, distinctiveness declines, and more and more generalization is required for their recognition and characterization. The point may finally be reached where cycles become more imaginary than real. Progressive transition from the concrete toward the abstract is evident, for example, in the preceding consideration of patterned sequences starting with simple alternations and varves and continuing to the greater complexity of cyclothems, megacyclothems, and hypercyclothems.

The desire to distinguish patterns that are useful for classification, interpretation, prediction, or other purposes seems to be a natural attribute of the inquiring human mind. It is evident in all the sciences and in many other unrelated fields such as stock market fluctuations and astrology. Undoubtedly there are variously distinct and variously significant valid patterns that can be recognized among natural phenomena and human activities. It is unsafe, however, to accept any of them without the most critical examination and careful testing as to their reality and meaning. Facts can be warped too easily by slightly altering the emphasis accorded them to produce patterns compatible with preconceived or favored notions or expedient conclusions.

The diastrophic cycle that has been believed to punctuate geologic time and to divide it into periods is considered briefly in the next chapter. The general acceptance of diastrophic periodicity led naturally to the conclusion that it should be paralleled by a sedimentary cycle. This cycle, unlike those that have been discussed previously, was considered to mark off world-wide divisions of geologic time as well as to consist of a more or less characteristically patterned succession of strata. The belief was held that a geologic system should be bounded by angular unconformities recording emergence of the continents and mountain building, that it should exhibit in its earliest and latest parts rapidly eroded detrital sediments, and that the central part should record a long interval of relative quiescence and stability. Some systems in some regions do present this pattern. For example, the Mississippian System of the upper Mississippi and lower Ohio valleys overlaps onto Ordovician strata and is in turn overlapped completely by the Pennsylvanian. Its lower part includes much detrital sediment, its middle part is almost uninterrupted limestone subdivided into very widely recognized formations, and its upper part again is dominantly detrital. If this pattern were a general one it would be most satisfying. Unfortunately it is not, and neither the Mississippian in other regions nor other systems generally are comparably constituted.

Sedimentary cycles were first visualized by geologists in the latter part of the nineteenth century at a systemic scale and in much the form just outlined. The absence, however, of a generally recurrent pattern of that type failed to shake widespread faith in the diastrophic cycle. Most geologists seemed to assume that if the proper pattern does not occur in one region it will be found in another and thus satisfy the demands of an accepted theory. Later, evidence accumulated indicating what appeared to be large-scale cyclicity that did not correspond with the established systems. This was accepted by some American geologists as proof that the systems were improperly constituted. European geologists were more conservative and concerned themselves less with such problems. During the first quarter of the twentieth

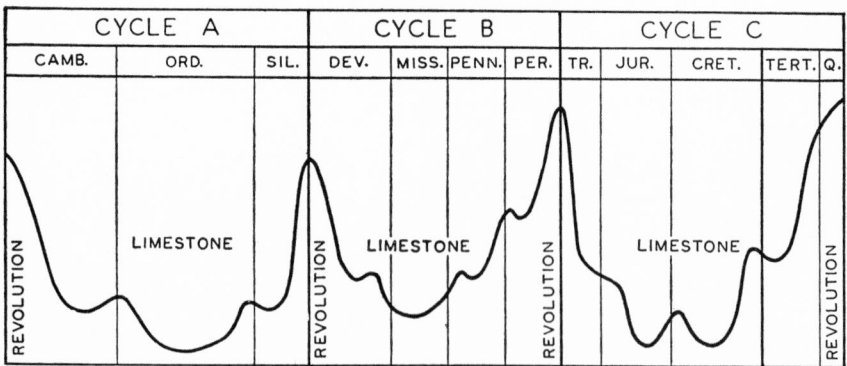

Figure 150. Curve intended to represent the variations in intensity of world-wide diastrophism since the beginning of Cambrian time. The peaks that are emphasized here serve to separate three great cycles which resemble each other in the patterns of sedimentary deposition occurring in western Europe and eastern North America. Compare with Figure 153, p. 389. (After Snider, 1932, *Earth history*, pl. after p. 74, by permission of Appleton-Century-Crofts, Inc.)

century several Americans attempted to reform stratigraphic classification in accordance with the diastrophic cycle as they understood it (see Figure 152, p. 389). Their proposals, involving the subdivision of old systems and the creation of more numerous new ones, failed to obtain much recognition and most of them are now forgotten.

An even grander cycle has been imagined that subdivides all geologic time since the beginning of the Paleozoic into three parts, as shown in Figure 150. The great orogenic "revolutions," late Precambrian, Caledonian, Appalachian, and Laramidian, which is considered to continue to the present, were used to bound them. Each cycle was supposed to possess transgressive and regressive phases, as in the systemic cycles, and an intervening limestone phase is provided by the Ordovician, Mississippian, and Cretaceous systems. These cycles are, of course, greatly generalized and not sharply set off from one another, but there is a good possibility that they have somewhat more reality than the supposed systemic cycles.

BIBLIOGRAPHY

Bradley, W. H. (1929), The varves and climate of the Green River Epoch, U.S. Geol. Surv., Prof. Paper 158, pp. 87–100.
  The author describes and interprets minutely laminated Eocene lake sediments in southwestern Wyoming and neighboring states.
Bradley, W. H. (1931), Non-glacial marine varves, Am. J. Sci., ser. 5, vol. 22, pp. 318–330.
  Alternate layers characterized by different amounts of organic matter identify annual sedimentary deposition.
Kelley, V. C. (1956), Thickness of strata, J. Sediment. Petrol., vol. 26, pp. 289–300.
  Nomenclature and classification of strata based on thickness of bedding are discussed.
Kuenen, P. H. (1950), Marine geology, New York, Wiley.
  See pp. 362–374 for discussion of stratification in marine sediments, its development and variations.
McKee, E. D. (1957), Primary structures in some recent sediments, Bull. Am. Assoc. Petroleum Geol., vol. 41, pp. 1704–1747.
  Stratification characteristics of a variety of modern littoral sediments including beach, dune, alluvial fan, lagoon, and tidal-flat deposits are described.
Moore, R. C. (1936), Stratigraphic classification of the Pennsylvanian rocks of Kansas, Geol. Surv. Kan., Bull. 22.
  See pp. 26–35 for original description and analysis of Pennsylvanian megacyclothems.
Shrock, R. R. (1948), Sequence in layered rocks, New York, McGraw-Hill.
  A thorough description of many stratification features, particularly those useful in determining tops and bottoms of beds.

Symposium, Studies related to the order and conditions of accumulation of the
    Coal Measures (1931), Ill. Geol. Surv., Bull. 60, pp. 161–289.
    Papers are by J. M. Weller, H. R. Wanless, Wilber Stout, D. B. Reger,
    G. H. Ashley, R. C. Moore, F. B. Plummer, David White, and A. C. Noé
    mostly discussing Pennsylvanian sedimentary cycles.
Twenhofel, W. H. (1950), *Principles of sedimentation,* 2nd ed., New York,
    McGraw-Hill.
    See pp. 542–554 for discussion of factors responsible for the development of
    stratification.
Twenhofel, W. H., and collaborators (1932), *Treatise on sedimentation,* 2nd
    ed., Baltimore, Williams and Wilkins.
    Stratification and rhythmic bedding are discussed on pp. 603–618.
Weller, J. M. (1956), Argument for diastrophic control of late Paleozoic cy-
    clothems, *Bull. Am. Assoc. Petroleum Geol.,* vol. 40, pp. 17–50.
    Theories are compared and explanations presented of processes responsible
    for development of Pennsylvanian cyclothems in the central and eastern
    United States.
Weller, J. M. (1958), Cyclothems and larger sedimentary cycles of the Penn-
    sylvanian, *J. Geol.,* vol. 66, pp. 195–207.
    The relations connecting Pennsylvanian cyclothems and megacyclothems in
    Kansas and Illinois are analyzed.
Young, R. C. (1957), Late Cretaceous cyclic deposits, Book Cliffs, eastern
    Utah, *Bull. Am. Assoc. Petroleum Geol.,* vol. 41, pp. 1760–1774.
    The development of regressive coal-bearing cyclothems is described and
    explained.
Zeuner, F. E. (1958), *Dating the past, an introduction to geochronology,* 4th
    ed., London, Methuen.
    See pp. 20–45 for descriptions of varves and varvelike bedding.

11

Unconformities

AN *unconformity* is a stratigraphic plane or contact that marks an important interruption of the stratigraphic record. Originally the only kind of unconformity recognized by geologists was a contact where older layers are beveled and overlain by younger ones that are angularly discordant with them. Later other evidences of unconformability were noted and this term was applied to stratigraphic discontinuities of other types. Erosion of preexisting rocks contributed to the development of most unconformities but it is not essential to them.

The stratigraphic record missing or destroyed at an unconformity may vary from exceedingly great, being equal to nearly the entire span of recorded geologic time, to some small lower limit that cannot be specified exactly. Ordinarily, minor or local discontinuities, although plainly evident, receive little notice. They are likely to be considered too unimportant to be remarked upon if they represent very short intervals of time, as, for example, the erosion associated with cross-bedding or cut-and-fill structures in a sandstone. Therefore in its practical application, the term *unconformity* is relative. The same surface of stratigraphic discontinuity which might be recognized as an unconformity in a detailed geologic study might pass unnoticed in a reconnaissance investigation. Breaks in the stratigraphic record of equal time value also may be accorded different treatment depending upon whether the apparent depth of erosion and resulting relief developed at a stratigraphic contact is large or small.

Hiatus

The time that is unrepresented in the stratigraphic record at an unconformity is a hiatus. As noted later, one part of a hiatus corresponds to the time during which sedimentary deposition was interrupted, and the other part is equivalent to the time value of formerly existing strata that were destroyed by erosion.

IMPORTANCE OF UNCONFORMITIES

Most stratigraphic sections are incomplete and consist of variably thick successions of continuously deposited sediments separated by interruptions of variable magnitude. Both the sediments and the stratigraphic breaks are records of geologic conditions and events. One or the other type of record may predominate, but both are important for the purposes of geologic interpretation.

Unconformities Compared to Formations

Unconformities and formations or other groups of strata alternate and intertongue. Both have areal extent and both represent intervals of time. Both are likely to vary in time value from place to place.

Like formations, unconformities can be correlated. Unlike formations, however, their correlation is dependent entirely on extrinsic evidence because no unconformity possesses peculiar features that set it apart certainly from all others. The identification of unconformities occurring at nearby localities and their correlation in more widely separated areas are dependent wholly upon the local relations existing between whatever rock units may be observed in contact. Thus, a particular unconformity can be known by its occurrence immediately beneath a certain formation, regardless of what may underlie it, or by its position immediately above a certain formation, regardless of what strata may succeed it. If different formations meet at an unconformity at different places, identity is determined if correlations of both underlying and overlying formations demonstrate that some part of the missing stratigraphic record corresponds from place to place.

Unlike formations and other rock units, unconformities cannot be arranged or classified in a hierarchical succession of increasingly more important and inclusive classes. Under some circumstances, however, they can be grouped. Thus, several less important unconformities may merge upon the border of some persistent structurally positive area, as a result of the wedging out of intervening strata, to form a single unconformity of much greater magnitude. Relations of this kind may provide information important for the recognition of extended intervals of variable structural activity in relatively stable or periodically uplifted areas and adjacent basins of subsidence and sedimentary deposition.

Unlike formations, unconformities are not named, although names have been applied to a few of the time intervals they represent. For example, that part of late Precambrian and early Cambrian time that is unrepresented in the stratigraphic record beneath the oldest Cambrian deposits has been called the Lipalian interval. If the term is to be accepted with its original meaning (p. 41), however, this is a misuse of it. Also an Eparchean interval has been recognized as being unrepresented at the unconformity between highly metamorphosed crystalline Archean rocks and less metamorphosed Algonkian strata. Because of uncertainties of correlation, there is much doubt that such an unconformity and its time correspond from one Precambrian region to another.

Unconformities generally are identified in terms of the rock units or time-rock units which they bring into contact. The names of both underlying and overlying units may be used, if reference is made to a local area, or if stratigraphic relations are not widely constant. Thus, on the eastern flank of the Ozark region there is a post-St. Louis–pre-Ste. Genevieve unconformity (Miss.). If overlapping conditions exist, only the name of the overlying unit is appropriate because different underlying formations occur at different places. For example, in Missouri and Illinois there is a pre-Grassy Creek unconformity which brings a black shale (Miss. or Dev.) into contact with a variety of formations ranging in age from mid-Devonian to mid-Ordovician. If these relations are reversed, only the name of the underlying unit is appropriate because of the occurrence of different overlying formations. The latter situation, however, is far less common.

Some of the greater or more important unconformities are identified in terms of larger stratigraphic units. In the upper Mississippi and lower Ohio valleys the pre-Chesterian unconformity (Miss.) brings one or more Lower Chesterian formations into contact with one or more older formations. Also, in Illinois the pre-Pennsylvanian unconformity overlaps from strata of late Mississippian to mid-Ordovician age. In the southern part of the state this might be termed the post-Mississippian and in the northern part the post-Ordovician unconformity, or in either area a combination of names could be employed. Because of the differing relations, the first term, pre-Pennsylvanian unconformity, is preferable. It alone is applicable everywhere. Generally identification in terms of an overlying stratigraphic unit serves more accurately to locate unconformities in terms of geologic time.

Note should be made that use of a name, like Pennsylvanian, implies the time-rock unit *system* and not the time unit *period*. There can be, of course, no such thing as a hiatus between the Mississippian and Pennsylvanian periods because there are no breaks in geologic time. The prefix *sub-*, indicating position in space, is preferable and more exact in combination with such a name as Pennsylvanian than *pre-*, which suggests position with respect to time. Its use, however, has not been common, and a corresponding prefix such as *super-* or *epi-* instead of *post-* has been employed even less commonly.

Unconformities in Stratigraphic Classification

Cessation of sedimentation in a depositional area for an appreciable time is a noteworthy change. If erosion also occurs, a complete reversal of geologic processes is evident. Angular unconformities indicate not only erosion but also a previous episode of structural disturbance and are particularly obvious and significant. The folded or otherwise deranged strata beneath many angular unconformities record diastrophism that may have reached mountain-forming proportions.

Angular unconformities were noted and interpreted correctly very early in the development of modern geologic science. Other less obvious unconformities were discovered only after paleontology or detailed regional studies demonstrated the absence of important parts of the stratigraphic section. As differentiation and classification of rock units gradually progressed, unconformities commonly were utilized wherever they were recognized as the most logical and practical stratigraphic boundaries.

Alternation of important parts of the stratigraphic section, such as geologic systems, and conspicuous unconformities, some of which record episodes of mountain building, suggest a definite periodicity in diastrophic activity. Three episodes of diastrophism in western Europe raised great mountain chains. These disturbances became known as (1) the Caledonian revolution, at the end of the Silurian Period (not evident in the United States), (2) the Hercynian revolution, at the end of the Permian Period (Appalachian revolution in North America), and (3) the Alpine revolution, at the end of the Cretaceous Period (Laramidian revolution in North America). The last two were largely instrumental in establishing the recognition of the post-Proterozoic geologic eras.

The idea of diastrophic periodicity has proved attractive to many geologists because (1) it accords with thoroughly ingrained early geologic interpretations which accepted catastrophism as a normal part of geologic development, and (2) it appears to furnish a rational basis for the subdivision of past time into geologic periods. The belief formerly was almost universal that geologic history records a succession of relatively long world-wide periods of quiescence, characterized by slow gentle epirogenic movements, separated by brief episodes of rapid and extreme orogenic disturbances acting synchronously in restricted, widely separated parts of the world. Less than fifty years ago the doctrine was generally accepted that such periodic diastrophism provides the only proper and practical basis for the natural division of geologic time into its larger units of world-wide applicability. With this view firmly established, geologists sought to complete a succession of "revolutions" or more moderate "disturbances" to set off all geologic systems from each other. Eventually all desired "disturbances" were discovered, each of which is evidenced by an angular unconformity noted in one or more areas.

In America they have become known by the names shown in Table 11 or other comparable ones.

TABLE 11.   Names of Mountain-Forming
Movements Supposedly Separating the
Geologic Systems as Identified in Most
American Textbooks

Post-Tertiary–pre-Pleistocene, *Cascadian*
Post-Cretaceous–pre-Tertiary, *Laramidian*
Post-Jurassic–pre-Cretaceous, *Nevadian*
Post-Triassic–pre-Jurassic, *Palisadian*
Post-Permian–pre-Triassic, *Appalachian*
Post-Pennsylvanian–pre-Permian, *Marathonian*
Post-Mississippian–pre-Pennsylvanian, *Ouachitaian*
Post-Devonian–pre-Mississippian, *Acadian*
Post-Silurian–pre-Devonian, *Caledonian* (Europe)
Post-Ordovician–pre-Silurian, *Taconian*
Post-Cambrian–pre-Ordovician, *Vermontian*
Post-Proterozoic–pre-Cambrian, *Killarneyan*

All diastrophic episodes in the history of the earth except the very recent ones are known only from either (1) the stratigraphic relations observed at unconformities or (2) the sediments, derived from ancient, newly uplifted areas, that were deposited and are still preserved in situations where they are now available for observation. Erosion that resulted in important unconformities and deposition of the sediments so produced could not have occurred simultaneously in the same areas, but both were equally the products of the same diastrophic movements. Although sediments recording diastrophic episodes probably are much more extensively preserved than are the corresponding erosion surfaces, unconformities have been more commonly sought and accepted as evidence of orogenic activity.

Periodic Diastrophism Questioned

Most geology textbooks have presented some simple sequence of intersystemic orogenies of variable intensity (see Figure 151). However, the foregoing tabulation is deceptive because (1) it emphasizes certain diastrophic episodes and ignores others, (2) it gives a false impression of the definite placement of these episodes in geologic time, and (3) it suggests that these episodes are all more or less equally important.

As new and more detailed information has accumulated, the realization has grown that geologic time has not been so clearly punctuated by a few outstanding but relatively brief episodes of disturbance separating the recognized geologic systems. Several of the orogenies listed in Table 11 are not known outside of very local areas. Many of these probably are no more important than others which have not been dignified with names because they do not coincide with geologic boundaries previously considered to be important. For example, at least two disturbances of considerable magnitude occurred during Cretaceous time in the Rocky Mountain region. Furthermore, it has become increasingly clear that the orogenies of the conventional series neither are as accurately dated nor were of as brief duration as was formerly believed. The more spectacular "revolutions" particularly have been found

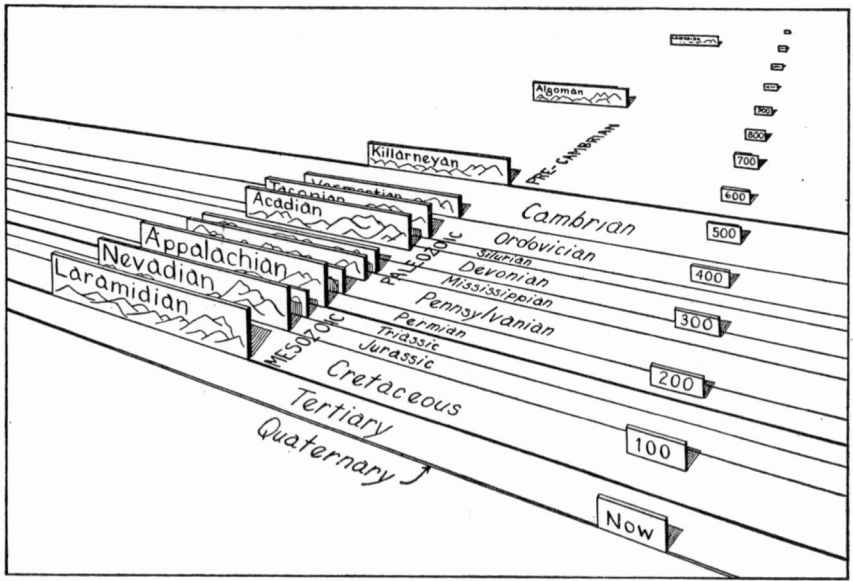

Figure 151.   Illustration of the common and convenient concept presented in many textbooks of the past that orogenic episodes are markers separating the geologic periods. (Modified by permission from *Introduction to historical geology* by Raymond C. Moore, 1st ed., p. 32, fig. 26. Copyright, 1949. McGraw-Hill Book Co.)

to consist of several related episodes spaced at intervals through a total time span more than equal to some geologic periods.

The hypothesis of periodic world-wide diastrophism has been questioned with increasing frequency since the early 1920's. Some geologists who adhered to this hypothesis attempted to work out a sequence in greater and more acceptable detail by correlating orogenic movements throughout the world. About forty are supposed to have been distinguished (see Figure 3, p. 14). Each has been thought to represent about 300,000 years and all of them thus would account for only 2½ percent of post-Proterozoic time. The intervening comparatively quiescent periods thus were believed to be about forty times as long, averaging about 12 million years each in duration. Other geologists approached the problem in a different way. They attempted to distinguish and correlate the strata of successive cycles consisting of transgressive and regressive halves that were believed to mark world-wide movements of the epicontinental seas. The Paleozoic alone has been considered to consist of twelve or more such systems presumably separated from each other by diastrophic episodes (see Figure 152).

Belief in world-wide "revolutions" and supposedly relatively brief periodic "disturbances" is now regarded by many geologists as a relic of early ideas that necessitated calling upon catastrophes to account for all major diastrophic activity. These geologists have been influenced by increasing doubts to reject this hypothesis. They do not deny that diastrophic activity has varied from time to time over the earth as a whole or that it has been more or less irregularly periodic within restricted regions. They recognize, however, no convincing evidence in favor of distinct world-wide periodicity, and they suggest that diastrophism of orogenic proportions probably was in progress somewhere at all times, (see Figure 153).

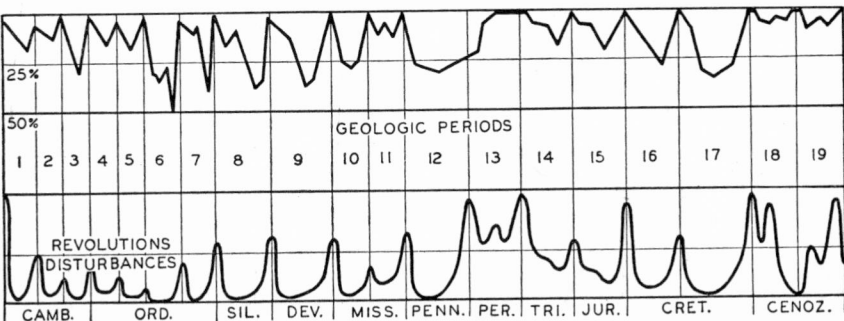

Figure 152.   Schuchert's diagram of diastrophic revolutions and disturbances separating geologic periods. His inclination to subdivide such standard periods as the Cambrian and Ordovician was influenced by the views of E. O. Ulrich. Later he revised his opinions and reverted to a more conventional viewpoint. The lower curve shows the presumed relative intensity of mountain-forming movements. The upper one indicates the approximate proportions of North America submerged by shallow seas during the intervals of relative stability. (After Schuchert, 1915, A text-book of geology, by Pirsson and Schuchert, 1st ed., vol. 2, p. 980, fig. 520, by permission of John Wiley and Sons; and 1918, The evolution of the earth and its inhabitants, p. 53, fig. 3, by permission of Yale University Press.

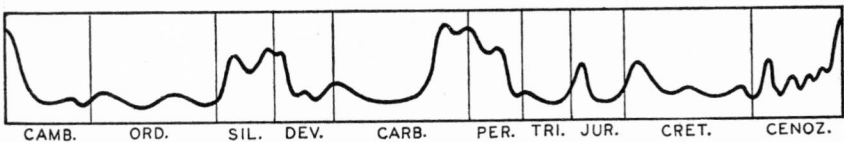

Figure 153.   Umbgrove's diagram showing the variable intensity of diastrophism during post-Proterozoic time. The horizontal scale of this diagram has been adjusted so that it corresponds with Schuchert's diagram in Figure 152 and direct comparison can be made. This interpretation gives little indication of distinct periodicity or the general occurrence of major diastrophic movements at the divisions between the systems. (Adapted from Umbgrove, 1947, The pulse of the earth, table 2, by permission of Martinus Nijhoff.)

Rejection of the hypothesis of diastrophic periodicity does not diminish the significance of unconformities in restricted regions. There they furnish evidence of the complete interruption and reversal of prevailing geologic processes and conditions. Commonly they record the temporary withdrawal of epicontinental seas. They constitute the best and most unequivocal stratigraphic boundaries. Unconformities generally are considered so important that most of them are almost automatically recognized as stratigraphic boundaries. Few formations are considered to be properly constituted if they are known to include unconformities that are conspicuous, extensive, or representative of more than minor interruptions in sedimentary deposition.

Unconformities are the boundaries of most of the larger time-rock units in their type areas. In the past, geologists have shown strong preference for unconformities as markers of the same or comparable boundaries in other regions (see Figure 166, p. 442). In this they have been influenced by a common desire for uniformity and order and by the general belief in diastrophic periodicity. Thus, unconformities in widely separated areas have been considered equivalent if they occur at approximately similar positions in the stratigraphic section and if paleontology does not clearly indicate their difference. Many correlations of this kind are now recognized to be more or less uncertain.

CLASSIFICATION

Several attempts have been made to classify unconformities on a genetic or dynamic basis, and various names have been proposed to distinguish different types. These efforts have not produced a classification that is entirely practical and they have resulted in confusion of nomenclature.

No sharp distinction can be made between different types of stratigraphic discontinuities. In a general and relative way, however, the following subdivision can be suggested:

A. Relatively important stratigraphic discontinuities
    1. Not produced by erosion
    2. Produced in part by erosion
       a. Adjacent strata parallel
       b. Adjacent strata not parallel
B. Relatively unimportant stratigraphic discontinuities

Unconformity

A general term is needed for all important stratigraphic discontinuities and *unconformity* has been so commonly used in this way that its proposed restriction to those exhibiting angular discordance seems undesirable.

The entirely relative distinction between important and unimportant discontinuities has been noted. No sharp demarcation can be made with respect to either time or physical relations. Importance can be judged and evaluated only in reference to the particular conditions existing in an area and the objectives that have governed its investigation.

Erosion is evident at many unconformities, and the common definition of an unconformity includes a statement that erosion resulting from emergence contributed to its development. Some important stratigraphic discontinuities, however, present no conclusive evidence of erosion even though they may be believed to represent erosional intervals because strata presumed to have been present formerly are now missing. Also, the differentiation of submarine and emergent erosion may not be possible. Common uncertainty as to whether, to what extent, and how erosion actually was accomplished is such that it does not seem desirable to include a statement in the definition that emergence and erosion are necessary to produce an unconformity.

Disconformity

Disconformity is a term originally proposed to designate an unconformity, in the broad sense, which separates strata whose beds are parallel (see Figure 154). Some geologists would restrict it to an irregular plane of un-

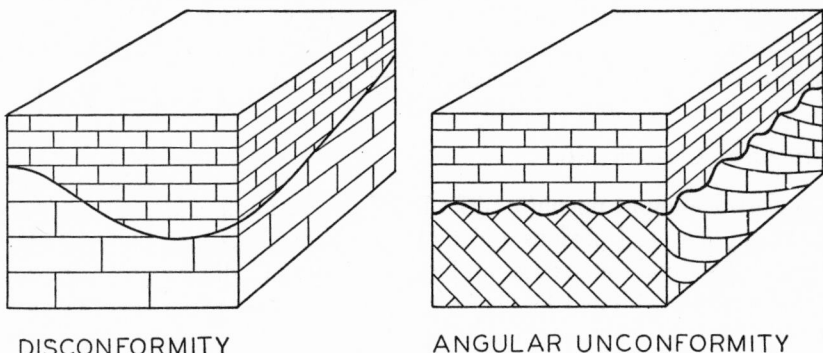

DISCONFORMITY   ANGULAR UNCONFORMITY

Figure 154. Block diagrams illustrating the differences in structural relations occurring at disconformities and angular unconformities. The actual surface of unconformity may be plane or highly irregular in either case.

conformity that provides clear evidence of erosion. Such restriction does not appear to be desirable because the character of any unconformity may be expected to vary considerably within short distances.

Angular Unconformity

The proposal has been made to restrict the use of *unconformity* to stratigraphic discontinuities that bring together angularly discordant strata. Because restriction of a term that has long been employed loosely is confusing and because an inclusive name is useful, this proposal has not gained general acceptance. Instead *nonconformity* has been suggested as the designation for an angular unconformity. This term, however, is unnecessary because the descriptive expression *angular unconformity*, whose meaning is unmistakable, is available and has been much used.

The contact between stratified rocks and underlying igneous rocks, or not clearly stratified metamorphics, likewise has been called a nonconformity and some geologists have desired to restrict the term to contacts of this kind. Such contacts cannot be misinterpreted and they are not exactly comparable to contacts within a stratigraphic sequence.

Diastem

The term *diastem* was introduced for a nonevident discontinuity between parallel marine strata. Originally it carried the idea of interrupted deposition not accompanied by erosion and not resulting from emergence. Because evidence of minor erosion or the lack of it generally is very obscure and because a similar concept is useful in connection with non-marine strata, this definition has been broadened.

Minor or local stratigraphic discontinuities are likely to escape notice even though evidence of their existence might be recognized by careful observation. Therefore, no sharp distinction can be made between diastems and disconformities. Thus, any minor stratigraphic discontinuity not considered important enough to be an unconformity may be termed a diastem.

Structural Classification

A classification of unconformities based on erosion and emergence is not practical. The most obvious and significant differences are structural. Two types of structural differences can be recognized: (1) differences in the topographic relief exhibited by planes of unconformity and (2) differences in the angular concordance or discordance of strata at these planes. Both types show extreme gradations and both may characterize a single unconformity. Topography varies progressively from a condition of practically perfect flatness to great irregularity and high relief. Inclination of strata varies from perfect parallelism to great and rapidly changing degrees of angular discordance. The influence of erosion in the development of unconformities becomes increasingly more obvious, but not necessarily more important, as relations deviate from flatness of surface and parallelism of strata.

Angular discordance at an unconformable surface is particularly significant because it is evidence of diastrophic disturbance preceding or accompanying erosion. The angular relations of strata at unconformities serve to identify and discriminate between regions of different tectonic characters, such as the relatively stable continental platforms on the one hand and portions of the relatively unstable mobile zones that were deformed, uplifted, and subjected to severe erosion on the other. The following classification reflects these differences. It is simple, meaningful, based on wholly objective criteria, and not subject to misinterpretation.

Unconformity—any important stratigraphic discontinuity

Disconformity—adjacent strata parallel

Angular unconformity—adjacent strata angularly discordant

Disconformities are characteristic of stable platform areas. Most of them were related to the ebb and flow of shallow epicontinental seas. Few exhibit absolute concordance of adjacent strata, but angular discordances related to gentle and slow warping are generally so slight that they are not discernible except by tracing for long distances. Disconformities may grade laterally into angular unconformities in the direction of rising mobile zones or pass into diastems and disappear in the uninterrupted sediments of subsiding depositional basins.

Angular unconformities occur upon the flanks of mobile zones and serve to outline them. As they approach the centers or axes of diastrophic activity, they are likely to record longer episodes of more active erosion, and their accurate dating in terms of geologic time units becomes less certain. They merge with other unconformities where intervening strata thin and disappear. At last they are lost in a great void of the stratigraphic record corresponding to the sum of all physiographic transformations of the uplifted area.

Environmental Classification

A classification of unconformities based on the interplay of environments is not useful in developing a system of terminology but it is important in directing attention to characteristics that may be significant in geologic interpretation. A more detailed and complex classification could be constructed but the following is adequate for all ordinary purposes:

A. Radical change in environment
   1. Marine regression and transgression
   2. Marine regression
   3. Marine transgression
B. No radical change in environment
   1. Submarine
   2. Terrestrial

Unconformities of these various types share common characteristics and are not separable with entire or equal certainty. Many of the features that may serve to distinguish them are matters of degree rather than absolute differences.

Marine Regression and Transgression

Marine beds constitute much the greater part of the preserved stratigraphic record. The most commonly recognized type of unconformity resulted from the more or less temporary withdrawal of the shallow epicontinental seas. The generally low featureless topography of those parts of the continental platforms that were subject to repeated marine submergence permitted the strand line to shift widely in response to comparatively minor fluctuations of relative sea level. Such movements have produced disconformities of wide extent at many positions within the stratigraphic section. Because erosion appears to have been slight, many disconformities are revealed more surely by paleontologic and lithologic evidence than by the local physical features of a stratigraphic contact. The amount of erosion was controlled in part by the local vertical measure of relative sea-level fluctuation and by the length of time of exposure to subaerial agencies. Both of these factors were related to and varied with local structural warping. Consequently the nature and distinctness of a single unconformity may vary considerably from place to place.

As deformed mobile zones or importantly uplifted areas are approached, the number of disconformities at first is likely to increase. Then as intervening strata wedge out and disappear, a progressively less complete stratigraphic section is interrupted by fewer and more prominent discontinuities that are likely to become angular unconformities.

Marine Regression

Non-marine strata may succeed marine without noteworthy interruption as in a growing delta adjacent to a relatively stable coastline. In other situations a more or less important discontinuity commonly separates these types of strata. Unconformities occurring at such positions are likely to be well marked. Relations may vary from disconformable to angular and generally they are similar to those characterizing regressive-transgressive unconformities.

Marine Transgression

The transgression of marine strata over non-marine may occur at an obvious unconformity produced by the erosive action of waves, tides, and currents in a littoral zone that shifted progressively inland. Unconformities of this kind may be similar to those previously discussed. Commonly, however, local sedimentary material was reworked and, if a low coastal plain has been submerged, the discontinuity may not be discernible.

Submarine

Unconformities may be produced by the erosive action of waves and currents in very shallow water without emergence. An unconformity also may result from by-passing or lack of sedimentary deposition for an appreciable time. Submarine unconformities are likely to develop only in relatively restricted areas or in comparatively narrow zones because currents strong enough to remove sediments or to prevent their deposition generally are localized. Conditions suitable for the production of such an unconformity may occur adjacent to a coast or at some other place where currents of oceanic circulation or those generated by the tides are constricted and consequently accelerated. Tides and currents, however, probably were not important in most inland seas of past ages, just as they are not important now in the Baltic and Mediterranean. Wave-cut unconformities adjacent to coasts probably would be marked by pebbles or cobbles of local derivation, if the bottom consisted of consolidated rock. These might be preserved as a basal conglomerate in succeeding sediments.

Submarine unconformities are likely to pass into diastems or be lost in uninterrupted sediments. If they were produced adjacent to a coast they may be continuous with more important unconformities related to terrestrial exposure and erosion. Differentiation of submarine and regressive-transgressive unconformities is likely to be difficult and uncertain. The occurrence of stratigraphic discontinuities representing lack of deposition for considerable intervals of time and throughout wide areas generally is questionable but may be indicated by the presence of glauconite and phosphatic nodules.

Terrestrial

The land is a realm of dominant erosion, and sedimentary deposition above sea level generally is temporary and local. Important sedimentary accumulation has occurred, however, in special situations, as in enclosed basins, in areas of low surface gradient adjacent to highlands being actively eroded, and upon expanding deltas and growing coastal plains. Most deposits of this type are destroyed eventually but in especially favorable situations some have been preserved for long periods of time. Opportunities for destruction increase with passing time, and in a general way terrestrial deposits appear to be progressively less and less well represented in the older rocks.

Both wind and glaciers accomplish erosion on the land and may contribute importantly to the development of unconformities. Some terrestrial deposits resulted from wind and glacial action and others accumulated in lakes where conditions resemble those prevailing in the sea. Most terrestrial strata, however, were closely related to flowing water. Deposition was caused by slackening of currents.

Flowing water on the land varies from year to year, with the seasons, and in shorter and more irregular cycles produced by storms. In regions of deposition, stream currents vary and change course repeatedly because some areas are aggraded slightly and streams are diverted to lower levels. This irregularity and repeated change is reflected in the sedimentary deposits, which commonly are marked by seemingly erratic variations and gradation, both laterally and vertically, in coarseness, composition, and other characters. Planes recording local and brief erosion are common but of little significance. Important stratigraphic discontinuities, if they occur, are likely to be difficult to identify. At some times and in some areas, however, more conspicuous erosion may have occurred and produced deep channeling. Nevertheless most sedimentary breaks worthy of being considered unconformities are only locally recognizable or are very unequally developed from place to place.

Composite Unconformities

Much thicker stratigraphic sections occur on some parts of the continents than on others. The tracing and correlation of formations between such areas generally show that the thick sections identify depositional basins which subsided slowly but somewhat irregularly for long periods of time. The thinner sections occur in areas which sank much less or were alternately depressed and elevated with respect to sea level. The differences in thickness of strata are accounted for in part by thinning of individual stratigraphic units such as formations from the basins toward the positive areas, but, more importantly, the stratigraphic record preserved in the basins is likely to be more complete. Thus deposition in the basins probably was more rapid and was interrupted less often and for shorter intervals of time. The interruptions are marked by unconformities or occur at diastems.

Some unconformities may extend throughout a basin and record complete withdrawal of the epicontinental sea. Other fluctuations of the strand line were not so great. They served to interrupt the stratigraphic record only outside of the central basin and toward the flanks of adjacent positive areas that stood somewhat higher topographically. Outward from the center of a basin the number of unconformities can be expected to increase as new ones appear at new positions.

Commonly some of the stratigraphic units present on the flanks of positive areas wedge out. Their edges are overlapped by other, more extensive units. Relations of this kind are likely to vary from place to place and may be quite complex. If a unit is bounded above and below by unconformities, these approach each other as the unit thins and merge along a line where the unit wedges out. The disappearance of several units in this way may result in the merging of a number of unconformities.

A *composite unconformity* produced by such merging differs in no essential from any of the less important unconformities with which it is laterally continuous except that it is a greater discontinuity in the stratigraphic record. The historical implications of a composite unconformity, however, are much different. It represents not one interruption of sedimentary deposition and one episode of possible erosion but several. No feature of a composite unconformity, however, indicates the number or relative importance of these interruptions and episodes. The recognition of a composite unconformity and its interpretation in terms of geologic history are wholly dependent upon deductions made from evidence obtained at other places where the stratigraphic record is more complete.

Several good examples of composite unconformities occur on the flanks of the Ozark region. Throughout the entire Paleozoic Era, this was a comparatively stable or at times mildly positive structural element of the continental platform surrounded by subsiding basins where greater thicknesses of sediment accumulated. The stratigraphic section is most complete and has been studied most carefully on the eastern flank (see Figure 155). A large number

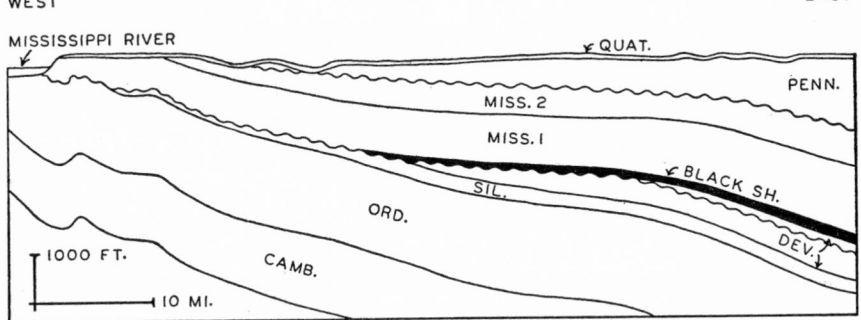

Figure 155. Much-generalized stratigraphic and structural section in southwestern Illinois showing beds rising on the flank of the Ozark region. Two particularly important unconformities are indicated. Both are composite unconformities where they outcrop because, as strata are traced eastward into the Illinois basin, formations and even whole systems that are themselves separated by less important unconformities appear as wedges and thicken to provide a more complete stratigraphic section. (After Weller, 1945, *Geologic map of Illinois*, Ill. Geol. Surv., cross section E-E'.)

of unconformities has been reported there. All of them are classed as disconformities because angular discordance is not apparent at the outcrops. Two of the unconformities are particularly significant because they mark planes of conspicuous overlap and record important readjustments in the structural relations of the Ozark dome and the Illinois basin. One below the Pennsylvanian System cuts across most of the Upper Mississippian Series in which seven rather minor unconformities occur. Where this unconformity outcrops 10 million or more years are unrepresented in the stratigraphic record. The one below the Middle Mississippian was produced by the merging of an equal number of more important unconformities, one of which, in the midst of the Devonian, alone represents as much time as the sub-Pennsylvanian unconformity. Altogether this great sub-Mississippian unconformity represents more than 100 million unrecorded years. More than 1000 feet of strata known in nearby areas are missing at each of these composite unconformities. On the Ozark plateau isolated remnants of Pennsylvanian and

Mississippian strata overlie still older formations and the locally missing record corresponds to at least 150 and 120 million years respectively. In neither case is this gap in the record related to only one interval of nondeposition and erosion.

EVIDENCE OF UNCONFORMITY

Unconformities vary greatly in their distinctness and the certainty of their recognition. Reliability in the identification of unconformable relations in general increases in proportion to (1) time interval or (2) thickness of beds missing from the stratigraphic record, and (3) structural discordance, (4) topographic relief, or (5) evidence of weathering at the unconformable surface. As these measures suggest, different types of evidence are variously serviceable and in doubtful cases no one type of evidence may be conclusive. The kinds of evidence important in the recognition of unconformities are listed in Table 12.

TABLE 12.   Types of Evidence
Important in the Recognition
of Unconformities

A. Evidence of unrecorded interval
   1. Gap in paleontologic record
   2. Gap in stratigraphic record
B. Evidence of erosion
   1. Structural discordance
   2. Topographic irregularity
C. Evidence of old land surface
   1. Weathering
   2. Old soil zone
   3. Silicification
   4. Solution
   5. Basal conglomerate

Unrecorded Interval

Positive evidence of unconformity is provided by the occurrence of fossils of different ages on the two sides of a plane of stratigraphic contact. The distinction in age must be definite, and a lower limit to the reliability of paleontologic evidence is set by the rate of evolutionary progress. Many differences in the faunas and floras which characterize parts of typical stratigraphic sections or other well-known sequences reflect variations in ecologic conditions or possibly changes in the geographic relations of land and sea rather than differences in age. In many regions the absence of fossils identifying strata comparable to the usual formational unit is not by itself sufficient to establish certainly the occurrence of an unconformity.

Erroneous conclusions are possible if the compared fossils are not present in closely adjacent strata. For example, an unconformity has been reported to separate the Bailey Limestone (Dev.) from the underlying Bainbridge Limestone (Sil.) in southeastern Missouri because the faunas described from these formations have been judged to indicate neither earliest Devonian nor latest Silurian time. Both formations, however, are generally unfossiliferous and the zones that have furnished most of the specimens are separated by more than 100 feet of barren strata. No good evidence of a physical break between these formations has been recorded. The unfossiliferous strata may fully represent the time that has been believed to separate the faunas.

Another example of possible misinterpretation is provided by the Devonian-Mississippian boundary on the east side of the Allegheny plateau (see Figure 156). There detrital strata generally identified as Pocono sandstone

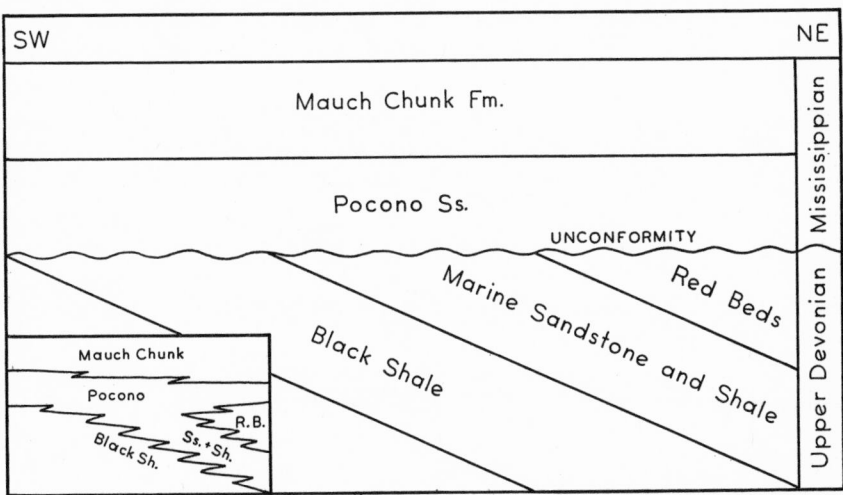

Figure 156. Stratigraphic relations of Devonian and Mississippian formations along the eastern side of the Allegheny plateau. The large diagram shows the conventional interpretation of Mississippian strata unconformably overlapping successively older Devonian formations. The physical evidence of such an unconformity has not been reported. The inset shows an alternative interpretation conforming to the stratigraphic relations occurring in the Catskill delta to the west.

(Miss.) have not furnished fossils similar to species of the Lower Mississippian formations of the upper Mississippi Valley. This sandstone overlies Upper Devonian formations that, in a southwestern direction, are first Catskill-like red beds, then Chemung-like sandstone, and finally Chattanooga-like black shale. This apparent overlap and the absence of Lower Mississippian fossils has been interpreted as evidence of an important unconformity although no actual physical evidence of stratigraphic discontinuity substantiating this conclusion has ever been reported. Possibly the Devonian formations are laterally transitional facies like those in the Catskill delta of Pennsylvania and New York. If so, there may be no real overlap. The Pocono fossils may differ from those of the Mississippi Valley because of important environmental differences.

Good evidence of unconformity may be provided by the local absence of distinctive strata characterized by either lithologic or paleontologic peculiarities, or both. The fossils of all such strata are an indication of environmental conditions just as the lithologic features are, and their full temporal range may be much greater than the narrow zone of their local occurrence. Evidence of this type is not conclusive because facies change and integrade laterally. If, however, the apparently missing strata are persistent in nearby areas, they may reasonably be thought to have been more extensive originally. Conclusions based on such evidence are strengthened if careful measurements demonstrate that a more inclusive stratigraphic unit has become thinner by an amount equal to the thickness of the supposedly missing strata.

Abrupt change in the lithologic character of strata and the absence of intergrading material of intermediate type may indicate unconformity. Abrupt lithologic change between formations characterized by different types of rock may be significant, and many unconformities have been postulated on no better evidence. Similar abrupt changes occur commonly, however, in formations of heterogeneous composition. Contacts of this type may record the alteration of physical conditions without any noteworthy interruption in sedimentary deposition.

More or less prolonged static conditions with very little deposition of sediment may be indicated by some thin zones marked by the occurrence of glauconite and black phosphatic nodules. Because these materials are believed to have formed slowly on the sea bottom, they may identify sedimentary interludes not related to emergence or erosion. A zone of this kind is widespread at the top of the Chattanooga Shale (Dev.-Miss.) east of the Mississippi River.

Erosion

The truncation of sedimentary layers at a stratigraphic contact is unmistakable evidence of discontinuity. If the beds are angularly discordant, the contact is likely to be particularly significant.

Four types of angular discordance (see Figure 157) must be distinguished as follows: (1) discordance above originally horizontal strata that have been diastrophically deformed and eroded—angular unconformities; (2) discordance at an unevenly eroded but unwarped surface to which the layers of later deposited strata conform—initial dip at disconformities; (3) discordance above strata that were deposited in an inclined position—cross-bedding; (4) discordance produced by slumping or interstratal flow. These are not likely to be mistaken for each other except possibly in very limited outcrops. Cross-bedding and slump-and-flow structure affect only restricted thicknesses of strata and should not be confused with disturbed beds occurring beneath an angular unconformity. Cross-bedding is rare except in sandstones and some shallow-water fragmental or oolitic limestones. Initial dip is rarely per-

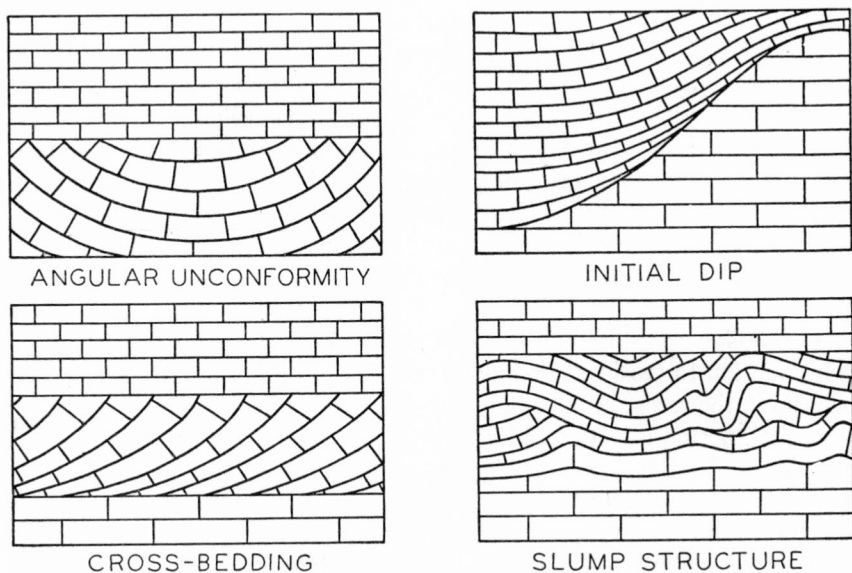

ANGULAR UNCONFORMITY   INITIAL DIP

CROSS-BEDDING   SLUMP STRUCTURE

Fig. 157. Four types of stratigraphic discordance that might be confused in small outcrops. Only the angular unconformity is evidence of structural disturbance. Initial dip and cross-bedding are features of original deposition possibly modified considerably by subsequent compaction of the sediments. Slump structure results from local and generally small-scale disturbance of newly deposited unconsolidated sediments and has no necessary connection with even the mildest kind of diastrophic movement.

fectly developed and disappears in overlying strata. Also slump-and-flow structures are likely to be exceedingly irregular and very local. All but the first type of angular discordance are produced in response to relatively temporary and local processes and conditions.

Angular unconformities record folding or other diastrophic disturbance of older strata that generally was related to important structural readjustments in more or less extensive regions. These structural movements involved the elevation of some areas and possibly they were accompanied by and certainly followed by erosion. Strata of all kinds and all older ages were affected. Angular unconformities are more conspicuous and they commonly represent more important breaks in the stratigraphic record than do most disconformities. They are utilized in most regions as means for subdividing geologic history, but many of them are difficult to date accurately because of the generally large gaps between the ages of the youngest underlying and oldest overlying beds.

The development of uneven topographic surfaces by the erosion of undisturbed or only gently warped strata also results in truncation. Disconformities preserve topography corresponding to all stages of the physiographic cycle ranging from undissected surfaces to near peneplanes. Sub-Pennsylvanian valleys in Illinois and western Kentucky were cut to depths of more than 300 feet but such valleys are exceptional. Buried relief resulting from erosion on the stable continental platform generally is more moderate. It rarely exceeds 100 feet. Few of the conspicuous intercyclical channels of the Illinois Pennsylvanian approach this figure. Disconformities may show many minor irregularities, but most of them are so subdued topographically that slopes are not apparent at ordinary outcrops. Details generally can be determined only by very careful measurement of formation thicknesses and elevations at many closely spaced localities.

Weathering

In addition to erosional irregularities, other results of subaerial processes may aid in the recognition of old land surfaces and the unconformities that mark their positions in the stratigraphic section. Most of these processes are included under the general designation *weathering* although chemical decomposition is relatively unimportant because sediments consist very largely of resistant minerals. Chemical weathering is more characteristic of igneous than of sedimentary rocks. Sediments overlying igneous rocks at some places do not show clear-cut lower boundaries. For example, the Fountain Formation (Penn.) in southeastern Wyoming consists of coarse reddish arkosic sands and sandy shales. Strata of these kinds locally grade downward without abrupt change in character through a poorly bedded zone to unstratified rubble that passes imperceptibly below into solid red granite. The oxidation of iron sulfides, probably related to former surface exposure, marks some unconformities and stains underlying strata red or brown. The concentration of manganese and black staining, as in some parts of Arkansas and Tennessee, also is believed to have been related to weathering of limestone while it formed part of an old land surface.

Some kind of soil probably developed on most land surfaces that persisted for an appreciable time. Old soils, however, are not commonly preserved as part of the stratigraphic record. Comparatively few good examples are known except beneath coals of the Pennsylvanian and at the surfaces of the earlier Pleistocene drift sheets. Soil is particularly vulnerable to destruction because it is loose material lying at the surface where it is constantly subject to erosion. Most regions achieve equilibrium between soil formation, by weathering, and erosion, but a change in conditions may result in the swift stripping away of the entire soil cover. Marine submergence of the land generally had this outcome. Advancing waves and shore currents removed all loose material from the underlying rock, transported it to some other location, and deposited it mixed with other sediments in such a form that its origin is rarely obvious. Consequently very few unconformities separating marine formations retain any trace of an old soil cover.

Remnants of old soils are more likely to be preserved in accumulations of terrestrial sediment. Soils require considerable time for their production, however, and they probably are absent from many non-marine formations because local aggradational and degradational processes were so continuously in operation that a well-developed soil had no opportunity to form. Pennsylvanian underclays have been recognized as old soils for many years. They are preserved either because they developed beneath accumulating peat or because peat swamps later provided a protective cover for them. In either case, they were produced mainly by the leaching of a low, flat, poorly drained land surface. If underclay development and peat accumulation were contemporaneous, both represent the same interval of time and no actual unconformity occurs. If on the contrary underclay formation antedated peat accumulation, the contacts between these beds record hiatuses and may be considered unconformities.

Pleistocene interglacial soils were produced by both leaching and chemical decomposition of glacial till. They have been widely preserved because of low topographic relief and poor drainage and because they probably were frozen when overridden by later glaciers. Useful information concerning the relative duration of the interglacial ages is furnished by measurements and comparisons of soil thicknesses.

Silicification and solution are other results of weathering that have affected surface rocks. They may furnish evidence of unconformity in limestone sequences. Disseminated silica present as sponge spicules or in other forms has been dissolved by ground water, transported for some distances, and redeposited. The concentration of silica at and near exposed limestone surfaces is not particularly obvious on casual inspection but it is so common that a secondarily silicified zone may aid in the identification of an overlying unconformity. Replacement of fossils or other limestone constituents such as oolites also has been common. Much chert probably was produced in this way.

Slowly circulating ground water is capable of dissolving much limestone, and gypsum and rock salt are even more readily soluble. The outcropping portions of many limestone formations are marked by sink holes, enlarged joints, and caverns. Limestone texture influences the manner in which solution acts. In formations consisting of fine-grained dense strata, solution is likely to be concentrated along joints and bedding planes, and relatively large openings may result. In coarsely crystalline or loose-textured limestone, solution generally is less concentrated and may be largely intergranular. This type of solution may result in the development of stylolitic seams or secondary porosity. Some important oil reservoirs have been produced in this way.

Solution of limestone is not necessarily restricted to a zone near the surface but may continue below the water table for hundreds of feet. The McCloskey oil "sand" of Illinois, a porous zone occurring at some places more than 150 feet below an unconformity at the top of the Ste. Genevieve Limestone (Miss.), is believed to be in part an example of secondary porosity. Also joints and sink structures that originated on an old land surface have been greatly enlarged after subsequent burial and as they grew they were filled with material gradually squeezed downward from above. This kind of solution has occurred in limestone and dolomite at many places beneath the sub-Pennsylvanian unconformity in Illinois and Missouri and possibly also beneath the sub-Chattanooga unconformity (late Dev.) near Chicago.

Basal Conglomerate

Many unconformities are overlain by conglomerates that form the base of a formation, and basal conglomerates are commonly cited as evidence of unconformity. Some conglomerates are so conspicuous that they have dictated the placement of formation boundaries. Others are much less prominent or less continuous. Some conglomerates of this kind would attract little attention if they did not occur at boundaries chosen for other reasons. Others have influenced the selection of a particular horizon as a stratigraphic boundary approximately where a boundary was desired. Conglomerates of these latter types actually may be no more significant than some others that have been little noticed because they lie in the midst of what has been considered to be a stratigraphic unit. The term *basal conglomerate* has very little meaning, therefore, beyond referring to a deposit constituting the lowest part of some recognized stratigraphic unit.

Many conglomerates mark interruptions in sedimentary deposition but others do not. Few of them provide much information concerning the magnitude or importance of a possible stratigraphic discontinuity. Pebbles of local derivation may indicate no more than very brief interruption of deposition and slight nearby erosion. For example, shale pebbles, common in many non-marine sandstones, generally were produced by temporary channel cutting. Limestone pebbles in limestone probably record a hiatus and at least brief exposure to the action of subaerial agencies. Lime sediments are not known to become sufficiently consolidated on the sea floor to develop material cohesive enough to produce pebbles. Such conglomerates may be differently evaluated. Thus, a thin limestone conglomerate noted at several places in western Illinois and northeastern Missouri within the St. Louis Limestone (Miss.) has never been considered particularly significant. Discontinuous patches of similar conglomerate in western Kentucky, however, are believed to mark a widespread but generally obscure unconformity between the Renault and Ste. Genevieve limestones (Miss.) which can be located at most places only by paleontologic means.

Residual gravel also is of local derivation, but if a conglomerate of this type is distinguishable, it generally can be accepted as evidence of noteworthy unconformity. Residual gravel was produced by local weathering and should contain no foreign pebbles. It is likely to overlie an uneven surface and be concentrated irregularly in depressions of that surface. Some reworking probably took place before sedimentary deposition was resumed and this material became a basal conglomerate, but the gravel was not moved far enough for the pebbles to become much worn and rounded. Chert gravel on a limestone surface may constitute a conglomerate of this kind. A good example occurs near St. Louis where angular chert fragments derived from the weathering of the underlying Mississippian limestone are locally present to a thickness of twenty feet or more at the base of the Pennsylvanian System. Chert pebbles also occur fifty miles to the south in the midst of the Mississippian limestone succession but some of them contain Devonian fossils. Obviously these pebbles were transported and they do not provide evidence of weathering or erosion at the place where they now are found.

Conglomerates consisting of foreign pebbles have different implications. In the course of transport such pebbles are much worn. If they have come long distances, only the harder, tougher, and less soluble types are likely to have survived. Conglomerates of this kind are most commonly associated with non-marine sandstones. They may overlie an unconformity but they are almost as likely to occur within a rapidly deposited detrital sequence where their irregular distribution is a reflection of the variability of local current action and not necessarily of any interruption of deposition. Conglomerates consisting of well-rounded quartz pebbles derived from some distant area are characteristic, for example, of lower Pennsylvanian sandstones in the southeastern part of the Eastern Interior basin. Most conglomerates of this kind were deposited from flowing water. Some may have been reworked by waves and currents along a beach. Otherwise the presence of foreign pebbles in a marine formation requires some special explanation. Such "erratic" pebbles generally are supposed to have been transported frozen in ice or entangled in floating vegetation.

Subsurface Evidence

All criteria useful for the recognition of unconformities in outcropping strata also are significant in the identification of subsurface unconformities. The records of wells and borings which provide most available information concerning buried formations, however, constitute such minute and isolated samples of the stratigraphic section that recognition and interpretation of evidence generally are difficult and uncertain. The kinds of records available for study are important. Cores furnish more and better information than cuttings, and electric logs are least satisfactory. For example, a conglomerate is readily recognizable in cores, but chert cuttings may have come from the pebbles of a conglomerate or from undisturbed concretionary nodules. Neither pebbles nor nodules would be revealed by an electric log.

Although well records generally provide less detailed information, they are superior to outcrops in one important respect: they present uninterrupted sections through complete formations. Thus, thicknesses of formations and variations in thickness are shown much more accurately than at most outcrops. Also compiled data from many wells may reveal the regional relations of unconformities very satisfactorily. The overlapping relations of strata at prominent unconformable surfaces and the features of topographic irregularity commonly can be traced with detail that is limited only by the distribution and proximity of wells.

Under most circumstances, unconformities are difficult to recognize in subsurface stratigraphic sections. Those known at outcrops may be traceable for long distances beneath the cover of younger formations, but identification of unconformities not known at outcrops is likely to be doubtful. The subsurface Mayes Formation (Miss.) of Oklahoma provides an example of uncertainty and disagreement. Some geologists believe that it is separated from the underlying Boone Chert (Miss.) by an erosional unconformity cutting across the older formation and thus overlapping it. Others interpret these same relations as the lateral intergradation of two characteristically different facies in strata of equivalent age.

MAGNITUDE AND MEASUREMENT

The magnitude or importance of an unconformity can be appraised in terms of (1) time, (2) thickness of missing strata, (3) differential relief resulting from erosion, (4) areal extent, (5) structural discordance, and (6) distinctness of development. The first four of these measures can be expressed to some extent numerically and are most readily compared. The last two, however, are wholly relative. All are independent variables. Although there are certain obvious possible relationships, as, for example, between time value and thickness of missing strata or between relief or angular discordance and distinctness, no one can be translated accurately into terms of another. Satisfactory measurement of an unconformity cannot be expressed in any of these terms alone. The importance of an unconformity can be evaluated only when all its features are considered in conjunction after each feature has been weighted in some way according to individual circumstances.

Time and Thickness of Missing Strata

The time that is unrepresented by strata at an unconformity consists of two parts whose differences must be recognized: (1) the time during which sedimentary deposition produced strata that were removed later by erosion and (2) the time during which there was no deposition and when erosion may have been accomplished (see Figure 158). The second time interval is

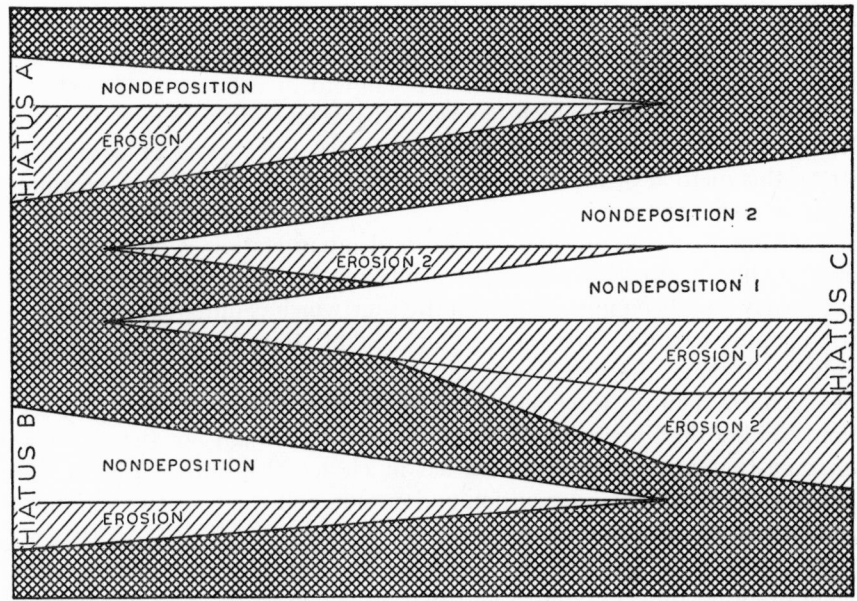

Figure 158.   Schematic diagram showing the relations of nondeposition and erosion to unconformities. Hiatus A and hiatus B are equal, but the relative importance of the non-depositional interval and depth of erosion are reversed. C represents the hiatus at a composite unconformity produced by the merging of two simple unconformities.

likely to have been more or less uniform throughout considerable parts of the area of any unconformity. The first interval, however, may have varied between wide extremes depending upon the depth of erosion at different places.

The most obvious or gross time value of an unconformity is indicated by the difference between the ages of the youngest underlying and oldest overlying strata. This may be an adequate local descriptive value, but it is not significant for geologic interpretation because the two time components are not differentiated. Identical unconformable relations might result from either (1) a long interruption of sedimentary deposition accompanied by little or no erosion or (2) rapid and deep erosion during a short interval of time. Ordinarily an unconformity furnishes little evidence concerning the relative importance of such events although some hints may be provided. Thus, secondary silicification suggests long static exposure, and a basal conglomerate of residual gravel indicates considerable local erosion. Also an unconformity may be composite and represent a complex history of depositional, nondepositional, and erosional episodes all of unknown relative duration.

Measurement of an unconformity in terms of the thickness of locally missing strata may be appealing to the imagination because strata can be visualized. This is, however, only an indirect means of expressing time relationships. It is imprecise because the standard of measure is the rate of sedimentary deposition, which has varied between wide extremes. In addition to uncertainties of lateral variation in the thicknesses of equivalent strata, this method of measurement shares all the uncertainties of measurement in terms of time.

The time that is significant for historical interpretation is only the time during which deposition actually was interrupted. This was generally less and it may have been much less than the time which is unrepresented in the stratigraphic record. Moreover the thickness of strata that is significant is only the thickness destroyed and removed by erosion. This is less and it may be much less than the thickness of the total locally missing stratigraphic section. Neither the time value of strata removed by erosion nor the thickness of strata that never were deposited has much actual meaning. Finally, the number of episodes of interruption and erosion and their relative durations and intensities are important.

Reconstruction of the series of episodes that contributed to the development of an unconformity must be based on details of the stratigraphic record preserved at other places. This involves interpretation based on the most probable of possibilities, and the results inevitably are uncertain. Also because conditions and happenings may have varied much from place to place, an interpretation which seems probable for one locality may not meet either the apparent or the unrecognized requirements at another.

Uncertainties inherent in the interpretation of unconformities can be illustrated by a consideration of overlap in the east central United States of the Chattanooga Shale (Dev.-Miss.) and its laterally continuous formations onto strata that locally are as old as the Middle Ordovician. The most obvious interpretation is as follows: (1) Gentle warping in late Devonian time uplifted the borders of the major sedimentary basins of the continental platform. (2) This was accompanied or followed by erosion which removed all Devonian, all Silurian, and some Ordovician strata from the most elevated areas. (3) Subsequently the region was submerged and black shale was deposited on the old land surface.

Alternatively the following explanation is possible: (1) General lowering of sea level in late Silurian time was accompanied by subsidence in the deeper basin areas. (2) Early Devonian deposition was restricted to these deeper basin areas; at the same time erosion was active on the emergent portions of the continental platform and all Silurian and some Ordovician strata were locally removed. (3) Rising sea level in mid-Devonian time resulted in general submergence and a relatively thin cover of Middle Devonian strata overlapped this old land surface. (4) Sea level fell again in late Devonian time and these thin deposits were eroded from most of the higher interbasin areas. (5) Near the end of the Devonian Period resubmergence occurred and black shale was deposited on the stripped surface of the old unconformity.

Both of these explanations account for the observed unconformable relations. The first postulates a major erosional episode in late Devonian time, and stratigraphic evidence on the east flank of the Ozark region seems to favor it. The other postulates a major episode of erosion in early Devonian time and a later minor one. It appears to be favored by stratigraphic evidence on the west flank of the Cincinnati arch and elsewhere.

Relief of Unconformable Surface

The differential topographic relief developed by erosion and subsequently buried at an unconformity can be determined fairly accurately from elevations corrected for irregularities resulting from later warping. The relief at a disconformity also is shown by the variable thickness of underlying beds providing that the unit measured was originally uniformly thick. Similar measurements of overlying strata generally are satisfactory if relief on the eroded surface is moderately low. If it is high, later sediments may have lapped upward on the slopes of topographic prominences or differential compaction may have compressed the thicker sediments deposited between these prominences so that differences between maximum and minimum measurements are too small.

The importance of an unconformity in terms of time or depth of erosion is not indicated by its topographic relief. If ancient land surfaces were exposed to the action of erosion long enough, they passed through a cycle of physiographic and topographic stages ranging from youth to maturity and finally to old age. Various stages of maturity may be distinguishable on the basis of the shapes of buried ridges and valleys and the steepness of their slopes. A very young uneroded surface, however, may be quite similar to one that is very old and peneplaned. Topography developed on Precambrian rocks shows that great relief is not necessarily indication of a longer period of erosion. For example, the generally featureless sub-Cambrian unconformity in Wisconsin is almost a peneplane and probably records a much longer period of erosion under stable conditions than does the sub-Cambrian unconformity in the Missouri Ozarks where a maturely dissected surface bears hills rising to heights of 1000 feet or more. Perhaps the Ozark region was elevated in early Cambrian time and erosion destroyed the old flat surface and produced a hilly region that was buried by Upper Cambrian sediments.

Structural Discordance

The gross measure of an angular unconformity in terms of either time or thickness of missing strata varies considerably from place to place because discordant structure brings different parts of the underlying stratigraphic sequence into contact with overlying beds. The maximum depth of erosion in dipping strata must have been greater and it may have been much greater than the thickness of beds locally destroyed. Relatively severe erosion was required to produce most angular unconformities. The duration of emergence and nondeposition, however, probably was generally much less than the time value of the locally missing strata. For all of these reasons, neither time nor stratigraphic thickness is a particularly useful measure of angular unconformities.

Angular unconformities are observed most commonly upon the flanks of disturbed areas. In one direction they are likely to be lost because later erosion has cut down to lower levels. In the other, structural discordance becomes less pronounced and unconformities pass into a stratigraphic sequence as inwedging strata separated by disconformities appear. This passage commonly occurs beneath a cover of younger formations where its details are not readily determinable. Consequently the integration of angular unconformities with the general stratigraphic record is likely to be difficult and uncertain within somewhat wide time limits.

In the interpretation and evaluation of angular unconformities, the diastrophic disturbance responsible for structural discordance generally overshadows all stratigraphic features. Such disturbance involved folding, possibly overthrusting, and uplift. These cannot be measured accurately by the structural features observable in any single area. A review of both stratigraphic and structural relations evident at such an unconformity throughout an extensive region, however, may serve to indicate the relative magnitude of the angular unconformity and the diastrophism that produced it.

Distinctness of Expression

Structural discordance, marked variations in topographic relief, or the presence of prominent basal conglomerates makes some unconformities conspicuous. Many disconformities, however, are more or less obscure. Some occur at sharp contacts between different kinds of strata, but such a contact is not a sure sign of an unconformity. Others bring beds of almost identical lithologic character into contact and these are very difficult to recognize. A widespread but relatively minor disconformity, for example, separates the Ste. Genevieve and Renault limestones (Miss.) in the lower Ohio Valley.

At a few places irregularities of this contact have been observed. At others there is a thin basal conglomerate of rounded limestone pebbles. Elsewhere this break in the stratigraphic sequence can be located only by paleontologic means.

Near Valmeyer in southwestern Illinois, the Mississippian disconformably overlies the Upper Ordovician (see Figure 155, p. 397). More than 1000 feet of strata present only 50 miles away are missing from the section here. This disconformity lies near the contact of reddish shaly and cherty Fern Glen Limestone with underlying greenish-brown Maquoketa Shale. There is an abrupt lithologic change but no clear physical evidence of any stratigraphic interruption. As seen in outcrop, the bedding is parallel in these formations and no irregularity at any bedding surface is apparent. The actual unconformity probably is marked by an obscure one-inch sandy zone lying about a foot below the limestone under a cover of reworked greenish shale.

This is a major unconformity—one of the greatest stratigraphic breaks known in the upper Mississippi Valley. It is an excellent illustration of the fact that the magnitude of an unconformity is not necessarily matched by its distinctness. In contrast erosional channels filled with Pennsylvanian sandstone (see Figure 178, p. 483) cut steeply and abruptly across underlying strata, but the stratigraphic discontinuities that are so clearly revealed are very greatly inferior in both time value and thickness of missing strata.

Areal Extent

In general a widely extensive unconformity is likely to be more significant than a local one because it records important changes in conditions throughout a larger area. It may not be more distinct, however, and it may represent a smaller time break in a stratigraphic sequence.

Submarine and non-marine unconformities which require no radical environmental change rarely are extensive. Local unconformities also may result from minor fluctuations in sea level or from local crustal warping. Extensive unconformities, on the other hand, generally are of the marine regressive-transgressive type. They record sea-level changes of sufficient magnitude to first drain and later flood large areas. If they can be traced or otherwise identified, they are especially important for correlation.

OBSCURE UNCONFORMITIES

Almost every report on areal geology records the existence of unconformities. A few are clear and unmistakable but many others are more or less obscure. Presumably most stratigraphic successions also are interrupted by an unknown but large number of unrecognized diastems. Perhaps the sediments preserve a much less complete stratigraphic record than is commonly believed.

Between the obvious unconformities and the great majority of diastems that resulted from interruptions too brief to be of much individual importance is an intermediate group of discontinuities. This includes various grades of obscure, dubious, and undetected unconformities. In total they may account for an appreciable fraction of geologic time in many regions. Their recognition and interpretation are important for both the subdivision and classification of stratigraphic units and the reconstruction of geologic history.

An understanding of the geologic record is clouded by both the postulation of doubtful unconformities based on inadequate or nonexistent evidence and the oversight or disregard of evidence pertinent to the actual presence of unconformities. A common tendency for geologists to accept orthodox formations as unequivocally natural rock units and a desire for precise boundaries leads to the postulation of unconformities on insubstantial evidence. Similar or even better indications of unconformability at positions that are not considered formation boundaries are likely to be ignored. The recognition of minor disconformities is not easy, and even after careful study the status of a possible disconformity may remain in doubt. In every case, however, evidence regarding the occurrence of a disconformity at some preferred position in the stratigraphic section should be judged on its own merits without preconceived ideas and without prejudice resulting from former interpretations or the opinions of others.

BIBLIOGRAPHY

Blackwelder, Eliot (1909), The valuation of unconformities, *J. Geol.*, vol. 17, pp. 289–299.
     The author compares and analyzes unconformities with respect to structural discordance, stratigraphic hiatus, and duration of erosion.
Blackwelder, Eliot (1914), A summary of the orogenic epochs in the geologic history of North America, *J. Geol.*, vol. 22, pp. 633–654.
     Three Precambrian and nine post-Proterozoic orogenies are recognized.
Chamberlin, T. C. (1909), Diastrophism as the ultimate basis of correlation, *J. Geol.*, vol. 17, pp. 685–693.
     Physical changes responsible for the evolution and migration of ancient faunas were the results of periodic diastrophic episodes.
Gilluly, James (1949), Distribution of mountain building in geologic time, *Bull. Geol. Soc. Amer.*, vol. 60, pp. 561–590.
     Evidence supporting the conclusion that orogenesis has not been clearly periodic is presented.
Grabau, A. W. (1936), Oscillation or pulsation, 16th Intern. Geol. Congr., Washington, Rept. vol. 1, pp. 539–553.
     Transgressions and regressions of the sea identify 10½ geologic systems of Paleozoic age.

Krumbein, W. C. (1942), Criteria for subsurface recognition of unconformities, *Bull. Am. Assoc. Petroleum Geol.*, vol. 26, pp. 36–62.
  Thirty-five types of evidence suggest unconformable relations.
Schuchert, Charles (1927), Unconformities as seen in disconformities and diastems, *Am. J. Sci.*, ser. 5, vol. 13, pp. 260–262.
  Many unrecognized stratigraphic discontinuities must occur because sediments are too thin to account for all geologic time.
Shepard, F. P. (1923), To question the theory of periodic diastrophism, *J. Geol.*, vol. 31, pp. 599–613.
  Orogenesis has been almost continuous from at least Ordovician to present time.
Stewart, W. A. (1950), Unconformities, in *Subsurface geologic methods*, 2nd ed., edited by L. W. LeRoy, Golden, Colo. School of Mines, pp. 32–51.
  Nomenclature, genesis, recognition, and importance of unconformities are considered.
Swain, F. M. (1949), Onlap, offlap, overstep and overlap, *Bull. Am. Assoc. Petroleum Geol.*, vol. 33, pp. 634–636.
  Several types of unconformable relations and the terms applied to them are discussed.
Twenhofel, W. H. (1936), Marine unconformities, marine conglomerates, and thickness of strata, *Bull. Am. Assoc. Petroleum Geol.*, vol. 20, pp. 677–703.
  The author describes the characteristics and discusses the implications of marine unconformities and conglomerates.
Wheeler, H. E. (1958), Time-stratigraphy, *Bull. Am. Assoc. Petroleum Geol.*, vol. 42, pp. 1047–1063.
  Emphasis is on nondepositional and erosional aspects of unconformities and their application to concepts of time and time-rock units of stratigraphy.

12

Stratigraphic Classification

CLASSIFICATION is necessary in stratigraphy for three reasons:

1. It furnishes a standard of reference with which rocks and geologic events everywhere can be compared.

2. It systematizes knowledge and provides a pattern that can be mastered without the necessity for remembering a great mass of intricate and more or less unrelated details.

3. It serves to distinguish different types of concepts that must be kept clearly separated from each other if confusion is to be avoided.

Classification provides a series of compartments or pigeonholes for arranging and relating information in a logical manner. The compartments are of different types and of different grades of importance. There are large and inclusive compartments, which are subdivided into smaller and progressively more exclusive ones. Chapter 3 explains how the larger stratigraphic units of one kind, the systems, came to be recognized.

Stratigraphic classification is certain to be arbitrary and artificial to some extent. It has no meaning or importance except as it promotes and clarifies the description, mapping, and interpretation of stratified rocks and aids in the reconstruction of geologic history.

ROCKS AND TIME

Stratigraphers are concerned with both rocks and time. These are very different but they are closely related to each other. A stratum, formation, or any other rock unit possesses a variety of physical characters: thickness, extent, composition, color, and so forth. It can be observed, measured, mapped, described, and analyzed. In addition such a unit required a certain time for its formation and, therefore, represents that particular interval of time. The rock unit preserves a record of some of the conditions that existed, some of the processes that were active, and some of the events that occurred during that time. Except for the most recent happenings in geologic history, it is the chief remaining record.

Thus stratigraphy deals with two quite different things but because these are related three concepts arise in their consideration: (1) rocks alone, (2) time alone, and (3) rocks and time in relation to each other.

Terms are needed for each of these concepts in order to make it clear which one is being referred to at any moment.

Concept of Rock Units

All terms introduced by the early stratigraphers were simply rock terms. They used the indefinite designations *formation, group, series,* or *system,* as well as some others, more or less indiscriminately. These are all common words familiar to everyone and originally they had no specific technical stratigraphic meanings.

The word *formation* was originally used in geology by Füchsel for a continuous succession of strata produced under similar conditions. It implied both origin and stratigraphic position. Werner employed this term, however, in a strictly petrographic sense. Thus all limestones or all sandstones constituted a formation which recurred again and again in a stratigraphic sequence. In contrast, he grouped strata into *suites*—mutually exclusive and successive stratigraphic units. In France *formation* had a similar meaning and *terrain* was used instead of *suite.* In England De la Beche employed *group* whereas Murchison used *system* in the latter sense. Von Humboldt reverted to the original meaning. He considered that a formation had both genetic and petrographic identity and also possessed time value (see p. 421).

Later stratigraphers appear to have chosen one of these words rather than another for a particular stratigraphic unit because it seemed appropriate. Thus *group* or *series* suggested greater lithologic heterogeneity than *formation* but less thickness than *system.* Usage was not consistent and until the latter part of the nineteenth century little need was felt for a graded sequence of terms each more inclusive than the last. Even some twentieth-century reports employ *group* and *series* in the old informal way that does not correspond to accepted modern usage.

Concept of Time Units

The time concept involved in historical interpretation was vaguely realized before the dawn of modern geology, as explained in Chapter 2, but its application to rocks in general was long delayed. This concept is evident, for example, in the early belief that marine fossils on the land owed their existence to Noah's flood. Much later, as the successive rock systems were distinguished, the subdivision of geologic time into corresponding periods was a natural and necessary development. Originally *period* had no particular significance beyond its common indefinite dictionary meaning, and other words such as *epoch, era, time,* and *age* were also loosely and indiscriminately used. Gradually, however, *system* and *period* acquired more restricted technical meanings and became more closely linked. Finally, the relations now recognized by geologists were established and corresponding systems and periods were identified by the same formal proper names.

DEVELOPMENT OF CLASSIFICATION

As field studies resulted in the progressive subdivision of rock units and advances in paleontology permitted more precise correlations, the need for a graduated stratigraphic classification became pressing. Slowly, and mainly by custom of usage, some terms gained precedence over others. Thus in the latter part of the nineteenth century a *series* came to be recognized as a subdivision of a *system* and a *formation* came to be accepted, in America at least, as the basic stratigraphic unit which, when combined with others, became part of a *group.* These were all rock terms but, insofar as rock units were considered to represent certain parts of geologic time, they were employed as time-rock terms also. At this stage little if any distinction was made between rock and time-rock terms.

Older Classification

Simultaneously with standardization of rock-unit classes, *epoch* came into use as a time term corresponding to any rock unit subordinate to system, and *era* was employed as a more inclusive time term comprising several periods. A few other terms gained less general acceptance. Until about 1940 most American stratigraphers recognized a dual classification of time and rock units, as shown in Table 13.

TABLE 13. Twofold Classification of
Geologic Time and Rock Divisions
Recognized Before About 1940

Time Divisions	Rock Divisions
Era	
Period	System
Epoch	Series
Epoch	Group
Epoch	Formation
	Member

Modern Classification

Increased stratigraphic and paleontologic knowledge eventually demonstrated that some well-established rock units do not everywhere represent even approximately uniform intervals of time. This is particularly the case in areas where formations or groups exhibit noteworthy lateral lithologic changes. Consequently such formations or groups are not time-rock units and their previous consideration as such had resulted in important inaccuracies of correlation.

This situation first became clearly apparent in New York and Pennsylvania where a great delta was built in late Devonian time. As the delta extended farther and farther westward a succession of different sedimentary environments gradually moved in that direction. They are represented by strikingly different types of rock (see Figure 159). In order to clarify these relations some geologists advocated the abandonment of the old time-transgressing formations or groups. In place of these lithologic units they attempted to differentiate a larger number of more or less local stratigraphic

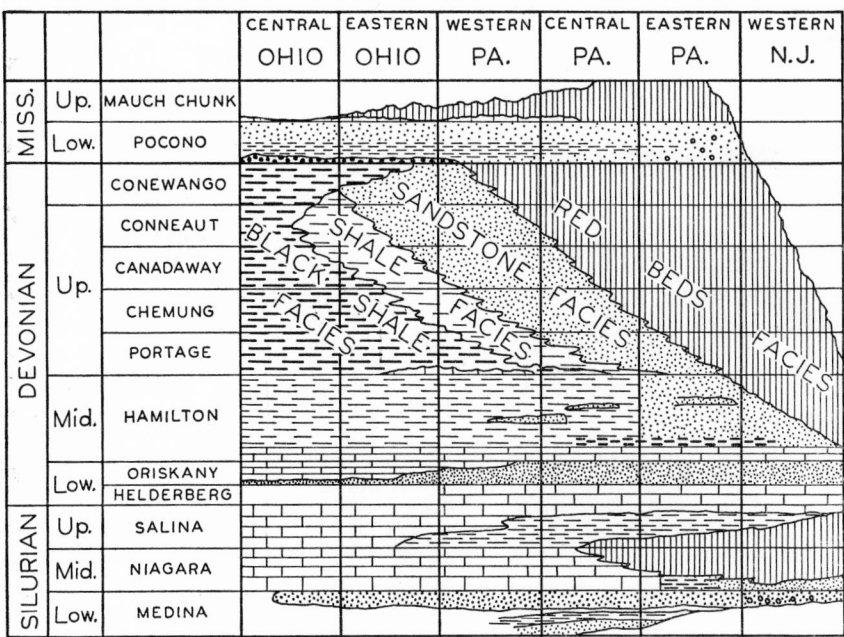

Figure 159. Diagram showing the time-transgressing relations of Upper Devonian strata in the Catskill delta. This figure illustrates the general lithologic characters of strata deposited simultaneously in several zones that gradually shifted westward. It does not indicate the relative thicknesses of these strata at different geographic localities (compare Figure 192, p. 502). (After Ashley, 1938, *Bull. Am. Assoc. Petroleum Geol.,* vol. 22, p. 422, fig. 5.)

units that were intended to be both rock and time-rock units. Their efforts resulted in many disagreements over details and by shifting attention away from the more general stratigraphic relationships they did little to improve understanding of the geology in that region.

Elsewhere the realization that rock units, as generally understood, are likely to be inconsistent when viewed in terms of time was very slow in coming. The confusion in some areas has been serious, and failure to distinguish clearly between rock units and time-rock units still persists in the thinking of some stratigraphers.

Operations in the California oil fields and studies of Tertiary sediments elsewhere in that state again focused attention on the stratigraphic complications arising from rapid and important lateral lithologic changes. Thick sediments that accumulated in several more or less separate basins had been subdivided in the usual way into lithologic units whose relations to each other proved to be irregular. When faunal zones were traced they were found to cross some formation boundaries. It became apparent, therefore, that these formation contacts are not time planes or unconformities, as some had been interpreted, but facies boundaries that had shifted laterally with the passage of time. In California, however, no attempt was made to substitute new rock units for old ones. Instead a new stratigraphic subdivision was worked out based on changes in the fossil faunas and without respect to lithologic characters. Thus a biostratigraphic classification was developed independent of but parallel to the lithologic classification. Comparison of the lithologic units with biostratigraphic units, which were considered to approximate time units closely, plainly revealed the variable time values of the rock units.

Careful analysis of these relations indicated the importance of making clear distinction between rock units and time-rock units, which are based on quite different methods of subdivision. To show these relations, the three-fold classification of Table 14 was developed and is now generally recognized.

TABLE 14. The Modern Threefold Classification of Geologic Time, Time-Rock, and Rock Units

Time Units Chrons	Time-Rock Units Chronoliths	Rock Units Geoliths
(Eon)		
Era	(Sequence)	
Period	System	
Epoch	Series	
(Age)	Stage	Group
	(Substage)	Formation
	(Zone)	Member
		(Bed)

This classification is not complete. Several obvious pigeonholes are not provided with distinctive names. Their lack, however, indicates that there is little need for them. Terms enclosed in parentheses are comparatively little used or require special explanation. *Group* was once recommended as a time-rock term corresponding to *era* but it has persisted as a rock term and now is generally so recognized.

RELATIONS OF STRATIGRAPHIC UNITS

Time and time-rock units are coordinate and directly comparable. For each time unit there is a time-rock unit and vice versa although all of them are not identified by distinctive names. Time units generally are defined by particular rock units as the latter are recognized at their type localities or in their type areas. At these places the rock units are time-rock units also. Elsewhere the time-rock units are limited by boundaries corresponding to the time planes that bound the rock units at their type localities. The time planes do not necessarily correspond with the lithologic boundaries of the rock units at other places. Together time and time-rock units provide a system of reference frames to which rock units are compared and by which they are correlated.

The larger time-rock units, systems and series, are represented by definite rock units at their type localities but not necessarily elsewhere. Boundaries of the rock units and the corresponding time-rock units may diverge when they are traced outward away from the type localities because the boundaries of rock units are likely to vary in time value from place to place. The smaller time-rock units, *stages*, *substages*, and possibly *zones*, may or may not be similarly related to definite rock units. Many of them are defined by paleontologic characters rather than by reference to any recognized rock unit. These are in part biostratigraphic units.

No direct comparison can be made between the various classes of rock units and the classes of time-rock units. A rock *group* may be more or less equivalent locally, in terms of included strata or represented time, to any one of the larger classes of time-rock units. Likewise a time-rock *stage* may be more or less equivalent locally to any but the smaller classes of rock units. The relations of actual rock and time-rock units at any place depend upon (1) local lithologic development, which generally is the basis of rock-unit classification, and (2) the locally recognized time classification, which is based on stratigraphy at the more or less distant type localities of appropriate time-rock units and correlation with the local stratigraphic section. Relations between rock and time-rock units are not necessarily constant and they are likely to vary from place to place.

Fossils rather than lithology are basis for the recognition of biostratigraphic units, which provide an important connecting link between rock units and time-rock units. Biostratigraphic units, like rock units, are objective. They are not defined by time but they furnish time limitations for the rock units that contain them. The relations of biostratigraphic units are not shown in Table 14 because these units are somewhat variable in nature and cannot be arranged in any formal classification.

The suggestion has been made that stratigraphic classification should be extended to include another category. This would consist of *rock-time* units, termed *geochrons*, corresponding to rock units just as time units correspond to time-rock units. The formal recognition of units of this kind almost certainly would be confusing and appears to be inadvisable. Such units would be of more or less variable time value or they would be indefinite because of inconstant boundaries. If reference to such units is desired the indefinite and informal term *time* can be appended to the geographic proper name of a rock unit.

Stratigraphers have not yet completely freed themselves from old confusions related to the failure to make clear distinction between rock and time-rock units. Rock units are the ones that are studied in the field and mapped. They generally are distinguished on the basis of their physical characters but the notion still persists to some extent that they should be time-rock units also. This view is impractical and has been the cause of considerable unnecessary difficulty. Paleontologists and stratigraphers with strong paleontologic interests have a particular weakness in this respect.

ROCK UNITS

No absolute distinction can be made between a group, a formation, and a member because the differences are only relative. A group consists of two or more formations, and a formation may be subdivided into members. The terms *lentil* and *tongue* also have been used for subordinate parts of formations. They are members of particular geometric form. Ordinarily the three-dimensional relations of minor rock units are not known well enough to justify the use of such descriptive terms although *tongue* may be convenient to express relationships where contrasting sedimentary facies integrade (see Chapter 14). With decreasing rank, rock units become both less inclusive and generally thinner but they also are likely to be more homogeneous lithologically.

In different areas or in the same area at different times the same sequence of strata may be designated a group, a formation, or a member. As more detailed stratigraphic studies are completed, more and thinner rock units generally are recognized. Old units are subdivided to form new ones. Thus a unit originally considered a formation may become a group and be subdivided into new constituent formations, or a member may become a formation and new more restricted members may be distinguished within it. History of the classification of the Madison Limestone (Miss.) in the northern Rocky Mountains provides a good example (see Figure 160). This rock unit, consisting of thick limestone that outcrops prominently on many of the mountain flanks, was originally described and mapped as a formation. Later it was divided into members and then in certain areas into formations, which were provided with new names. Thus the Madison Limestone has become a group in some areas although it is still considered a formation elsewhere.

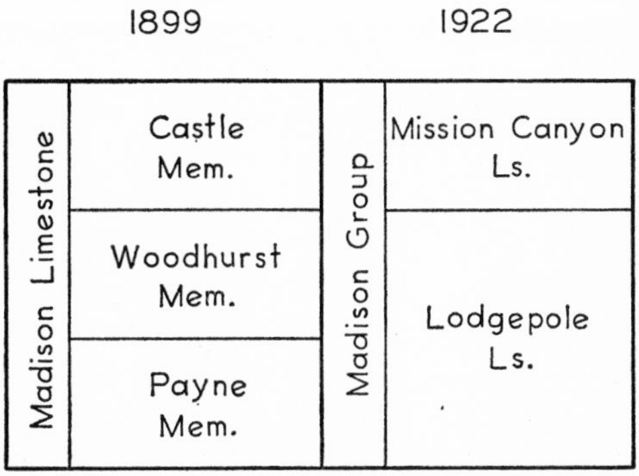

1899		1922
Madison Limestone	Castle Mem.	Mission Canyon Ls.
	Woodhurst Mem.	Lodgepole Ls.
	Payne Mem.	

(left column labeled "Madison Limestone"; right column labeled "Madison Group")

Figure 160. The Madison Limestone (Miss.) of the northern Rocky Mountains has been varriously subdivided in some areas, but the application of this name has not been restricted and its meaning has not been changed. In some areas the subdivisions are considered to be members of the formation. In others they are treated as formations and the Madison is a group. This illustrates the essential similarity of all rock stratigraphic units whose ranking is only relative.

Formations

The formation is the fundamental rock unit of stratigraphy. Its recognition goes back to the time of Füchsel and Werner, who defined each formation lithologically (see p. 415). Early in the nineteenth century von Humboldt, one of Werner's students, wrote, "The word formation denotes an assemblage of mineral masses so intimately connected that it is supposed they were formed at the same epoch and they present, in the most distant parts of the earth, the same general relations, both of composition and of situation, with respect to each other." This statement is not considered inappropriate today by many stratigraphers except for the belief that formations have universal extent.

The word *formation* in its original and still common general meaning is a noun of action implying origin. As applied to rocks it carries the idea of similar origin and, therefore, similar character. Many geologic definitions of formation have emphasized this idea. A committee of the International Geological Congress in 1882 expressed the opinion that "the word formation entails the idea of genesis and not that of time." Shortly after the founding of the United States Geological Survey a system of principles was drawn up to guide the stratigraphic work and geologic mapping of that organization. They provide that a formation is a "structural" but not a time unit of cartography discriminated primarily on the basis of its lithologic nature.

The so-called American Stratigraphic Code published in 1933 by a committee representing the Association of American State Geologists, United

States Geological Survey, Geological Society of America, and American Association of Petroleum Geologists states, "A formation is considered as a genetic unit formed under essentially uniform conditions or under an alternation of conditions" and it is not necessarily "of precisely the same age at different localities, and there may be marked differences in age from place to place." This is the view still held by most American stratigraphers.

The present American Stratigraphic Commission has stated that the "concepts of geologic time-spans properly play no part in differentiating or determining the boundaries of any rock unit" and "the definition of rock units should be independent of time concepts."

In accordance with the foregoing and other statements and definitions, the term *formation* embodies in varying degrees the following five ideas, which are not necessarily compatible: (1) similarity of lithologic composition, (2) similarity of genesis, (3) similarity of vertical relations to other formations, (4) similarity of time of deposition, and (5) practicality in mapping.

The emphasis on genesis, so conspicuous in the past, is theoretically attractive but it is misleading. Very few formations actually have been discriminated because of differences in origin except indirectly insofar as differences in composition indicate differences in origin. Emphasis on genesis is impractical because it does not furnish a sound basis for a primary stratigraphic classification of factual data. A genetic classification requires interpretation of facts. Interpretations are likely to be mistaken and are almost certain to be disputed or to change. Therefore, a genetic classification is practically sure to be unstable. Consideration of genesis is important and should not be ignored but genesis does not furnish a satisfactory basis for the definition of formations.

Discrimination of Formations

Every geologic formation was originally discriminated because someone believed it to be a convenient or significant rock unit for description, mapping, correlation, or interpretation. If other geologists shared this opinion, the formation gained more or less wide recognition. If not, it generally was ignored and may have been quickly and completely forgotten. The actual reasons that motivated the discrimination of individual formations have been extremely varied. Among other factors, the nature of the formation recognized and the boundaries selected for it have depended upon the following:

1. Kind of geologic work being done. A reconnaissance study probably would result in thicker and more generalized formations than would studies involving more detailed work.

2. Scale of mapping. Large-scale mapping would permit the recognition of thinner and more numerous formations.

3. Topography of mapped area. Mountainous relief probably would require the recognition of thicker and fewer formations.

4. Geologic environment. Monotonous sediments as in a geosynclinal region would be less readily divisible into thin formations than those of a platform area.

5. Adequacy of outcrops. Many and good outcrops provide a basis for better and more detailed discrimination of formations.

6. Purpose of investigation. Direction of attention to economic or structural problems or to general geologic history, and so forth, would influence both the types of formations recognized and the kinds of boundaries selected to separate them.

7. Chief interests of geologist. Paleontologic, sedimentologic, or other interests would exert much the same type of influence as the last.

8. Training and habits of geologist. Background and previous experience would influence later practice.

The association and joining together of strata in formations or other rock units imparts some degree of individuality to these units and implies that more or less important differences distinguish them from others. The particular characters providing formations with individuality cannot, however, be specified in any way. First and last a great variety of characters has been employed to define formations or to distinguish them from each other. Among them are:

A. Common geologic features
    1. Lithologic characters
    2. Vertical continuity of deposition
    3. Lateral continuity of similar strata
    4. Unconformable contacts or other boundaries
    5. Abrupt changes in lithology
    6. Sequential relations to other formations
    7. Presence and persistence of key beds
    8. Cyclic repetition of strata
B. Mass properties
    9. Chemical composition
    10. Mineralogic composition
C. Contained peculiarities
    11. Characteristic fossils
    12. Pebbles, oolites, chert concretions, etc.
    13. Direction of cross-bedding, ripple marks, joints
    14. Size and type of granular constituents
    15. Heavy minerals
    16. Varieties of clay minerals
    17. Insoluble residues
    18. Trace elements
    19. Concentration and chemistry of brines

D. Physical properties
    20. Color
    21. Degree of consolidation
    22. Resistance to weathering and erosion
    23. Topographic expression
    24. Nature of residual soil
    25. Porosity and permeability
    26. Electric properties
    27. Magnetic properties
    28. Transmission of seismic waves
    29. Radioactivity
    30. Thermoluminescence
E. Interpretative distinctions
    31. Genesis
    32. Age and time value

These characters are not of equal value. Not all of them have been employed in the definition of formations but all have been used for correlation and, therefore, for the identification of formations. All except the characters of category E, interpretative distinctions, are objective and less likely to be subject to differences of opinion than are the interpretative ones. Consequently, they provide better bases for a useful and stable classification of formations and other rock units.

Practical Formations

Long-standing emphasis by the United States Geological Survey on the practical nature of formations, based primarily on lithologic characters, has strongly influenced American stratigraphic practice. This appears to be one of the principal reasons for the relative preoccupation of most American geologists with rock units and particularly with formations. In the United States, formations are commonly correlated from place to place with other formations rather than with a standard time-rock sequence. European geologists, on the other hand, generally regard formations as more local and less important units. Thus they are more likely to make correlations directly with the time-rock sequence. These different attitudes are not entirely incompatible. Each possesses virtues as well as disadvantages. American practice may not make distinction between rock and time-rock units as obvious as is desirable. Nevertheless it is practical and well adapted to geologic investigations in a large country which exhibits almost endless variation in local stratigraphic development and relations.

Like many other common concepts, the formation cannot be defined in a way that will satisfy everyone. At present many geologists consider a formation to be, most simply, a *mappable rock unit*. This is not a real definition because it tells nothing about the formation. It is revealing, however, because it implies a practical quality considered by most American stratigraphers to be important.

In order to be practical, a formation should be identifiable and distinguishable from adjacent formations by virtue of reasonably obvious characters that can be recognized by any competent geologist. Most commonly, gross lithologic characters are relied upon although there are numerous exceptions. The ideal formation consists of a single distinctive kind of rock sharply set off from different but equally distinctive rocks both above and below. The black Chattanooga Shale (Dev.-Miss.) and its equivalents in much of the central United States is an almost perfect formation of this kind.

Formation Boundaries

The most desirable formation boundary is an unconformity that records an important and widespread break in sedimentary deposition. The separation of strata of distinctively different lithologic types by such an unconformity, in combination with a more or less uneven contact surface, makes recognition sharp and clear. This is by no means a common situation. Some unconformities that are considered to be important, like that between the Ste. Genevieve and Renault limestones (Miss.) in the lower Ohio River valley, may be inconspicuous and difficult to locate because adjacent strata are very similar lithologically. On the other hand, some locally prominent unconformities, such as most of those in the coal-bearing portions of the Pennsylvanian System, are discontinuous and relatively unimportant in terms of time. They may be ignored in favor of other types of contacts.

Most formations consist of a variety of strata. One type may dominate, or there may be a characteristic heterogeneity or combination of lithologic types. If such formations are sharply limited above and below, they are almost as practical as lithologically homogeneous formations. Many, however, grade into each other through a transitional zone where no sharp boundary can be drawn. The St. Louis and Ste. Genevieve limestones (Miss.) of the lower Ohio Valley are transitional. Their boundary is indefinite and may be drawn at different levels by different persons. If it is placed below the lowest occurrence of oolite, which is considered to be a characteristic feature of the Ste. Genevieve, the boundary is not likely to be the same as if it were located above the highest layer of sublithographic limestone, which is considered to be characteristic of the St. Louis.

In sequences of mixed sedimentary rocks, boundaries may be established at key strata or members. The Chilhowee Group (L. Camb.) of eastern Tennessee consists of three transitional formations described as being characterized by arkosic conglomerate below, shale in the middle, and quartzite above. Detailed field work has shown, however, that formations of these types are not readily distinguishable because of both vertical and lateral lithologic changes. In some areas the formation boundaries are now determined by two ridge-forming quartzite members without regard to other lithologic characters.

Key beds have been employed to subdivide some thick heterogeneous sequences into groups or formations having few if any distinctive lithologic differences. For example, coal beds have been chosen as boundaries within the Pennsylvanian System in Illinois, Indiana, Ohio, and elsewhere. The selection of coals as key beds reflects, in part at least, the economic aspects of much Pennsylvanian stratigraphic work in those states. Somewhat similarly, limestones have been utilized in Nebraska, Kansas, and northern Oklahoma and sandstones in southern Oklahoma and parts of the Appalachian region because strata of these kinds outcrop most commonly and are relatively easily traced from place to place.

Transitional formations and formations bounded by key beds are less satisfactory than more sharply contrasted lithologic units or those that are separated by persistent unconformities. The recognition of transitional formations is necessary, however, to reduce some thick stratigraphic sequences to units of useful magnitude.

Paleontologic Formations

Some well-established formations are identified by index fossils with more or less disregard of lithologic characters. Such fossils generally are considered to imply time equivalence but they do not prove it because these organisms may have followed a favorable but restrictive environment that shifted in geographic position with the passage of time. An example of a formation whose paleontologic features are particularly important is the St. Louis Limestone (Miss.) as now restricted, which includes the so-called *Lithostrotion* zone from Alabama to Iowa. Except in Iowa, where shale is present, the St. Louis consists almost exclusively of somewhat cherty limestone. It lies in the midst of a more inclusive limestone sequence and its limits are very rarely sharp or clear. Boundaries commonly are placed at zones of rather subtle lithologic change that are of different character in different areas. These are believed, however, to be fairly consistent with respect to time, and thus the St. Louis Limestone is much more nearly a time-rock unit than it is a distinct lithologic formation.

Some formations have always had a strictly paleontologic basis. Since the days of the earliest collectors, the neighborhoods of Burlington and Keokuk, Iowa, have been famous for their fossil crinoids. Although closely related, the species found at these places are not the same and some differences in the other fossils also have been noted. The Burlington and Keokuk limestones (Miss.) are defined by these faunas but slight differences in lithologic characters serve to differentiate them in their type areas and in nearby parts of Illinois and Missouri. Elsewhere, comparable lithologic differentiation is not possible and fossils are neither so abundant nor so well preserved. Consequently these formations cannot be distinguished clearly although local faunas observed here and there serve to identify the extension of zones believed to be of Burlington and Keokuk ages in a thicker limestone sequence known by other names.

Time-Transgressive Formations

Most definitions state that uniform time value is not the most important attribute of a formation, and most stratigraphers recognize that a formation need not be of exactly the same age everywhere. Many formations are bounded above by erosional unconformities at which variable thicknesses of formerly existing strata have been destroyed and removed, leaving remnants representing different spans of time from place to place. Also inequalities at underlying unconformities, particularly those involving the gradual onlapping of strata related to marine transgression, create inequalities in the time value of formations as they are developed in different areas. More important, however, are the relations occasioned by lithologic changes resulting from the lateral shifting of depositional environments within sedimentary basins.

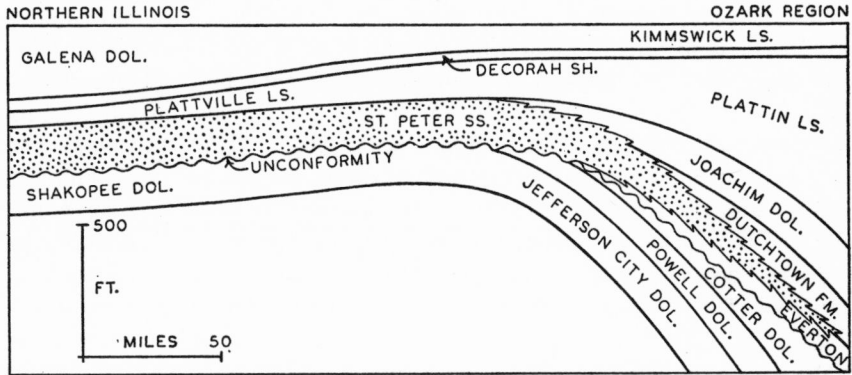

Figure 161. Generalized section showing stratigraphic relations of the transgressive St. Peter Sandstone (Ord.) to adjacent formations in the upper Mississippi Valley. The St. Peter overlaps the truncated edges of older formations unconformably and it also becomes progressively younger as it is traced northwards. As sand was deposited in the shoreward part of the advancing sea, sediments of different character simultaneously accumulated in the deeper offshore area. These sediments are recognized as constituting other formations distinguished lithologically from the St. Peter.

A few well-established formations appear to transgress time planes or time zones more or less notably. An excellent example is the St. Peter Sandstone (Ord.) of the upper Mississippi Valley, whose variable time value is related to both onlap and lithologic change (see Figure 161). This formation was deposited in the shoreward shallow part of a transgressing sea that gradually spread northward. It is a continuous lithologic unit easily identified by remarkably uniform characters. Deposition began to the south. As it progressed northward, different types of sediment were laid down contemporaneously in deeper water of the offshore zone. These have been distinguished as two other formations that overlie the St. Peter Sandstone to the south but are equivalent to it in age in parts of its northern range.

The time-transgressive nature of formations like the St. Peter Sandstone generally is not obvious. Relations of this type, however, are to be expected for many lithologic units whose deposition was related to near-shore or shallow-water conditions in either transgressive or regressive seas. Transgressive deposits are more likely to be preserved than are regressive ones because of the protective cover of vertically continuous later sediments. Most extensively developed marine sandstones probably are transgressive formations.

Time-transgressive and -regressive formations, more than most others, are likely to be good examples of true genetic units whose loci of accumulation at any time were determined by restricted physical environmental conditions. By virtue of similarity in both lithologic character and genesis, such formations meet two of the commonly recognized requirements of a formation.

The abandonment of several formerly recognized formations or groups that transgress time demonstrates the persistent failure of some stratigraphers to concede that formations, or other rock units, need not necessarily be time-rock units also. One of the best examples is furnished by the Upper Devonian deposits of New York and Pennsylvania in the famous Catskill delta region (see Figures 159, p. 417, and 192, p. 502). There early geologists mapped four thick formations that were distinguished lithologically and faunally. From the base upward they consist of (1) black shale, (2) greenish shale and sandstone, (3) gray sandstone and shale, and (4) red beds. These are now known to be regressive deposits marking concentric environmental zones where sediments accumulated simultaneously. The red beds, or Catskill Formation, are the deposits of a low alluvial fan on the eastern or landward side of the shoreline. The other formations are marine and mark zones of increasingly deep water to the west. As the delta grew, the shoreline moved westward and each zone, characterized by its own particular type of sediment and fauna, moved westward with it.

Each of these formations becomes progressively younger westward. They differ from the St. Peter Sandstone because none of the boundaries is an unconformity. They grade into each other through zones of lithologic change that are inclined to time planes. The preservation of shallow-water regressive strata is not common because ordinarily such sediments were soon exposed to erosive action above water level and destroyed. The Upper Devonian strata of this region have been preserved because gradual subsidence was accompanied by deposition of an expanding alluvial fan. Deposition exceeded subsidence, which accounts for the regressive relations of the lithologic units (see Figure 190A, p. 500).

In eastern Pennsylvania the red beds began to accumulate in Middle Devonian time. Slowly this environment moved westward until, several million years later, it reached the western part of the state. This important age discrepancy has been considered by some geologists to indicate that the Catskill red beds constitute an improper stratigraphic unit. Several proposals have been made to restrict the use of this name to strata that are equivalent in age to the red beds of the type Catskill region. If this were done, it would leave the younger western red beds without a designation. Consequently, a considerable number of subordinate red-bed units have been distinguished and named at various places where they were believed to constitute different age divisions of the old Catskill (see Figure 162). The other formations that un-

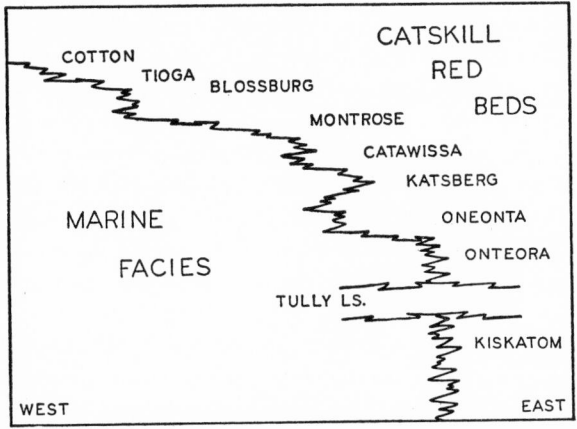

Figure 162. Diagram showing the order and relative stratigraphic and geographic positions of subdivisions of the Catskill Red Beds. Many of these were distinguished and named because of the desire to provide time-rock units in place of a lithologic unit that was recognized as being importantly time transgressive. (After Fisher, 1956, *J. Geol.*, vol. 64, p. 621, fig. 2.)

derlie the red beds have been treated in a similar way. As a result, the larger and more important stratigraphic relations of this delta region have been obscured by details that are poorly understood and differently interpreted by persons who are best acquainted with them. The old lithologic divisions remain, however, and they are still as well-marked rock units as they ever were.

Time-Transitional Formations

Several formations distinguished and mapped on the basis of their lithologic characters are more or less certainly known to include strata lying upon both sides of an important standard time plane. Formations of this type that are transitional across a systemic boundary introduce a problem in classification because, as units, they cannot be assigned to one particular system. They are awkward to handle, for example, in a table of formations summarizing a stratigraphic column or in the legend of a map. Although such difficulties are apparent, they are not overly important. They only reflect the failure of actual rock units in some areas to conform to a conventional classification based on stratigraphic relations observed in another region where the sequence of geologic developments may have been quite different. Nevertheless, the desire for complete conformity and an apparently irrational faith in the perfection of a system of classification, whose arbitrary qualities are imperfectly understood, have led many geologists to conclude that formations transitional between two systems are improper. Other formations crossing less important time planes may be regarded similarly but they have received much less notice.

The name Caney Shale was given originally to a thick lithologic unit in Oklahoma that was later determined to include strata of both Mississippian and Pennsylvanian ages. No distinctive separation of these parts that is consistent from place to place seems to be possible. Upper and lower divisions, however, came to be referred to respectively as the "Pennsylvanian Caney" and the "Mississippian Caney" as though these were two formations. Later the designation Springer Shale was adopted for the upper division and the name Caney was restricted to the lower one in spite of the expressed opinion that only the upper division outcrops at the Caney type locality.

The Amsden Formation of Wyoming and Montana is a lithologic unit consisting mainly of red beds that separates undoubted Mississippian and Pennsylvanian formations. The age of the Amsden is disputed because its few fossils are not certainly diagnostic. It has been referred entirely to one system or to the other by different persons. The lower part contains fossils at some localities that probably are Mississippian, and most geologists believe that Pennsylvanian strata are included in its upper part. The desire to separate the Amsden into two parts at the Mississippian-Pennsylvanian time plane and efforts to adjust nomenclature accordingly have resulted in much confusion (see Figure 163). Thus, in Montana the proposal has been made to restrict usage of the name Amsden to the lower or Mississippian portion and to expand the overlying Quadrant Sandstone to include the upper or Pennsylvanian part of the Amsden. In Wyoming, on the other hand, restriction of the name Amsden to the upper, supposedly Pennsylvanian, strata has been favored and expansion has been suggested of the Sacajawea Formation, which originally included only some beds uncertainly identified as Middle Mississippian, for the underlying older portion. Regardless of how this problem may finally be decided, the original Amsden Formation remains a well-marked and useful rock unit. The systemic time plane believed to divide it probably never can be determined accurately.

A black-shale unit of wide distribution in central North America occurs between fossiliferous Devonian and fossiliferous Mississippian strata. Termed Chattanooga Shale at many places, it also has a variety of other local names. This shale is almost unfossiliferous except for different kinds of conodonts which mark three zones. Agreement is general that the lower zone is of late Devonian age and the upper zone is early Mississippian, but the age of the middle zone is disputed. The middle zone extends much farther to the west than do the others. The lower zone appears to wedge out in that direction, whereas the upper one grades laterally into different types of strata. In the upper Mississippi Valley and in some other areas, the middle zone succeeds a profound unconformity and overlaps onto strata as old as Middle Ordovi-

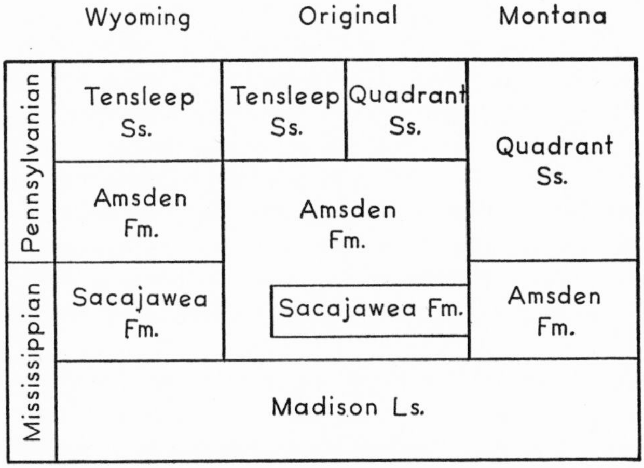

	Wyoming	Original		Montana
Pennsylvanian	Tensleep Ss.	Tensleep Ss.	Quadrant Ss.	Quadrant Ss.
	Amsden Fm.	Amsden Fm.		
Mississippian	Sacajawea Fm.	Sacajawea Fm.		Amsden Fm.
	Madison Ls.			

Figure 163. Diagram showing the results of uncoordinated attempts to subdivide and restrict a lithologically well-characterized rock unit that is transitional across an important time-stratigraphic boundary.

cian. Mainly because of these physical relations, the middle zone is generally considered to constitute the base of the Mississippian System in those areas. In the northern Appalachian basin, however, where no similar unconformity occurs, the middle zone commonly has been referred to the Devonian. Efforts have been made to subdivide this black-shale sequence at a few places but the results do not seem to be particularly satisfactory or very practical. Regardless of its age and the zones present in typical lithologic development, this black shale is an excellent distinctive and generally sharply limited rock unit.

It would be convenient if all major time planes of the standard stratigraphic classification coincided with the lithologic boundaries of rock units because the age assignments of formations and their correlations would be simplified. Many of them do not, however, and attempts to achieve conformity by the subdivision of time-transitional formations have not been uniformly satisfactory or acceptable. Many such formations are largely unfossiliferous. Even if fossils do occur they are likely to be transitional between older and younger faunas and, therefore, indecisive. It is not reasonable to expect time planes to be revealed equally everywhere by lithologic or faunal changes. Consequently, it would be surprising if some locally well-characterized formations did not cross them. The transitional nature of such formations does not impair their local usefulness or make them less important in the interpretation of geologic history if their true time relations are correctly understood.

Conclusions

In actual practice, almost any succession of strata distinguished for almost any reason can be designated a formation. Recognized formations vary from very thick to very thin. Some, like the Fern Vale Limestone (Ord.) of the Mississippi Valley, are so thin they cannot be mapped without exaggeration. Some are lithologically homogeneous, like the Chattanooga Shale (Dev.-Miss.), but others consist of extreme mixtures of lithologic types, like many Pennsylvanian formations. Some are sharply defined by unconformities or abrupt changes in lithologic character; others are gradually transitional, like the St. Louis and Ste. Genevieve limestones (Miss.). All were originally distinguished for some reason that appeared to be good to the person who first described and named them. For one purpose a formation may be a logical and useful unit and for another it may not be. No one can surely decide for others that any particular formation is misconstituted. He can judge only for himself whether or not it is well suited to his purposes. The more useful a formation proves to be for many persons, the more likely it is to win a generally recognized place in the system of stratigraphic classification.

The variously constituted formations currently recognized in any area are variously distinct and variously useful. Some are such well-marked lithologic units that almost any geologist would have defined them in exactly the same way. Others may be so unclear that they appear to owe their recognition to historical circumstances generally related to the authoritative opinion of some influential person. Such formations are accepted more by force of habit than by reason.

Formations defined solely by lithologic characters and others defined by fossils or key beds may occur in the same stratigraphic section. Association of some formations that are nearly or quite similar in age everywhere and others that are not is likely to result in conflict and confusion. The apparent difficulties, however, exist mostly in the minds of geologists who fail to recognize the important distinctions between such formations and who seek to force all into a single pattern. If every formation were simply a convenient lithologic unit, a sound and uncomplicated basis for most local geologic studies would be provided and problems of detailed local and more general regional correlation could, in the main, be made the responsibility of experts with paleontologic knowledge. This is not the case, and stratigraphers must make the best possible use of many long-recognized formations of different types. The facts that these formations have gained wide acceptance and have been used for many years are evidence that they are not without merit even if they are not perfect in every way.

Many problems are involved in the subdivision of a stratigraphic section into its constituent formations. No set of rules can be drawn up that will overcome all difficulties. Thoughtful consideration of desirable objectives, however, may aid in avoiding many difficulties. The following principles can be suggested:

1. Formations should be recognized as practical rock units.

2. Very thick and very thin formations are undesirable but no limits as to thickness should be set.

3. Formations should, if possible, be defined by lithologic characters.

4. Lithologic distinctions may be supplemented by paleontologic and structural, that is unconformable, relations.

5. If faunal or structural features take precedence over lithologic characters, they should be unusually clear and unequivocal.

6. Formations should be so constituted that their boundaries are as sharp and distinct as possible.

7. If key beds are employed as boundaries, they should be persistent and easily identifiable.

8. It is desirable that formations be of approximately the same age throughout their extent, but no actual or implied time limits should be set.

9. Formations should not be redefined or have their boundaries changed without more than ordinarily good reasons, and redefinition should make them more distinct and practical rock units than they were before.

10. Well-established formations should not be abandoned even if they contravene the foregoing principles unless a much clearer and more practical stratigraphic subdivision can be substituted.

Groups and Members

Rock units either more or less inclusive than formations share many of the qualities of formations and in general they are considered and treated similarly. Ideally a *group* consists of two or more successive and contiguous formations. A formation, however, is not necessarily subdivided into *members*.

Groups

Recognized groups have originated in two ways. First, any one or more of the same considerations that influence the association of strata to produce a formation may lead to the joining of formations in a group. Second, the upgrading of an old formation, and generally its subdivision into new and more restricted formations, may result in the recognition of a group. For purposes of distinguishing between them, these types may be termed *synthetic* (resulting from combination) and *analytic* (resulting from separation) groups respectively.

Formations generally have been combined in synthetic groups because of the close relations of their fossils, their lithologic similarity, or the occurrence of important unconformities that serve as punctuation marks in an otherwise more or less uninterrupted stratigraphic sequence. Grouping on the basis of fossil faunas has been most common. Groups so formed are rock units in their type areas, but if they are traced and identified elsewhere by their fossils, rather than by their constituent formations, they possess the qualities of biostratigraphic and perhaps time-rock units and should be considered stages. The subordinate position of a group to a series in the old twofold classification demonstrates the unconscious merging of rock and time-rock concepts at this point. Many so-called groups of the synthetic type require careful scrutiny to determine whether they are proper rock units or, instead, time-rock stages or substages.

The formations of an analytic group are much more likely to share lithologic similarities. These groups, therefore, generally are more distinct lithologic units than most synthetic groups and there is less possibility of their being confused with time-rock units.

Some currently recognized groups have been created by the upgrading of old formations without subdivision into new subordinate formations. This rather anomalous procedure has resulted because old rock units were considered too thick or too inclusive to be proper modern formations. Examples are provided by the Pottsville, Allegheny, Conemaugh, and Monongahela divisions of the Pennsylvanian in the northern Appalachian region. These units were formations for many years but now they commonly are accorded the rank of group or series.

The constituent formations of a group may change from place to place as different treatment of its content warrants. Reasonable continuity, however, should mark its top and bottom. In this way a group resembles a formation.

Members

Comparatively unimportant and more or less local rock units included within formations are designated members. If desirable, such units can be distinguished and named but a formation need not be subdivided and most formations are not.

A formation may be subdivided into several parts and only some of these, considered to be of particular interest for one reason or another, be designated members. Thus, it is not necessary for named members to be successive and contiguous, and a formation may consist in greater or less part of undifferentiated and unnamed strata. The Pennsylvanian System in the eastern United States contains many coal beds, limestones, and prominent sandstones that have been named and are best considered members. Other intervening strata, mainly shaly, remain undivided and unnamed.

Tongues are wedge-like, lithologically identified rock units, that interfinger with complementary tongues of different lithologic character in a zone of lateral facies change. They are in a sense members of one formation that occur in stratigraphic sequence with members of another formation.

Lentil is a little-used term for minor rock units or members of distinctive type that wedge out lenslike in all directions. Because detailed observations of such minor units generally are restricted to cross sections of strata in zones of outcrop, truly lenticular shape rarely can be determined.

Beds

The smallest rock stratigraphic unit is a bed. As this word has been employed, difficulty commonly is encountered in determining whether somewhat formal or informal usage was intended. *Bed* also has been used in the sense of *zone*, and in the plural it may be equivalent to *member*.

BIOSTRATIGRAPHIC UNITS

Biostratigraphic units consist of strata that are defined and identified solely on the basis of their fossils and without respect to any lithologic characters. They are wholly objective and not dependent upon interpretative considerations of the type used to determine the boundaries of time-rock units. In this way they are similar to rock units. Biostratigraphic units differ from rock units, however, because (1) they are not adapted to arrangement in a hierarchical succession and (2) their mutual relations generally are more variable and more complex.

Although time concepts are not directly involved in the recognition of biostratigraphic units, the latter commonly have been considered to approximate time-rock units closely if not to correspond to them exactly. For this reason, the important distinction between biostratigraphic units and time-rock units has not been emphasized sufficiently. Many persons, both stratigraphers and paleontologists, have mistakenly regarded most biostratigraphic units as special types of time-rock units.

The dependence of time-rock units on detailed paleontologic correlation increases as descent is made in the scale from larger to smaller units because greater precision is required for their recognition. Thus the relations of time-rock units and biostratigraphic units appear to become closer, and a gradual merging of corresponding concepts commonly occurs. At the lowest level of time-rock classification, a practical distinction actually is difficult to make.

Zones

The word *zone* is used in geology with a variety of meanings. In a geographic sense it is a relatively narrow area or band such as the zone of outcrop of a dipping formation. In a strictly geologic sense it refers broadly to almost any distinctive body of rock which is narrow in one dimension in comparison with its much greater extent in others. Thus sheared zones occur along many faults, and contact metamorphic zones are recognized adjacent to many igneous intrusions. In stratigraphy this word is used for strata of more or less restricted thickness which are differentiated from others in some specific way. Among the many kinds of zones are shaly zones, fossiliferous zones, impervious zones, and ferruginous zones.

Zone also has been adopted as the formal designation of a biostratigraphic

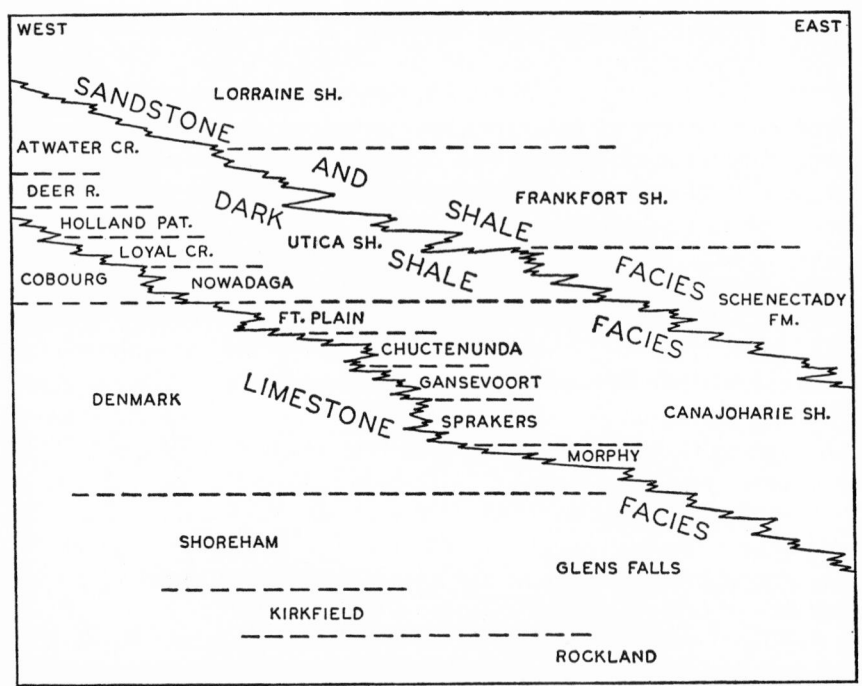

Figure 164. Schematic diagram showing the time relations of some of the Middle Ordovician stratigraphic units in New York. Before the discovery of intertonguing facies only a small number of lithologic formations was recognized. Later numerous supposedly time-rock units were named in an attempt to clarify these relations. Many of the units cannot be differentiated lithologically and are identifiable only by their fossils. This is particularly true of the dark-shale units containing distinctive graptolites. These, therefore, are biostratigraphic zones. They should not bear geographic names like those of rock or time-rock units but should be designated by the names of their most characteristic fossils. (After Fisher, 1956, *J. Geol.*, vol. 64, p. 620, fig. 1.)

unit. It was first used consistently in this way by Oppel in the mid-nineteenth century for subdivisions of the Jurassic System in Germany. Since then biostratigraphic zones have been employed extensively in stratigraphic correlation. Before clear distinction was made between rock and time-rock units, successive zones defined by fossils commonly were considered to represent definite intervals of geologic time.

Theoretical considerations have led to the recognition of a variety of biostratigraphic units, most of which are termed zones of one kind or another. Few of these units are of much practical value in stratigraphy except for purposes of correlation (see Figure 164). Also complete agreement regarding their relationships has not been reached and the nomenclature applied to them is rather confused. The principal types of biostratigraphic units that can be recognized are (1) range zones, (2) assemblage zones, (3) abundance zones, and (4) barren zones.

The presence of fossils in biostratigraphic zones was determined by (1) local biologic environment, (2) possibilities of migration or introduction from other areas, (3) local extinction, and (4) evolutionary change. Only the last has broad time significance. In addition to these factors, the absence of characteristic zonal fossils may have resulted from the destruction of the remains of organisms. Consequently it is unlikely that many zones of broad extent approximate time-rock units as closely as has been supposed.

Range Zones

The simplest kinds of biostratigraphic units are range zones. These consist of all beds included between the lowest and highest stratigraphic occurrences of any fossil, which may be a species, genus, or some larger taxonomic group. A range zone can be recognized for every variety of fossil. Range zones generally are not successive units because almost every one is overlapped by others. Also one range zone may include several other range zones of lesser thickness. In actual practice, however, only a few zones that are considered to be especially significant or useful are selected for more or less formal recognition. Generally an effort is made to choose nonoverlapping zones that succeed each other without important gaps.

An objective range zone includes no strata at any place that lie above or below the actual local range limits of the zonal fossil. Because these limits are likely to have been controlled by environmental conditions that were not uniform from place to place, the boundaries of such zones rarely coincide with time planes. Two objective range zones may overlap in one area and be separated in another by strata that belong to neither of them. Range zones of this kind generally have been termed *teilzones*. This name also has been used, however, in a restricted way for the strata through which a fossil ranges at a particular locality. In this sense a teilzone has no lateral extent and a fossil may have a different teilzone at every place where it is found.

A range zone also may be considered to consist of all strata deposited during the existence of the zonal organism, whether or not fossils are present in the strata. A zone of this kind has been termed a *biozone*. It is the only kind of biostratigraphic unit that is necessarily a time-rock unit and it possesses all of the subjective qualities of other time-rock units. A teilzone of the first type is equivalent, from place to place, to some variable fraction of the corresponding biozone as thus defined.

Assemblage Zones

Assemblage zones consist of strata characterized by the occurrence of two or more particular zonal fossils, commonly species or genera. They do not necessarily include beds equivalent to the entire range of any fossil and, therefore, they generally are more restricted stratigraphically than many range zones. Three kinds of assemblage zones are (1) overlap zones, (2) negative association zones, and (3) faunal or floral zones.

Overlap zones are defined by the associated occurrence of two zonal fossils whose stratigraphic ranges are not the same but overlap or, more rarely, by a larger number of fossils that may substitute for each other. The boundaries of such zones correspond with the boundaries of the range zones of these fossils. Thus the boundary of one range zone marks the upper limit and the boundary of the other marks the lower limit of the assemblage zone.

A *negative association zone* is that part of the range zone of one fossil that is neither overlapped below by the range zone of a second fossil nor overlapped above by the range zone of a third. It is marked by the presence of one zonal fossil and the absence of others. Assemblage zones of these two kinds, that are selected for recognition, generally succeed each other without overlap.

Faunal and *floral zones* are characterized by the occurrence of an entire fauna or flora or at least by its principal members. Although other assemblage zones may overlap, faunal or floral zones do not, but they may recur at different positions in the stratigraphic section. These zones are more directly related to particular combinations of environmental conditions than any others.

Abundance Zones

The term *epibole* has been understood to mean a biostratigraphic zone consisting of strata supposedly deposited during the *acme* or *climax* but not the entire existence of some particular organism. In practice the greatest number of preserved fossil specimens commonly has been considered to identify the acme. Except within small areas, however, such a zone is not likely to represent a closely restricted identical interval of time. An epibole is equivalent to a small and probably variable fraction of a corresponding range zone.

Barren Zones

Even in highly fossiliferous strata, some layers or successions of beds are likely to lack whatever zonal fossils are employed for biostratigraphic differentiation. Barren zones may occur within range zones and assemblage zones but these rarely require separate recognition. Barren strata, however, may intervene between fossiliferous zones of any kind. If barren zones are thin, boundaries between adjacent fossiliferous zones may be placed arbitrarily at some intermediate position. If barren zones are thick, they may be considered important enough to be distinguished in a zonal succession.

Zonules

Although *zonule* has been used with other meanings, it ordinarily designates a subdivision of a major zone. It is more or less equivalent to *subzone*, and this is the only example of hierarchical order in biostratigraphy. Thus an epibole might be regarded as a zonule or subzone within a range zone. Also a zonule might be characterized by fossils of less stratigraphic range or more restricted association occurring within a thicker zone defined by other fossils.

Horizon

The word *horizon* commonly has been used as a synonym of zone particularly with reference to the occurrence of vertically restricted fossils or as a synonym of *bed* in connection with some lithologically restricted type of rock. Thus there are such expressions as "the *Stricklandinia* horizon" in the Kankakee Dolomite (Sil.) of northern Illinois or "the red shale horizon" above Coal No. 6 (Penn.) in central Illinois. The word *horizon* means most strictly a bounding line or limit. It is properly used by geologists in a comparable way to identify a plane or a position within a stratigraphic succession. It is correct to refer to "the horizon of Coal No. 6" at places where this coal is missing. Use of *horizon* instead of *zone* dulls its meaning and is unnecessary. The American Stratigraphic Code and subsequent declarations by the American Stratigraphic Commission recommend that horizon be recognized as being without thickness.

TIME-ROCK UNITS

Time-rock units are actual successions of strata bounded by theoretically uniform time planes regardless of the unit's local lithologic development. Time planes generally are located as closely as possible on the basis of fossil evidence.

It has been pointed out that time-rock units as defined in theory and as recognized in practice are not the same. True or ideal time-rock units are bounded by time planes that are independent of all material things. The actual or practical time-rock units of stratigraphers, however, depend upon whatever material evidence is available to approximate the ideal, and the term *para-time-rock units* has been suggested for them. It is important that this difference be understood, but no change in terminology seems necessary because the practical time-rock units are the only ones with which stratigraphers actually deal.

Systems and Series

Geologic systems are time-rock units based on stratigraphic successions present in certain historically important areas (see Chapter 3). Although they are considered to be of world-wide applicability, there are large regions where the recognition and separation of some of the standard systems has not been accomplished satisfactorily.

Systems are divided into series whose type areas commonly have been chosen because the stratigraphic sections there are fully developed, fossiliferous, and well known as the result of early and continuing study. Generally the recognized series are of less than world-wide extent but they should be applicable throughout large major stratigraphic provinces. Thus, in different continents or in different parts of the same continent a system may consist of different series that are not equivalent to those in other regions. For example, the dominantly terrestrial Pennsylvanian System of the Appalachian region and the mainly marine Pennsylvanian of the Mid-Continent area are differently divided into time-rock units and in neither of these regions are the units the same as those recognized in Europe (see Figure 165).

In their type areas, the major time-rock units are rock units also. Their boundaries correspond with the boundaries of certain locally developed formations. The boundaries that are chosen generally are important structural or faunal breaks or more than ordinarily conspicuous changes in lithologic characters. Many of them are unconformities.

Away from their type areas the major time-rock units may not be so distinctive or easily separated. An unconformity may become less important or disappear entirely, and a considerable thickness of strata may occur that is intermediate in age between the uppermost and lowermost parts of contiguous units as these are represented in the type area. In America, the European Carboniferous System has been divided into two new systems because of stratigraphic relations in the central United States. There a great unconformity separates the Mississippian and Pennsylvanian systems, which are quite differently developed lithologically. At this unconformity the Pennsylvanian overlaps 5000 feet or more of strata ranging in age from late Mississippian to Middle Ordovician (see Figure 259, p. 635). There is no comparable unconformity in the Appalachian region or any similar lithologic change and a considerable thickness of transitional strata probably occurs. This is the type area of the Pennsylvanian. Because the greater part of the transitional beds are non-marine, they generally are assigned to that system.

Fossils are rare and of little service in separating the Mississippian from the Pennsylvanian in the Appalachian region. Even if they did occur abundantly, they probably would not be certainly diagnostic because the fossils

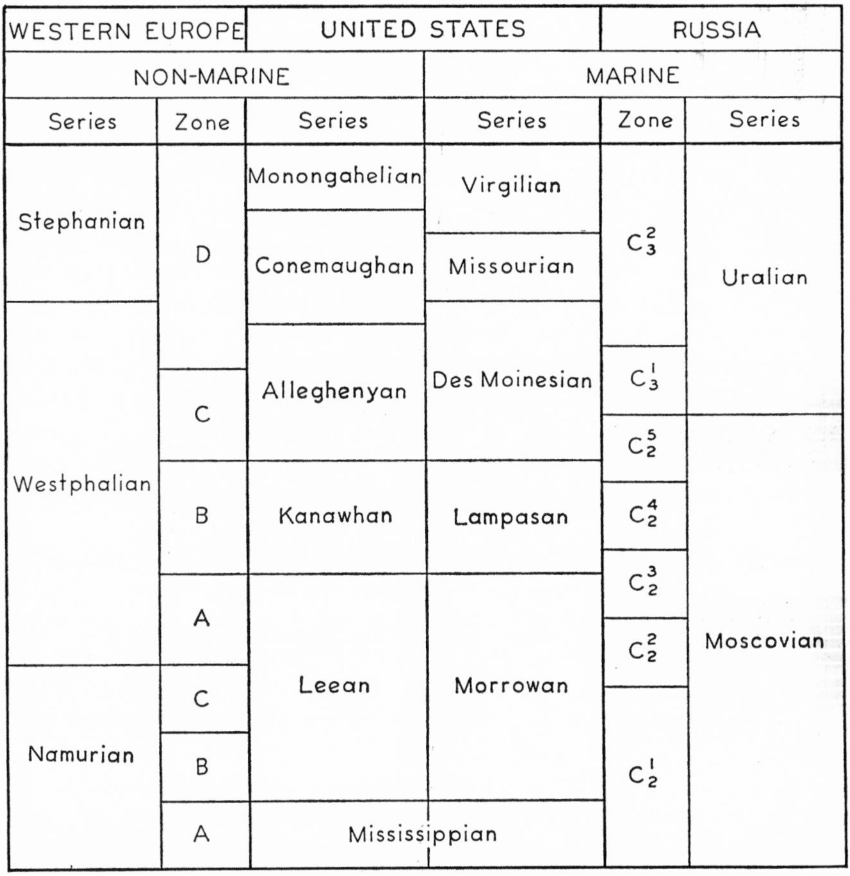

WESTERN EUROPE		UNITED STATES		RUSSIA	
NON-MARINE			MARINE		
Series	Zone	Series	Series	Zone	Series
Stephanian	D	Monongahelian	Virgilian	C_3^2	Uralian
		Conemaughan	Missourian		
Westphalian	C	Alleghenyan	Des Moinesian	C_3^1	
				C_2^5	
	B	Kanawhan	Lampasan	C_2^4	
	A			C_2^3	
		Leean	Morrowan	C_2^2	Moscovian
Namurian	C				
	B			C_2^1	
	A	Mississippian			

Figure 165. Correlation diagram showing the approximate time relations of the principal time-rock divisions of the Upper Carboniferous in Europe and America. Different regional lithologic developments and differences in the fossils useful for correlation in marine and non-marine strata have resulted in the recognition of different classifications. (After Pennsylvanian Correlation Chart and other sources.)

of transitional beds are likely to be themselves transitional and fail to indicate a sharp division between older and younger faunas. In such situations, a time-rock boundary may be placed for convenience at the boundary separating two local formations. On the other hand, the boundary may be believed to lie somewhere within a local formation such as the Caney Shale or Amsden Formation. A time-rock boundary of either type probably would no more than approximate a true time plane because almost certainly it would vary somewhat in time value as it is recognized from place to place. Different conclusions may be drawn by different persons who do not agree about the interpretation of fossil or other evidence. Also, the discovery of new evidence may result in the shifting of a time-rock boundary that is supposed to correspond with a standard time plane.

Unconformities commonly are favored as time-rock boundaries outside of type areas if they occur at approximately the proper stratigraphic position because they record the kind of physical break that many geologists expect or at least desire at these major boundaries. The unconformity below the black shale in the Mississippi Valley has been mentioned (p. 408). Another example is the unconformity beneath the Edgewood Limestone (Sil.) of southern Illinois (see Figure 166). The Girardeau Limestone below this unconformity contains a fauna that has been referred to the Silurian by some paleontologists, but this formation is completely transitional downward into strata of Ordovician age.

Systems and series are large units representing long intervals of time. They contain strata that accumulated in a great variety of environments. From zone to zone and from place to place, therefore, they tend to carry a considerable variety of fossil assemblages. Quite different index fossils may be relied upon for the identification of these larger units in different areas. Because the stratigraphic ranges of these fossils are not identical, the boundaries based upon them also are unlikely to have exactly the same time value everywhere.

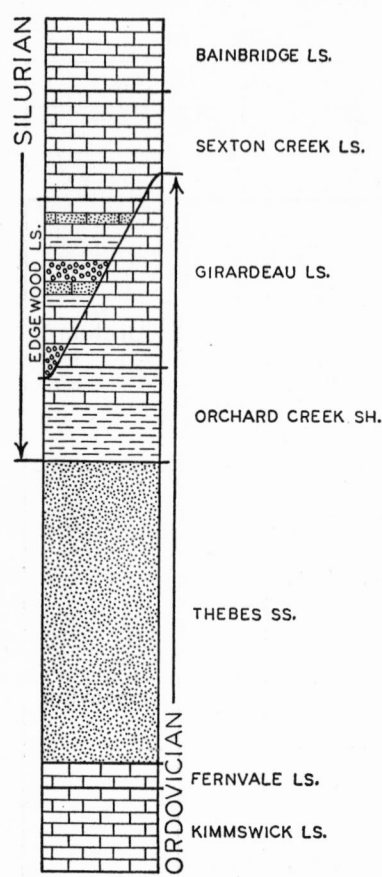

Figure 166. Generalized columnar section showing the relations of formations near the Ordovician-Silurian boundary in Union and Alexander counties of southern Illinois. The boundaries between these systems as interpreted from physical and fossil evidence do not correspond.

Even in some type areas, the proper boundary between two time-rock units may be disputed, as at some places where characteristic and contrasting faunas grade into each other or are separated by faunas that are quite different from those occurring above and below. Good examples are furnished by the Warsaw and Ste. Genevieve limestones (Miss.) in the upper Mississippi and lower Ohio valleys (see Figure 167). For faunal or other reasons, these for-

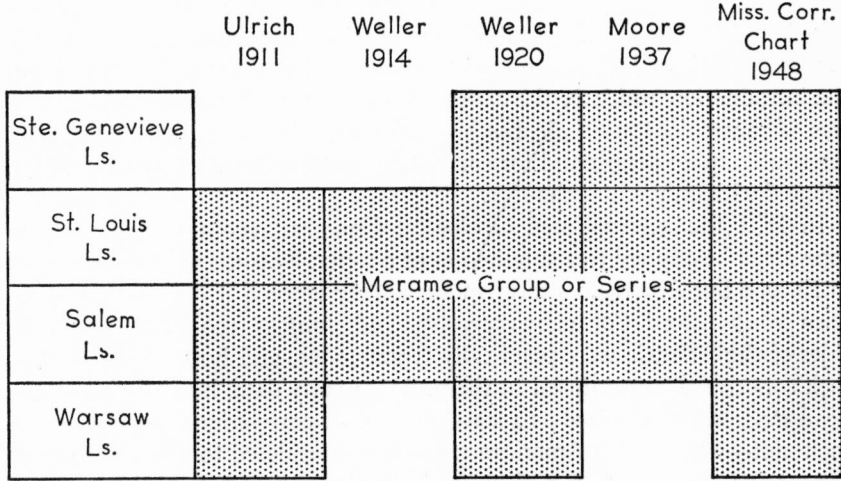

Figure 167.   Opinions regarding the boundaries of the Meramec Series (Miss.) have differed considerably. Both paleontologic and physical evidence have been cited in favor of different views. Until agreement is reached concerning the formations that constitute this series in the type area, important discrepancies in the classification of equivalent strata are certain to occur elsewhere. Before distinction was made between the rock and time-rock qualities of groups and series, these terms were used more or less indiscriminately.

mations have been both included and excluded at the bottom and top respectively of the Meramec Series. Of course if disagreement of this kind occurs in type areas, considerable discrepancies of interpretation may be expected elsewhere.

Stages

Biostratigraphic zones are combined to form larger units termed stages or substages. Stages built up in this way may also be considered biostratigraphic units, but objective in their formation is to create time-rock units. These larger units provide a means of long-range correlation extending far beyond the ranges of their constituent zones, which are not likely to persist throughout large regions. Such stages are built up by observing the lateral extent and overlapping relations of individual zones. Thus, as one zone becomes unrecognizable, another closely adjacent one takes its place and correlation is carried on. Stages constituted in this way generally possess some unifying paleontologic characteristics and, therefore, may themselves be considered zones of a grosser type.

The concept of stages as time-rock units was originated in Europe by d'Orbigny in 1850. He sought to sweep away confusions resulting from both lithologic and faunal facies changes in Jurassic rocks and to substitute paleontologic units of universal extent for local formations characterized by varied faunas. He believed that each of the stages that he recognized recorded first the introduction and later the extinction of a complete fauna. This concept was, of course, far too simple, but his stages proved to be so useful in organizing stratigraphic details and for correlation that eventually they were widely adopted with only minor changes.

In 1881 the International Geological Congress recommended that the term *stage* be applied to a subdivision of a series. This usage became general in Europe but American stratigraphers largely ignored it and employed the term *group* instead. For many years *stage* and *group* as recognized on the two sides of the Atlantic were practically synonymous, and both rock and time-rock concepts were confused in them. At an early date, however, the European *stage* was recognized as a standard unit of correlation—that is, a time-rock unit—whereas the American *group* was considered to consist of several formations—making it a rock unit. This difference in emphasis probably was related to the ease of Mesozoic stratigraphic zonation in Europe, based on ammonites, and progress in Paleozoic stratigraphy in America, where detailed correlations generally are less clear.

Few fossils other than the ammonites make possible the recognition of world-wide stages. Except in the Mesozoic systems, therefore, different stages have been set up in different regions. Successive stages are based on somewhat similar fossils, but different systems of subdivision based on different kinds of fossils may be recognized in the same region. Such units are comparable in rank but they need not correspond because noteworthy changes in different fossil groups are not likely to occur at the same stratigraphic levels. Thus in California, the upper half of the Cenozoic has been divided into unrelated foraminiferal, molluscan, and mammalian stages (see Figure 168).

In America, *stage* was first used consistently for Pleistocene subdivisions (see p. 499). Later this term became more familiar in connection with the correlation of post-Paleozoic strata with standard European sections. Recently it has been used increasingly by Paleozoic stratigraphers in the United States as conflicts in rock and time-rock concepts have been resolved. Complete distinction between *stage* and *group*, however, does not yet appear to have been accomplished.

	Mammalian Stages	Molluscan Stages	Foraminiferal Stages
Pleistocene	Rancholabrean		Upper Hallian
	Irvingtonian	Tulare	Lower
Pliocene	Blancan	San Joaquin	Wheelerian
	Hemphillian	Etchegoin Jacalitos	Venturian Repettian
	Clarendonian	Neroly Cierbo Briones	Delmontian Mohnian
Miocene	Barstovian	Tremblor	Luisian Relizian Saucesian
	Hemingfordian		
	Arikareean	Vaqueros	Zemorrian

Figure 168. Stages of the Upper Tertiary and Pleistocene recognized in California. Time-rock stages generally are defined and identified by their fossils. Different types of fossils are likely to suggest different stratigraphic subdivisions, and several different systems of subdivision may be useful within a single area. In the molluscan column are the names of formations, which lack the -ian ending that is proper for time-rock units. Many of the other names also are derived from formations and they are a possible source of confusion (see Figure 171, p. 456). (After Savage, 1955, *Univ. Calif. Publ. Geol. Sci.*, vol. 31, p. 7, fig. 3.)

TIME UNITS

Geologic time units are intervals that followed each other like hours of the day or days of the month. Unlike these familiar examples, however, geologic time units are not of equal length. The time scale presented in Chapter 1 shows that some periods were of very much greater duration than others (see p. 15). Thus there is no standard length for any of the classes of geologic time units. An epoch of one period, like the Cambrian, may have exceeded another entire period, such as the Jurassic.

The time assigned to any time unit is determined by the rocks of the corresponding time-rock unit. Time and time-rock units are directly comparable and for each unit of one kind there is a corresponding unit of the other although all classes of them have not been named.

Most time units, except possibly some of the smallest, are incompletely represented in local stratigraphic sections. Most rock sequences are interrupted by discontinuities of nondeposition or erosion, and many rock units are separated by unconformities. In contrast, there were no interruptions of geologic time. The flow of time has been continuous and there can be no intervals between successive time units. When one unit was completed, the next one immediately began. Thus the rocks of two systems, as locally developed, may be separated by an unconformity that represents a time hiatus, but no corresponding interval separates the periods represented by these rocks.

The recognition of instants in time separating successive geologic time units poses a theoretical and abstract problem which parallels the practical problem of recognizing consistent and uniform time-plane boundaries between time-rock units in areas of continuous deposition. There were such instants and there are such planes. Their proper placement involves consideration of both actual rock sequences and time correlations. The identification of a stratigraphic horizon with a standard time plane, or vice-versa, is an ideal that is very rarely or never attained outside of a type area. Differences of opinion regarding observations are to be expected and revisions of interpretations are certain to be made. As stratigraphic and paleontologic knowledge increases, however, the ideal should be approached more and more closely.

Pennsylvanian-Permian Boundary

A good example of some of the theoretical and practical problems involved in the separation of two major time units, and the selection of a stratigraphic horizon or time plane separating time-rock units with which it corresponds, is furnished by the boundary between the Carboniferous, or Pennsylvanian, and the Permian systems. Presumably, this boundary should be determined by conditions and relations existing in the type areas of these systems. The type areas, in England and northeastern Russia respectively, are 2000 miles apart and the Permian System is developed in different facies in these two areas. Also, an important unconformity occurs beneath the Permian beds in England but deposition probably was essentially continuous in Russia.

Murchison originally placed this boundary at the base of a succession of sandy strata in Russia. He differentiated the Permian System because of the occurrence of fossils different from, and younger than, fossils similar to Carboniferous forms known in England. Later, limestone underlying the sandy beds was discovered to contain a distinctive fusulinid ("*Schwagerina*") fauna which also is younger than any English Carboniferous fauna. The question then arose: Should the "*Schwagerina*"-bearing strata be assigned to the Carboniferous or to the Permian? Some Russian geologists lowered the basal Permian boundary because the "*Schwagerina*" beds were not included in the typical Carboniferous. Others retained Murchison's original boundary

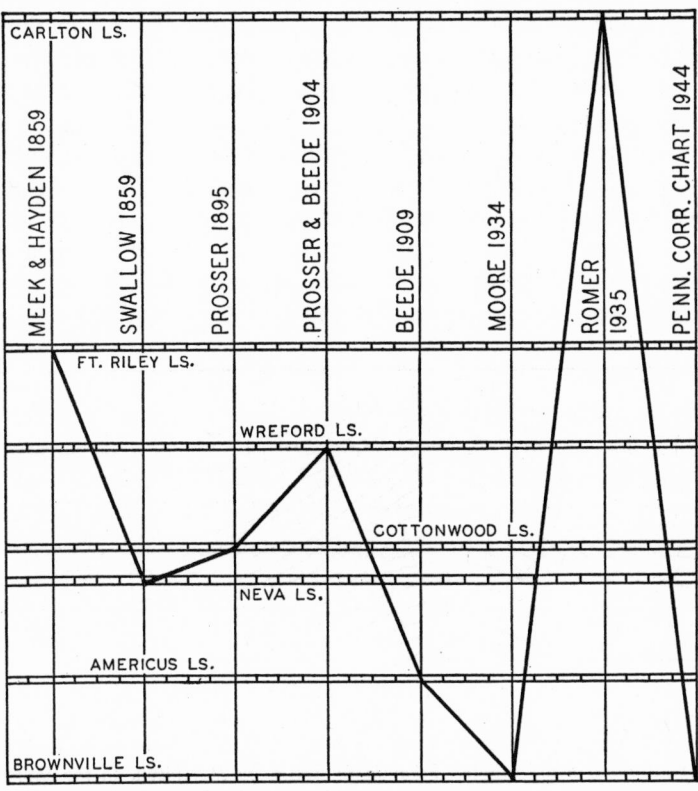

Figure 169. Chart showing different positions advocated for the Pennsylvanian-Permian boundary in the Mid-Continent region. (Modified from Moore, 1940, *Bull. Am. Assoc. Petroleum Geol.*, vol. 24, p. 300, fig. 3.)

because the "*Schwagerina*" beds were not included in the typical Permian or because they believed that this boundary coincided with an important unconformity.

Since the discovery of Permian fossils in the Mid-Continent region of the United States in 1857, there has been much uncertainty over the proper position of the Pennsylvanian-Permian boundary as shown in Figure 169. At various times and by different persons, this boundary was placed at several different levels within a stratigraphic interval of about 1000 feet. The stratigraphic section in this region is essentially complete, and fossil zones adjacent to the boundary in both Russia and the United States have been correlated confidently. The boundary as recognized in America has varied because (1) the "*Schwagerina*" beds were considered to be basal Permian by some and uppermost Pennsylvanian by others, (2) the lower limit of the range of "*Schwagerina*" was not determined accurately, and (3) various more or less persistent thin limestone members were selected as key beds to mark the base of the Permian. More recently, an inconspicuous and perhaps local unconformity was chosen as a supposedly more significant boundary in part of the Mid-Continent region.

American participants in the 1937 International Geological Congress visited the Russian Permian region. They concluded that the sandy beds and the "*Schwagerina*" limestone are at least partly transitional facies of similar age and further that the supposed unconformity separating them reflects structures produced by large organic reefs which rise above the general level of the "*Schwagerina*" limestone (see Figure 170). The Americans favored

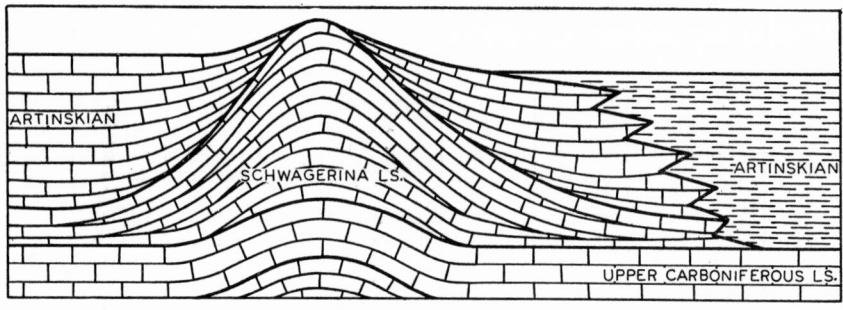

Figure 170. Greatly generalized section showing the relations of the "*Schwagerina*" Limestone to the Upper Carboniferous and Permian in Russia. These strata, which include large organic reefs, are younger than the original Carboniferous of England but they were not included in the original Permian of Russia by Murchison. In the United States strata of equivalent age are generally considered to be lower Permian. Compare with Figure 181, p. 489. (Data from Dunbar, 1940, *Bull. Am. Assoc. Petroleum Geol.*, vol. 24, pp. 237 to 281, and other sources.)

inclusion of the "*Schwagerina*" beds in the Permian System, which corresponds to American practice, as the best solution to the long-standing Carboniferous-Permian boundary problem. If general agreement with this conclusion should be reached, which seems possible, an example will be provided of an important stratigraphic and geologic time boundary whose accepted position has been strongly influenced by evidence derived from a region far from the type locality of either system.

Larger Time Units

The *period* is the principal unit of geologic time and all other units are combinations or subdivisions of this one. An *era* corresponds to a time-rock *sequence* of several periods, such as the Paleozoic or Mesozoic, but the latter term has not gained general acceptance. Above this, all geologic time is divided at the beginning of the Cambrian period into two *eons*, Cryptozoic and Phanerozoic, but these terms are little used. *Epoch,* formerly employed for any time unit smaller than a period, is now recommended as the equivalent of *series* only.

Minor Time Units

Age is recognized as the time term corresponding to the time-rock *stage*. It has the disadvantage of being a very common word that is certain to be used with other less restricted meanings. Beneath this, a considerable variety of terms has been proposed to correspond to zones (see p. 436). The ending *-chron* has been used for several of them. Thus *faunichron, biochron,* and *teilchron* correspond to *faunal zone, biozone* and *teilzone* respectively. None of these terms has gained more than very limited or local usage. The time term corresponding to epibole is *hemera*. This is a geochron (see p. 420) rather than a true time unit because an epibole, which marks the "climax" of a species as indicated by abundance of fossil specimens, does not represent the same time everywhere.

GLACIAL STRATIGRAPHIC UNITS

Glacial geologists generally are more concerned with physiographic features than with stratigraphic successions. They distinguish and map till plains, moraines, shorelines, and outwash channels rather than such lithologic units as till sheets and loess blankets. Rock units comparable to those that play such an important part in conventional stratigraphy, therefore, have been little emphasized. Attention has been directed principally to the relations of topographic forms, glacial deposits, and the physiographic processes that responded to the rhythmic alternation of glacial action and interglacial repose.

In Pleistocene glacial studies the time element is predominant. Local time divisions are unequivocal and not dependent upon the more or less arbitrary grouping of rock units as in conventional stratigraphy. Each principal time division, that has commonly been termed a *stage*, is defined in any area as either a glacial or an interglacial time unit and the sedimentary or rock unit corresponds with it exactly. Therefore, the rock divisions appear to be time-rock units rather than simple rock units.

The glacial stage has been considered a time unit and not a time-rock unit as in conventional stratigraphy. This usage of the term has been so general and was so firmly established by long practice that the American Stratigraphic Code of 1933 made special provision for its recognition. No comparable or corresponding terms were generally adopted for glacial time-rock or rock units.

Careful analysis shows that the glacial time division *stage* is actually a geochron and not a true time unit comparable to those recognized in conventional stratigraphy. This is so because it has not been defined with respect to uniform time planes. As glaciers slowly advanced or retreated, the time values of glacial and interglacial stages varied from north to south and thus the interstage boundaries transgress time planes. Consequently the glacial stage, as recognized in the past, is a variable unit. Also, the glacial rock divisions actually are rock units and not time-rock units.

Attention directed to these discrepancies has resulted in suggested action intended to bring Pleistocene glacial classification into conformity with general stratigraphic practice. Thus, *age* is substituted for the old time term *stage*, and the latter is employed here also as a time-rock term. In addition, *age* is defined not in terms of local glacial or interglacial conditions but by time planes. Theoretically, these are selected so that they bracket the active lives of the glaciers that periodically pushed southward. Such time planes are not clearly revealed by any of the features of the glaciated areas. Presumably, however, glacial expansion and contraction was accompanied by corresponding fall and rise of sea level. Therefore, the standard glacial and interglacial ages presumably should find their most accurate expression in coastal regions where episodes of regularly fluctuating sea level alternated with episodes of stable strand-line conditions.

Such a reform seems logical but it may be unnecessarily impractical. It substitutes ideal indefinite units for those that are real and evident. There is no certainty that Pleistocene glacial geologists will recognize such changes.

Ordinarily, the deposits of a glacial stage, as this is now recognized, do not require stratigraphic subdivision into vertically successive units. Instead, different types of material, such as till, outwash, lake beds, and loess of more or less equivalent age accumulated in different areas. Each is characteristic of a different and distinctive environment, and little or no intergradation occurs. Consequently, the interrelations of rock units of different lithologic character are fairly simple and glacial stratigraphy is not complicated by many of the problems that arise in connection with the study of older strata.

BIBLIOGRAPHY

Arkell, W. J. (1933), *The Jurassic System in Great Britain*, Oxford, Clarendon. Chapter 1 is a historical account of the development of the concept of biostratigraphic and time units in the Jurassic System.

Arkell, W. J. (1956), *Jurassic geology of the world*, Edinburgh, Oliver and Boyd.

Chapter 1 includes explanations of stage and zone.

Ashley, G. H., and others (1933), Classification and nomenclature of rock units, *Bull. Geol. Soc. Amer.*, vol. 44, pp. 423–459; *Bull. Am. Assoc. Petroleum Geol.*, vol. 17, pp. 843–863; reprinted, 1939, *ibid.*, vol. 23, pp. 1068–1088; Stratigraphic nomenclature in reports of the U.S. Geological Survey, by Geologic Names Committee, U.S. Geol. Surv., 1953.

This is the so-called American Stratigraphic Code.

Chadwick, G. H. (1935), Summary of Upper Devonian stratigraphy, *Am. Midland Natur.*, vol. 16, pp. 857–862.

The many locally named stratigraphic units are briefly related.

Chadwick, G. H. (1936), History and value of the name "Catskill" in geology, N.Y. State Museum Bull. 307.

This report documents stratigraphic and nomenclatoral confusion in the Catskill Mountains.

Cooper, C. L. (1948), Lower boundary of Mississippian System, *Bull. Geol. Soc. Amer.*, vol. 59, pp. 102–104.

New Albany (Chattanooga) conodont correlations are summarized.

Dunbar, C. O. (1940), The type Permian: Its classification and correlation, *Bull. Am. Assoc. Petroleum Geol.*, vol. 24, pp. 237–281.

The nature of the sub-Permian boundary in Russia is discussed.

Frye, J. C., and Leonard, A. B. (1953), Definition of time line separating a glacial and interglacial age in the Pleistocene, *Bull. Am. Assoc. Petroleum Geol.*, vol. 37, pp. 2581–2586.

Physical and time relations of glacial units are explained.

Hedberg, H. D. (1948), Time-stratigraphic classification of sedimentary rocks, *Bull. Geol. Soc. Amer.*, vol. 59, pp. 447–462.

Consideration is given to stages in relation to other stratigraphic units.

Hedberg, H. D. (1954), Procedure and terminology in stratigraphic classification, Comptes rendus, 19th Intern. Geol. Congr., fasc. 13, pp. 205–233.

This is an excellent presentation.

Hedberg, H. D. (1958), Stratigraphic classification and terminology, *Bull. Am. Assoc. Petroleum Geol.*, vol. 42, pp. 1881–1896.

The more fundamental aspects of stratigraphic classification are reviewed.

Kleinpell, R. M. (1938), *Miocene stratigraphy of California*, Tulsa, Am. Assoc. Petroleum Geol.

This includes an extended discussion of Miocene biostratigraphy.

Mallory, V. S. (1959), *Lower Tertiary biostratigraphy of the California Coast ranges*, Tulsa, Am. Assoc. Petroleum Geol.

The strata are zoned by foraminifera and ecologic interpretations are made.

Miser, H. D. (1934), Carboniferous rocks of Ouachita Mountains, *Bull. Am. Assoc. Petroleum Geol.*, vol. 18, pp. 971–1009.

Age and correlation of Caney Shale are discussed.

Moore, R. C. (1940), Carboniferous-Permian boundary, *Bull. Am. Assoc. Petroleum Geol.*, vol. 24, pp. 282–336.

A history of Pennsylvanian-Permian boundary placement in the Mid-Continent region is presented.

Powell, J. W. (1890), Conference on map publication, in Report of the director, U.S. Geol. Surv., 10th Ann. Rept., pt. 1, pp. 56–79.

An explanation of stratigraphic classification and nomenclature adopted by the U.S. Geological Survey is given.

Schenck, H. G., and Muller, S. W. (1941), Stratigraphic terminology, *Bull. Geol. Soc. Amer.*, vol. 52, pp. 1419–1426.

First presentation of the time-rock concept appears in this article.

Sutton, A. H. (1940), Time and stratigraphic terminology, *Bull. Geol. Soc. Amer.*, vol. 51, pp. 1397–1412.

The older twofold classification is explained.

Teichert, Curt (1958), Some biostratigraphic concepts, *Bull. Geol. Soc. Amer.*, vol. 69, pp. 99–120.

This gives a theoretical discussion of the principles and concepts of biostratigraphy.

Wheeler, H. E. (1958), Primary factors in biostratigraphy, *Bull. Am. Assoc. Petroleum Geol.*, vol. 42, pp. 640–655.

The author differentiates and classifies biostratigraphic units comparably to lithostratigraphic units.

Wheeler, H. E., and Beesley, E. M. (1948), Critique of the time-stratigraphic concept, *Bull. Geol. Soc. Amer.*, vol. 59, pp. 75–86.

Emphasis is on the time-transgressive nature of formations and unconformities.

Wheeler, H. E., and others (1950), Stratigraphic classification, *Bull. Am. Assoc. Petroleum Geol.*, vol. 34, pp. 2361–2365.

The possible time-transgressive nature of stages and zones is pointed out.

Willard, Bradford (1939), The Devonian of Pennsylvania, Pa. Geol. Surv., ser. 4, Bull. G 19.

Chapter 8 discusses stratigraphy of the Catskill continental facies.

Williams, J. S. (1954), Problem of boundaries between geologic systems, *Bull. Am. Assoc. Petroleum Geol.*, vol. 38, pp. 1602–1605.

This is a brief general discussion.

Willman, H. B., Swann, D. H., and Frye, J. C. (1958), Stratigraphic policy of the Illinois State Geological Survey, Ill. Geol. Surv., Circ. 249.

A practical system of stratigraphic classification and nomenclature adapted to geologic conditions in Illinois is explained.

AMERICAN COMMISSION ON
STRATIGRAPHIC NOMENCLATURE

(published in *Bull. Am. Assoc. Petroleum Geol.*)

REPORTS

[These reports do not constitute parts of a stratigraphic code. They have been prepared and published as recommendations in an attempt to achieve uniformity of opinion and to promote discussion. They are subject to alteration and, after possible revision, they will provide the basis for a new American code.]

1. Declaration on naming subsurface stratigraphic units, vol. 33 (1949), pp. 1280–1282.
2. Nature, usage, and nomenclature of time-stratigraphic and geologic-time units, vol. 36 (1952), pp. 1627–1638.
3. Nature, usage, and nomenclature of time-stratigraphic and geologic-time units as applied to the Precambrian, vol. 39 (1955), pp. 1859–1861.
4. Nature, usage, and nomenclature of rock-stratigraphic units, vol. 40 (1956), pp. 2003–2014.
5. Nature, usage, and nomenclature of biostratigraphic units, vol. 41 (1957), pp. 1877–1891.
6. Application of stratigraphic classification and nomenclature to the Quaternary (with expression of disapproval), vol. 43 (1959), pp. 663–675.

NOTES

[These notes present information, opinions, and discussions pertinent to the development of a new American stratigraphic code. They do not constitute either recommendations by or opinions of the full American Commission.]

1. Organization and objectives of the Stratigraphic Commission, vol. 31 (1947), pp. 513–518.
2. Nature and classes of stratigraphic units, vol. 31 (1947), pp. 519–528.
3. Rules of geological nomenclature of the Geological Survey of Canada, vol. 32 (1948), pp. 366–367.
4. Naming of subsurface stratigraphic units, vol. 32 (1948), pp. 367–371.
5. Definition and adoption of the terms stage and age, vol. 32 (1948), pp. 372–376.
6. Discussion of nature and classes of stratigraphic units, vol. 32 (1948), pp. 376–381.
7. Records of the Stratigraphic Commission for 1947–1948, vol. 33 (1949), pp. 1271–1273.
8. Australian code of stratigraphical nomenclature, vol. 33 (1949), pp. 1273–1276.
9. The Pliocene-Pleistocene boundary, vol. 33 (1949), pp. 1276–1280.
10. Should additional categories of stratigraphic units be recognized? vol. 34 (1950), pp. 2360–2361.
11. Records of the Stratigraphic Commission for 1949–1950, vol. 35 (1951), pp. 1074–1076.
12. Divisions of rocks and time, vol. 35 (1951), p. 1076.
13. Third Congress of Carboniferous Stratigraphy and Geology, vol. 36 (1952), pp. 169–172.
14. Official report of round table conference on stratigraphic nomenclature at Third Congress of Carboniferous Stratigraphy and Geology, Heerlen, Netherlands, June 26–28, 1951, vol. 36 (1952), pp. 2044–2048.
15. Records of the Stratigraphic Commission for 1951–1952, vol. 37 (1953), pp. 1078–1080.
16. Records of the Stratigraphic Commission for 1953–1954, vol. 39 (1955), pp. 1861–1863.

17. Suppression of homonymous and obsolete stratigraphic names, vol. 40 (1956), pp. 2953–2954.
18. Records of the Stratigraphic Commission for 1955–1956, vol. 41 (1957), pp. 130–133.
19. Status of soils in stratigraphic nomenclature, vol. 41 (1957), pp. 758–763.
20. Problems in applying standard stratigraphic practice in nonmarine Quaternary deposits, vol. 42 (1958), pp. 1979–1983.
21. Preparation of new stratigraphic code by American Commission on Stratigraphic Nomenclature, vol. 42 (1958), pp. 1984–1986.
22. Records of the Stratigraphic Commission for 1957–1958, vol. 43 (1959), pp. 1967–1971.
23. Need for rock-stratigraphic units larger than groups, vol. 43 (1959), pp. 1971–1975.
24. Unconformity-bounded units in stratigraphy, vol. 43 (1959), pp. 1975–1977.

13

Stratigraphic Nomenclature

STRATIGRAPHIC NAMES

ALL stratigraphic units require distinctive names or comparable designations in order that they may be identified and differentiated from each other. In former times stratigraphic names were derived indiscriminately from places or other geographic features, distinguishing physical features, or characteristic fossils. Thus, the Joliet Limestone (Sil.) was named for a city in Illinois, the Helderberg Limestone (Dev.) for a low range of mountains in New York, the Saccharoidal Sandstone (Ord.) of the upper Mississippi Valley for its sugary appearance, and the Archimedes Limestone (Miss.) of western Illinois and Iowa for a peculiar bryozoan. Nongeographic names given long ago remain in use in some other countries but in the United States the practice of the United States Geological Survey of designating all rock units, and most of the stratigraphic units of other categories, by geographic names has been followed almost invariably. Old descriptive names have been replaced; the Saccharoidal is now the St. Peter Sandstone and the Archimedes is now the Warsaw Limestone.

Construction of Stratigraphic Names

General Rules

Stratigraphic names consist of two parts: (1) a geographic or other name that is invariably capitalized, and (2) a class name such as *period*, *series*, or *formation*, that may not be. The American Stratigraphic Commission has recommended that the second word be capitalized also but in the past this has not necessarily been done. Capitalization of the second part of every formal stratigraphic name emphasizes its technical usage and distinguishes this from the common more general meaning of the word.

Time and Time-Rock Units

The geographic or other names identifying corresponding time and time-rock units are identical. Distinction is shown by use of the appropriate class name—for example, Devonian Period and Devonian System. The class names, however, may be omitted to avoid repetition if confusion is unlikely, and reference is made simply to "the Devonian."

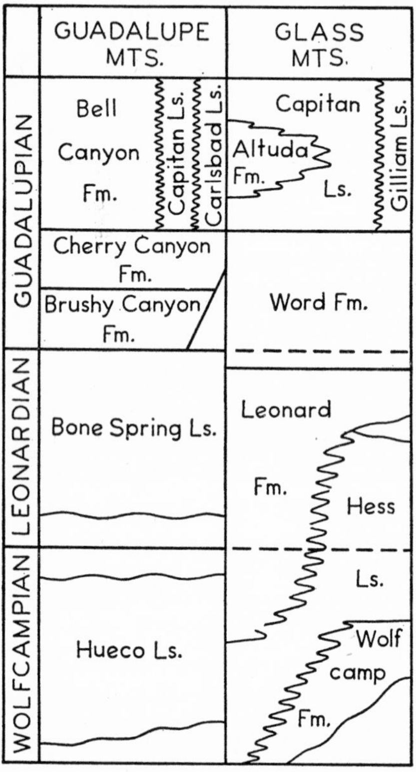

The initial parts of names of time and time-rock units are changed to adjectival form by adding a suffix such as -an, -ian, -ic, -ous, or -ary. A few attempts at systematization and uniform use of suffixes have not proved popular and the original terminations are in general use. Thus, among the systems there are Ordovician, Jurassic, Carboniferous, and Tertiary. A few names of classical derivation end in -cene or -gene: Pliocene and Neogene.

Most geographic names are in their modern forms although a few European names are Latinized. Examples are Vindobonian, named for Vienna, and Pontian, named for the Black Sea.

A very few names have not been changed to adjectival form because the results would be uneuphonious —for example, Finger Lakes Stage (Dev.).

	GUADALUPE MTS.	GLASS MTS.
GUADALUPIAN	Bell Canyon Fm. / Capitan Ls. / Carlsbad Ls.	Capitan / Altuda Fm. Ls. / Gilliam Ls.
GUADALUPIAN	Cherry Canyon Fm.	
GUADALUPIAN	Brushy Canyon Fm.	Word Fm.
LEONARDIAN	Bone Spring Ls.	Leonard Fm. / Hess
WOLFCAMPIAN	Hueco Ls.	Ls. / Wolf camp Fm.

Figure 171. Correlation chart showing the relations of Lower and Middle Permian strata in west Texas. Stratigraphic boundaries of the Leonard and Wolfcamp formations do not correspond with the boundaries of the Wolfcampian and Leonardian series. This chart illustrates the possible confusion that may result from the use of the same geographic names for both rock and time-rock units. (After Batten, 1958, Bull. Am. Mus. Nat. Hist., vol. 114, art. 2, p. 163, fig. 1.)

Rock Units

Geographic names employed for rock units are not changed to adjectival form or altered in any way.

Rock units have no necessary time connotations. Therefore, the same geographic names cannot be used for them and either time or time-rock units without danger of confusion (see Figure 171). A rock unit such as a group may be equivalent to a time-rock unit such as a stage as its type locality, but the boundaries of these units are likely to diverge as they extend into other areas. If a single name were used for two units having these relations, it might identify different sequences of strata at any locality other than the type.

Because the distinction between rock and time-rock units has not been clearly realized in the past, there have been many instances of the duplication or shifting of names in or between the rock and time-rock categories of stratigraphic units. The Pottsville, Allegheny, Conemaugh, and Monongahela divisions of the Pennsylvanian provide examples. The names originally identified formations but subsequently they also have been indiscriminately used in the sense of both *group* and *series*. This particular situation is not so serious as some others because the Pennsylvanian rock units are identified by tracing key beds or by paleobotanic correlation; they are very similar, therefore, and perhaps actually identical to practical time-rock units. Nevertheless, in order to eliminate all possibility of confusion, no duplication of names in rock and time-rock categories should be permitted.

Formations

The class name *formation* ordinarily is replaced by a lithologic term, most commonly *limestone, sandstone,* or *shale* but others such as *dolomite, oolite, red beds,* or *graywacke* may be used. These lithologic names generally indicate the dominant or most conspicuous kind of rock present in a formation and do not necessarily imply that the entire formation consists of this material. Some so-called limestones, for example, are predominantly shale, but their softer layers are likely to be less well exposed than the more resistant beds. Thus an erroneous idea as to the nature of a formation may arise. Some formations are so heterogeneous that no lithologic term is appropriate and the unspecific class name *formation* is used for them.

According to the practice of the United States Geological Survey, the combination of geographic and lithologic terms in a formation name is invariable. This may result in names that are inappropriate in some areas for formations of variable lithologic development. An example is the Paint Creek "Limestone" (Miss.) of southern Illinois and western Kentucky. At its type locality this formation includes more shale than limestone. Elsewhere it grades laterally into solid limestone at some places and into continuous shale at others. In the latter places the designation "Limestone" is an obvious misnomer. Many geologists do not adhere to the Geological Survey's standard practice in this respect.

Members

Members constitute an exception to the rule that stratigraphic names consist of two words because the name of a member properly consists of three:

(1) a geographic name, (2) a lithologic term, and (3) the class name *member*. Only in this way can the distinction between formation and member be made clear. Informally and to avoid repetition, however, the word *member* may be omitted if confusion is unlikely or if distinction is unimportant, or the lithologic term may be omitted if it is unnecessary for clarity of meaning.

Zones

In contrast to other stratigraphic units, all biostratigraphic zones are named for their characteristic fossils. These may be either genera or species. A genus name is a single word that is capitalized. A species name consists of a capitalized generic name and a second or specific name that is not capitalized. Both names should be italicized. The use of a second or specific name without its generic designation is both improper and confusing because species belonging to different genera may have the same second or specific name. Without indication of the particular genus, therefore, such species cannot be distinguished (see Figure 215, p. 560). Unnecessary repetition can be avoided by abbreviating the generic name, which commonly is represented by its initial capital letter, providing that the full generic name has been used at least once and that confusion with other genera is unlikely.

In the past many zones have been designated by the second or specific name of a zonal fossil without any indication of its genus and the name may or may not have been capitalized or italicized. Modern practice requires the stratigrapher to adhere uniformly to the proper method of writing the names of fossils when they are used for the names of zones.

A review of actual practice in the construction of stratigraphic names shows that few invariable rules have been recognized. Procedure has been governed more by custom than by consistency.

Priority

A stratigraphic unit may be known by two or more names given to it at different places or at different times. If synonymous names exist and a choice must be made between them, it is advisable to select the best-known and most widely used name. American stratigraphers generally are agreed that it is not necessary to employ the oldest name. Stability of nomenclature is considered more important than priority. Otherwise various well-established and familiar names might be required to give way for older obscure or forgotten ones.

As an example, the youngest division of the Mississippian System is known as the Chesterian Series. The name Chester was first given to a Mississippian sandstone in 1858 which is now termed Palestine. In 1860 a Chester limestone was described and in 1866 this name was employed for a group of strata including shale and sandstone as well as limestone. This group later became the Chester Series. Earlier, however, in 1857, the name Kaskaskia

Limestone had been proposed for these same strata. In this case Chester is neither the oldest name introduced for Upper Mississippian rocks nor is it used for the beds to which it was originally applied.

Homonyms

The use of any name for more than one stratigraphic unit creates homonyms, results in confusion, and, therefore, is not permissible. There are, however, many examples of homonyms in stratigraphic literature. Most homonyms among the older names, created before any rules were recognized, have been eliminated because all but one usage of a name have been abandoned. In modern practice only the first usage of a name is proper although redefinition or restriction of the stratigraphic unit may have been considered necessary. This applies to names in different categories of stratigraphic units and to names in different classes of the same category as well as to those in a single class. It is advisable also to avoid the use of different but somewhat similar names for units of the same general age occurring anywhere or for units of any age that are present in the same general region.

For example, the name Battle Mountain Formation was introduced for certain Pennsylvanian strata in Colorado in 1941. In 1942 the Upper Cretaceous Battle Formation was described in western Canada. These names are distinct enough so that confusion is not likely between formations of different ages in different areas. In 1951, however, the name Battle Formation was used again for Pennsylvanian beds in Nevada. This created homonyms. Also Battle and Battle Mountain are so similar that formations of similar age in the same general region are likely to be confounded. Another example is provided by the name Kinkaid Limestone of the Mississippian first used in Illinois in 1920. In 1933 a very similar name, Kincaid, was given to an Eocene formation in Texas. Although these names are slightly different and identify formations of different ages in quite different areas, they are so much alike that difficulty may result.

The United States Geological Survey has published lexicons listing all formation names used in America through 1955. The Committee on Geologic Names of the Survey also maintains an up-to-date catalog of all stratigraphic names published in this country. Inquiry addressed to the committee concerning names tentatively selected for new units will reveal which if any have been used before and thus prevent the publication of a name that has been preempted.

Symbols

In some European countries more or less complex systems of symbols consisting of letters or numbers with superscripts and subscripts have been employed to designate stratigraphic units. Generally these are time-rock units identified by their fossils, or strata correlated with such units by other means.

The symbols, therefore, may take the place of names for series, stages, and zones.

In Russia the Carboniferous System is divided into major parts designated C1, C2, and C3. Subdivisions are indicated by the symbols C_1^1, C_1^2, and so forth (see Figure 165, p. 441) and still smaller divisions by $C_1^{1\alpha}$, and $C_1^{1\beta}$. In contrast, divisions of the English Carboniferous are distingushed by the initial letters of the generic names of characteristic fossils such as Z1 and Z2, for *Zaphrentis*, a coral; S1 and S2 for *Seminula*, a brachiopod now known as *Composita*; H for *Homoceras*, a goniatite; and so on. Other systems using Roman numerals and Greek letters also have been employed.

Symbols may serve as a sort of shorthand for stratigraphic names in long-studied and complete stratigraphic sections if their detailed developments are well known and they are not complicated by important lateral facies changes or broken by important stratigraphic discontinuities. Most systems employing symbols, however, lack the flexibility provided by names because they indicate order and continuous succession. Once they have been set up, revisions of the stratigraphic section or additions to it of newly discovered beds intermediate between any of the older units are difficult or impossible. Systems of symbols do not seem to be suitable to stratigraphic classification in such a large and varied country as the United States, where many stratigraphic details remain to be determined.

Informal Names

The designations of coal beds and oil sands generally have been considered to fall outside of the field of formal stratigraphic nomenclature. Consequently the rules and conventions governing the use of other stratigraphic names commonly have not been applied to them. Most of these strata are, however, well-marked lithologic units and there seems to be no good reason why they should not be accorded at least the status of members.

Coals have been named and numbered and some coals are designated in both ways, as, for example, the Springfield or No. 5 coal of Illinois. Names are commonly geographic, but some refer to physical peculiarities, such as the Fireclay coal of eastern Kentucky, which is marked by a persistent thick clay parting. Some names are used for more than one bed, like the Lower, Middle, and Upper Mercer coals of Ohio. Thin coals lying close above thicker ones may be termed "rider" beds, as in West Virginia and Pennsylvania, where the Pittsburgh coal is followed by the Pittsburgh rider coal.

Generally numbers applied to coals progress from below upward in stratigraphic order. Thin, local, or commercially unimportant beds may be skipped, however, so numbers do not indicate the actual succession of coal beds present. Coals occurring between numbered beds may be identified by letters. Thus No. 5a coal lies between the No. 5 and No. 6 coals of southern

Illinois, and Coal III A intervenes between Coal III and Coal IV in Indiana. In contrast, the coals of some districts, as in northern Illinois, are numbered in reverse order. Progressively deeper beds are known there as the First, Second, and Third vein coals.

Many oil sands are identified by the name of the farm upon which the first producing well was drilled. Geographic names, however, also are common— for example, the Robinson sand of Illinois and the Bartlesville sand of Oklahoma. Some oil sands carry the names of the producing formations, like the Aux Vases sand of southern Illinois, but generally these constitute only a part of the complete formation. Although some miscorrelations have resulted in the misapplication of such names, once established in subsurface terminology they are likely to persist even after the mistake in identification has become well known. One name may be used for several oil sands. Thus there are the First, Second, and Third Venango sands in Pennsylvania. Less commonly numbers only are used, like First pay, Second pay, and so on. As applied to oil sands, numbers progress downward and indicate the order in which they were reached in drilling. Any oil-producing bed is likely to be termed a *sand*. The use of this word does not necessarily indicate that it is sandstone. Thus, the McCloskey sand, which is an important and widespread producer in Illinois, is a porous zone in limestone.

Strata other than coals and oil sands encountered in drilling may be useful as key beds for correlation or identification of position in the stratigraphic section and some are named. These may correspond to rock units known in outcrop but be given different names because correlation was not understood at first. On the other hand, they may be either more or less inclusive than surface units. The names are quite variously derived. Some are farm names like the Barlow lime of Indiana. Others are old-time drillers' terms, such as the Big Lime and Pencil Cave of the northern Appalachian region. Most names of this kind antedate the advent of the petroleum geologist. Some have persisted because they were widely employed and are still useful.

In some areas the Pennsylvanian System has been subdivided into cyclothems (see Chapter 10) that have been given geographic names and may be treated as if they were standard formations. Each cyclothem consists of several lithologic members, as many as eleven being recognized in Illinois (see Figure 145, p. 372). Some of the members also have received geographic names but the naming of all of them would create a system of nomenclature of unnecessary complexity and be almost impossible to remember. Consequently, the members commonly are identified by the name of the cyclothem and distinguished by their lithologic nature and position. Thus in the Brereton Cyclothem there is a Brereton sandstone, a Brereton underclay, a Brereton coal, and so on. In the Shumway Cyclothem there are among others a Shumway middle limestone, middle shale, and upper limestone. The rules of stratigraphic nomenclature prohibit the use of the same name for a unit and a subdivision of that unit, but this system of cyclothemic designation is simple and convenient and can be accepted on an informal basis.

Many of the geologic systems are divided more or less informally into lower, middle, and upper parts. If, as in the Cambrian, the system is composed of three series, these words substitute for series names, are capitalized, and are recognized as formal designations for these time-rock units. Some systems include a larger number of series. If, as in the Devonian, there is agreement regarding assignment of the series, an equally definite tripartite division may be recognized, and these words are capitalized and similarly employed in a standardized formal way. Otherwise the uncapitalized words identify only successive, somewhat indistinct divisions. In some systems, like the Pennsylvanian, agreement has not been reached, and even if Lower, Middle, and Upper are used formally, their meanings are not consistent and they vary in different regions or as used by different persons. In such a system as the Mississippian, division into either two or three parts may be made. Thus Middle Mississippian may or may not be recognized. Others, like the Cretaceous, consist of only two series; there is no Middle Cretaceous. In any case capitalization of these terms indicates formal and supposedly standardized usage whereas non-capitalization is informal and indicates only relative position. The words *lower, middle,* and *upper* are employed in the subdivision of series in exactly the same way.

Time divisions corresponding to the lower, middle, and upper parts of systems and series also are recognized. The terms properly applied to them are *early, middle,* and *late* respectively, although the prefix *mid-* or the word *medial* or *median* may substitute for *middle*. These words are rarely capitalized. Finally, the capitalized prefixes *Eo-, Meso-* and *Neo-* are used in the same way for both time and time-rock units. Even though these relative terms are capitalized and employed in a formal sense, their exact meanings may be somewhat uncertain. Therefore the use of geographic names for parts of time and time-rock units generally is preferable if they are available.

Obsolete or Abandoned Names

Many stratigraphic names included in all classes of all categories are not in current use. Some gained little or no recognition after their original introduction because:

1. They were ill suited to stratigraphic needs.
2. They resulted from stratigraphic misinterpretations.
3. They apply to areas that have received no further attention.

Other names formerly more or less familiar to geologists are no longer in use for these same reasons or because:

4. They have been superseded by synonymous names.
5. They have been employed so variously or have been so miscorrelated that they are no longer useful.

6. A stratigraphic unit has been subdivided and no present need is felt for a former name.

7. An entirely different classification is now recognized.

Almost any obsolete name may be revived under some circumstances and win renewed acceptance.

TYPE LOCALITIES

Ideally every rock unit and particularly every formation should have a type locality. Type localities are important because they provide specific stratigraphic sections that serve as standards of reference showing the typical lithologic characters of a rock unit and its typical relations to others. At a type locality there should be no question as to the identity of a unit and its boundaries.

Some formations and members have been carefully defined with exact type localities specified and type sections measured and recorded. Many, however, originally did not have precise type localities designated for them. Consequently stratigraphers cannot be certain exactly what was intended when such a unit was first discriminated. If particularly good and complete exposures were selected later, these now may be accepted as the type sections of such units.

Groups and larger rock units, corresponding to time-rock units at their type localities, generally are defined in terms of the smaller units that constitute them but they also may have recognized type areas or regions. Most time-rock units other than zones have geographic names derived from such places. Because they generally are synthetic, these time-rock units rarely have specific type localities or type sections.

Zones, which are named for characteristic fossils, do not necessarily have type localities.

Derivation of Names

The names of rock units are derived from the names of places or other geographic features at or near type localities. If a formation has had no exact type locality specified, the place for which it was named presumably indicates approximately the position of the type locality. If the name is that of a town or some other restricted geographic feature, the nearest good exposure may be suitable. If, however, the name was taken from a more or less extensive political subdivision or geographic area or from such a feature as a mountain range or river, there may be any number of possible type localities. Under these circumstances there is likely to be much uncertainty, and different geologists may choose different places for the type. Some units are not adequately exposed at any single place and at best they can be said to have only type areas or regions.

The lack of a precise type locality may result in much confusion. For example, a thin black shale of Mississipian or possibly Devonian age exposed at Louisiana, Missouri, has been termed Grassy Creek Shale and is recognized throughout a considerable area. Obviously the name was derived from a stream a few miles distant from Louisiana. Black shale exposed along this stream, however, is a dark member in the Maquoketa Shale of Ordovician age.

Names of stratigraphic units generally are selected from published maps. Some areas, however, are incompletely or inadequately mapped. Others are without suitable geographic names that have not already been used elsewhere. Consequently the selection of names for new units may pose problems. The lack of a suitable new name near an excellent exposure may necessitate the choice of a less desirable place for a type locality.

Some geographic names that are well known locally but have never appeared on maps have been used as formation names. In the lower portion of its valley, the Kaskaskia River of Illinois is known as the Okaw, and this name was given to an Upper Mississippian limestone formation. Elsewhere local features too unimportant to be recorded on a map have furnished names for rock units. Examples are the Confederate and Union Dairy Limestone members of the Hoxbar Formation (Penn.) of the Ardmore basin in Oklahoma. These names were derived from an old soldiers' home and a dairy farm. In some areas lacking suitable names, a local feature has been christened informally and then this name has been applied to a rock unit. Examples are the Spergen Limestone (Miss.) of Indiana, misspelled from the name of a hill on a former Mr. Spergeon's farm, and the Darty Limestone (Miss.) of southern Illinois, named from a small creek that flows near Mr. Darty's house.

In an indirect way, a few formations have provided their own names. The Galena Dolomite (Ord.) received its name from the city of Galena, Illinois, which in turn was named for the mineral extensively mined from this formation before the Civil War. Also the Checkerboard Limestone Member of the Coffeeville Formation (Penn.) of northern Oklahoma was named from a creek in whose bed regular joints enlarged by solution separate this limestone into large rectangular blocks. Some stratigraphic units bear geographic names that are now obsolete and practically forgotten. An example is the Borden Group (Miss.) of Indiana. This was named for the town of Borden, whose name was changed many years ago to New Providence. The latter name was later given to a shale formation included in the Borden Group so these two units received their names from the same place.

Subsurface Formations

Most formations and other stratigraphic units are characterized by and were named from surface outcrops. Some rock units noted in well drilling, however, are not known at the surface or are uncertainly related to exposed stratigraphic sections. In the study of subsurface geology, particularly in oil fields, such units may be important and require names for convenient identification. Some of them have been named from the farm upon which a well was drilled. This becomes the type locality, and the record of the well becomes the type section. Most subsurface units are of only local importance but a few have received wider recognition by stratigraphers and have gained acceptance as units comparable to more conventional units based on surface exposures. A formation of this type is the Charles Limestone (Miss.) of Montana.

A few names derived from outcrops but no longer much employed for surface units continue to be used for parts of the subsurface stratigraphic section. An example is the Mayes Formation (Miss.) of eastern Oklahoma, which is recognized in wells on the basis of its lithologic character and stratigraphic position. The vertical relations of this formation to its neighbors and its possible lateral equivalence to differently developed and constituted strata are not agreed upon. It is doubtful if exposures at the old Mayes type locality, where the strata now are known by other names, are characteristic of this formation as recognized in the subsurface.

PERSISTENCE OF STRATIGRAPHIC UNITS AND NAMES

Most stratigraphic nomenclature originated in more or less restricted areas that include the type localities of stratigraphic units. In these areas useful or significant units were distinguished and their vertical relations to other units were determined. Here names were applied to them. From these areas the units were traced laterally and the names were carried throughout expanding regions. Thus a name identifies strata included between fairly definite upper and lower boundaries, but the lateral limits of the unit are not determined.

Because time-rock units are defined by time planes, they can be recognized as far as the time planes can be approximated and they pose no problems beyond the identification of those planes, difficult though this may be. Most rock units and particularly formations, however, are distinguished by lithologic characters, and changing relations resulting from both vertical and horizontal lithologic variations introduce many complexities.

Names and Individuality

Sedimentary deposition may be continuous throughout very wide regions, but environments are not uniform. Thus any rock unit, if it can be followed far enough, is sure to change in lithologic character, in thickness, and in its relations to adjacent units. Consequently, as a rock unit is traced laterally from its type locality, its differentiation from others may become less sharp and clear and its identification may even become impossible. Different units in the same area or the same unit in different areas are not equally distinct, equally thick, or representative of equal intervals of time. Some units, of course, are much more uniformly developed than others and are recognizable throughout much larger areas.

Because of these differences, all formations or other rock units are not equally objective or equally important. The identification of a unit by name, however, provides it with a subjective individuality that serves to set it apart from all other similar units. Also the identification of the several parts of a stratigraphic section by different but strictly comparable names seems to establish all units of a single class upon an equal footing. Finally, the extension of a stratigraphic name from its type locality to other places, where lithologic characters or vertical relations are not the same, serves to disguise these differences and obscures the fact that the unit is not exactly the same as at its type locality and cannot be defined in exactly the same way.

The naming of strata and the application of the names throughout extensive areas may convey a greater appearance of consistency to the parts of a more or less arbitrarily subdivided stratigraphic section than is warranted. Attention may become so focused on a name that its dependence upon actual stratigraphic individuality is neglected. In extreme cases, a name may come to be considered more important than the strata it is intended to identify.

The relations between a name and the strata it represents are so close that one cannot be considered without the other. The question of the limited or extensive use of a rock-unit name should be answered on the basis of (1) the lateral limits of the unit that the name identifies, and (2) the minimum requirements with respect to similarity in development necessary for the differentiation of the unit from others of its kind.

Lateral Limits

Some rock units are remarkably uniform and the extensive use of single names for them appears to be appropriate. Other strata change greatly in short distances and one or more related changes in name may seem desirable or necessary. A logical decision regarding the lateral limits to be recognized for any unit and the areal applicability of its name must take into consideration (1) lateral lithologic consistency, (2) continued suitability of boundaries, and (3) time equivalence of strata.

The relative emphasis given to these three factors varies considerably. In actual practice, lithologic consistency generally takes precedence in the characterization of a rock unit. Important and abrupt changes in boundaries or time value, however, may seriously impair the practical usefulness of a unit thus defined. The ideal rock unit that is both a consistent lithologic unit and a time-rock unit rarely occurs except in very restricted areas.

Lithologic Consistency

Lithologic consistency is important because most rock units are recognized primarily by their lithologic characters. Continuous strata of similar composition and appearance are likely to bear a single stratigraphic name as far as such similarity warrants. In spite of all that can be said, however, the use of a single stratigraphic name suggests to many geologists both lithologic similarity and time equivalence. Both are important, and the violation of either implication necessitates increased reliance on the other if the unit is to be a useful one.

Many lithologically defined formations have boundaries above and below that deviate somewhat with respect to time planes. These formations consequently do not represent exactly the same time intervals from place to place. Some, such as the St. Peter Sandstone (Ord.), transgress time planes importantly and probably such formations would not prove to be useful if they were not unusually well-marked lithologic units.

Formations that are defined lithologically are likely to be indistinctly limited laterally by gradual changes in their characters. They may wedge out between unconformities, however, or between converging formations of different lithology. Also they may be split into two or more smaller units by the introduction of strata of different types or merge into larger units where boundaries similar to the original ones become unrecognizable.

Consistent Boundaries

A formation defined by sharp boundaries such as unconformities, key beds, or abrupt changes to contrasting adjacent formations may be recognized and known by the same name in spite of important differences in lithologic composition in different areas. The nature of boundaries may change from place to place but, if it does, relations at the boundaries should be clear. Abrupt steps upward or downward of important magnitude are undesirable.

In many areas the boundaries are likely to approximate time planes rather closely. If they are unconformities, the time value of a formation may be somewhat variable from place to place but it is definitely limited. Thin persistent key beds are likely to be time-rock units. Similar abrupt lithologic change throughout a considerable area suggests a uniform, nearly simultaneous change in some important physical factor related to deposition; otherwise the sediments would change more gradually and exhibit lateral transition. The Paint Creek Limestone (Miss.) is a unit of this type. It is characterized by extreme lithologic variability but is confined by sharp boundaries between persistent overlying and underlying sandstones.

Rock units defined by abrupt boundaries are limited laterally at points where their boundaries become indistinct or unrecognizable. Although such units may wedge out beneath or between unconformities, they are more likely to merge laterally into stratigraphic sections that are differently subdivided.

Time Equivalence

Time equivalence is the basis for the identification of time-rock units wherever they are recognized. Some rock units or units treated like rock units also have been defined on a similar basis. Their boundaries are supposed to approximate time planes, and a single name may be applied extensively to strata of diverse lithologic development not enclosed between any consistent physical upper and lower limits. A unit of this kind has no logical lateral limits but it may wedge out above, between, or below unconformities.

A time-defined formation may be a lithologic unit at its type locality, but its identification elsewhere generally depends upon what have been believed to be exact paleontologic correlations. For example, similar fossils occur in three comparatively thin Silurian formations that outcrop in areas hundreds of miles apart. These are the Brassfield Limestone of central Kentucky, the Sexton Creek Limestone of southern Illinois, and the Kankakee Dolomite of northern Illinois. These formations do not resemble each other in appearance and it is doubtful that they can ever be proved certainly to be of exactly the same age, but some geologists advocate using the Kentucky name for all of them.

Another limestone rarely as much as five feet thick in southeastern Missouri and the neighboring part of Illinois carries the same fossils as the shaly Fernvale Formation (Ord.) of central Tennessee. Because of confident correlation in the past, the southern name was carried into the Mississippi Valley, where it is still in use in spite of present opinion that ages of the strata in these two areas are not the same.

The Glen Dean Limestone (Miss.) is marked by certain faunal peculiarities in southern Illinois and western Kentucky, where it has been extensively recognized and mapped. Similar fossils have been found at a few places east of the Cincinnati arch in eastern Kentucky and the western tip of Virginia. The name Glen Dean has been applied to a formation of heterogeneous lithologic composition in the latter state, where its boundaries are not similar to those in the type area and it almost certainly represents a considerably longer interval of time.

The Salem, or Spergen, Limestone (Miss.) of Indiana is a well-marked rock unit identified by its oolitic character and peculiar fossils. Similar limestone occupying a similar stratigraphic position but without the fossils occurs in the Mississippi Valley south of St. Louis, where the same names have been used. Farther north in western Illinois and Iowa these names also have been applied to entirely nonoolitic and somewhat shaly and sandy strata that exhibit no similarity to the original Indiana formation although they are believed to be approximately time equivalent. In each of these examples, a formation name has been extended much farther than seems advisable. There is very little reason to approve such practice.

Intertongued Units

Many stratigraphic successions consist of alternating beds of two contrasting kinds of rock such as shale and sandstone or shale and limestone. If the beds are thin or impersistent they may be too unimportant to be considered rock units in any classification, and together they are regarded as constituting a formation or a member. Change in texture or composition of such beds or wedging out may occur gradually, and an important change in the lithologic proportions or the complete disappearance of one kind of rock may be considered sufficient to warrant the recognition of different rock units. The gradual nature of such lateral change, however, provides no sharp boundary, and separation of the units must be made in some more or less arbitrary way.

If the alternating rocks are thick or if they are important for some other reason, the alternations may be regarded as rock units and receive formal stratigraphic names. If the stratigraphic section changes laterally as just described, the alternating units of one lithologic type no longer will be separated from each other by units of the other type that have wedged out. Where similar units come together, differentiation may be impossible and the new, more inclusive units may require recognition. One kind of rock may be eliminated in one direction and the other may disappear in the opposite direction. Thus two thick lithologically contrasting units may pass into each other by intertonguing (see Figure 191, p. 501). Such relations provide problems in nomenclature. These may be approached from the standpoint of either (1) the smaller alternating units or (2) the larger composite units.

Pennsylvanian Shales in Kansas

In parts of the Pennsylvanian System of eastern Kansas and Nebraska, cyclothems are incompletely developed and important portions of the stratigraphic section consist of alternating shale and limestone beds. Most of these occur at definite stratigraphic positions and are persistent for long distances. Many have been recognized and named as members of somewhat complexly constituted practical formations that do not correspond to cyclothems (see Figure 172). As they are traced southward, many of the limestones thin, and some wedge out and disappear. Where this occurs, two or more shale members merge and lose their individual identity. Here the names of the separate shale members are useless; larger composite shale members require recognition. New names might be provided for the new units but if this were done a multitude of names of only local applicability would greatly complicate an already burdensome nomenclature. In order to avoid this unwelcome possibility and to keep nomenclature relatively simple, the composite members are designated by hyphenated names. If one limestone disappears and two shale members merge, their names are joined

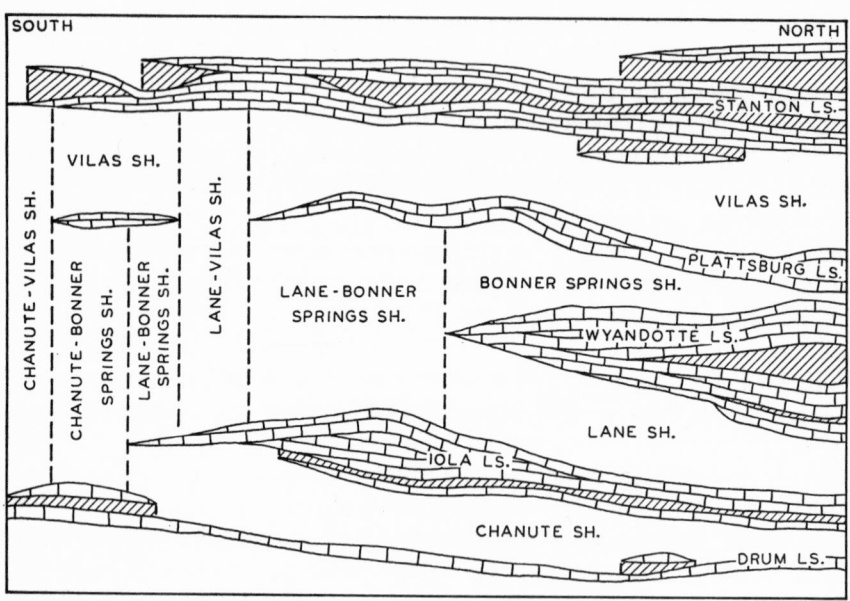

Figure 172. Diagram showing lateral variations in the stratigraphic relations of formations and some of their principal members in part of the Pennsylvanian System of eastern Kansas and the nomenclature applied to them. Compare with Figure 238, p. 615. Notice that boundaries of limestone formations cut vertically across shale members at places where the upper or lower limestone members wedge out and disappear. This conforms to the practice of arbitrary vertical cutoff used to define the limits of some stratigraphic bodies in areas of lateral lithologic transition (see Figure 194, p. 509). (Adapted from Moore, 1936, Kan. Geol. Surv., Bull. 22, p. 36, fig. 4A.)

by a hyphen to identify the new unit. If several limestones pinch out and several shales coalesce, the names of the uppermost and lowermost shale members are hyphenated and thus define the stratigraphic span of the new unit. This system is very flexible and can be applied to almost any situation that arises in an intertonguing sequence.

Mancos–Mesa Verde Transition

Early field work in the southern Rocky Mountains region revealed the existence of a thick body of marine Upper Cretaceous shale in some areas and a thick succession of coal-bearing Upper Cretaceous sandstones in others. These were named and mapped as the Mancos Shale and the Mesa Verde

Sandstone. Later investigations proved that these formations are approximately equivalent and grade into each other by large-scale intertonguing. Lithologic complexity of the Mesa Verde Sandstone led to its being upgraded to a group, and some of its subordinate formations have been subdivided into members. The Mancos Shale, however, is much more uniform and has maintained its status as a formation, but several tongues have been named that persist for many miles between extensions of Mesa Verde members.

Although the stratigraphic relations in the zone of intertonguing are not particularly complicated (see Figure 191, p. 501), they have resulted in disagreement concerning proper classification and nomenclature of the alternating lithologic units. The trouble seems to be that emphasis has been placed upon "formations" which conventionally overlie each other in regular order regardless of whether their boundaries are planes of equal or transgressing time. According to this concept, stoutly maintained by some stratigraphers, lithologic bodies may intertongue, but formations cannot do so. Consequently it has been considered necessary to limit the formations laterally by arbitrary vertical cutoff planes and to consider Mancos Shale tongues that extend beyond the boundary to be shale members of the Mesa Verde Sandstone or vice versa.

Such a convention under these circumstances seems to be unnecessary as well as artificial. If emphasis is transferred to the tongues, which are the units of local importance, they can be named, mapped, and described in as much detail as is required. In this way they introduce no more difficulties than if they were members of a conventional formation consisting of alternating lithologic units. In this particular case, however, no such formation would be recognized in the intertonged area because it would only obscure significant lithologic relations. Instead of being considered a member of a mixed formation, each unit can be recognized for what it really is, a lateral offshoot from a larger, well-characterized lithologic unit. The distinction between a member and a tongue should be kept clear: A *member* is a subordinate stratigraphic unit *within* a formation. A *tongue* is a lateral extension of a portion of a formation lying *between* units that are not members of that formation.

Extensive Versus Restricted Formations

The application of stratigraphic names and the recognition of rock units throughout wide geographic areas have obvious advantages because the number of units thus is minimized and the necessity of remembering a multitude of names and their definitions and mutual relations is reduced. If, however, the extensive use of a few names obscures or distorts the true nature of ever-changing stratigraphic relationships, which stratigraphers attempt to decipher and interpret, one of the most important objectives of stratigraphic investigation is seriously endangered.

The details of local stratigraphic relations can be shown best in terms of rock units closely adapted to local developments that rarely are exactly the same in any two areas. If stratigraphic subdivision were to be made only on this basis, however, a bewildering multiplicity of formations and formation names would be required and little if any sense of unity would be apparent. Consequently, an intermediate position must be sought. There must be a compromise between a desire, on the one hand, for simplicity in nomenclature that emphasizes regional similarities and a wish, on the other, for detailed accuracy with respect to local relations.

With these objectives in mind, several principles may be suggested to aid in the selection of desirable lateral limits of formations, and other rock units, and in the extension of their names, where strata are laterally continuous or are presumed to be of similar age. Because it is desirable to recognize units and to employ names throughout as large areas as is reasonably practicable, and thus hold their number to a minimum, these principles are stated negatively.

1. Ordinarily a unit should not be recognized beyond a point where important lateral lithologic change occurs and the strata no longer possess those particular lithologic features which serve to characterize the unit at its type locality.

2. If precise boundaries are relied upon to define it, a unit should not be extended beyond the areas where these boundaries or closely similar ones are clearly recognizable and continuous.

3. Ordinarily a rock unit should not be extended or identified solely on the basis of paleontologic characters.

4. A unit should not be extended beyond a single basin of deposition or into remote separated regions.

5. In the absence of evidence of subsurface continuity, a unit should not be recognized in outcropping zones on opposite sides of a large basin unless the strata are similar and the stratigraphic relations are clearly the same.

6. Similar restraint should be exercised with respect to strata that are separated from each other on the opposite flanks of broad anticlinal structures like the Cincinnati arch; the same name should not be used unless the strata closely resemble each other lithologically and the stratigraphic relations are clearly similar.

Subsurface Requirements

Stratigraphic classification and nomenclature are largely the products of surface stratigraphic studies conducted by field geologists who have observed outcrops and traced outcrop continuity. The outcrops so studied generally extend in bands or zones along the strike of dipping strata. Consequently, lateral gradation and lithologic changes commonly have been considered examples of simple linear variability. Outcrop bands occur, on the one hand, on the flanks of uplifted areas from which strata have been stripped by erosion or across which deposition was not continuous and, on the other, along the margins of downwarped areas or basins into which the strata extend under the cover of younger beds. The proportion of strata of any age that actually are available to direct observation in the bands of outcrop is relatively small in comparison with the total extent of these strata either as they formerly occurred or as they now remain. When the areal extent of strata is considered, the problem of lateral gradation and lithologic change acquires a two-dimensional aspect that is much more complicated than the linear relations observable in outcrops.

Stratigraphers, of course, are concerned with these larger problems although many field geologists seem to lack appreciation of them. Subsurface geologists, however, are accustomed to dealing with areal problems and lateral variability that occurs in two dimensions. Also they commonly are interested in relatively extensive regions constituting indivisible units. Consequently subsurface requirements with respect to stratigraphic classification and nomenclature are likely to be more difficult and more demanding than those that satisfy the needs of surface stratigraphy and ordinary geologic mapping.

Somewhat areally restricted, laterally gradational formations may be most suitable for outcrop studies and surface mapping but are inconvenient or unsatisfactory for subsurface work. Even the recognition of two nearly identical formations and two almost synonymous names is likely to be confusing in a basin area whose depositional and structural history is being considered as a whole. An example is provided by the Galena Dolomite and Kimmswick Limestone (Ord.) of the upper Mississippi Valley. These formations outcrop in different areas. Each is a well-marked lithologic unit possessing characteristics different from those of the other. Both names are well known and have been used consistently for many years. Beneath the cover of younger beds, however, these formations are transitional. The change occurs so gradually that no satisfactory abrupt division between them can be made. In the subsurface they constitute a single continuous unit that needs a single name.

Stratigraphic units that do not correspond with conventional surface formations may be more useful in some subsurface studies than those which do. Some horizons or thin zones identified in electric logs or by other means may be traced across areas of lithologic change where the relations of formations are irregular or obscure. Strata between such horizons or zones provide informal supplementary stratigraphic units for which the term *format* has been proposed. Formats are rock units, although possibly many of them may approximate time-rock units closely.

Political Boundaries

The subdivisions recognized in equivalent parts of a stratigraphic section and the names applied to the resulting rock units change in different areas because (1) lateral lithologic variations or changed structural relations require different treatment, and (2) units and names that originated in different areas have been extended until they meet.

Lateral lithologic changes are inevitable in any extensive region of sedimentary deposition. The changes may be abrupt or very gradual. In either case they may make changes in stratigraphic classification and nomenclature desirable or necessary. If lithologic transition is abrupt, there may be no question where these changes should be made. If, however, it is gradual, there may be considerable areas where either of two systems of classification and nomenclature might be employed with equal satisfaction.

Most of the early stratigraphic studies and geologic mapping in the eastern and central United States was accomplished under the auspices of the several state geological surveys. Much of this work lacked coordination from state to state or even from area to area within a single state. Many different stratigraphic sections were built up that varied greatly among themselves with respect to the rock units recognized and the names selected for them. With the

Wooster 1877	Winchell 1888	Ulrich 1914	Twenhofel and Thwaites 1919
Sandstone	Dresbach Ss.	Dresbach Ss.	Dresbach Ss.
trilobite bed Eau Claire		Eau Claire Fm.	
grit	Hinckley Ss.	Mt. Simon Ss.	

Figure 173. Diagram showing variations in the nomenclature applied to the basal part of the Upper Cambrian in the upper Mississippi Valley. Confusion in use of the name Dresbach is particularly noticeable. Subdivisions of this section have been considered formations or

passage of time, some of these differences have been eliminated but others still remain as the result of different local requirements or because of habits and prejudices inherited from former days. Thus it is not uncommon for strata on the two sides of a state line to be joined differently into rock units, for the same units to be known by different names, or for the same name to be used in different ways.

As an example of adjustment, the old name Mitchel Limestone (Miss.) formerly used in Indiana has been abandoned for strata equivalent to the St. Louis and Ste. Genevieve limestones of the Mississippi Valley and these names have now replaced it. In southern Wisconsin, the Dresbach Formation (Camb.) is divided into three members, but across the state line in Illinois these members are considered to be formations and formerly the name Dresbach was used for only one of them (see Figure 173). Coal No. 6 is one of the most important coals in Illinois. In Indiana this same bed is known as Coal VA and in western Kentucky it is No. 12 coal.

Political boundaries are not likely to correspond with natural lateral stratigraphic boundaries. The changes in stratigraphic treatment at such places may give the erroneous impression that lithologic changes are more abrupt and more important there than they really are (see Figure 174). If changes in stratigraphic subdivision or nomenclature are required, however, and no more logical dividing line is indicated, a state line may be an advantageous place to effect the change. It may be possible thus to preserve some old, useful, and well-known names and avoid the confusion that commonly attends changes in nomenclature.

Anderson 1919	Ulrich and Resser 1930		Trowbridge and Atwater 1934	Illinois Geological Survey
Jordan Ss.	Dresbach Ss.	Dresbach Formation	Galesville Mem.	Galesville Ss.
St. Lawrence Fm.	Eau Claire Ss.		Eau Claire Mem.	Eau Claire Fm.
Dresbach Ss.			Mt. Simon Mem.	Mt. Simon Ss.

members of a single inclusive formation by different persons at the same time. (Data from Thwaites, 1927, Ill. Geol. Surv., Rept. Invest. 13, p. 10, table 1, and Raasch, 1935, 9th Ann. Field Conf., Kan. Geol. Soc., p. 304, fig. 212.)

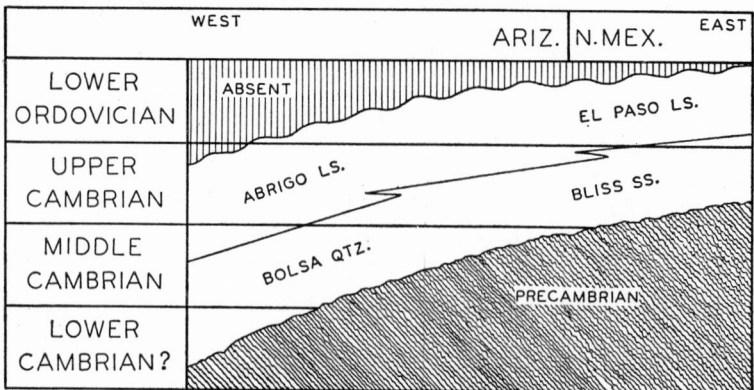

Figure 174. Much-generalized diagram showing the time and lateral relations of early Paleozoic formations in parts of Arizona and New Mexico. Formations of different ages recognized in these neighboring states are now believed to have been laterally continuous. Both the lower sandstone and upper limestone units appear to transgress time planes and become younger as they are traced from west to east. (After Sabins, 1957, *Bull. Am. Assoc. Petroleum Geol.,* vol. 41, p. 471, fig. 4.)

Conclusions

The preceding discussions clearly show that the method of subdividing and grouping strata into rock units and the selection of names to be used for them are neither simple nor certain. Many aspects of the problems involved are viewed differently by different persons. Divergent opinions are inevitable. If it is realized that no system of classification and no selection of names can meet the needs and desires of all stratigraphers, some of the inadequacies and discrepancies of the many systems now in use will be understood and viewed more leniently. These systems have grown up gradually over the years through the uncoordinated work of many geologists, and some of their features have as much historical as natural significance. Details of these systems have been changed in the past and more changes undoubtedly will be made in the future. In this way systems of classification and nomenclature have evolved and they will continue to evolve into increasingly more useful and meaningful patterns.

REDEFINITION OF STRATIGRAPHIC UNITS

Many stratigraphic units of all categories and classes have been redefined or had their boundaries shifted with the purpose of correcting some real or imagined fault in a former definition or of improving the understanding of a stratigraphic section. Some have been altered repeatedly. Any change in the application of a name to strata, however, invites misunderstanding and confusion because the meaning of the name is changed. Thus what appears to be a single definite unit may actually have been quite different at different times and, if a proposed revision of boundaries were not recognized by all, a single name might identify different units to different persons at the same time.

The Carbondale Formation or Group (Penn.) of Illinois provides an example of revisions that first corrected a mistake in correlation and later shifted boundaries to conform to a different system of stratigraphic classification. This name was introduced for a formation extending from the base of Coal No. 2 to the top of Coal No. 6 because this interval was recognized to include most of the commercially important coals of Illinois. Moreover paleobotanic correlation indicated age equivalence to the well-known Allegheny Formation of the northern Appalachian region. After many years the discovery was made that Coal No. 2 at Murphysboro in southern Illinois is not the same as Coal No. 2 at Colchester in western Illinois but lies approximately 200 feet lower stratigraphically. The Murphysboro coal can be identified in only a comparatively small area and therefore is not a satisfactory key bed to mark a boundary. Consequently, the much more persistent Colchester coal was accepted as the base of the Carbondale and this formation was restricted correspondingly in southern Illinois. The lower Allegheny flora, however, that was one of the main considerations in the original definition of the Carbondale Formation occurs associated with the Murphysboro coal, so the change of boundary altered the definition of the formation in this way also. Later, when the Pennsylvanian of Illinois was subdivided into cyclothems, the Carbondale became a group. Its boundaries were shifted to the base of the sandstone underlying the Colchester coal and to

Old Classification	Modern Classification
Kaskaskia Ls.	Chesterian Series
St. Louis Ls.	Ste. Genevieve Ls.
	St. Louis Ls.
	Salem Ls.
Archimedes Ls.	Warsaw Fm.

Figure 175. The old St. Louis Limestone (Miss.) of the upper Mississippi Valley has been subdivided, and the use of the name has been restricted to the middle part of this stratigraphic section. The lower and upper parts are now recognized as distinct formations known by other names. Thus the meaning of the name St. Louis has been radically changed.

the base of the sandstone overlying Coal No. 6 in order to make them conform to the boundaries of cyclothems.

Greater adjustments are required if a unit is restricted within limits much narrower than those it originally possessed. The St. Louis Limestone (Miss.), for instance, once included all strata in the upper Mississippi Valley lying between Chester beds above and the Warsaw Limestone below, as shown in Figure 175. Later the Ste. Genevieve and Salem limestones, first recognized as separate formations in distant areas, gained broad acceptance, and strata present in the upper and lower parts respectively of the original St. Louis were assigned to these formations. Use of the name St. Louis was then restricted to the remaining intervening beds. In contrast, the Madison Limestone of the Rocky Mountain region (see Figure 160, p. 421) was subdivided, but new names were provided for all its parts.

Alabama 1890	Alabama 1926	Georgia 1942
Bangor Ls.	Pennington Sh.	Pennington Sh.
	Bangor Ls.	Bangor Ls.
	Hartsell Ss.	
	Gasper Ls.	
Ft. Payne Chert	Ste. Genevieve Ls.	Ft. Payne Chert
	St. Louis Ls.	
	Warsaw Ls.	
	Ft. Payne Chert	

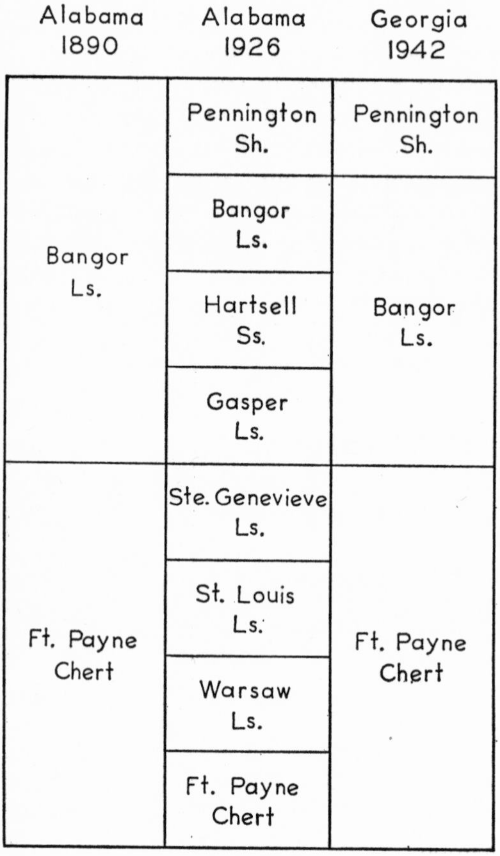

Figure 176. Chart showing the Mississippian stratigraphic units in the southern Appalachian region as recognized by different persons at different times. Much confusion in the application of such names as Bangor Limestone and Ft. Payne Chert is the result of variable usage. This is not apparent in the literature unless close attention is paid to the author of a report, the time of its publication, and the particular area described. (After Weller and others, 1948, *Bull. Geol. Soc. Amer.*, vol. 59, chart after p. 196.)

The Mississippian System in northern Alabama originally was separated into two formations, an upper calcareous unit, the Bangor Limestone, and a lower siliceous unit, the Ft. Payne Chert (see Figure 176). Subsequently the upper unit was divided into four formations and the name Bangor was restricted to one of them. Still later, in the neighboring part of Georgia, three of the last formations were not distinguished and the name Bangor was used in a much broader sense approaching but not equaling its original definition.

Many so-called groups, more properly considered stages, have been altered and revised repeatedly by the addition or subtraction of formations. Generally these changes have resulted from the acquisition of new or the re-evaluation of old information with respect to the relations of fossil faunas. Opinions as to whether a particular fauna is more similar to the fauna of overlying or underlying beds are likely to vary and be disputed. The not uncommon lack of agreement in these matters indicates that the boundaries of many units are very arbitrary.

The fact that revisions and restrictions of stratigraphic units have altered the meanings of many stratigraphic names is likely to escape the notice of those who are not well acquainted with the history of stratigraphic investigations and all the literature dealing with the geology of an area. The exact definition of a stratigraphic unit and the exact meaning of a stratigraphic name are very important in correlation and stratigraphic interpretation. In order to be certain in these matters, it may be necessary to take careful note of the author and date of a geologic report and also of the location of the area concerned.

BIBLIOGRAPHY

Forgotson, J. M., Jr. (1957), Nature, usage and definition of marker-defined vertically segregated rock units, *Bull. Am. Assoc. Petroleum Geol.,* vol. 41, pp. 2108–2113.
  The problem of nomenclature of subsurface stratigraphic units traced across facies boundaries is considered.
Moore, R. C. (1936), Stratigraphic classification of the Pennsylvanian rocks of Kansas, Geol. Surv. Kan., Bull. 22.
  For methods used in classifying and naming rock stratigraphic units in a complex section see pp. 15–40.
Wheeler, H. E., and Mallory, V. S. (1953), Designation of stratigraphic units, *Bull. Am. Assoc. Petroleum Geol.,* vol. 37, pp. 2407–2421.
  The geometric form and lateral relations of rock stratigraphic units are discussed.
Wilmarth, M. G. (1938), Lexicon of geologic names of the United States (including Alaska), U.S. Geol. Surv., Bull. 896 (2 pts.), reprinted 1951 and 1957.
  All geologic names published through 1935 are listed, with references and notations.
Wilson, Druid, Sando, W. J., and Knopf, R. W. (1957), Geologic names of North America introduced in 1936–1955, U.S. Geol. Surv., Bull. 1056-A.
  This supplements Wilmarth's Lexicon but lacks notations.

See also Reports of the American Commission on Stratigraphic Nomenclature listed at end of Chapter 12.

14

Lateral Variation and Facies

ONLY casual observation is required to demonstrate that sediments of the most diverse types are accumulating simultaneously today at different places. It is also evident that the kind of sediment being deposited at any place is determined by local circumstances and conditions. These relations are not unique to present time but have existed through all past ages. Accumulating sediments have always varied laterally. Likewise conditions have changed from time to time at any place and these changes are reflected by vertical sedimentary variation.

Vertical change in lithologic character is apparent at almost every outcrop. It is so familiar to all geologists that it is accepted without reserve as an almost universal feature of sediments and sedimentary rocks. All geologists also realize that lateral variation must occur. Some, however, lose sight of this fact because they are conditioned to think in terms of formations that persist throughout more or less extensive areas with a considerable degree of uniformity and because lateral variation generally is not abrupt or obvious. Although lateral facies variations have been recognized for more than a century, habits of thought inherited from the Wernerian era have been difficult to shake off completely.

William Smith's demonstration that similar fossils identify the same formation at different places induced the countertheorem that different fossils indicate formations of different ages. Though the first generally is correct, the second conclusion is neither logical nor true but it has contributed to neglect of the appreciation that lateral change rather than uniformity is the rule. This viewpoint has survived into the present century and there have been influential paleontologists and stratigraphers who minimized the possibilities of important lateral variation. The satisfactory untangling of various misinterpreted stratigraphic relations, such as some of those involving lower Paleozoic formations in the Appalachian region, has required the development of newer viewpoints by younger minds.

Lateral variation and facies changes obscure stratigraphic relations and are responsible for many uncertainties and disagreements. Understanding of the importance of facies relations in sedimentary rocks, however, has gradually increased. These relations are now recognized to be particularly significant in connection with correlation problems and the interpretation of environmental conditions and paleogeography.

LATERAL VARIATION

Lateral variation in sedimentary deposits is expressed in (1) changing lithologic characters, (2) changing thickness, and (3) irregularities of structure resulting from deposition on uneven surfaces.

Lithologic Variation

Lateral lithologic variation in sediments and sedimentary rocks may be gradual or abrupt, the differences depending upon distinctness of boundaries separating depositional environments of diverse types. Because of rather characteristic differences in local interenvironmental relations, distinction generally can be made between lateral variations in (1) fluvial deposits, (2) littoral deposits, and (3) marine deposits. Deposition in large lakes varies much like that within the sea.

Fluvial Deposits

Fluvial deposits may be divided into channel and flood-plain facies. The more or less constant shifting of channels is likely to result in complex associations. Deposition in both environments is controlled by currents. In channels the currents are relatively strong and extremely variable from place to place and from time to time. Consequently deposits are equally variable and consist of relatively coarse sediments in irregular beds of limited extent. Individual beds commonly are lenticular or show rapid textural gradations and they are likely to be separated by minor erosional surfaces. Complete channel fills are long, generally narrow and somewhat sinuous bodies of coarse sediment that either grade laterally into finer material or occupy depressions eroded in older deposits (see Figures 177 and 178). In areas of very active aggradation, as on growing alluvial fans, well-marked channels are less likely to develop and deposition occurs irregularly over broad surfaces accompanied by much local scouring that produces cut-and-fill structures.

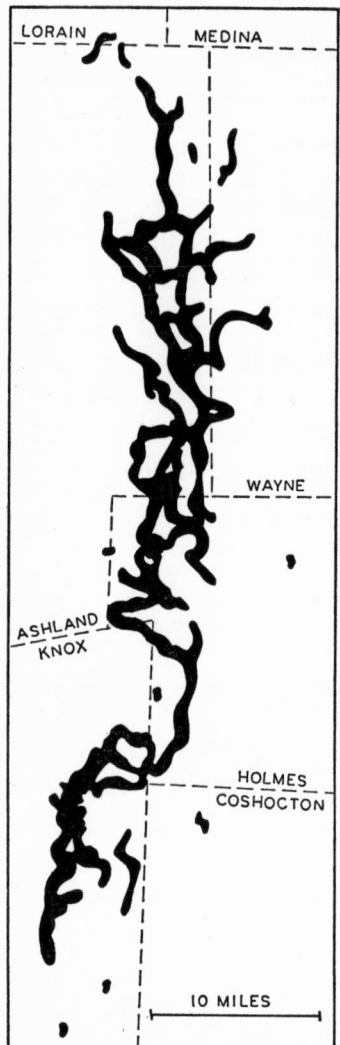

Figure 177. Map showing the distribution and relations of Berea Sandstone (Miss.) channels in part of north central Ohio. The pattern indicated here suggests shifting channels similar to those that have been occupied successively by modern rivers. (After Pepper and others, 1954, U.S. Geol. Surv., Prof. Paper 259, p. 47, fig. 28.)

More or less slack-water conditions occur, or currents are very gentle, outside of channel-ways at times of flood. Therefore, flood-plain deposits are characteristically both finer textured and more regularly bedded than those of channels. Sediments may occur in alternating coarser and finer layers in a varve-like manner. In the absence of channels, flood-plain deposits may be difficult to distinguish from sediments laid down in a shallow littoral environment protected from the action of strong waves.

On the whole, fluvial deposits are marked by great irregularity. Facies differentiation is likely to be imperfect and indistinct except in local areas and restricted stratigraphic zones.

Littoral Deposits

Deposits of the shore and shallow-water littoral zone are not abundantly available for observation in ancient sediments. This is a zone across which most marine detrital sediment must pass, but little finds a permanent resting place there unless sea level is rising or sediment is especially abundant. Deposits of this zone become immediately subject to erosion when sea level declines and are likely to be rapidly destroyed. If they remain, the deposits of this relatively narrow zone rarely coincide with outcrop trends.

Littoral deposits generally record restricted environments that are related to nearness of the shore, depth of water, and effectiveness of wave action. Lateral variation is most pronounced in zones parallel to the shore. Sand commonly is deposited in a relatively narrow band extending outward from the beach to a depth of not much more than thirty to forty feet, where it gives way to silty or muddy sediment. Thus marine sands mark shorelines or occur in bars built in very shallow water. If sea level fluctuates, the sandy near-shore zone shifts back and forth accordingly and may result in the intertonguing of sandy and muddy sediments (see Figure 179). If the supply of coarse detrital sediment is small, sand is likely to be concentrated near the point where it is delivered to the sea by streams and it grades laterally to finer sediment along the coast. A large supply provides sand and silt that may be built out into a delta, from which sand is spread for a considerable distance along the shore. Continued deposition may produce a faithful record of how the position of the shoreline changed. An excellent example is provided by the intertonguing Mancos Shale and Mesa Verde Sandstone (Cret.) of Utah and Colorado. Most extensive sandstone formations with little or

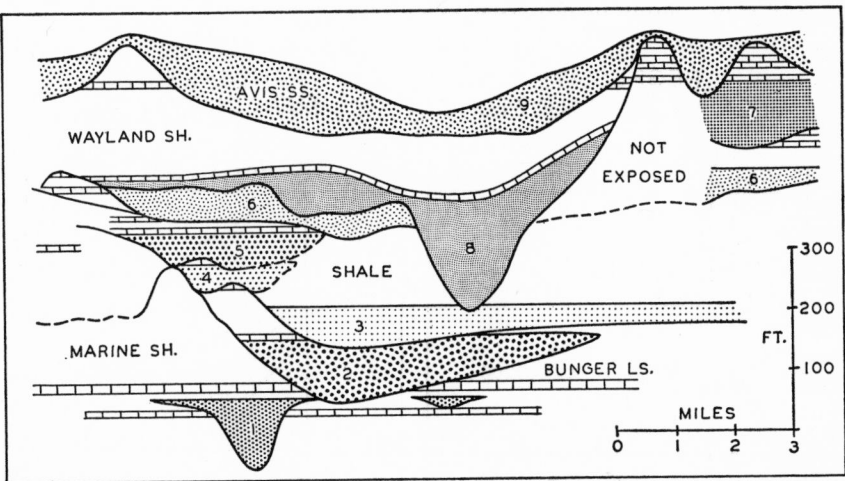

Figure 178. Diagram showing the stratigraphic relations of nine successive unconformable sandstones that occupy channels in the Graham Formation (Penn.) of northern Texas. (After Lee, 1938, Univ. Tex. Publ. 3801, pl. 2.)

no interbedded shale are marine deposits that followed a shifting shoreline, probably a transgressing one, or filled a very shallow-water area. Seaward they grade into finer-textured strata.

In the absence of detrital sediments, calcium carbonate may constitute deposits of the littoral zone. This can occur importantly only in tropical or subtropical regions. It is particularly characteristic near coastal reefs from which this sediment is derived. Size sorting is likely to be accomplished by wave and current action along such coasts but lithification may mask lateral gradation and facies are not so well developed nor do they show up so clearly in calcareous sediments as in littoral detrital deposits. Also lateral gradation in calcareous sediments does not certainly identify a coastal zone because such sediment can originate and accumulate in shallow water far from any land.

Marine Deposits

Environmental conditions in the sea are much more broadly uniform, and lateral variations generally are gradual except in near-shore, very shallow-water areas. In landlocked epicontinental seas, where tidal flow is small and wave action is less severe than in the open oceans, uniformity may characterize even fairly shallow-water deposition. This is the type of general environment represented by many of the marine formations of the continental platform regions. The more conspicuous lateral changes that do occur commonly are related to such factors as depth of water, distance from sources of detrital sediments, and direction of sediment-distributing currents.

As a rule, marine depositional conditions have altered much more con-

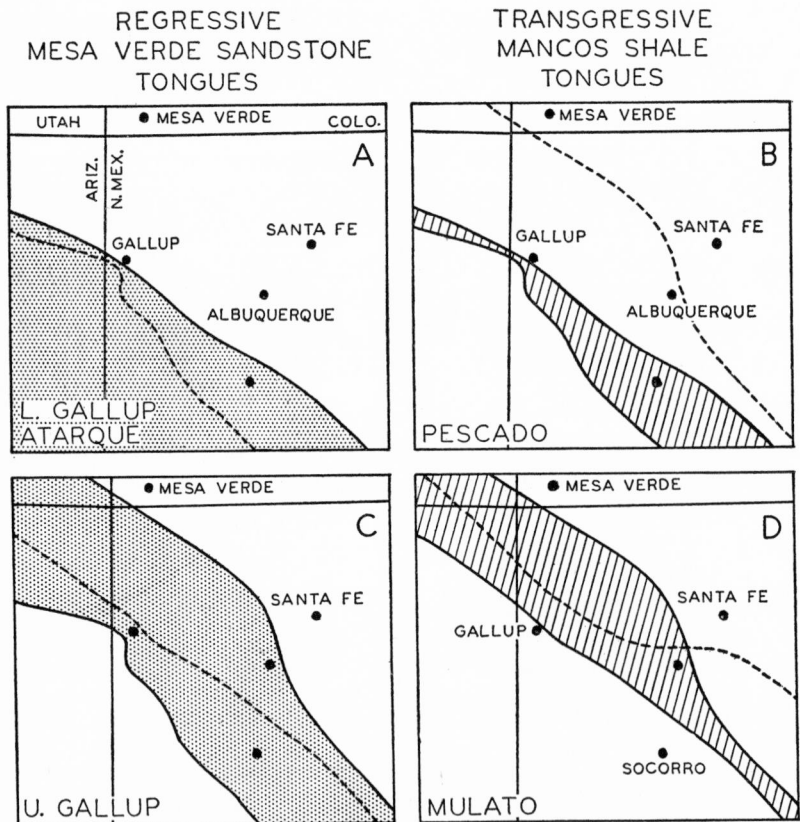

Figure 179. Maps showing the areal extent of interfingering tongues of Mesa Verde Sandstone and Mancos Shale (Cret.) in northwestern New Mexico and neighboring regions. The shaded areas in A, C, E, and G are sandstone tongues wedging out northeastward. In B, D, F, and H they are shale tongues wedging out to the southwest. These maps do not show the patterns of shifting shorelines because the

spicuously and abruptly with passing time than they have from place to place contemporaneously. Vertical changes in the lithologic characters of strata reflect such variations as fluctuating sea level, altered extent and topographic conditions in sediment-producing lands, and climatic changes. Marine facies are likely to consist of several vertically successive, more or less contrasting kinds of sediment, but stratigraphic units generally are extensive laterally and smoothly intergrade. Zones in which facies changes may occur shift gradually across an area or remain fairly constant for considerable intervals of time.

Although the marine environment commonly is characterized by maximum uniformity, it also exhibits some very striking and abrupt changes related to biologic activity. Bioherms result from the presence of communities

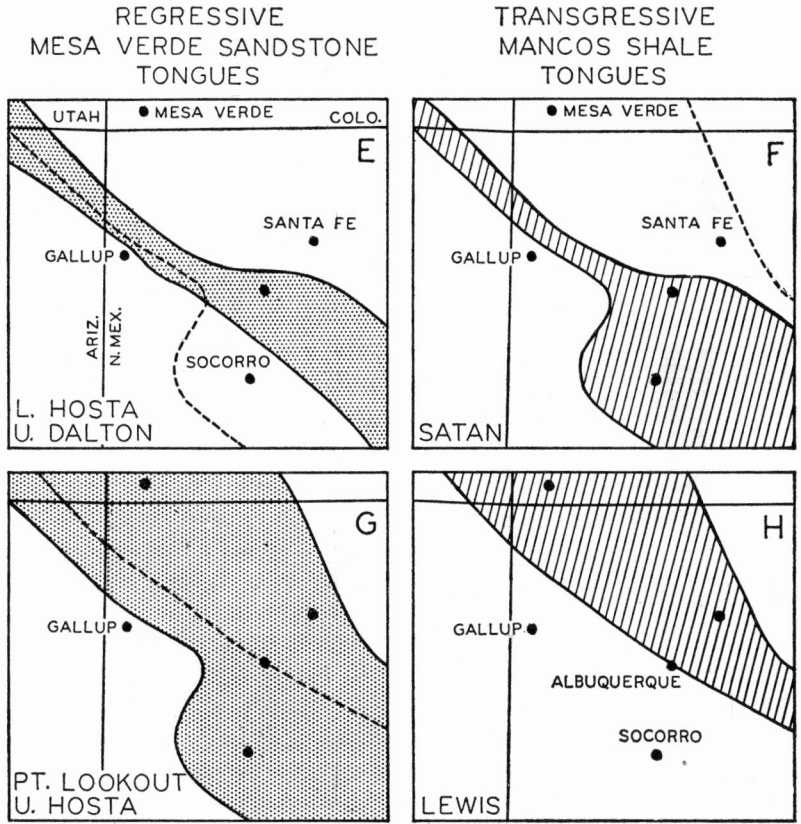

sandstones are largely if not entirely marine. The actual shore, however, probably shifted in a somewhat similar way but was located a little farther to the southwest. (After Pike, 1947, Geol. Soc. Amer., Mem. 24, p. 94, fig. 7.) See also Figure 191, p. 501.

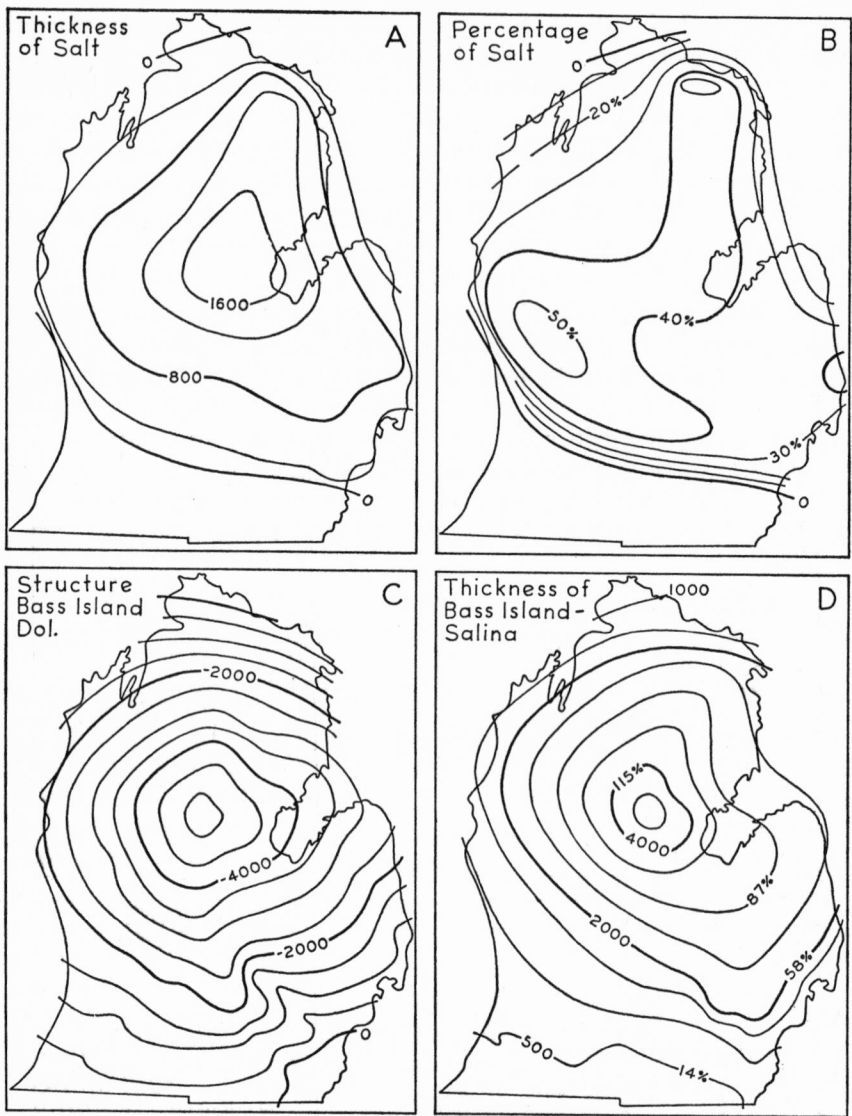

Figure 180. Maps showing features of the subsurface Silurian geology of Michigan.
A. Isopachs showing the total thickness of salt in the Salina Formation.

B. Map showing the proportions of the Salina and Bass Island formations that consist of rock salt. It was constructed from the data provided by A and D.

C. Structural contour map of the top of the Bass Island Dolomite. Structure at the bottom of the Salina Formation can be calculated by subtracting the thicknesses shown in D. Comparison with Figure 107, p. 280, showing the position of the Precambrian surface in Michigan, indicates that sinking in the Michigan basin occurred about one-third in pre-Salina time, about one-third in Salina-Bass Island time, and about one third in subsequent Paleozoic time.

of organisms that became established locally on the sea floor and by altering the prevailing environment perpetuated themselves there. Structures of these kinds generally are confined to restricted parts of the stratigraphic section and occur in more or less well-marked areas. Where they are present, however, they introduce complexities that are likely to be baffling until the lateral relations of very different kinds of strata have been determined.

Thickness Variation

In continental areas the thicknesses of most marine sediments seem to have been controlled through all the geologic past by downwarping of the basins. This is most marked in geosynclinal regions where many thousands of feet of dominantly marine sediments accumulated but none bears conclusive evidence of deposition at a depth of more than a few hundred feet. Some thick black shales have been interpreted as abyssal sediments because they lack benthonic fossils but such strata probably indicate anaerobic or toxic bottom conditions rather than great depth. These relations suggest some measure of isostatic control but this could not have been perfect because sedimentary loading by itself is incapable of maintaining continuous subsidence in any basin. The comparison of geosynclines to deep oceanic trenches adjacent to modern island arcs also fails to indicate close parallelism.

Detrital sedimentary rocks thicken in passing from platform regions into geosynclines and the supposition is rather common that such deposits thicken toward the source of sediments. That this is not necessarily true is shown clearly by thickening of Tertiary strata in the southern states toward the Gulf of Mexico (see Figure 103, p. 275). Also many formations, including limestones and other non-detrital deposits, increase in thickness from all sides inward toward the centers of continental basins. An excellent example is provided by the Silurian System of Michigan as shown in Figure 180D. Thickness variations suggest corresponding differences in the rate of sedimentary deposition, but the occurrence of unconformities and diastems may result in underestimation of these rates. The lateral thinning or perhaps the complete wedging out of a rock unit may indicate either lithologic change or unconformable relations. Erroneous interpretations are certain if such relations are misidentified.

Lateral variation in the thickness of sedimentary rocks generally is expressed in terms of recognized rock units such as formations or groups. Measurements of the same unit at different places, however, may not be strictly

D. Isopach map showing thickness of the Bass Island–Salina strata. Thickness is indicated in feet and also as percentages of the thickest stratigraphic section encountered in deep wells.

(A, C, and D after Landes, 1945, U.S. Geol. Surv., Oil and Gas Invest., Prelim. Map 40, figs. 4, 1, and 3.)

comparable because (1) the measured unit is not necessarily a time-rock unit, and (2) it may be bounded by unconformities and be interrupted by other stratigraphic discontinuities. Determination of the thicknesses of time-rock units, which is necessary for accurate comparison, may be difficult if not impossible. Thickness relations in areas of rapid lateral lithologic change where the stratigraphic section is subdivided into different sequences of practical rock units are likely to be especially uncertain.

Thickness variations of stratigraphic units such as those compiled to produce isopach maps commonly are employed as the basis for studies of the structural evolution of platform and basin areas. To be meaningful for this purpose it must be assumed that the units measured are time-rock units, that the strata included in them were deposited in a horizontal position, and that appreciable compaction has not occurred. The results are accurate only insofar as these assumptions are true. If boundaries of the units deviate importantly from time planes, conclusions are almost certain to be erroneous. Consequently great care is necessary in order that boundaries may be selected which can be correlated most certainly on the basis of time rather than lithologic nature and continuity.

Structural Variation

Non-tectonic structural variation mostly involves bedding and bedding characters. These commonly are related to ordinary lithologic variations, which require no further consideration here. There remain, however, erosional channels filled with sandstone and limestone masses termed reefs and bioherms. These display complications involving abrupt lateral transitions and extreme variations in bedding characters and inclination (see Figure 181 and also Figures 170, p. 448, and 178, p. 483). They have resulted in much stratigraphic confusion in areas of inadequate outcrops and have been variously misinterpreted where the details of facies interrelations are not clearly shown.

The word *reef* has been used in many ways. Even among stratigraphers its meaning is not uniform. It has been loosely applied to (1) almost any limestone mass that swells into a reeflike mound or ridge surrounded by sedimentary material of a different kind, and (2) other limestones that do not have this form but contain the abundant fossilized remains of organisms, such as corals, which commonly are believed to be reef builders. In an effort to make this distinction clear, two new words were coined and introduced into the technical vocabulary of geologists. *Bioherm* was proposed for the organic reeflike mounds to distinguish them from other reefs that are not stratigraphic bodies or are of nonorganic origin, and *biostrome* was proposed for obviously organic limestone that occurs in ordinary layers. Both of these words have been much used but the first does not distinguish between two entirely different kinds of structure and the second is not required as a special technical designation.

According to its original definition, a bioherm may be either (1) a true organic reef that was built by animals and plants and grew steeply upward from the sea bottom as a potentially wave-resistant mass or (2) a more or less irregular limestone lens consisting of fragmental organic debris that accumulated locally on the sea floor but never rose much above the general sedimentary surface and was not wave resistant. Typical examples of these

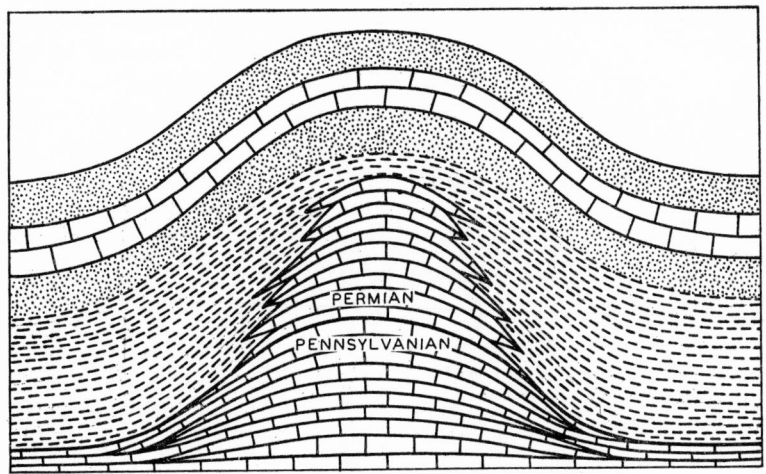

Figure 181. Diagrammatic section showing an organic reef of Wolfcampian age (Perm.) rising from the top of a Pennsylvanian reef in the Wellman oil field of Terry County, Texas. No scale provided but the Permian reef is from 1000 to 1500 feet high. (After Anderson, 1953, *Bull. Am. Assoc. Petroleum Geol.,* vol. 37, p. 520, fig. 11.)

two kinds of structure are the Silurian limestone reefs of the Great Lakes region (see Figures 182 and 183) and the crinoidal limestone mounds occurring in the Borden Group (Miss.) of southwestern Indiana (see Figure 187, p. 497). Coral beds in the lower part of the Jeffersonville Limestone (Dev.) at the Falls of the Ohio near Louisville, Kentucky, are a well-known example of a so-called biostrome.

The discovery of oil in buried reeflike limestone bodies has focused attention on these structures but the nomenclature applied to them is confused and many geologic reports do not make adequate distinction between the different kinds. These structures have been termed both organic reefs and bioherms rather indiscriminately but it is preferable to distinguish true organic reefs wherever possible. Although *bioherm* can be retained as a structural rather than as a genetic term to include both kinds of mounds, it is most useful as a designation for limestone bodies of doubtful wave-resistant types. The actual nature of many bioherms, particularly those that do not outcrop, is uncertain. These should not be described as reefs unless their nature is well established.

Organic Reefs

True organic reefs are rigid structures that rise more or less steeply above the sea bottom and grow upward almost to water level. The designation *coral reef* commonly applied to them actually is a misnomer, particularly for some ancient reefs, because careful investigation proves that corals have not been the most important reef builders and rarely do their skeletons constitute as much as one-fifth of the reef mass. The remains of many other kinds of organisms are much more prevalent. Calcareous algae rather than corals have played the most important role both in contributing calcium carbonate to modern reefs and in binding calcareous debris derived from other organisms into a wave-resistant structure.

Calcareous algae cannot exist except in shallow lighted water, and modern reef corals cannot live in water whose temperature falls below 68°F. or at a greater depth than about 250 feet. Both kinds of organisms require clear water of nearly normal oceanic salinity. Corals thrive best where waves and currents bring them an abundant and continuous supply of oxygen and food. It is generally assumed that fossil reef-building organisms also had similar requirements but this is not certain. Paleozoic corals differ importantly from modern ones and their zoologic relations are not considered to be very close. Some modern corals are abundant locally in deeper, colder water. Consequently ancient corals may not indicate a similar environment although there is no evidence that they lived under conditions greatly different from those occurring on modern reefs.

The growth of all organic reefs is believed to have started in fairly shallow water. The great thicknesses that many of them attain, therefore, indicate that these structures grew upward as sea level rose or as the sea floor sank. Modern reefs are estimated to be capable of rising one foot in about ten years. If sea level rises, they must keep pace with it or they will drown. Deep drilling on Eniwetok Atoll in the Pacific revealed more than 4000 feet of reef material before igneous basement rock was reached. Most known fossil reefs are not so thick, but some of the Silurian reefs in Illinois grew upward almost 1000 feet (see Figure 182) and the Permian reefs of west Texas and New Mexico continue through 2000 feet or more of stratigraphic section. These thicknesses do not necessarily indicate that the reefs ever stood so high above the bottom because as they grew interreef sediments accumulated between them and lapped up on their sides.

Organic reefs characteristically consist of more or less structureless cores and dipping flank beds (see Figure 183). The cores are massive, and commonly porous or even cavernous. Their framework was built by living organisms but diagenesis, and in many reefs dolomitization, has destroyed almost all traces of their original organic structure. These also are the parts whose upper growing portions are battered by waves and produce large

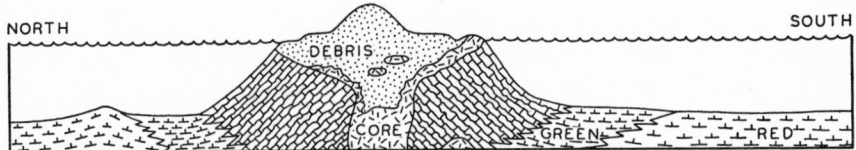

Figure 182. Reconstruction of the Marine reef of Niagaran age (Sil.) in Madison County, Illinois, as interpreted from well records. The form of this reef indicates that upward growth occurred first rapidly and then more slowly on its southern side. This suggests that during the later stage of reef development prevailing winds and currents were from the south. The dominantly red interreef sediments become greenish in an area surrounding the reef. The color change probably resulted from the reducing action of organic matter derived from the prolific organic community responsible for the reef's growth. No scale provided. (After Lowenstam, 1950, J. Geol., vol. 58, p. 464, fig. 8.)

quantities of calcareous debris, much of which accumulates as talus on reef flanks. The finer debris is swept away by currents and settles in deeper water or is redissolved. Thus three lithologic facies can be distinguished in and about most mature organic reefs: (1) the massive structureless reef core, (2) the more or less coarse-grained, fragmental, outward-dipping reef flank

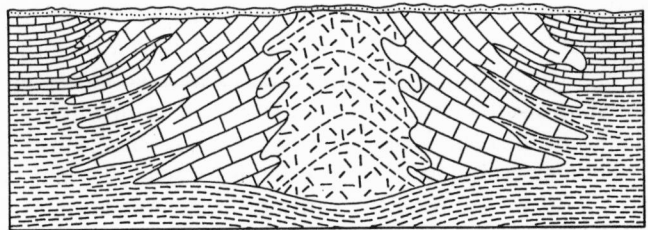

Figure 183. Generalized cross section showing the form and structure of a typical Niagaran (Sil.) reef in northern Indiana. This reef is shown transgressing the boundary between the Mississinewa Shale and Liston Creek Limestone. It consists of massive core rock and flanking beds that dip outward and interfinger with non-reef sediments. The top of this reef has been destroyed by erosion and its original thickness is not known. Strata represented in this section are about 150 feet thick. (After Cumings and Shrock, 1928, Bull. Geol. Soc. Amer., vol. 39, p. 598, fig. 7.)

strata, and (3) the fine-grained interreef and deeper-water deposits. These represent three corresponding environments: (1) a very shallow, rough-water, well-aerated zone, (2) an intermediate semi-rough-water zone, and (3) a deeper, quiet-water zone that may have been oxygen deficient or toxic and unsuited to the existence of an abundant benthonic fauna. In addition a fourth facies and environment may occur in a back-reef or enclosed lagoon. This generally is a relatively quiet-water, very shallow zone in which fine-grained sediments accumulate. Depending upon the situation, sediment may be entirely calcareous or this may grade into detrital material. The back-reef water may not be normal in salinity, and some back-reef deposits include evaporites (see Figure 185, p. 495). On the whole, the lithologic characters, structures, and fossils of the four environments are quite different and distinctive.

Laterally equivalent strata in reef and interreef deposits are difficult to recognize because sediments of the different environments vary rapidly and greatly, both in character and in thickness. Also they are difficult to trace because deposition occurred upon an uneven surface and strata may rise or fall considerably within short distances. Uniformity of level, which indicates approximate continuity in most stratigraphic situations, is meaningless with respect to reefs because this leads outward from reef cores into younger and younger strata. In the absence of excellent outcrops or very closely spaced subsurface records, structures are easily misinterpreted. The first Silurian organic reefs observed in northern Indiana were believed to be abrupt tectonic folds, and reefs near the boundary between the Carboniferous and Permian systems in eastern Russia were formerly considered limestone hills produced by erosion and marking an important unconformity (see Figure 170, p. 448).

Much of the material that has accumulated in the dipping beds that flank most reefs is talus broken from reef summits by the waves. It consists mainly of sand-size and larger particles ranging upward to large blocks of tumbled reef rock standing at all angles. Extensive slumping of this material has occurred and adds to the complexity of reef structures. One great slide on the flank of the Permian reef in west Texas extends for ten miles and locally has a thickness of 100 feet. Talus on the flanks of modern reefs generally stands with slopes of 15 to 20 degrees although slopes up to 35 degrees have been observed locally. Some ancient reefs possess flanking beds dipping at much steeper angles. Slopes of 45 degrees are not uncommon about the Silurian reefs of Illinois and Indiana, and 60-degree dips have been reported. This rather noteworthy difference suggests that differential compaction, perhaps partly after burial by post-Silurian strata (see Figure 120, p. 305), has accentuated the draping structure of the reef flanks. Some Silurian reefs in northern Illinois, however, lack flanking strata. They are believed to have grown in a very shallow sea where turbulence and currents were strong enough to prevent the local accumulation of reef debris, which was moved away and scattered over the bottom of interreef areas. Large reefs founded on fine-grained sediment may sink into this material, and some are margined by surrounding ridges formed by the outward squeezing of unconsolidated mud.

The growth of reefs is controlled by relative sea level. Their fate and the forms they assume depend upon its stability or fluctuation. Three general situations can be compared, as shown in Figure 184.

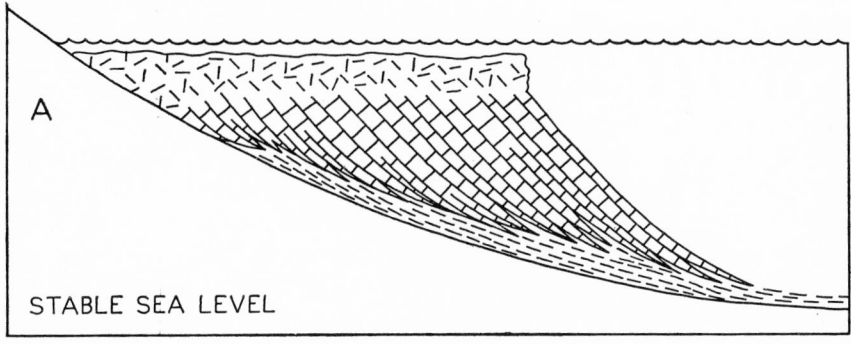

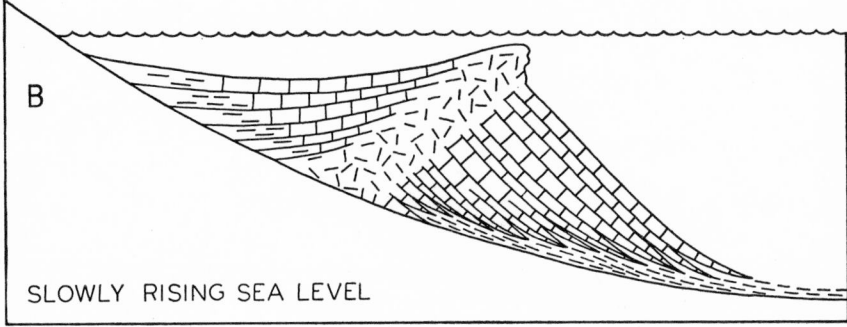

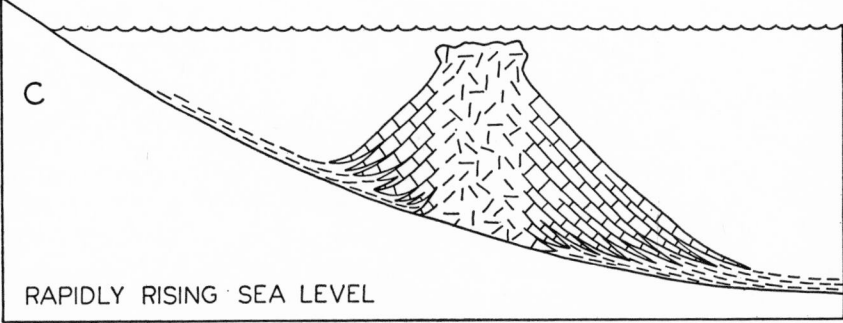

Figure 184. Idealized diagrams showing the influence of stable or rising sea level on the growth form of organic reefs. If sea level should fall, the reef would be exposed and the community of organisms responsible for its growth would die. If sea level should rise too rapidly for reef growth to keep pace with it, an environment unsuited to reef-building organisms would develop and the reef would cease to grow.

1. Stable sea level. The most favorable position for the existence of reef-building organisms is along the outer exposed side of a reef just below the surface of the sea where water is in almost constant motion. The way this margin grows determines the kind of reef developed. If sea level is stable, growth can only occur outward horizontally. The expanding reef, however, requires a foundation for its support and this is provided by the reef talus that accumulates upon its flanks. If water is shallow, flanking deposits may be built out rapidly. If it is deep, the same amount of debris must form much longer slopes, and reef growth is retarded correspondingly. In either case a flat-topped reef develops whose surface lies at approximate low-tide level.

2. Rising sea level. If sea level rises slowly, a similar relationship is maintained between reef rock and debris, but the reef grows upward as well as outward. These are the relations exhibited by the Permian reef in the Guadalupe Mountains of Texas and New Mexico. If sea level rises so rapidly that reef growth can just keep pace with it, the reef will grow vertically and debris accumulates on its flanks in greater thickness. The Leduc reef (Dev.) of Alberta in Canada appears to be of this latter type. In either case an upward-growing reef is likely to develop as a submerged ridge enclosing a lagoon. If rising sea level exceeds reef growth the reef will drown.

3. Falling sea level. If sea level falls, reefs are exposed, die, and become subject to erosion. The opinion has been expressed that a succession of reef ridges or barriers could develop parallel to the shoreline of a regressive sea and that this situation can be identified by the occurrence of red beds and evaporites in resulting back-reef lagoons. This explanation appears to be extremely unlikely if not impossible and is unnecessary to account for this type of back-reef facies. Such relations occurred behind the Permian reef of west Texas and New Mexico but no evidence of regression has been recognized there.

Reef Types

Three types of modern reefs generally are recognized: (1) fringing reefs that have grown outward from a shore in the form of a horizontal shelf, (2) barrier reefs that parallel a coast and rise as a ridge separating a back-reef lagoon from the open sea, and (3) atolls, most of which rise from great depths in the open ocean and enclose more or less circular lagoons. To these a fourth type must be added: (4) patch or platform reefs (the name depending upon their size), which are variable in shape, are flat topped, and occur as shallowly submerged archipelagos rising from a shallow sea bottom. The first and last types have developed in response to comparatively stable sea-level conditions. The others grew where sea level rose or the bottom sank.

Ancient reefs resembling fringing reefs and atolls are not well known. This is not surprising because ancient shorelines are rarely well exposed and typical atolls are not likely to have developed in continental platform regions. The Permian reef of Texas and New Mexico is a barrier reef at least 300 miles long. In some ways it is comparable to the Great Barrier Reef of Australia, which is more than 1000 miles long and is the world's best example of this type. These reefs differ, however, in several important respects, and the Permian reef is not duplicated by a modern one. For example, it did not face the open sea but grew within an embayment and surrounded an enclosed basin about 100 miles in diameter which was connected with the ocean through one or two restricted channels (see Figure 185). The dark-colored and poorly fossiliferous sediments of this basin show that it was occupied by water whose lower layers were stagnant. The Permian reef

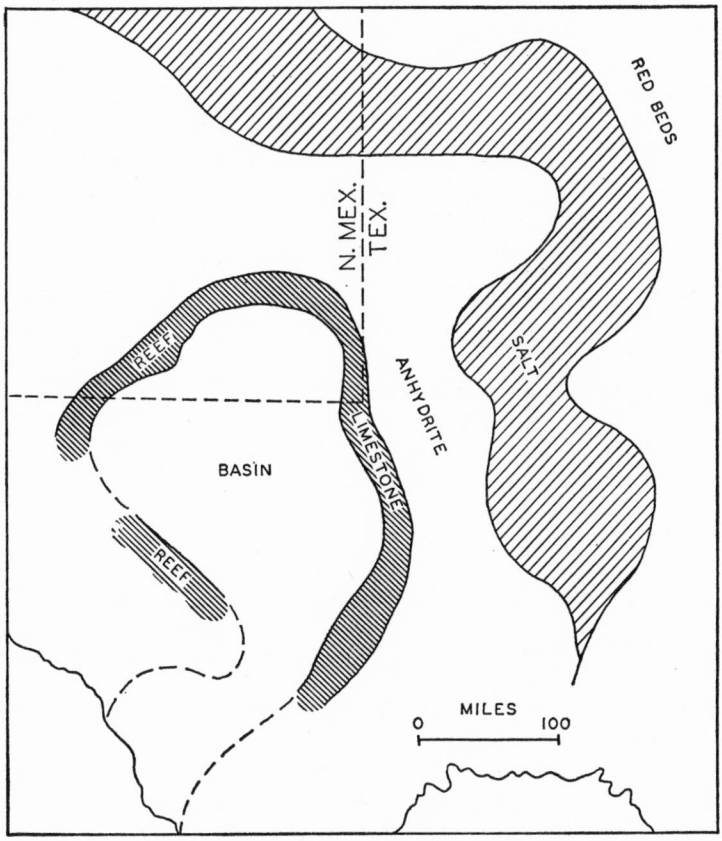

Figure 185. Generalized map of west Texas and adjacent New Mexico showing the relations of the great Permian reef to its enclosed basin and the surrounding back-reef areas of shallow water where detrital sediments and evaporites accumulated. (After King, 1942, *Bull. Am. Assoc. Petroleum Geol.*, vol. 26, p. 747, fig. 32.)

probably was more continuous than the Australian reef. Possibly it was not broken by channels that would have allowed more or less free circulation of surface water between the basin and wide back-reef lagoons where super-saline conditions existed. The Permian reef also is much thicker. Several other ancient reefs, however, are closely similar to it. One of the best examples occurs in the Mississippian System of northern England. The Devonian reefs of western Canada also resemble the Permian reef in some respects.

The Silurian reefs of the Great Lakes region extending at least from the Gulf of St. Lawrence in one direction to Hudson Bay in the other (see Figure 186) are the greatest aggregation of patch and platform reefs either

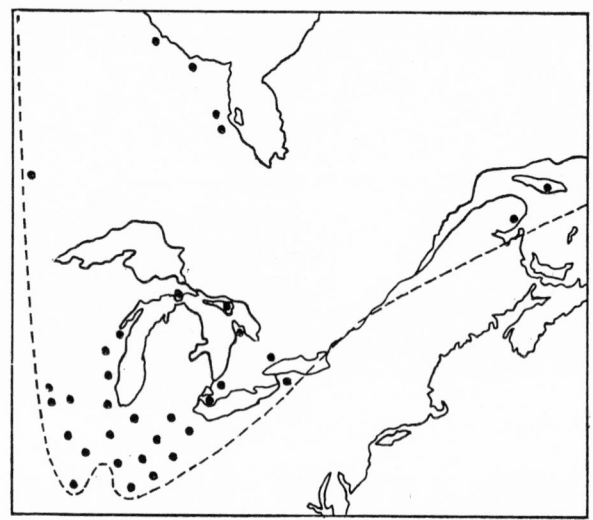

Figure 186. Map of the Great Lakes region and areas to the north and east showing the known distribution of Niagaran (Sil.) reefs. Several of the reefs in southern Illinois and southwestern Indiana are not exposed but have been discovered by drilling (see Figures 120, p. 305, and 182, p. 491). (After Lowenstam, 1950, J. Geol., vol. 58, p. 480, fig. 11.)

ancient or modern known anywhere in the world. They vary in size from an acre or less to several square miles in area and probably rose from a sea bottom rarely more than about 200 feet deep. The great thicknesses of some of these reefs, particularly the most southern ones, probably are more a measure of basin subsidence than of water depth.

Other Bioherms

The most common kind of bioherm consists largely of the remains of organisms, including algae, stromatoporoids, archaeocyathids, sponges, corals, brachiopods, bryozoans, crinoids, and pelecypods. Although some of these same organisms contributed importantly to the growth of true reefs, there is no evidence that other bioherms rose much above the surrounding bottom at any time during their development. Such bioherms are enclosed in sediment of some contrasting kind which accumulated contemporaneously and to which organisms contributed less importantly (see Figure 187). The

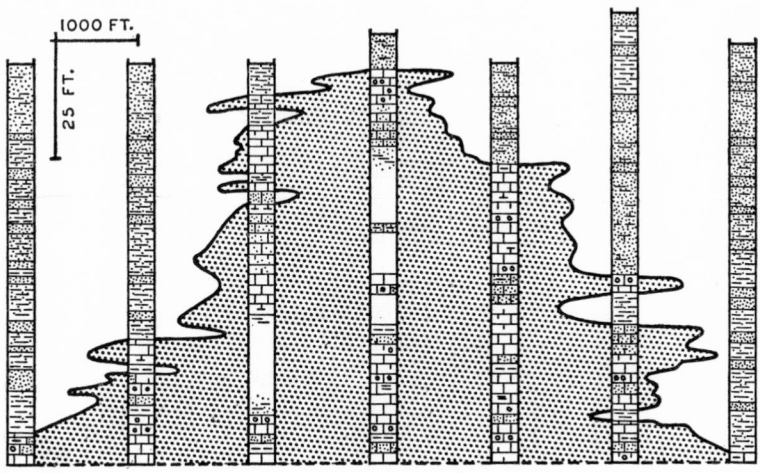

Figure 187. Diagram showing the form of a bioherm in the Edwardsville Formation (Miss.) of Indiana as based on detailed stratigraphic sections measured at about quarter-mile intervals. (After Stockdale, 1931, *Bull. Geol. Soc. Amer.*, vol. 42, p. 714, fig. 2.)

most conspicuous examples occur in the midst of shaly, silty, or sandy strata. Somewhat similar bodies are present in calcareous formations, as shown in Figure 188, but because they do not stand out so clearly they are likely to be overlooked.

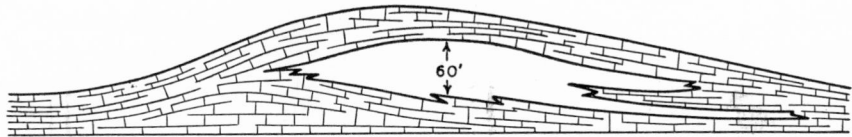

Figure 188. Cross section drawn to true scale of a bioherm in the St. Joe Limestone (Miss.) of northeastern Oklahoma. This bioherm consists of massive crinoidal limestone enclosed in thin-bedded crinoidal limestone. (After Harbaugh, 1957, *Bull. Am. Assoc. Petroleum Geol.*, vol. 41, p. 2537, fig. 7.)

The Mississippian bioherms of Indiana have been carefully studied. They are composed of variously massive beds of variously pure limestone formed mainly of disarticulated crinoids and broken bryozoans. Each bioherm appears to represent an isolated organic community that created a specialized environment and survived in the midst of an area where conditions were unfavorable for the existence of a widespread benthonic fauna of lime-secreting organisms. The vicissitudes of the community's precarious existence are recorded by interfingerings of the surrounding detrital sediment, the variable intermixture of this material with the accumulating calcareous debris, and the final contraction and extinction of the community. Bioherms in Indiana range up to about two miles in diameter and attain thicknesses of as much as seventy feet.

The structural relations of these bioherms and surrounding sediments are much simpler than those of organic reefs because contemporaneous strata of different kinds pass into each other laterally in perfectly normal ways. Gradation or intertonguing, however, commonly is more or less abrupt and may be accomplished between two fairly closely spaced outcrops. Generally there is little evidence that differential compaction has altered these relations importantly unless the surrounding material is relatively non-silty shale. Bioherms may begin at different horizons within a formation and continue upward through zones of different thickness. Some may extend without interruption across the boundary between two recognized formations.

Basin Filling

Persistent sedimentary deposition requires the maintenance of both a supply of sediment and a basin in which the sediment can accumulate. This means that a tectonic balance between uplift and erosion on the one hand and subsidence and deposition on the other must be preserved. One is as important as the other, but geologists see only the basin and its deposits. From these they must judge how well the balance has been maintained and in what manner it has varied from time to time.

The final disposition of most sediment deposited on the continental platforms is controlled by sea level. This provides a datum from which relative uplift and subsidence can be estimated. Littoral deposits mark the approximate position of sea level and furnish the most direct evidence bearing upon its fluctuations. Sea-level movements are, of course, relative. There is no sure method of distinguishing between fluctuations that are eustatic and those produced by more or less local tectonic activity without any actual change in water level. Somewhat similar relations are shown by the sediments deposited in large lakes but they do not have the same significance because lake levels commonly respond to climatic changes or other strictly local factors. The tectonic implications of fluvial deposits are wholly different.

All basin filling by water-borne detrital sediments is similar. It involves more or less sorting, the deposition of coarse material in a shallow littoral zone, and the settling of finer sediment in deeper-water, offshore areas. Lateral changes in the sediments may show patterns that reflect tectonic balance or eustatic sea-level movements although these may be variously modified if non-detrital sediment is abundant. As lateral changes are viewed from the standpoint of the basins and their deposits, three possibilities require consideration: (1) stable sea level, (2) falling sea level, and (3) rising sea level (see Figures 189 and 190).

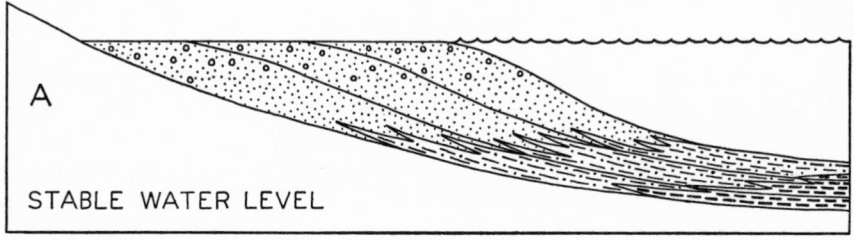

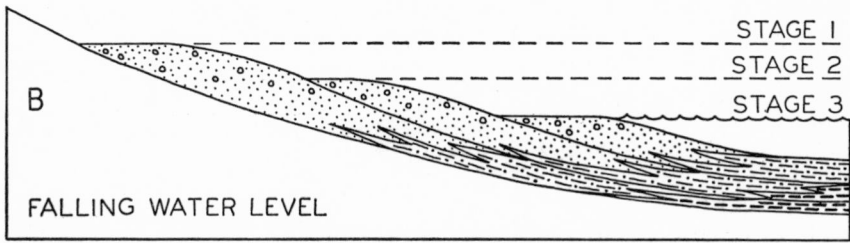

Figure 189. Schematic diagrams showing the lateral gradation of sediments and the interfingering of lithologic facies in situations where water level is stable or falling.

Stable Sea Level

Under conditions of stable sea level, deposition results in a shoreline that shifts as the marginal part of the basin is filled in. The coarser near-shore sediment gradually extends basinward above previously deposited finer material, from which it is separated by a time-transgressive lithologic boundary that is approximately horizontal. This is a typical regressive relationship. The rate of sedimentary supply and deposition makes no difference because whether it is slow or rapid the shoreline retreats accordingly in exactly the same way.

Falling Sea Level

If sea level falls, either constantly and gradually or by small successive stages, the results are very similar to those previously described. Advance of the shoreline is more rapid, however, because both withdrawal of the sea and basin filling contribute to this movement. If deposition is slow, the first

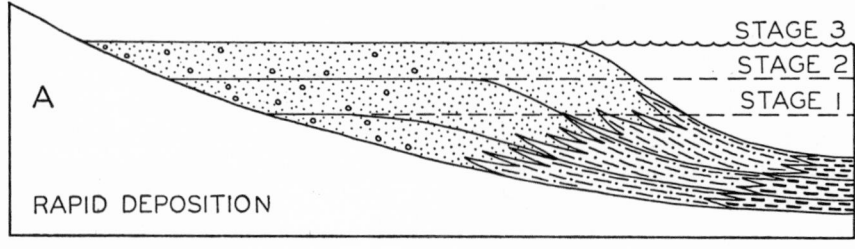

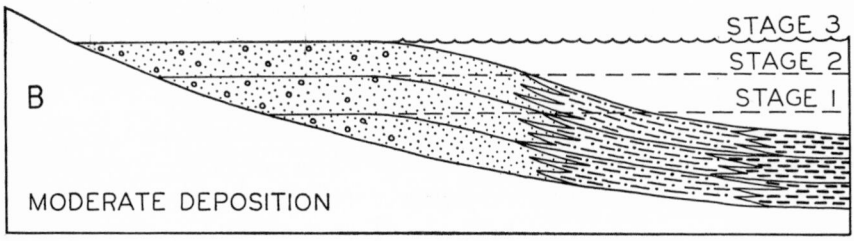

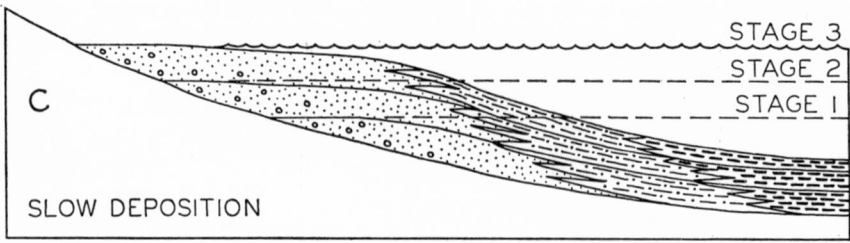

Figure 190. Schematic diagrams illustrating three possible types of lateral sediment gradation in a basin with rising water level. Transgressive lithologic facies as shown in C can develop only if rise in water level is not compensated by the deposition of new sediment.

factor is most important. If it is very rapid, the second dominates. In either case a regressive relationship develops and a time-transgressive lithologic boundary dips gently into the basin.

Rising Sea Level

With rising sea level, a different type of situation is presented and the rate of sediment supply and deposition determines the resulting stratigraphic relations. Three possibilities require consideration:

1. Rapid sedimentation. Rising sea level commonly results in retreating shorelines and the enlargement of submerged basins. Sedimentary deposition, however, may fill the margins of a basin at such a rate that enlargement does not occur, and if it is rapid enough the shoreline may actually advance. This also would result in basinward extension of coarse near-shore sediment and regressive stratigraphic relationships. In this situation a time-transgres-

sive lithologic boundary would rise inward toward the center of a basin.

2. Moderate sedimentation. If sediment were delivered at just the proper rate, the shoreline might be held stationary, neither advancing nor retreating, and the lithologic boundary would rise vertically. This situation is extremely unlikely, because deposition and rising sea level would have to remain in exact balance for a very considerable length of time.

3. Slow sedimentation. Marginal deposition in a basin with actively rising sea level generally is not sufficient to halt a retreating shoreline but only to reduce enlargement of the basin to some extent. In this case coarser sediment is deposited in a zone that gradually shifts outward and upward as submergence progresses and this sediment is subsequently buried beneath finer material deposited in deeper water farther from the shifting shoreline. Although the lithologic boundary dips inward toward the basin, as it does when sea level is falling, the vertical relations of coarse and fine sediment are reversed. This is the only situation that can produce the transgressive shifting of laterally equivalent sedimentary zones.

Intertongued Sediments

The intertonguing of differently constituted sediments like that which characterizes the lateral transition from Mesa Verde Sandstone to Mancos

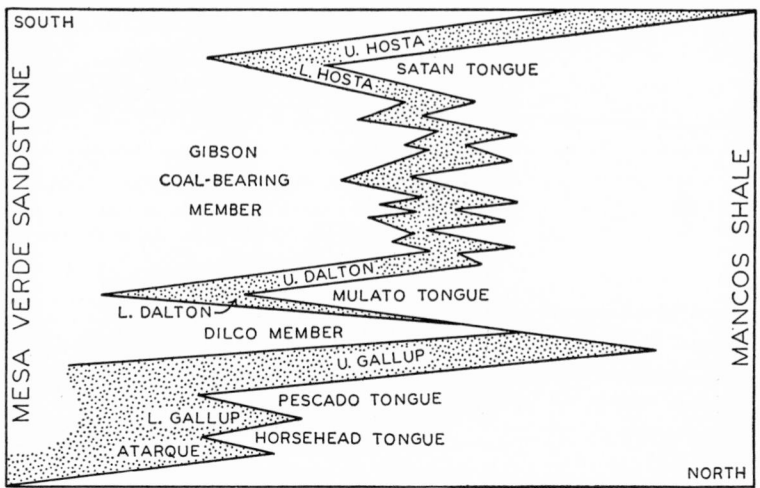

Figure 191. Diagrammatic cross section showing the intertongued relations of the Mesa Verde Sandstone and Mancos Shale (Cret.). See also Figure 179, p. 484. (After Pike, 1947, Geol. Soc. Amer., Mem. 24, p. 13, fig. 2.)

Shale (Cret.) in Utah, Colorado, and neighboring states (see Figure 191) results from the reversal or alternation of some of the depositional and sea-level relations previously outlined. The regressive extension of a Mesa Verde Sandstone tongue into the Mancos Shale might have occurred

whether sea level rose, fell, or remained steady. The deposition of a transgressive Mancos Shale tongue projecting into the Mesa Verde Sandstone,
however, is much surer evidence of rising water level.

The Mesa Verde and Mancos formations both attain thicknesses of several thousand feet and they thicken greatly toward the west. Neither possesses characters suggesting that any part of them was deposited in deep water. Consequently it is safe to conclude that the depositional basin was
downwarped tectonically and it is fairly sure that sea-level changes were related to tectonic action. Under these circumstances the stratigraphic relations present two main possibilities: (1) that intertonguing resulted from
intermittent subsidence of the basin or (2) that it resulted from strong fluctuations in the amount of sediment delivered to a constantly and more or
less regularly subsiding basin, the fluctuations being controlled by intermittent uplift or some other periodic change of conditions in the sedimentary
source area. Possibly both types of action participated.

The intertongued sandstone and shale members furnish little or no basis
for a choice between these possibilities. Evidence must be sought elsewhere.
The Mesa Verde Sandstone grades laterally into a very thick succession of
piedmont and other terrestrial strata. These include several coarse conglomeratic zones and they are interrupted by at least one important erosional unconformity that becomes markedly angular to the west. The source area
must have been uplifted greatly to have furnished the enormous amount of
detrital sediment delivered to the basin, and the unconformity is additional
proof that this did occur. Also the conglomerates suggest that uplift was
intermittent. These irregularities have not been correlated with Mesa
Verde Sandstone tongues. If they were, there would be no necessity to conclude that subsidence of the basin was strongly intermittent or was inter-

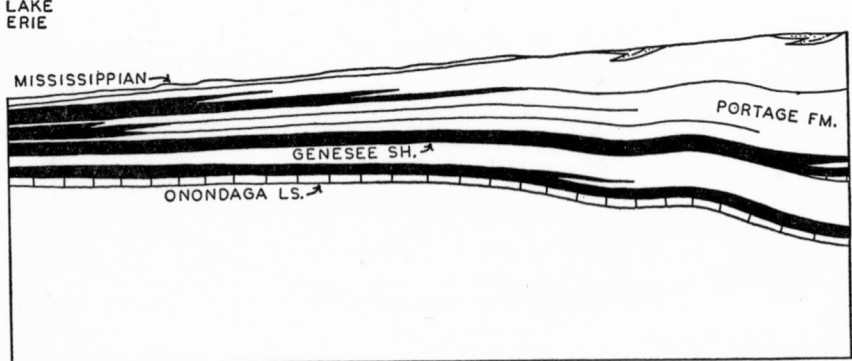

Figure 192.   Generalized cross section of the Catskill (Dev.) delta and related strata
in southern New York and northern Pennsylvania. This shows the regressive interfingering
of terrestrial red beds with marine deposits that, in a westward direction, grade from

rupted by reverse movements. On the other hand, these possibilities would not be eliminated.

The Devonian Catskill delta of the northern Applachian region exhibits relations somewhat similar to those evident in the Mesa Verde–Mancos transition of the west (see Figure 192). In both instances sedimentary deposition exceeded the subsidence of a basin, and dominantly regressive stratigraphic relations were the result. Regular intertonguing of sandstone and shale, however, has not been recognized to the same extent in the eastern region as in the west. This suggests that Catskill deposition progressed more regularly and was less influenced by intermittent basin subsidence or possible sharp pulses of uplift in the sediment-producing region.

Consideration of basin filling, and particularly the Mesa Verde–Mancos example, emphasizes sandstone-shale lithologic relations because they are conspicuous and can be correlated with shifting littoral environments. Limestone and shale also intertongue in a similar fashion. Changes in the areal distribution of strata of these kinds undoubtedly are related to varying detrital sediment supply, changing water depth, and other environmental fluctuations. They cannot be connected so surely, however, with shifting shorelines. Consequently their interpretation is much less certain. Some at least may have been related to local warping of the continental platform rather than to the migration of a distant shore.

FACIES

The common meaning of *facies* is *general appearance*. This word has been used in geology in connection with the differentiation of more or less

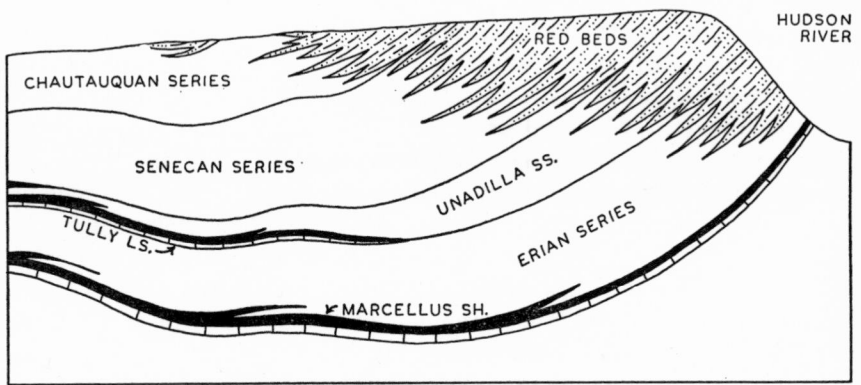

sandstone into gray or greenish shale and finally into black shale. Compare with Figure 159, p. 417.

similar associations among the rocks or organisms of any area or of any interval of past time. A facies implies variation. It has no significance, therefore, except as it is contrasted with one or more related facies. As this word is used in stratigraphy with reference to rock bodies, *facies* also implies a certain degree of constancy and continuity within whatever rocks are being

WEST   EAST

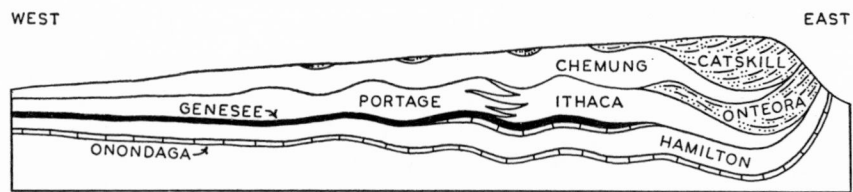

Figure 193.   Generalized cross section of the Catskill delta showing how the Upper Devonian stratigraphy of New York and Pennsylvania was usually interpreted before about 1930. The time-transgressive nature of the lithologic formations generally was not recognized. Western outliers of the red beds, for example, were considered to be remnants of the Catskill Formation preserved in synclines. Compiled from old maps and reports.

compared with or differentiated from others. Facies differences in stratified rocks have been recognized for more than a century, but the word *facies* has been used in so many different ways that its meaning is vague in spite of a general desire to restrict its technical application.

Stratified rocks vary in character both vertically and laterally. Vertical variation is obvious in most outcrops, and changes are abrupt at many bedding planes. The grosser features of vertical variation provide the basis for differentiating most formations and other rock-stratigraphic units. These variations are evidence of change in geologic processes and conditions that occurred during the course of passing time, and reconstruction of the local geologic history of a region is dependent upon their interpretation. Lateral variation within beds of equivalent age generally is much more gradual and it is not so plainly apparent. Lateral variations in lithologic and biologic characters are particularly important, however, because they give evidence of contemporaneous environmental differences upon which the interpretation of paleogeography is based. The numerous uncertainties attending lateral variation introduce complications with respect to stratigraphic relations, subdivision, nomenclature, correlation, and interpretation that as a whole are commonly recognized as constituting the facies problem.

Since about 1930 increasing awareness of lateral lithologic variation in stratified rocks and more critical interest in lateral facies relationships, and the problems that they present, have developed in America among both stratigraphers and paleontologists. In this time facies have been considered from different viewpoints both theoretical and practical and different ideas regarding them have evolved. Although several efforts have been made since 1948 to clarify and systematize useful facies concepts and the nomenclature to be applied to them, little uniformity of opinion has resulted and much confusion and disagreement concerning them persist.

Facies Concepts

The word *facies*, as commonly applied in stratigraphy, and other more restrictive terms have been used in such ways that they embody four related but different concepts: (1) the *appearance* of a rock body, (2) the *composition* or actual nature of a rock body, (3) the rock body *itself* as identified by its appearance or composition, and (4) the *environment* that is recorded by a rock body. The ways in which facies terms have been used by different persons or by the same person at different times show that meanings shift back and forth between these ideas or include more than one of them.

Facies have been distinguished at widely divergent scales or levels of importance. The differences recognized may be of any kind. They range from the plainly obvious to the very subtle. Facies may be generalized and refer to a varied assemblage of associated elements or they may be highly exclusive and be identified by a complete set of specific, detailed characters. Thus, facies concepts related to sediments and rocks range all the way from large bodies of more or less heterogeneous but characteristic composition to thin and restricted beds or parts of beds of uniform composition, texture, structure, biologic content, and so forth.

Stratigraphic literature provides examples of facies that have been differentiated or identified in many different ways. Among the diagnostic features utilized are (1) lithologic characters, (2) metamorphic alteration, (3) biologic composition, (4) stratigraphic relations, (5) temporal sequence, (6) structural form, (7) environmental influences, (8) tectonic control, (9) genetic interpretation, (10) geographic occurrence, and possibly others. Most of these features furnish valid basis for some kind of differentiation but all are not equally objective or equally significant in stratigraphy.

Lithologic Facies

Fundamentally, most facies of interest in stratigraphy are lithologic because lithologic characters are objective and they furnish the basis for most differentiations including those that involve interpretations. Lithologic characters consist of all observable features of the rock ranging from the most obvious to the most obscure. Included among them are all general features such as composition, color, bedding, and so forth, and all petrographic and some biologic details.

Lithologic facies may be considered (1) without regard to their relations to each other, (2) as variations in a vertical sequence, and (3) as lateral variations.

Rocks of similar composition and appearance have been distinguished as a particular facies regardless of where they may occur or of their relations to other rocks. Such distinction is classificatory only. It implies nothing except that rocks can be differentiated on the basis of certain chosen characters. Expressions like "red beds facies" or "black shale facies" or the even more general "limestone facies" or "sandstone facies" may apply to either (1) all rocks of a particular kind, no matter where they may occur, or (2) particular rock bodies of unspecified form and extent whose relations to other facies are indeterminate. Similar terms also have been used in a vague way to designate environments in which particular kinds of sediment accumulated. It is, of course, important to distinguish different kinds of rock and to relate similar rocks that occur at different places but such unsupplemented observations are not likely to have much bearing on either lithologic variations or the problems of stratigraphic relations resulting from variation.

The association of facies in vertical sequences or their transitions laterally involve stratigraphic considerations that are discussed in a later section.

The term *lithofacies* was introduced as a substitute for *lithologic facies*. It has been employed in the several different ways that have been noted. Generally, however, *lithofacies* is considered to apply to rocks, and only indirectly and incidentally to environment. Lithofacies have been regarded as either including or excluding the biologic contributions to sedimentary rocks. The biologic aspects of lithologic character cannot be excluded entirely because they have been of dominating importance in determining the composition of such rocks as limestones and they have strongly influenced rock colors, as in carbonaceous shales. Biologic features that do not find expression in such physical characters of rocks as composition, texture, and color can be eliminated, however, from the concept of this kind of facies. Actually no practically meaningful, strict separation of the physical and biologic elements that have contributed to sediments can be made. Their interrelations are so intimate that the consideration of one to the entire exclusion of the other is almost impossible.

Metamorphic facies are a special type of lithologic facies. Ordinarily they find more application in a consideration of tectonics than in stratigraphy. They record, however, the advanced stages in a series of alterations that began with the diagenesis of sediments, and no sharp or entirely satisfactory division can be drawn. Various diagenetic changes such as those involving dolomitization and chertification commonly are recognized as bases for lithologic facies differentiations of importance in stratigraphy.

Biologic Facies

Biologic facies, like lithologic facies, are objective because they are based solely on observable characters. They may be defined as either (1) strictly biologic, consisting only of organisms associated in faunas and floras, or (2) geologic, consisting of rocks characterized by their organic contents without respect to any lithologic features. Facies that are strictly biologic are important in paleontology and paleoecology but they have little direct application in stratigraphy except in connection with correlation. Biologic facies that are also geologic overlap and grade into lithologic facies because, as already noted, the kind and amount of organic products present in sediments may strongly influence the resulting deposits. Conversely those physical and chemical factors that are recorded by the nonbiologic elements of sediments are an essential part of any biologic setting, and the distribution of organisms is more or less strongly influenced by them. The distribution of organisms, however, also responds to other ecologic factors that are not recorded in the sediments and some of these may be of predominating importance. Variations in these latter factors result in biologic differences not necessarily paralleling changes in lithologic facies. Thus, one type of rock may contain several different assemblages of fossils. Also, but more rarely, similar assemblages may occur in different types of rock.

Like lithologic facies, biologic facies have been considered either with or without reference to each other. They have been regarded as either collective facies defined by particular organic assemblages, wherever these may be present, or specific biologic or geologic units that occur in vertical sequence or intertongue or intergrade laterally. No sharp distinction ordinarily has been made between biologic facies that are assemblages of fossils or bodies of rock and the environments that are recorded by the objective facies. Finally, the term *biofacies* has been introduced as a substitute for *biologic facies*.

Stratigraphic Facies

Both vertical and horizontal variability in sedimentary rocks are aspects of stratigraphy recording differences that are related in time and in space respectively. Both kinds of variability can be expressed either in terms of conventional stratigraphical units or in terms of facies. The most practical facies also are stratigraphic units and they do not differ importantly from the more familiar rock stratigraphic units except as their mutual relations are emphasized. Thus ordinary stratigraphic units are considered principally in vertical sequence whereas the lateral relations of facies are primarily important.

Each kind of material stratigraphic unit is paralleled by a kind of stratigraphic facies as follows:

Stratigraphic Unit	Stratigraphic Facies
Rock unit	Lithologic facies
Biostratigraphic unit	Biologic facies
Time-rock unit	Temporal facies

Most rock and biostratigraphic units are somewhat generalized facies because they are characterized by certain unifying lithologic or biologic features. Time-rock units are not because, theoretically at least, they are independent of all material considerations. The stratigraphic facies generally are laterally contiguous, differently constituted, areal subdivisions of these units.

Stratigraphic facies need not correspond, however, with any formally recognized stratigraphic unit. For example, a stratigraphic unit may be subdivided into successive vertical parts, each of which is differentiated separately into facies. These parts may be determined by any features that are distinctive. If no such features permit consistent subdivision, the unit may be sliced into horizontal parts, each of which constitutes some arbitrary fraction of the whole unit's thickness. More general units also may be recognized for operational purposes which combine several formations or even transcend systems. Altogether great latitude is possible in the selection of stratigraphic units that are to provide the basis for stratigraphic facies differentiation. The units chosen are likely to be determined equally by the limitations of practical stratigraphy and by the purposes motivating a particular facies study.

Structural Facies

Stratigraphic structures like bioherms also are a kind of facies because they differ from surrounding rocks in much the same ways that stratigraphic facies differ among themselves. Structural facies, however, are not likely to be such well-marked subdivisions of ordinary stratigraphic units because they may be completely enclosed within a unit or they may continue from one unit into another. Therefore the relations between such structural facies and interbiohermal facies are not so regular or simple as the relations between adjacent or successive stratigraphic facies.

Facies Boundaries

One of the most important problems in connection with facies concepts concerns boundaries. It has both practical and theoretical aspects and has been approached by different persons from different standpoints. The natures of horizontal boundaries separating facies that succeed each other vertically in a stratigraphic section and vertical boundaries separating laterally adjacent facies require separate consideration.

Accurate reconstruction of paleogeography and geologic history requires that comparisons be made between temporally equivalent facies. The best that ordinarily can be done is to compare lateral facies subdivisions of time-rock units whose boundaries approximate time planes. The boundaries most commonly utilized to limit practical stratigraphic facies, however, are those that define recognized rock stratigraphic units. Some boundaries of this kind transgress time planes importantly, especially those related to episodes of transgressive or regressive marine movements. Others are unconformities at which variable parts of the stratigraphic record are unrepresented. Any deviation from exact time equivalence of the facies compared is likely to cause some inaccuracy of interpretation. Correspondence may be so imperfect between distant parts of a large area that resulting comparisons are seriously misleading.

Lateral facies boundaries generally are gradational. If boundaries are drawn in such a way that adjacent stratigraphic facies have mutually exclusive areal relations, the boundaries are arbitrarily located vertical planes that cut across the bedding (see Figure 194). This method of arbitrary cutoff

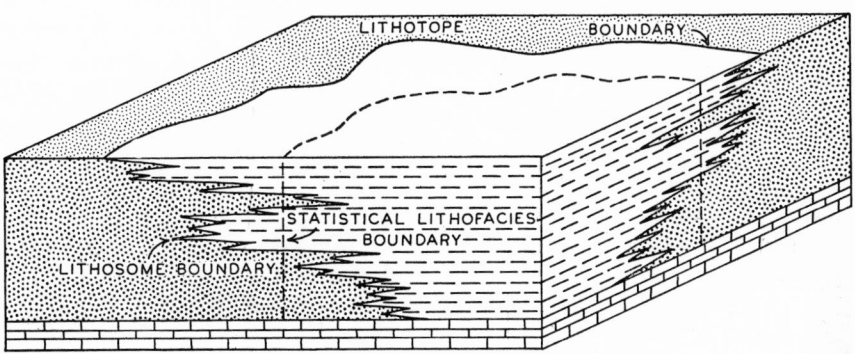

Figure 194. Block diagram illustrating the relations of intertongued lithosomes and statistically defined lithofacies that are terminated at an arbitrary vertical cutoff boundary. In this example a sandstone and a shale lithosome are distinguishable. The statistical boundary is drawn so that the lithofacies on one side is more than 50 percent sandstone and on the other more than 50 percent shale. The boundary between the two kinds of sediment at any depositional surface separates two lithotopes. (Modified from Wheeler and Mallory, 1956, *Bull. Am. Assoc. Petroleum Geol.,* vol. 40, p. 2714, fig. 2.)

may be accomplished either (1) qualitatively, in such a manner that adjacent facies differ in some general way (see Figures 195 and 196), or (2) quantitatively or statistically, so that a boundary separates two facies, characterized by some measurable objective feature, in such a way that the numerical value of this feature is greater than some arbitrary quantity in one facies and less in the other. For example, two qualitative facies of this kind might be distinguished depending upon whether or not prominent sandstone beds are present. The boundary between them will be more or less indefinite and it might be drawn at different places by different persons. In contrast two statistical facies might be separated on the basis of whether or not sandstone exceeds 25 percent of the total stratigraphic thickness at any place. Such a boundary is much more definite and the accuracy with which it can be drawn depends only upon the number, distribution, and perfection of outcrops and subsurface records. More complex facies differentiation, particularly of the statistical type, may be based on variations of several features simultaneously considered (see Figure 197, also Figure 206, p. 533).

The term *lithofacies* has been employed most commonly for lithologic stratigraphic facies of this kind.

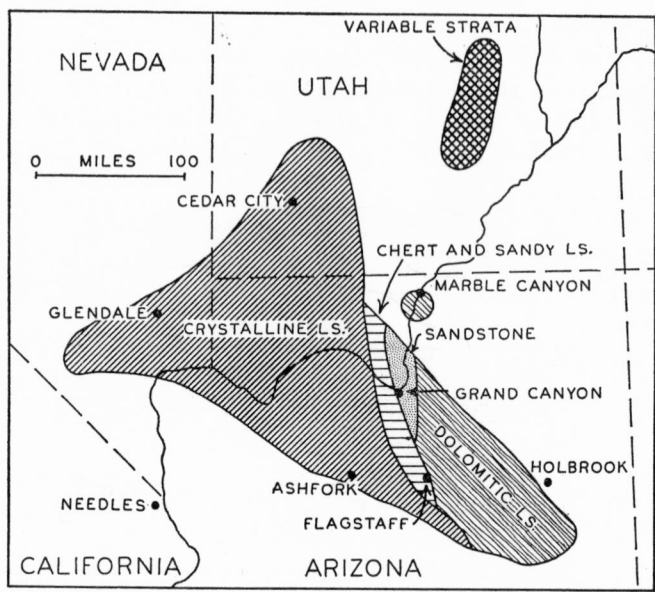

Figure 195. Map of the Grand Canyon and neighboring regions showing the different lithologic developments of the middle member of the Kaibab Formation (Perm.). This is a good example of a qualitative lithofacies map. Changes occur gradually and the boundaries are arbitrary. The divisions are not made systematically. They appear to be more distinct than they actually are. (After McKee, 1938, Carnegie Inst. Washington Publ. 492, p. 45, fig. 22.)

Lateral transition may involve the gradual change of some objective feature such as coarseness of sediment or lithologic composition. It may also be accomplished by intertonguing and wedging out of unlike strata in opposite directions. If lateral facies boundaries are drawn at the actual contacts between intertonguing bodies of contrasting characters, the facies are likely to

Figure 196 (*opposite*). Lithofacies and thickness maps of the Maquoketa Shale (Ord.) in Illinois. The Maquoketa Shale was more or less arbitrarily divided into three members that vary in thickness from place to place. The upper is mainly greenish shale, the middle one dolomite or limestone, and the lowest brownish shale. None of them is consistent in lithology. Each grades laterally into or encloses other kinds of material. The maps show the dominant lithologic character of each member and its variations and indicate noteworthy associations of different kinds of rock. The maps are entirely qualitative and have none of the quantitative features of statistical lithofacies maps of slices of a formation. (After Du Bois, 1945, Ill. Geol. Surv., Rept. Invest. 105, p. 8, fig. 1, and p. 10, fig. 3.)

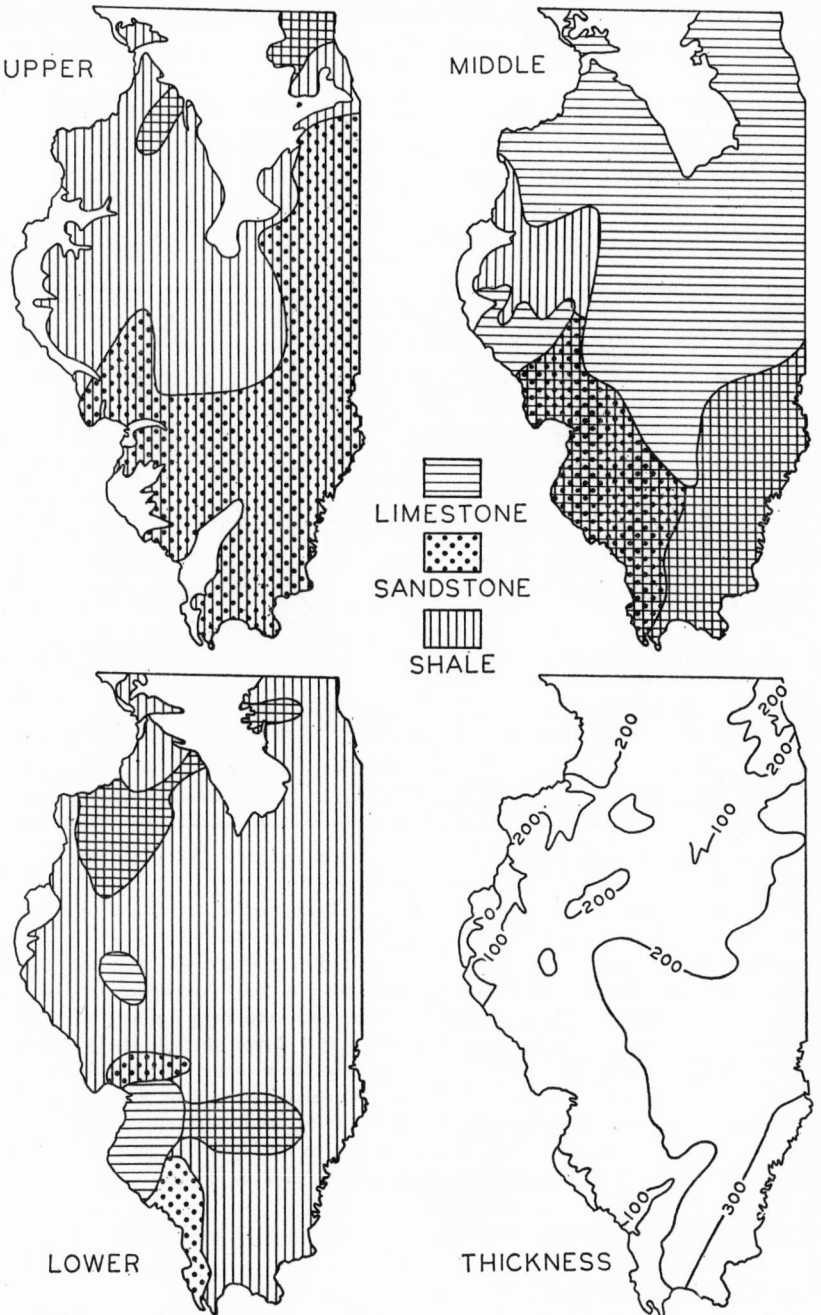

UPPER

MIDDLE

LIMESTONE

SANDSTONE

SHALE

LOWER

THICKNESS

be very irregular and they interpenetrate each other in transitional zones. Such relations can be mapped, but geologic maps of facies of this kind show repeated alternating members of the same units and not a simple vertical succession of different stratigraphic units like formations. The term *lithosome* has been introduced for lithologic stratigraphic facies of this kind to distinguish them from the more simply related statistical lithofacies (see Figure 194, p. 509). In many situations laterally transitional facies might be differentiated either as intertongued lithosomes or as statistical lithofacies.

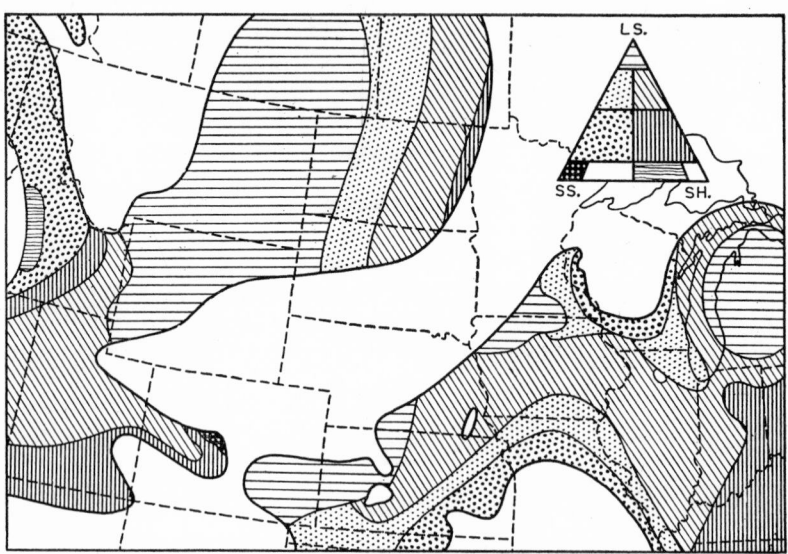

Figure 197. Statistical lithofacies map showing average lateral variations in the composition of strata of equivalent age throughout a very large region in the north central United States and adjacent areas. The accurate correlation of strata in all parts of such a region presents many difficult problems. No thin or restricted part of the stratigraphic section can be recognized everywhere with desirable certainty. Consequently a thick sequence representing a long interval of time was selected for study and analysis. The sequence considered here includes all beds of the Middle and Upper Ordovician, Silurian, and Devonian systems. This map differs in no respect from one that might be made for a thinner stratigraphic section. It averages out, however, the results of geologic conditions that probably changed importantly in many ways, at many places, and at many times. Consequently the significance of this pattern of lithologic variability is very obscure. (After Sloss and others, 1949, Geol. Soc. Amer., Mem. 39, p. 118, fig. 10.)

Structural facies, such as large non-reef bioherms, generally intertongue with enclosing strata. Because of uneven lateral expansion of their lower layers and similar contraction of their upper ones, these structures may not have regular upper and lower boundaries. Organic reefs also commonly intertongue, but transition occurs in the dipping strata of their flanks, and most reefs are surrounded by younger strata that are not part of a laterally equivalent interreef facies. In strata containing bioherms and in other stratigraphic-sections where lateral gradation is conspicuous, the boundaries between rock stratigraphic units are likely to be drawn at different positions in the section from place to place and the recognition of facies that are temporally equivalent and significant for direct comparison is very difficult.

Environmental Facies

Several kinds of environmental facies have been distinguished. Those noted most commonly are related to particular lithologic, biologic, and tectonic environments. Littoral facies, molluscan facies, and geosynclinal facies are examples. Most facies of these kinds are based upon objective features selected because of their inferred environmental significance. This interpretative element, which contributes importantly to their differentiation, separates them from purely objective facies. There is at least a theoretically significant difference between (1) a sandstone facies that is recognized simply because it differs lithologically from adjacent shale and (2) a facies that is recognized because sandstone is believed to identify a shallow-water, near-shore environment. The environmental concept of facies is important because it directs attention to interpretation. Some confusion exists, however, because it connects the concepts of rocks with concepts of the environments that rocks record, and adequate distinction between them generally has not been made.

Environmental facies of different kinds are not exactly comparable. Lithofacies are the simplest because lithologic features provide direct evidence of some important elements of the sedimentary environment. Other significant elements, however, are not recorded. Biofacies present much greater problems. Their environmental implications are mostly interpretative and they are less certain because of incomplete understanding of paleoecology and the possible occurrence of mixed faunas. Even where benthonic faunal elements from different places have not been intermingled, a biofacies may reflect two or more vertically stratified environments.

Because the distribution of species, genera, and higher taxonomic categories of organisms has been restricted in both space and time, similar ecologic roles have been played by different organisms in different areas and in different epochs. Consequently quite different biologic associations may indicate practically identical environments. If biofacies are considered environmentally, a particular biofacies might be represented by strata of any age that contain fossils indicating this environment even though the fossils are not the same. If they are viewed objectively, however, and defined by particular fossils, biofacies cannot be duplicated outside of a stratigraphic zone representing an interval of time too short to have witnessed appreciable evolutionary change, or in two areas where the organic communities were different.

Tectonic facies, or *tectofacies*, are even less objective than environmental lithofacies and biofacies because in many instances they are recognized only after interpretations have been made. In actual practice, principal reliance generally is placed on the variations in thickness of stratigraphic sections, and the actual characters of the rocks are of subordinate importance. Insofar as rock characters are employed in diagnosis, a tectofacies is only a special kind of lithofacies.

The importance of environments is widely recognized. Attempts have been made to emphasize them in facies considerations. *Biotope* is a term used by biologists for an area of uniform ecology and organic adaptation. It has been adopted in geology, and two companion terms, *lithotope* and *tectotope*, have been introduced with somewhat similar sedimentary and tectonic meanings. In spite of the etymology of these words, which indicates that they should refer to places, they have been used more or less indiscriminately for (1) areas, (2) environments, and (3) the records of environments. The term *lithosome*, which was originally defined as an intertonguing lithologic facies, has been employed for the rock record of a sedimentary environment. Also the similar words *biosome* and *tectosome* have been proposed for the records of biologic and tectonic environments. Much confusion among these concepts and terms is evident.

Facies Hierarchy

Facies are not well adapted to arrangement in a hierarchical succession like conventional stratigraphic units. Nevertheless the various facies concepts related to stratigraphy that have been discussed can be ordered in a sequence of diminishing generality. In expressing this order, difficulty is encountered in nomenclature because most terms applied to facies concepts do not have meanings that are exclusive and precise. If certain particular meanings are given preference, the following order is evident:

Facies 1—general association of certain related types of rock.
Facies 2—body of related rocks not defined with respect to others.
Lithofacies—stratigraphic unit, may consist of lithosomes.
Lithosome—particular kind of rock, may consist of lithostromes.
Lithostrome—bed of uniform character, the record of a lithotope.
Lithotope—area of uniform environment.

This list is concerned only with lithologic facies concepts. A different arrangement would result if different meanings of these terms were emphasized. Similar lists could be presented for comparable biologic and tectonic concepts but these would be less practical. The brief descriptions accompanying the terms are not intended to define them fully. Facies definitions are considered in a later section.

Genetic Facies

Facies also have been regarded from a genetic viewpoint. Genetic facies generally are highly interpretative and even less objective than environmental facies. They differ from most environmental facies because processes rather than conditions are emphasized in their differentiation. Thus turbidity current deposits constitute a facies defined by its mode of origin rather than by conditions existing at the site of deposition. Some facies might be viewed equally well in several different ways. For example, bioherms might be considered structural, environmental, or genetic facies. The concept of purely genetic facies has found few applications in stratigraphy.

Geographic Facies

The identification of rock facies only with modern geographic areas rarely has much meaning. Where there is some basis for such a differentiation, the facies are likely to be much generalized and to have inexact boundaries because few areas or large regions recognized today correspond closely with significant paleogeographic subdivisions of any kind. If identification is made with ancient areas, these will probably be defined structurally and the facies are more or less similar to tectonic facies. In any case geographic designations serve to conceal whatever actual distinguishing features there may be. Thus the Ozark and Wisconsin facies of the Upper Cambrian would be much more intelligibly described respectively as limestone and sandstone facies. If, however, somewhat similarly developed facies occur in other areas, the use of a supplementary geographic name might be advantageous, as, for example, in comparing the Wisconsin sandstone facies with an Adirondack sandstone facies.

Facies Classification

Patterns shown by the construction of various facies names indicate that a kind of facies classification has developed. Thus facies differentiated on the basis of one or another element of their nature which is regarded as important are identified by such terms as *lithofacies, biofacies,* and *tectofacies.* These may be considered to distinguish *facies aspects.* Facies differentiated on the basis of their form and mutual relations are identified by such terms as *lithofacies, lithosome, lithostrome,* and *lithotope.* These may be considered to distinguish *facies classes.* Differentiation of facies by aspects and into classes has produced a useful classification of facies concepts but it has not resulted in the development of a satisfactory system of nomenclature.

Much of the confusion in the unstandardized use of facies terms appears to be mainly a result of difference in the approach to general facies problems. From one point of view, laterally intergrading rock bodies are primarily stratigraphic units that should be integrated into the system of conventional stratigraphic classification and nomenclature. According to this idea, formations, lithofacies, and lithosomes are comparable units but they differ with respect to form and mutual relations. Units of this kind can be classified as shown in Table 15.

TABLE 15.   Classification of Facies as Stratigraphic Units

Stratigraphic Classes	Stratigraphic Aspects		
	Rock Units	Biostratigraphic Units	Time-Rock Units
Vertically successive stratigraphic units	Formations	Zones	Stages
Laterally intertongued rock bodies	Lithosomes	Biosomes	
Laterally equivalent, statistically differentiated rock bodies	Lithofacies	Biofacies	
Layers of uniform character	Lithostromes	Biostromes	

In contrast, facies may be viewed as environmental units which are important chiefly because their characters and differences are subject to interpretation and explanation. Units of this kind are classified in Table 16.

TABLE 16.   Classification of Facies as Environmental Units

Environmental Classes	Environmental Aspects		
	Physical	Biologic	Structural
Depositional areas of uniform environment	Lithotopes	Biotopes	Tectotopes
Bodies of rock recording uniform environments	Lithosomes	Biosomes	Tectosomes
Vertically bounded lateral parts (facies) of stratigraphic units	Lithofacies	Biofacies	Tectofacies

Facies Types

Stratigraphers are concerned primarily with facies that are stratigraphic units but they are interested in them mainly because, as environmental units, they are more useful in interpretation and in the reconstruction of paleogeography than are conventional stratigraphic units. A review of facies concepts reveals, however, that factors other than those utilized in the foregoing classifications are important in facies discrimination and that a broader viewpoint is desirable. Thus facies that are definitely stratigraphic units grade off into others that are not. In one direction they pass into petrographic facies, or some other comparable kind, and in the other they merge into facies concerned with environments and nothing else. Facies, therefore, can be differentiated in another way that appears to be more fundamental than division into classes or by aspects. Three different types of facies can be recognized:

Type I. Facies differentiated primarily on the basis of appearance or composition without respect to their form, boundaries or mutual relations. These may be termed *petrographic facies*. Even though some are characterized by their fossils, the fossils can be regarded as rock constituents. These are all generalized facies in the sense that (1) they are more or less characteristically heterogeneous or (2) stratigraphic continuity is considered to be unimportant and is ignored.

Type II. Facies of characteristic composition differentiated among themselves primarily on the basis of form, nature of boundaries, and mutual relations. These are all stratigraphic bodies of one kind or another. They may be termed *stratigraphic facies*. Most of the specialized kinds of facies that have been recognized by stratigraphers are included in this group.

Type III. Facies that are concerned solely with environments. These are not sediments, rocks, or stratigraphic bodies; in fact they are not material. They are related more closely to sedimentology, biology, or tectonics than to stratigraphy although their applications to stratigraphy may be important. In contrast, facies of Types I and II consist of rocks even though interpretation, and particularly environmental interpretation, may influence to a large degree their recognition and differentiation.

Facies Classes

Current concepts indicate that facies of Types I and II can be subdivided into classes. The two classes of Type I facies are the following:

Class A. Facies consisting of all rocks of a certain kind without any reference to their form or occurrence. There can be only one facies of each kind. These facies generally are less heterogeneous than those of Class B. Good examples are black-shale facies, oolitic limestone facies, and graywacke facies.

Class B. Facies consisting of actual large bodies of indefinite or unspecified form, extent, and mutual relations, identified by generalized features of their composition or appearance, that occur in certain areas and more or less restricted parts of the stratigraphic section. Examples are red-bed facies, evaporite facies, paralic facies, and geosynclinal facies. There are as many facies of each kind as there are separate rock bodies.

The three classes of Type II or stratigraphic facies are the following:

Class C. Facies occurring in vertical succession whose boundaries are more or less horizontal stratigraphic planes and whose lateral relations are unspecified. These commonly correspond to conventional stratigraphic units such as formations, stages, and zones.

Class D. Facies that are laterally intergrading parts of some kind of stratigraphic unit and are separated at more or less arbitrary vertical cutoff planes. These are the statistical, mappable facies that have become important in various kinds of facies analysis.

Class E. Facies generally of strongly contrasting characters whose lateral boundaries are irregular. They intertongue and record shifting transgressive and regressive relations.

This subdivision of stratigraphic facies appears logical but it is not entirely practical. Difficulties are encountered when an attempt is made to classify actual stratigraphic bodies. Facies of these classes are defined on the basis of their form but attention has been devoted almost exclusively to the mutual relations of adjacent facies and their boundaries, and consideration of the form of a facies as a whole has been neglected. Thus one facies might intertongue with a second in one direction and pass into a third in the opposite direction so gradually that division would be made by arbitrary cutoff. Such a facies would be classified as belonging to either Class D or Class E depending upon the direction of approach. Also a formation or other similar stratigraphic unit must terminate laterally somewhere. Unless it ends at an outcrop or is cut out at unconformities, it must be cut off arbitrarily or intertongue with another stratigraphic unit. Consequently it does not differ essentially in form from horizontally differentiated facies.

Facies of Type III constitute a single class.

Class F. Facies that are environmental areas and not sedimentary or rock bodies of any kind.

Facies Aspects

The aspect of a facies is determined by the kind of characters relied on for its recognition. The aspects that have been noted as shown by the classifications on page 516 are (1) lithologic, (2) biologic, (3) tectonic, and (4) chronologic. With few and comparatively unimportant exceptions, only lithologic facies have found applications in stratigraphy. Future studies, however, are likely to bring other aspects into greater prominence and increase their relative importance. It is also possible, however, to consider facies in terms of other aspects, particularly if lithologic characters are broken down into their components, such as chemical composition, mineralogic nature, textural details, and so forth.

The three facies aspects that have received most emphasis are not as distinct as the names *lithofacies, biofacies,* and *tectofacies* seem to indicate. As previously noted, many of the organic constituents of rocks may be regarded as either lithologic or biologic features. Also the tectonic category is a specialized lithologic aspect that is dependent upon interpretation. Finally, further possible subdivisions of facies aspects make logical distinctions increasingly less clear. Altogether, the recognition of different aspects does not aid in the development of a reasonably simple facies classification.

Conclusions

Consideration of the elements of facies classification indicates that the differentiation of facies concepts as applied to stratigraphy into types and classes and with respect to aspects and objectivity is no simple matter. A system like those presented in Tables 15 and 16 is not adequate to organize all current facies concepts and show their relations because too many variables are involved. Several of the concepts are not sharply distinguishable among themselves, and separate classification would indicate more clear-cut differentiation than actually occurs. In the interests of accurate thinking, an analysis of the factors on which some kind of differentiation can be made appears to be worth while, but no simple, practical pattern of relationships emerges.

Facies Nomenclature

As understanding and appreciation of the importance of facies relations in sedimentary rocks have grown, one concept after another has been recognized and formulated, and terms to express various facies relationships have appeared. As knowledge increased, ideas changed and multiplied. Old terms were judged inadequate to express the more complex relations that became evident. Some old terms acquired specialized meanings and others were redefined or used with more restricted or otherwise altered meanings. Because facies problems have been approached from more than one standpoint, however, redefinitions of old terms, expressed or implied, have differed. Careless or inexact definitions or ill-considered usages, also, have confused a variety of concepts under single terms. Consequently very few available facies terms have generally accepted and exact meanings that are adequate for identifying the concepts they are intended to represent. For example, the word *lithofacies* has been employed to designate each of the classes of facies listed above except the last. It also has been used to mean (1) lithologic appearance, (2) lithologic character, (3) a lithologic type, (4) sediments representing an environment, and (5) as an adjective, lithologic. On the other hand, a bed characterized lithologically has been variously referred to as (1) a facies, (2) a lithofacies, (3) a lithosome, (4) a lithostrome, and (5) a lithotope.

Altogether at least twenty-five words have been coined or adapted to designate supposedly different kinds of facies having some application in stratigraphy. Many other facies concepts remain unnamed, and obviously, if a term were to be provided for every possibly useful concept, the most retentive memory would be severely taxed and most geologists would agree that an intolerably burdensome nomenclature had been created. Actually, no such elaborate terminology is necessary. If proper attention is given to the selection of a small, basic, well-defined vocabulary, different shades of meaning can be conveyed by context and, where greater precision is required, common adjectives can be used to modify somewhat general terms and make distinctions clear.

Facies

Facies is a general term that finds application in many different ways as both noun and adjective. It was originally used in geology to refer to the general appearance or aspect of rocks as this is determined by both lithologic and paleontologic characters. It still is used in this way but more commonly, as a noun, it now means the actual rocks that are distinguished or differentiated from each other by some peculiarity in their aspect or composition.

A general term of this kind is useful in geology in other fields beside stratigraphy. Therefore, *facies* can be accepted as referring to rocks or sediments, their aspects, composition, or environments as these are differentiated in any way that seems to be interesting or important. In stratigraphy specifically, *facies* can be employed in four ways without much danger of confusion:

1. As a generic term to include all restricted or specialized kinds of facies. It can substitute for them where distinction is not essential or where confusion is unlikely. The need for such a term is demonstrated by the way this word is used throughout this chapter.

2. To indicate the more or less generalized appearance, composition, or aspect of any body of rocks whose characteristics or differences from others are noteworthy.

3. For all rocks of some particular kind without reference to their form, age, or geographic occurrence. Thus, all red beds represent a red-beds facies and all black shales a black-shale facies. In this sense, there can be only one facies of each kind.

4. For a particular body of rocks characterized in any way whose relations to other rocks of different type are not specified. In this sense there are as many red-beds or black-shale facies as there are bodies of these kinds. If it is desirable to limit a facies stratigraphically, use can be made of an expression like "the limestone facies of the Paint Creek Formation (Miss.) in western Kentucky."

Facies of interest in stratigraphy may be differentiated on the basis of any observable physical or biological feature of the sediments or rocks, including secondary features resulting from diagenesis or other alteration except those produced by weathering, structural disturbance, or metamorphism. Thus limestone or dolomite and cherty or non-cherty facies may be recognized.

Geographic names generally should not be used to identify indeterminate facies with the purpose of indicating that they are similar to some particular formation or other conventional stratigraphic unit.

Lithofacies

A lithofacies is a rock body. This word has been used for rocks of some particular kind, either collectively or individually, whose relations to others were not specified. More generally, however, a lithofacies has been defined as a lateral subdivision of some stratigraphic unit that is differentiated from adjacent subdivisions by its lithologic character. Restriction in the latter sense appears to be advisable.

The upper and lower boundaries of a lithofacies correspond to the limits of some stratigraphic unit. A lithofacies may be separated from others laterally in three ways:

1. Lithofacies may be separated qualitatively at more or less indistinct and arbitrary vertical boundaries on the basis of generalized lithologic differences. Such lithofacies may be provided with geographic names, like Irvine Lithofacies of the Brodhead Formation (Miss.). If they are named, they become formally recognized stratigraphic subunits.

Insofar as a formation is a lithologic unit it is a more or less broadly conceived facies. The naming of locally restricted lateral parts of a formation as lithofacies provides synonyms that may be useful in detailed stratigraphic work. These synonyms can be ignored, however, by anyone who is not concerned with details.

2. Lithofacies may be separated at statistical boundaries—arbitrary vertical cutoff planes. Differentiation may be made on the basis of any lithologic character or combination of characters that can be expressed numerically—for example, percentages of shale, sandstone, and limestone. Many other features can be used, but as differences become more subtle, numerical measures are more difficult to apply. Lithofacies separated in this way are *statistical lithofacies* and they are the kind most commonly recognized. They are mappable stratigraphic units but are not likely to be named.

3. Lithofacies also may be separated at intertonguing boundaries—irregular lithologic contacts of contrasting stratigraphic bodies exhibiting transgressive-regressive mutual relations. Lithofacies separated in this way are *intertongued lithofacies* that cannot be mapped like conventional stratigraphic units. Adjacent intertongued lithofacies commonly differ in very obvious lithologic characters. Thus one may consist of shale and the other of sandstone.

The stratigraphic unit that is subdivided into lithofacies may be of any kind. It may be a formally recognized rock, time-rock, or biostratigraphic unit. Also it may be a similar unit not recognized in conventional stratigraphic classification known as an *operational unit*. In addition, it may be some arbitrary vertical fraction of an otherwise indivisible stratigraphic unit that is termed a *slice*. Most intertongued lithofacies are subdivisions of time-rock units because rock units generally do not consist of sufficiently contrasting parts so arranged that lithofacies of this kind can be distinguished. Biostratigraphic units rarely are separated into lithofacies of either kind.

Biofacies and Tectofacies

Biofacies and tectofacies in stratigraphy are identical in all respects to lithofacies except that they are distinguished respectively on the basis of differences in biologic or tectonic features. Facies of these kinds may be interesting theoretically but they have very little practical value except possibly in a few highly specialized connections. As previously noted, tectofacies are lithofacies that are dependent upon interpretation. They are recognizable only as much generalized stratigraphic bodies and they are not readily differentiated either statistically or by intertongued relations.

The concept of biofacies overlaps that of lithofacies because many biologic features contribute importantly to lithologic character. Therefore there is no point in recognizing biofacies except on the basis of features that do not find expression in such a way. Features that can be used to differentiate biofacies, whose aspects are different from and complementary to those of lithofacies, are restricted to the taxonomic identity and environmental implications of fossils.

If biofacies are recognized on the basis of taxonomic differences, they may be compared with conventional biostratigraphic units but there are important differences. Biostratigraphic zones have upper and lower boundaries determined by fossil ranges and lateral limits that are less significant. In contrast, the upper and lower boundaries of biofacies correspond with the boundaries of some specific stratigraphic unit and their lateral limits are emphasized. In other words, biostratigraphic units are considered principally in vertical sequence, but the significance of biofacies is in their lateral relations.

Biofacies generally are of little value if they are considered from the standpoint of detailed environmental implications. Almost every stratigraphic unit, unless it is a very thin or restricted one, is likely to consist of various zones whose fossils differ. The biologic character of the stratigraphic unit as a whole is the sum of the characters of its zones. Consequently it is a mixture. Such a mixture is almost certain to present a confused picture of biologic relations whose interpretation is difficult if not impossible.

Lithofacies can be recognized and traced in the subsurface on the basis of drilling records. Generally biofacies cannot. Wells furnish such tiny samples of a stratigraphic section that they cannot be relied on to reveal the biologic characters of most strata adequately. Therefore, the differentiation of biofacies commonly is restricted to zones of outcrop. Very rarely is it possible to map biofacies with a reasonable degree of accuracy throughout any extensive region.

Lithosome, Biosome, and Tectosome

Lithosome was proposed originally as a structural term to identify an intertonguing stratigraphic body. Because lithosomes are characterized lithologically, this word carries facies implications and it has been used in the sense of a lithologic facies for rocks that record a particular sedimentary environment regardless of their form. The companion terms *biosome* and *tectosome* were introduced subsequently for rocks that similarly record particular biologic and tectonic environments. It may be convenient in some circumstances to regard a lithofacies, for example, as being composed of several different lithosomes. The same idea can be expressed more directly, however, in terms of strata or members of different lithologic character, so a technical term for this concept is not needed. Because biofacies and tectofacies are less practical than lithofacies, there is even less reason for the terms *biosome* and *tectosome* except possibly for use in some abstract or theoretical considerations. Similarity in form of the words *lithosome* and *lithostrome*, and their companion terms, is certain to cause confusion and this is an additional reason to avoid their use wherever possible.

Lithostrome and Biostrome

A lithostrome is nothing more than a minor rock stratigraphic unit. The words *layer*, *stratum*, *bed*, and *member* are all available and adequate to express the same idea. Biostrome was originally defined as a particular kind of lithostrome. If it were to be redefined in a biologic sense, it would be a biostratigraphic zone. There is no real need for either of these words. No similar term has been suggested for a tectonic layer.

Lithotope, Biotope, and Tectotope

Although these words have been used with various meanings, they are properly areas characterized by particular environments. *Lithotope* and *biotope* are both useful terms for simple concepts. *Tectotope* is much less practical because tectonic areas are generalized and extensive. They are not subject to differentiation comparable to that possible in the consideration or description of sedimentary or biologic environments. The tectotope concept is useful but this term is superfluous because *area* is adequate.

Lithotopes and biotopes are not sediments or rocks. Therefore, they are not measurable in a third dimension. They are more or less ephemeral areally and at any moment they are circumscribed by boundaries that are subject to expansion, contraction, or other shift in position. The record of a lithotope or biotope that persists for some appreciable time is a body of sediment or rock and its enclosed fossils that has been termed a lithosome or a biosome.

Bioherm

Bioherm should be used as a structural rather than as a facies term as originally intended. Insofar as it means only organic reef, no very good reason can be offered for its retention. Organic reefs have only a generalized facies significance because they are not homogeneous bodies but consist of structureless core rock and steeply dipping fragmental flanking strata. Possibly they also enclose nearly horizontal intrareef deposits. These parts differ greatly in lithologic characters and biologic contents and represent quite different environmental conditions. Other bioherms, however, have more definite facies significance.

Other Facies Terms

Other facies terms have been proposed. None of them is considered here because they have been little used, several have no accepted meanings, others represent concepts that are impractical, and all appear to be superfluous. General understanding of facies and their relations is not advanced by the development of a complex and highly technical vocabulary.

Appearance, Composition, and Environment

The indiscriminate use of specialized facies terms for *appearance, composition,* or *environment* is inadvisable. A variety of common words more accurately expressing intended meanings is available for reference to these attributes of facies. Particularly, *lithofacies* should not be used as a synonym for *lithologic character*.

Facies Analysis

A single facies can be interpreted in terms of environment but the results are much more meaningful if several related facies are considered with respect to the differences they reveal. The comparison of a sequential set of facies at one locality gives evidence of the changes in environment that occurred with passing time. In isolation from other localities or areas, however, the significance of these changes is not apparent. On the other hand, comparison of a set of time-equivalent facies throughout a region provides the basis for the interpretation of static paleogeographic relations. The recognition of changes in lateral facies relations throughout time is necessary for the reconstruction of geologic history. This requires the consideration of facies within a three-dimensional framework and the comparison of successive sets of time-equivalent facies.

The recognition of more or less well-differentiated facies is not necessary for an analysis of stratigraphic variations and the reconstruction of geologic history. Every alert field geologist makes some kind of interpretation every time he views an outcrop and compares it mentally with others. Although such comparisons are qualitative, many excellent and critical conclusions have been drawn from them and much current knowledge concerning paleogeography and geologic history has been based on them.

One of the most noteworthy advances in practical stratigraphy in recent years, however, is the development of methods of facies analysis. Facies defined in terms of rocks with more or less definite limits, no matter what these are or how they are determined, provide sets of units related in various ways that can be studied and compared. Facies analysis depends for its accomplishments upon the quantity and quality of available basic information. The comparison of carefully chosen statistical facies improves quality and

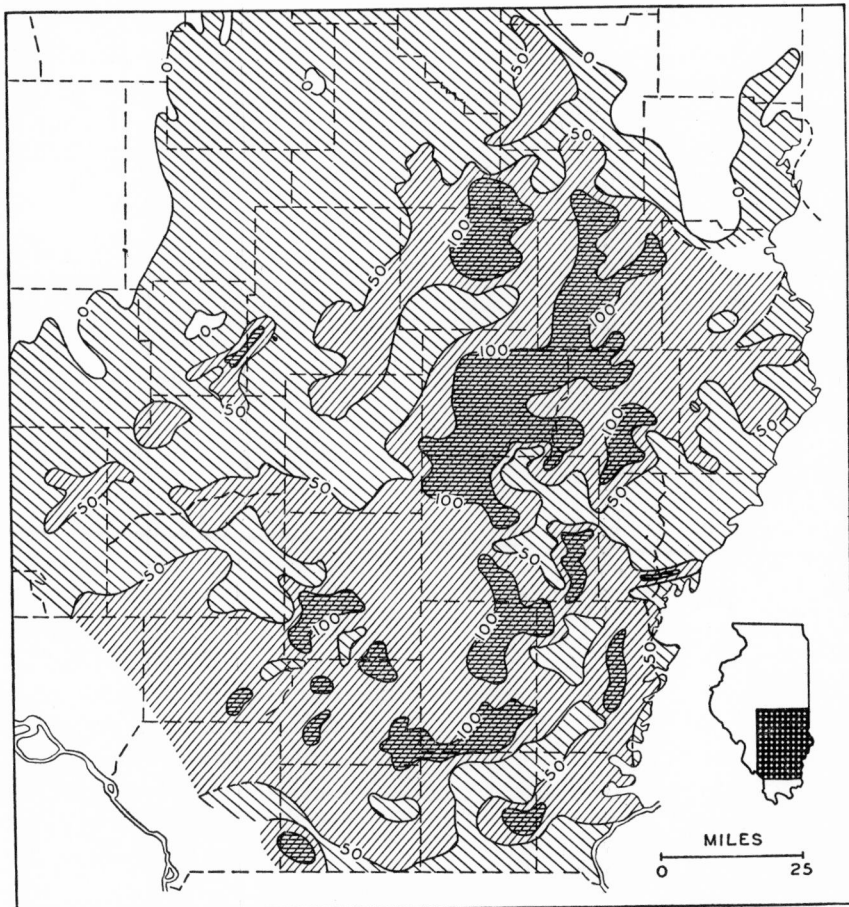

Figure 198. Isolith map showing the thickness of sandstone included in the Cypress Formation (Miss.) in southeastern Illinois. This formation is commonly designated a sandstone but it contains variable amounts of shale, which dominates the formation in some areas. Because the thickness of the Cypress is not constant, the relations of sandstone to the entire formation are not indicated by a map of this kind. A map showing the percentage of sandstone in the Cypress probably would be more significant for interpretative purposes (see Figure 180 A and B, p. 486). (After Pryor and others, 1957, Ill. Geol. Surv., Bull. 80, p. 61, fig. 6.)

furnishes a surer and more accurate foundation for interpretation than the comparison of qualitative facies. The degrees of similarity and difference of such facies can be determined quantitatively, and most subjective elements of comparison can be eliminated. This process, to be successful, requires good planning and logical reasoning in relating whatever facts can be determined.

Facies Mapping

Facies analysis is facilitated by the presentation of lithologic and other data in the form of maps that show lateral changes and make visual compari-

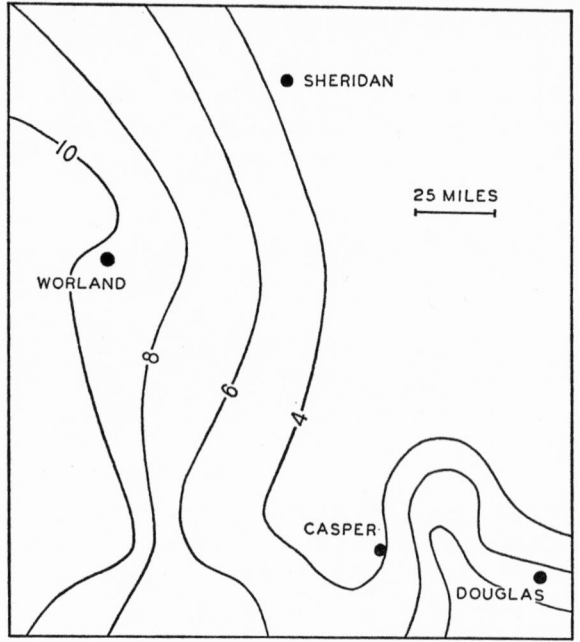

Figure 199. Map showing by contours the number of sandstones exceeding some unspecified thickness present in the Cretaceous System between the base of the Niobrara Formation and the base of the Dakota Sandstone in north central Wyoming. The results of statistical studies of the lithologic composition of a stratigraphic section of this kind can be shown on maps which indicate the center of gravity of sandstones within the section and the degree of their dispersion as well as other features of vertical variability. (After Krumbein and Libby, 1957, Bull. Am. Assoc. Petroleum Geol., vol. 41, p. 207, fig. 6.)

son of areal relations possible. Facies can be mapped on an entirely qualitative basis, but the results are not likely to be detailed or very accurate unless facies distinctions are strongly marked and lateral gradations are abrupt.

Much more useful results generally are obtained if facies are considered quantitatively. Statistical facies based on one or several related properties of the rocks can be differentiated more accurately and in greater detail. A series of maps showing the relations of such facies in successive stratigraphic zones provides a compilation of basic data that is particularly suitable for interpretation and the reconstruction of changing paleogeography.

Maps useful in facies studies are (1) contoured maps and (2) areal maps. Variation in any property of rocks that can be counted or measured is most simply shown by contours. These can be concerned with individual properties like the total thickness of a stratigraphic interval or unit, the total thickness (see Figure 198), percentage thickness (see Figure 180B, p. 486), or number of beds (see Figure 199) of one particular kind of rock, or the position within a stratigraphic interval where a particular kind of rock is concentrated. Also two properties can be compared, such as the relative proportions of two different kinds of rock within the same interval. Because origin and coarseness of sediments are particularly important in interpretation, two of the most useful measures of the latter type are the following, as shown in Figures 200 and 201:

$$Detrital\ ratio = \frac{noncarbonate\ clastic\ rocks}{carbonates + non\text{-}clastic\ rocks}$$

$$Sand\text{-}shale\ ratio = \frac{sandstone + conglomerate}{shale + siltstone}$$

Proportionate relations can be expressed either as ratios or in percentages. Generally relations of one property to the whole are calculated as percentages whereas the relations of two comparable properties are presented as ratios. Because a geometrical series of ratios is infinite, ratio contouring results in finer differentiation of large and small values. Contours at equal percentage intervals, however, are somewhat simpler for intermediate values—see Table 17.

TABLE 17.   Equivalent Percentages and Ratios

Percentage	Ratio	Ratio	Percentage
0	0.00	0.00	0
1	0.01	0.125	11
10	0.11	0.25	20
20	0.25	0.50	33
30	0.43	1.00	50
40	0.67	2.00	67
50	1.00	4.00	80
60	1.50	8.00	89
70	2.33	16.00	94
80	4.00	32.00	97
90	9.00	64.00	98
99	99.00	128.00	99
100	∞	∞	100

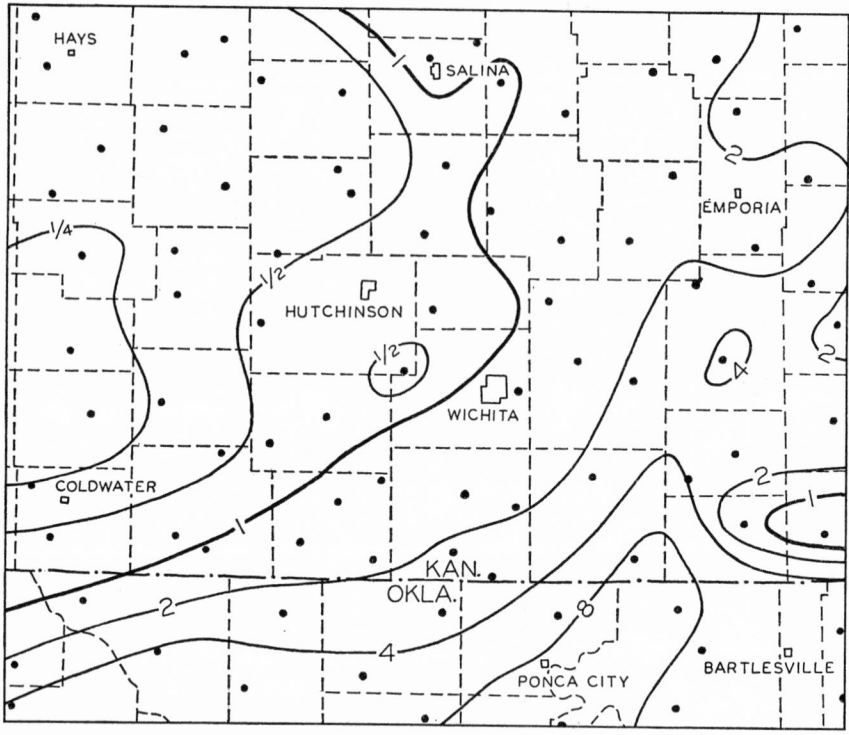

Figure 200. Detrital ratio map of all Pennsylvanian strata in part of south central Kansas and adjacent Oklahoma. The Pennsylvanian is overlapped by the Cretaceous in the western half of this area. In the eastern half, however, gentle west dips bring successively lower beds to the surface, and eastward the Pennsylvanian section becomes progressively more incomplete. This map, therefore, does not show relations in strata that are strictly comparable throughout its whole extent. The pattern of variation suggests that Pennsylvanian seas deepened somewhat to the northwest and that the source of detrital sediment lay to the south. A companion isopach map would be useful in evaluating these possibilities. (After Krumbein, 1955, J. Geol., vol. 63, p. 461, fig. 3 [upper].)

More complex relations within a stratigraphic unit cannot be shown by contours in a manner that is easily understood. Generally these relations are presented by what are more properly termed facies or lithofacies maps. The latter consist of patterned areas that are keyed to a legend presented most commonly in an arbitrarily subdivided triangular diagram (see Figures 197, p. 512 and 206, p. 533). Two or three related variables can be handled conveniently in this way. For example, one map may show variations in both the clastic and sand-shale ratios. Also a single map can show the relative proportions of limestone, sandstone, and shale or any other three kinds of rock that are considered important. It can be supplemented by similar constructions devoted to a single kind of rock showing, for instance, the proportions

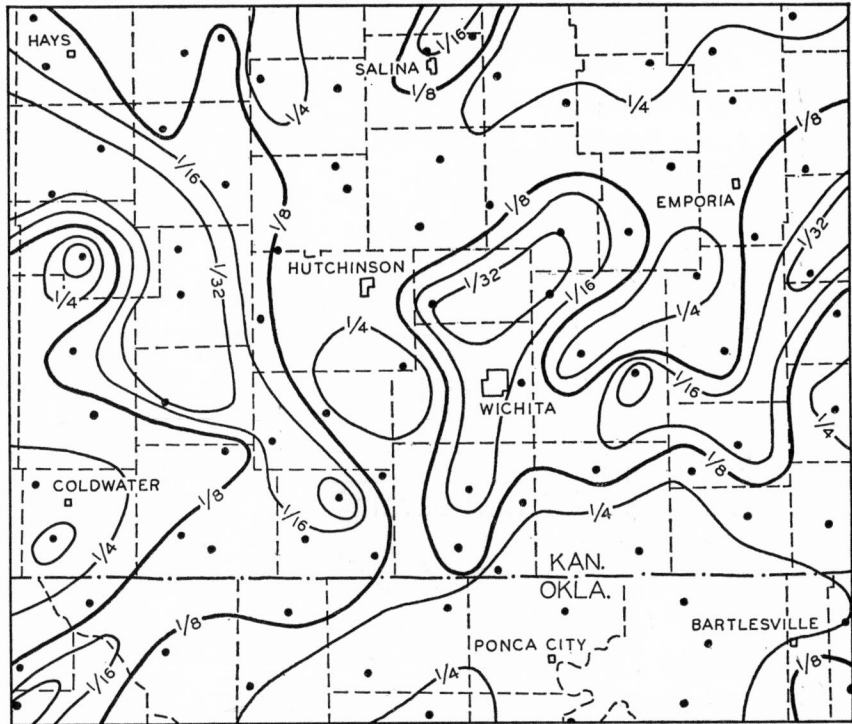

Figure 201. Sand-shale ratio map of all Pennsylvanian strata in part of south central Kansas and adjacent Oklahoma. This is a companion to the map shown in Figure 200. It reveals more irregular relations because Pennsylvanian sandstones are more erratically developed than the limestones. (After Krumbein, 1955, *J. Geol.*, vol. 63, p. 461, fig. 3 [lower].)

of red and gray shale or the relative abundances of quartzose, arkosic, and graywacke sandstones, and so forth (see Figure 202). It is possible, of course, to map more than three related properties in a similar way. Four kinds of rock can be related to the volumetric subdivision of a tetrahedron (see Figure 203). Maps of these types become confusing, however, because of the many patterns representing rocks or properties related in so many ways.

Maps of the kinds described show lateral variations within a stratigraphic interval and furnish the basis for paleogeographic interpretations. Similar comparisons can be made between two successive stratigraphic intervals to show the differences of detrital or sand-shale ratios or in the relations of any other quantitative measurements. Such maps indicate how paleogeographic conditions changed.

Single facies maps may be misleading because they do not reveal significant differences. For example, a stratigraphic interval in different areas might consist of two homogeneous units, one sandstone and the other shale, or of many alternating sandstone and shale strata in such proportions that the sand-shale ratios are the same (see Figures 204 and 205). Also important dif-

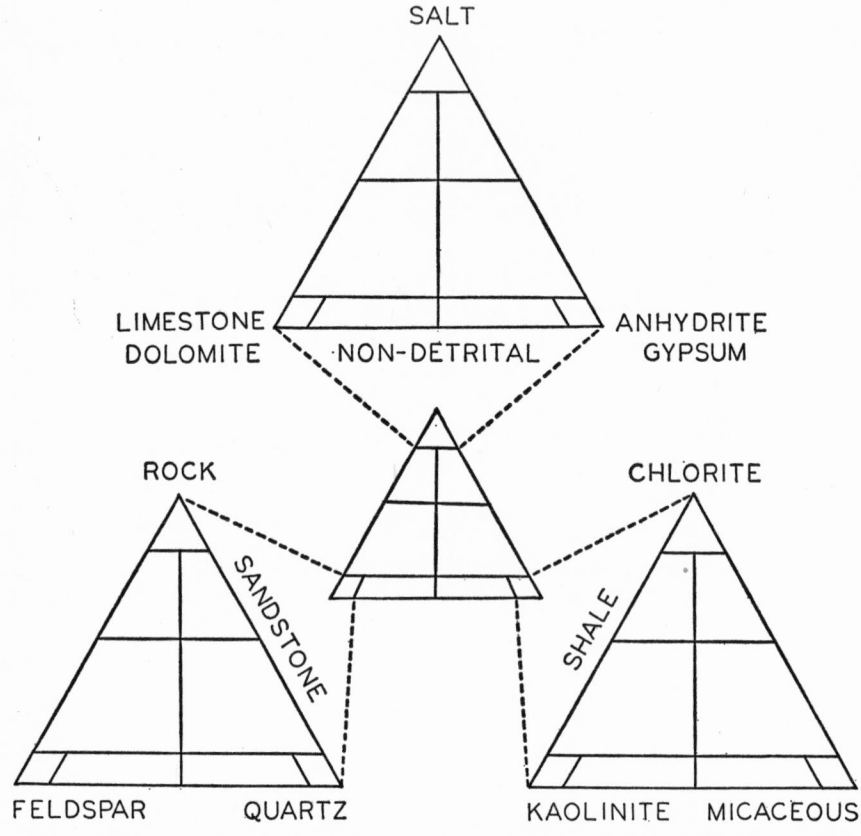

Figure 202. Three-component triangles used for plotting ratios in sedimentary analysis and lithofacies mapping. The smaller central triangle is the one most commonly employed (see Figure 236, p. 612). It shows the relations of detrital and sand-shale ratios. The others provide the means for refined analysis of the three generally recognized end members. Triangles with other end members may be more useful in some situations—see, for example, Figure 206, p. 533. Also different divisions of the triangle may be made (see Figure 234, p. 611). (Modified from *Stratigraphy and sedimentation*, p. 276, fig. 9–13, by W. C. Krumbein and L. L. Sloss. San Francisco: W. H. Freeman and Company, 1951. Also by permission of the authors.)

ferences such as those between clean sandstone of the general St. Peter type and dirty ones like those in the upper Pennsylvanian would not be revealed by an ordinary percentage map. On the other hand, differences like those between very argillaceous limestone and very calcareous shale might appear to be much more important than they actually are. Therefore, accurate facies analysis is likely to require consideration and comparison of the variability of several different properties or measurements. The usefulness of many facies maps can be increased by the superposition of a contour map showing varia-

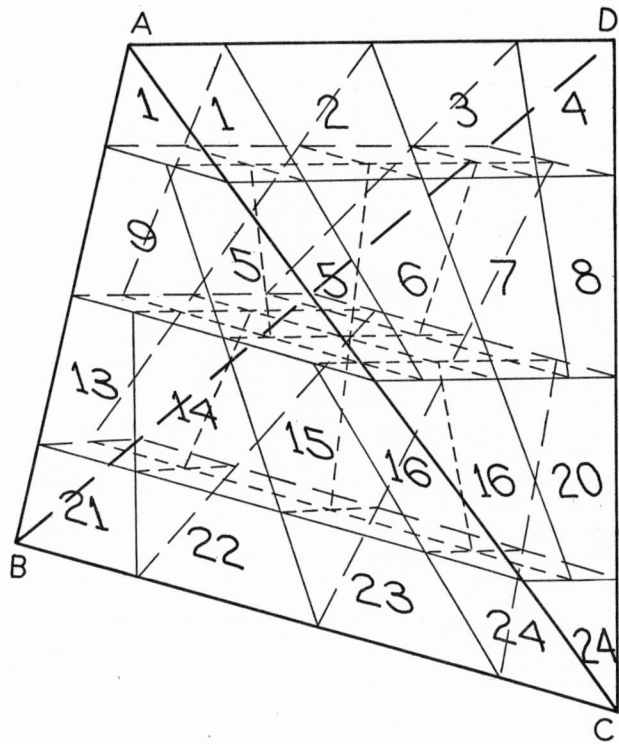

Figure 203. Four end members, e.g., A, limestone and dolomite, B, sandstone, C, shale, and D, evaporites, can be treated simultaneously within the solid body of a tetrahedron although such a system is difficult to visualize. Each side of the tetrahedron, however, is a simple three-component diagram.

tion in some other property (see Figure 206). One of the most common combinations is a lithologic facies map with added isopach contours.

So many possibilities exist for the presentation of lateral variability in the form of maps that they are limited only by an investigator's ingenuity and industry. Few maps are likely to be made, however, because of the amount of labor required for their preparation. The complete analysis of any stratigraphic section is practically impossible and results certainly would not adequately repay all of the necessary time and effort. Careful planning obviously is required to obtain the most satisfactory results. Judicious consideration of

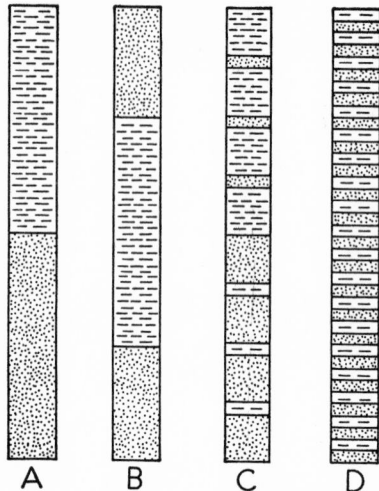

Figure 204. Four stratigraphic columns consisting of equal quantities of sandstone and shale. Although these columns are very differently constituted, they all provide the same sand-shale ratio of 1, and no distinction would be made between them in ordinary lithofacies analysis. There are, however, means of treating differences of this kind (see Figure 199, p. 526).

the general stratigraphic situation should suggest what features will provide the most useful and easily obtained information. The features selected for investigation do not need to be the same for all parts of a region or throughout the whole of a stratigraphic section that is to be studied.

Limitations of Facies Analysis

Because the vertical dimension in stratigraphy cannot be calibrated very accurately in terms of time, the fundamental weakness of facies mapping and analysis stems directly from uncertainties of correlation. Probably few formation contacts or other horizons that are utilized as boundaries separating stratigraphic facies are time planes, and as studies are extended throughout larger and larger areas uncertainties multiply and the likelihood of inaccuracy increases. Many formations of the continental platforms, however, probably are approximate time-rock units. No better standards for time control in carefully studied regions can be set up at present. Nevertheless, all formations are areally restricted, and any comprehen-

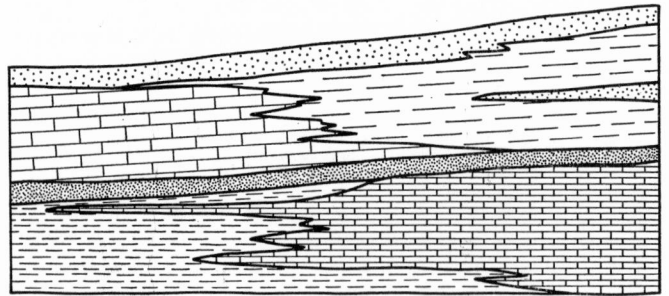

Figure 205. Schematic cross section with several different types of intertongued lithologic units. This section has been drawn so that the proportions of limestone, shale, and sandstone are the same everywhere regardless of lateral variations. Ordinary lithofacies analysis and mapping would give no hint of these very striking differences. (After Moore, 1957, *Bull. Am. Assoc. Petroleum Geol.*, vol. 41, p. 1784, fig. 7.)

sive comparison of facies is likely to extend beyond the lateral limits of recognized formations. This is the point at which correlation becomes crucial. Even if the most accurate possible correlations are established, however, the boundaries of laterally intergrading or supposedly equivalent formations recognized in different areas cannot be expected to correspond in time exactly. Consequently, parts of formations traced throughout an extended re-

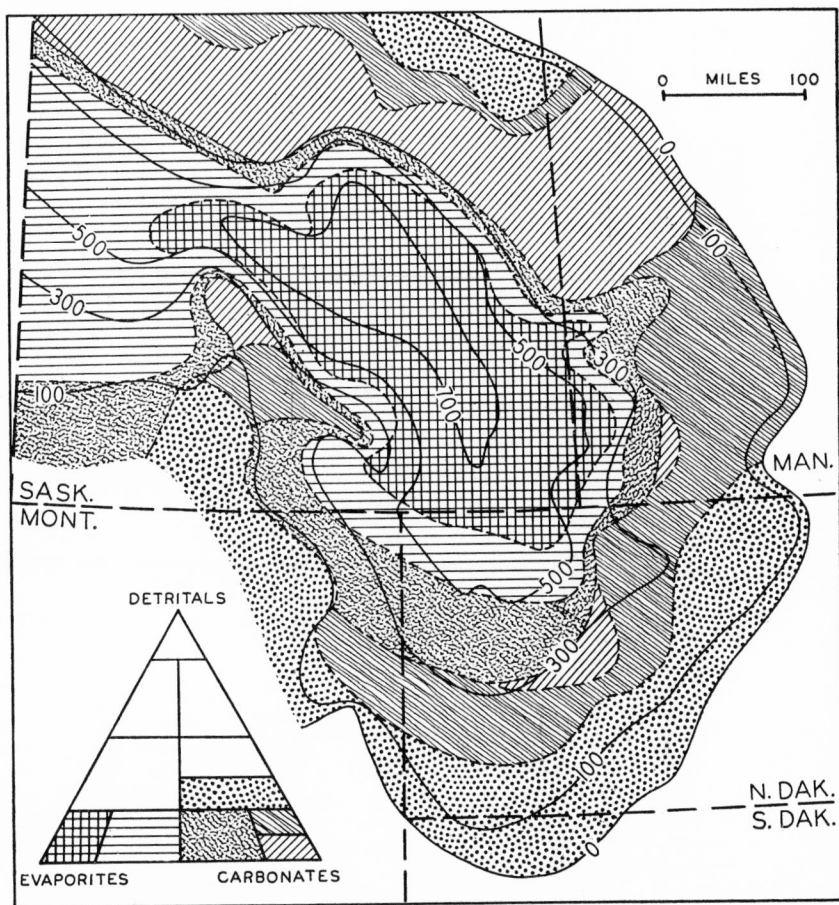

Figure 206.   Statistical lithofacies map of the Williston basin showing variations in the development of the Elk Point Group (Dev.). It is based on the relations of the detrital ratio and the evaporite-carbonate ratio. Maps of this kind are complicated and difficult to read and interpret without much practice. Note that the triangular diagram and its divisions that provide the basis for lithofacies differentiation are not the same as those most commonly used (see Figure 202, p. 530). The isopach contours showing the thickness of Elk Point strata furnish important additional information but they also serve to make the map more complicated. (After Baillie, 1955, *Bull. Am. Assoc. Petroleum Geol.,* vol. 39, p. 591, fig. 9.)

gion probably do not constitute a time-equivalent set of facies. Insofar as any deviation in time equivalence does occur, facies interpretations are bound to be inaccurate.

The precise time equivalence of facies is not so important in some economic applications as in paleogeographic interpretation. For example, in oil-producing regions, it is the lateral variability in physically continuous rock stratigraphic units rather than in time-rock units that is likely to be of inter-

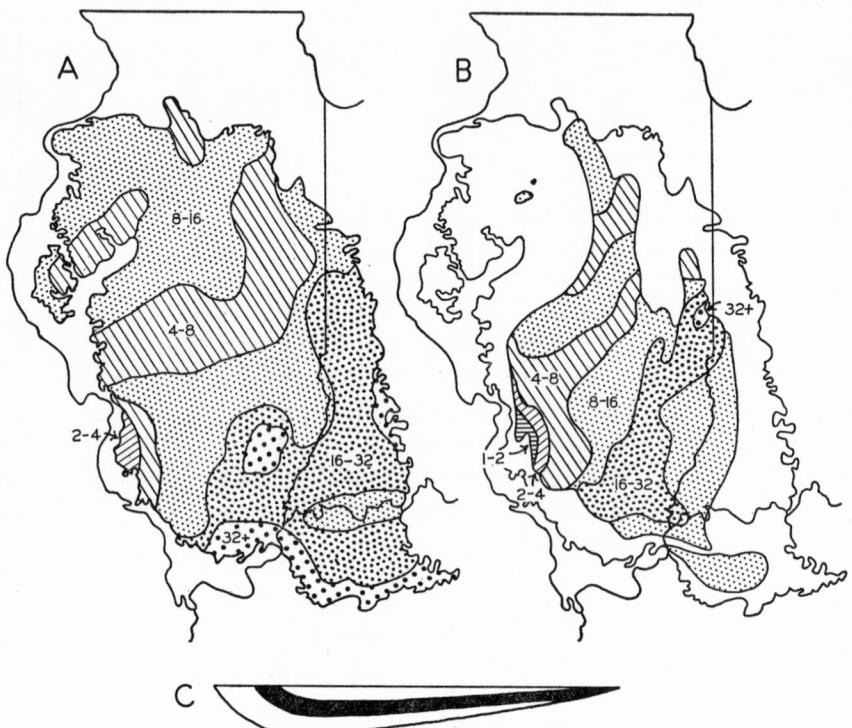

Figure 207.   Detrital ratio maps of the Pennsylvanian rocks in the Eastern Interior basin of Illinois, southwestern Indiana, and western Kentucky. A shows ratios for all Pennsylvanian rocks, B only for rocks of Des Moinesian age, which include much of the Tradewater, all of the Carbondale, and the lower parts of the McLeansboro groups, and C is a diagrammatic north-south cross section showing relations of Des Moinesian strata to the entire Pennsylvanian System as this is developed and preserved in Illinois. The first map does not deal with a uniform stratigraphic section because older strata are overstepped northward and erosion has removed unequal amounts of younger strata in different areas. Consequently significance of the pattern shown in A is not readily apparent and any interpretation based on it is likely to be erroneous. This objection does not apply to B, whose diagonally trending pattern with highest ratio to the northeast and lowest to the southwest suggests that detrital material was transported in the latter direction. (A and B after Wanless, 1955, Bull. Am. Assoc. Petroleum Geol., vol. 39, p. 1796, fig. 11.)

est, and the deviation of stratigraphic boundaries from time planes may not matter greatly. Also, as useful information can be obtained from areally less extensive studies, the problems of detailed correlation are less complex.

Unconformities provide some of the most ideal formation contacts but they are not nearly as satisfactory boundaries for sets of laterally related facies. Although unconformities may be continuous throughout wide areas, the time spans of adjacent stratigraphic units are almost certain to vary from place to place because deposition began at different times at different places, or it ended sooner, or erosion was more severe in some areas than in others. Facies above or below some unconformities, where overlapping or overstepping are particularly important, may be so unequal that comparisons are misleading. Facies studies of outcropping strata also yield unreliable results because they are based on extremely variable fractions of a complete stratigraphic unit. An excellent example of such discrepancies is furnished by the Pennsylvanian System in Illinois, which diminishes northward to a feather edge by both the thinning and wedging out of lower strata above an unconformity and the progressive erosion of upper beds (see Figure 207).

Further inequalities in facies are caused by variable stratigraphic relations within units chosen for analysis. Thus the removal of strata at local unconformities changes proportions of remaining rocks even though the proportions originally were identical (see

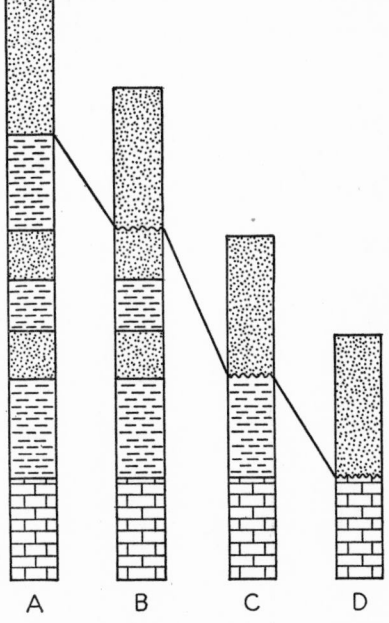

	DETRITAL RATIO	SAND-SHALE RATIO
A	5	1
B	4	1.7
C	2.5	1.3
D	1.3	∞

Figure 208. The unconformable sandstone shown in these four stratigraphic columns directly overlies older and older members of a lower formation because erosion has cut progressively more deeply into it. Differences in the detrital and sand-shale ratios that result are not necessarily related in any way to the conditions or history of deposition in the area of these columns. In actual lithofacies studies the results of unconformable relations can be mistaken for important lateral variations within continuously equivalent stratigraphic units.

Figure 208). Such variations do not indicate any differences in depositional environments. Changes in the rate of deposition from place to place also alter lithologic proportions and the results as indicated by the facies might be mistakenly interpreted as evidence of lateral environmental shifting (see Figure 209).

The comparison of facies differentiated in stratigraphic slices may lead to anomalous interpretations because the arbitrarily spaced planes of separation may deviate importantly from time planes. Figure 210 illustrates a possible

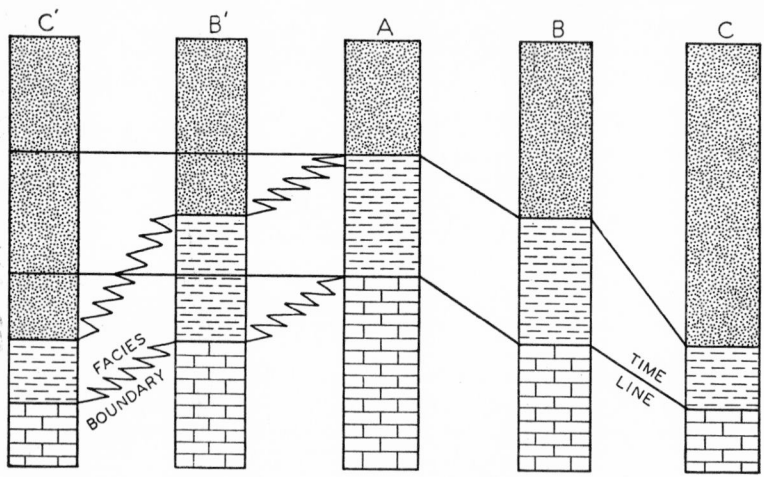

Figure 209. The stratigraphic columns on either side of A are identically constituted. Each pair, B and B' or C and C', provides the same detrital and sand-shale ratios. Lithofacies analysis and mapping makes no distinction between relations of these kinds where on the one hand strata do not vary lithologically from place to place but were deposited at unequal rates and on the other lateral variation in contemporaneous subunits is important.

situation where strata pinching out between two unconformities are considered as three slices with very different characters and relations. Lateral variations within these slices, if all were interpreted similarly, would yield erroneous conclusions. A somewhat similar rock association results from lateral lithologic gradation rather than unconformities. Facies similarly differentiated here also would lead to improper conclusions.

The foregoing rather obvious possible obstacles to accurate facies interpretation demonstrate that facies analysis should be most carefully planned and conclusions should be drawn with caution. In many actual situations doubts may not be serious but certainly no single formula for analysis can be relied upon to produce uniformly acceptable results.

One other aspect of facies analysis and interpretation requires explanation and understanding. In general, the smaller the time value of a stratigraphic unit, the less certain is its correlation. Conversely, if all due care is exercised, the greater the magnitude of a unit, the less important is uncertainty concerning the correlation of its boundaries even though more accurate correlation is not possible. If extensive facies studies are to be made, the limitations of correlation impose the practical necessity of working with stratigraphic units of considerable thickness such as those occurring between widely spaced unconformities or other major stratigraphic boundaries. Although the correlation of such units from place to place may be reasonably reliable, the

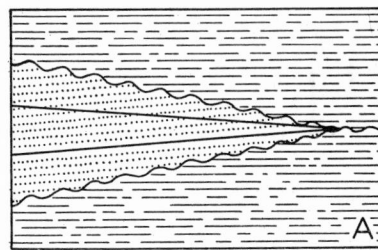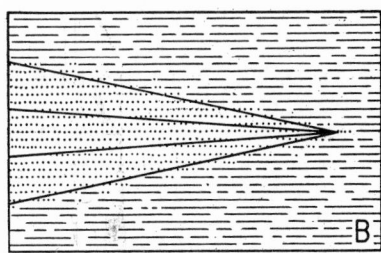

Figure 210. The subdivision of a large stratigraphic unit into arbitrary slices is likely to provide surfaces that are not time planes and smaller stratigraphic units that deviate importantly from time-rock units. The lithofacies mapping and interpretation of slices, therefore, should be undertaken with caution. In these schematic diagrams, A shows a lithologically distinctive wedge lying between unconformities and B shows a similar wedge that grades laterally into strata of a different kind. Each is divided into three equal slices. Only by chance does one of the slice surfaces correspond with a time plane.

facies differentiated within them will certainly be much generalized and important details of both areal and temporal environmental variations are sure to be obscured. As attempts are made to bring these details into better focus, generally by subdivision of the stratigraphic section, correlation becomes more important but it is relatively more difficult to achieve. Consequently the conclusion must be drawn that detail and accuracy are incompatible. As standards in one respect are raised, their decline in the other is almost inevitable.

BIBLIOGRAPHY

Cloud, P. E., Jr. (1952), Facies relationships of organic reefs, *Bull. Am. Assoc. Petroleum Geol.*, vol. 36, pp. 2125–2149.
  This article compares different kinds of reefs and describes the ways in which they grow.
Cumings, E. R. (1932), Reefs or bioherms? *Bull. Geol. Soc. Amer.*, vol. 43, pp. 331–352.
  The author describes and compares a variety of ancient reeflike limestone bodies.

Du Bois, E. P. (1945), Subsurface relations of the Maquoketa and "Trenton" formations in Illinois, Ill. Geol. Surv., Rept. Invest. 105, pp. 6–33.

   A subsurface lithofacies study is made of strata known by different names at outcrops.

Emery, K. O., Tracey, J. I., and Ladd, H. S. (1954), Geology of Bikini and nearby atolls, pt. 1, Geology, U.S. Geol. Surv., Prof. Paper 260-A.

   Detailed studies are made of modern organic reefs in the Marshall Islands of the Pacific Ocean.

Fairbridge, R. W. (1958), What is a consanguineous association? *J. Geol.*, vol. 66, pp. 319–324.

   This points out the important relations between paleotectonic and paleographic setting and the lithologic nature of sediments.

Fisher, D. W. (1956), Intricacy of applied stratigraphic nomenclature, *J. Geol.*, vol. 64, pp. 617–627.

   Examples and problems of lateral lithologic variation in the Paleozoic rocks of New York are discussed.

Guilcher, André (1958), Coastal and submarine morphology, London, Methuen.

   See pp. 118–136 for descriptions of coral reefs and a consideration of the theories proposed to account for their formation.

Krumbein, W. C. (1952), Principles of facies map interpretation, *J. Sediment. Petrol.*, vol. 22, pp. 200–211.

   Largely theoretical consideration is given to facies interpretation based on measurements of lithology and thickness.

Krumbein, W. C. (1954), The tetrahedron as a facies mapping device, *J. Sediment. Petrol.*, vol. 24, pp. 3–19.

   Methods of dealing with four variables in the differentiation of facies are explained.

Krumbein, W. C. (1956), Regional and local components of facies maps, *Bull. Am. Assoc. Petroleum Geol.*, vol. 40, pp. 2163–2194.

   An explanation is given of methods of eliminating effects of local variability from regional facies maps.

Krumbein, W. C., and Libby, W. G. (1957), Application of moments to vertical variability maps of stratigraphic units, *Bull. Am. Assoc. Petroleum Geol.*, vol. 41, pp. 197–211.

   Methods of showing by contours the position and concentration of a particular kind of rock within a stratigraphic unit are described.

Krumbein, W. C., and Sloss, L. L. (1951), *Stratigraphy and sedimentation*, San Francisco, Freeman.

   Sedimentary facies and facies maps are discussed in Chapters 9 and 13, pp. 252–286 and 403–419.

Longwell, C. R. (chairman) (1949), Sedimentary facies in geologic history, Geol. Soc. Amer., Mem. 39.

   This symposium consists of papers by R. C. Moore, E. D. McKee, S. W. Muller, E. M. Spieker, H. E. Wood, and L. L. Sloss, W. C. Krumbein, and E. C. Dapples with following discussions.

McKee, E. D. (1938), Environment and history of the Toroweap and Kaibab formations in northern Arizona and southern Utah, Carnegie Inst. Wash., Publ. 492.

The value of qualitative facies differentiation for stratigraphic interpretations is demonstrated.

McKee, E. D., and others (1956), Paleotectonic maps, Jurassic System, U.S. Geol. Surv., Misc. Geol. Invest., Map I–175, 9 plates and text (folio).

The first of a projected series, this has the most complete and detailed paleogeologic, facies, isopach, paleotectonic, and paleogeographic maps produced for any extensive region.

Moore, R. C. (1957), Modern methods of paleoecology, *Bull. Am. Assoc. Petroleum Geol.*, vol. 41, pp. 1775–1801.

The author discusses facies and points out some of the weaknesses of lithofacies mapping.

Pike, W. S., Jr. (1947), Intertonguing marine and nonmarine Upper Cretaceous deposits of New Mexico, Arizona and southwestern Colorado, Geol. Soc. Amer., Mem. 24.

Lateral variation and transition of the Mesa Verde Sandstone into the Mancos Shale are described.

Pugh, W. E. (ed.) (1950), *Bibliography of organic reefs, bioherms, and biostromes*, Tulsa, Seismograph Service Corp.

A list of over 1000 titles is indexed geographically and stratigraphically.

Shrock, R. R. (1939), Wisconsin Silurian bioherms (organic reefs), *Bull. Geol. Soc. Amer.*, vol. 50, pp. 525–562.

The composition, structure, and development of a variety of exposed Silurian reefs are described.

Spieker, E. M. (1946), Late Mesozoic and early Cenozoic history of central Utah, U.S. Geol. Surv., Prof. Paper 205-D.

The stratigraphic and structural relations of the Indianola Group and Price River Formation (Mesa Verde Sandstone) and the Mancos Shale are described.

Stockdale, P. B. (1939), Lower Mississippian rocks of the east-central interior, Geol. Soc. Amer., Spec. Paper 22.

In a comprehensive stratigraphic study the facies relations within formations receive particular attention.

Teichert, Curt (1958), Concept of facies, *Bull. Am. Assoc. Petroleum Geol.*, vol. 42, pp. 2718–2744.

The author reviews history and European opinions concerning varied facies concepts.

Weller, J. M. (1958), Stratigraphic facies differentiation and nomenclature, *Bull. Am. Assoc. Petroleum Geol.*, vol. 42, pp. 609–639.

This is an extensive review of literature and evaluation of facies nomenclature.

Young, R. C. (1955), Sedimentary facies and intertonguing in the Upper Cretaceous of the Book Cliffs, Utah-Colorado, *Bull. Geol. Soc. Amer.*, vol. 66, pp. 177–202.

Laterally transitional relations of the Blackhawk and Price River formations (Mesa Verde Sandstone) and the Mancos Shale are described.

15

Correlation

CORRELATION is the process of determining mutual relations. In stratigraphy this term commonly is used with a much restricted meaning and refers principally to the establishment of equivalent relations with respect to time. Correlation is one of the most obvious and necessary functions of stratigraphy. It is the first step beyond the relatively simple observational and descriptive processes that constitute the basic practical phases of stratigraphy. It serves to indicate which rocks in different regions are of the same age and arranges rocks of different ages in their proper sequence. Without correlation there could be no historical geology because it is the only means of relating happenings that occurred at different places and thus synthesizing a single regional or world-wide succession of geologic events. Many stratigraphers have considered correlation their ultimate objective.

EVIDENCE AND METHODS OF CORRELATION

Correlations should be based on every kind of pertinent evidence that is available. Paleontologic evidence commonly is emphasized but actually more different types of physical evidence are utilized. Fossils furnish the best means for effecting long-range correlations. Various physical features of the rocks, however, generally are more useful for short-range correlations and they may be superior to fossils in the detailed correlation of strata within individual sedimentary basins. Both kinds of evidence have their limitations and in several respects the limitations are similar.

All of the features useful in the recognition of formations (see p. 423) are also useful in correlation. The most important and most commonly employed types of evidence are listed in Table 18.

TABLE 18.   The Most Important
Kinds of Evidence Used for
Correlation

A. Physical evidence
    1. Lithologic similarity
    2. Continuity of strata
    3. Position in stratigraphic sequence
    4. Orderly variation in lithology
    5. Electric characters
    6. Unconformable relations
    7. Structural development
    8. Metamorphism
    9. Radioactivity
B. Paleontologic evidence
    10. Index fossils
    11. Paleontologic sequences
    12. Paleontologic similarity
    13. Evolutionary development

Physical Evidence

Physical evidence generally is relied upon for very short-range correlation. Although fossils have often been called upon for this purpose, the tracing of certain types of key beds such as bentonites may furnish even more secure assurance of time equivalence. As the distance between localities increases, however, the reliability of physical correlation rapidly declines unless the contemporaneity of strata can be substantiated by other means.

Lithologic Similarity

Different rocks resemble each other more or less closely in various respects: composition, texture, structure, color, and so forth. Similarity invites comparison and close similarity suggests correlation, particularly if the rocks under consideration occupy approximately corresponding positions in the stratigraphic section. Actually, lithologic similarity is a much more accurate index of similar genesis than it is an indication of contemporaneity. Within a single basin of deposition similar conditions may have prevailed simultaneously throughout large areas or they may have shifted gradually from one part to another, in either case being recorded by laterally continuous strata of similar characters and appearance. Also similar conditions may have occurred simultaneously in several isolated areas or may have recurred in different areas at different times, in either of these cases producing discontinuous bodies of similar strata.

Since the days of Werner many correlations have been made on the basis of lithologic similarity alone. Some very long-range correlations of this type —for example, between western Europe and eastern North America— proved to be reasonably accurate with respect to the larger divisions of the stratigraphic section. Such examples, of course, reflect the generally similar geologic histories of transatlantic regions, and corresponding similarities cannot be expected to occur in all other parts of the world. Less extensive and more detailed correlations have been variously successful. Generally substantiation is sought in paleontologic comparisons but many formations are deficient or entirely lacking in useful fossils. Commonly lithologic correlations are accepted tentatively and they are likely to be maintained with varying degrees of assurance until shown to be incorrect. In situations of this kind the burden of proof generally falls upon those who contest the accuracy of generally accepted lithologic correlations.

Most stratigraphic field work, consisting as it does of the identification and tracing of formations from outcrop to outcrop, involves short-range correlation. Lithologic similarity is chiefly relied upon, aided and checked by intermittent paleontologic observations. In a similar manner but on a somewhat extended scale, correlations are continued throughout the strata of a single basin.

There appear to be adequate reasons for concluding that some rather thin distinctive strata record a happening or a peculiar combination of conditions that affected very large areas practically simultaneously for brief intervals of time. Such strata include bentonites, believed to have resulted from falls of volcanic ash, and the coal beds and some limestones of the Pennsylvanian System that reflect phases of recurrent sedimentary cycles. Where present, these strata may provide a basis for detailed correlation of much greater certainty than fossils.

Continuity of Strata

The tracing of strata in most regions involves short-range lithologic correlation from outcrop to outcrop or from well to well. The tracing is not difficult in areas where stratigraphic units maintain general lithologic uniformity. Difficulties arise where differently constituted facies intergrade, and other evidence must be sought to establish lateral continuity.

Lateral continuity of strata, like lithologic similarity, suggests correlation. Generally, however, it is very difficult to determine whether or not the rock unit being traced is rising or falling gradually in the stratigraphic section. Identification of the unit is based either upon lithologic similarity, whose problems and uncertainties were discussed in the preceding section, or upon stratigraphic position relative to one or more other well-marked rock units, which is considered in the next section. In the latter case, lithologic characters may change.

Correlation by lateral continuity is common practice. It is particularly important in subsurface stratigraphic studies. Paleontologic checking of sub-surface correlations generally is impossible except in comparatively uncon-solidated marine strata of late Mesozoic or younger age whose foraminifera can be recovered from well cuttings. Therefore, the tracing of many sub-surface units must be carried from one outcropping area to another and the fossils in these areas must be collected and compared before the reliability of correlations can be assessed. In a region like that of the Gulf coast of the United States, where outcrop control occurs only on the northern side, cor-relations would be unsure were it not for the evidence furnished by fo-raminifera.

Stratigraphic Position

After the correlation of some strata seems to have been established satis-factorily, these strata serve as units of control for other correlations. If impor-tant unconformities do not intervene, strata immediately above or below these units generally can be correlated regardless of their local lithologic de-velopment, which may vary from place to place. If two closely spaced units are satisfactorily correlated, these serve as a double check on intervening strata. Thus, the correlation of two levels of fossiliferous beds may establish the correlation of an intermediate unfossiliferous sequence or of intervening fossiliferous strata exhibiting more or less extreme facies variation.

Correlations become progressively more uncertain as zones are more widely separated from control units. Rates of sedimentary deposition have varied greatly both from place to place during the same interval of time and from time to time within the same area. Numerous mistakes in correlation have resulted from assumptions that stratigraphic intervals remain approxi-mately constant. Many time-rock units thicken as they pass toward the cen-tral parts of sedimentary basins. Perhaps some allowance for such thickening can be made, or average rates of thickening can be determined, but the rates are not certainly predictable and they may change abruptly in accordance with obscure past structural trends.

Unconformities are likely to cut across older strata and to be succeeded by gradually transgressing deposits. Consequently, unconformities are compli-cating factors that must be given special consideration if correlations are based principally on relative stratigraphic position.

Orderly Lithologic Variation

Under some circumstances trends in lateral lithologic variation may be es-tablished. The grain size of sediments deposited commonly decreases off-shore in deeper water, or in areas farther from the land, producing zones of different sediments extending roughly parallel to a coast (see Figure 211). Thus, sandstone may grade through siltstone and shale to limestone in a single time-rock unit. If conditions changed so that sandstone is overlain by shale in one zone, the same sequence may consist of shale grading upward into limestone in another. Correlations based on changes in lithologic character of this type require knowledge of paleogeographic conditions and, of course, cannot be made beyond the confines of a single depositional basin.

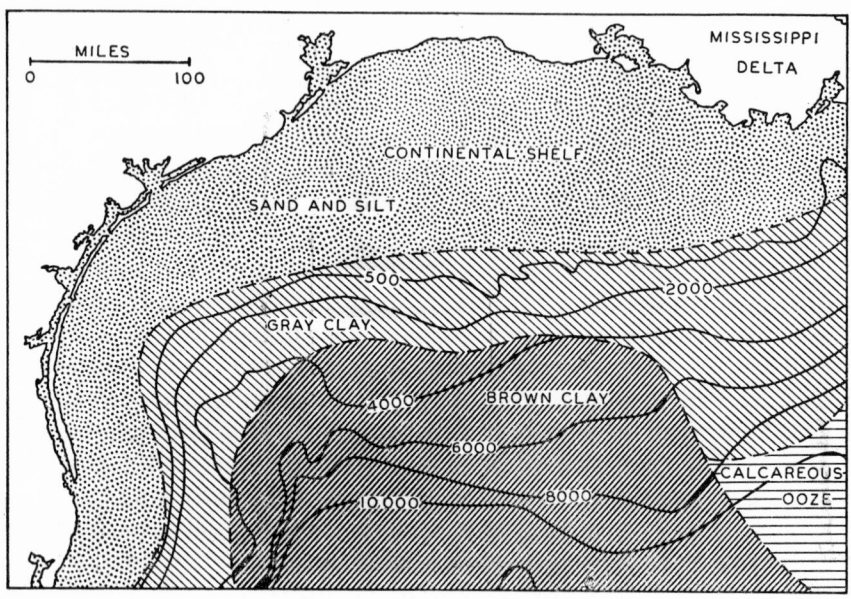

Figure 211. Map of the northwestern part of the Gulf of Mexico showing the relations of different kinds of modern bottom sediments to distance from shore and depth of water. The area of calcareous ooze in the southeast corner is continuous with calcareous sediments that extend to the coast of Florida (see Figure 22, p. 85). The general westward drift of currents carries detrital sediment delivered to the Gulf by the Mississippi River in this direction. (After Greenman and LeBlanc, 1956, *Bull. Am. Assoc. Petroleum Geol.*, vol. 40, p. 828, fig. 8.)

Electric Characters

Electric well logs have largely replaced lithologic logs in routine subsurface correlations. The electric characters that are recorded in these logs are dependent upon certain physical characters of the rocks, such as porosity, permeability, fluid content, and so forth, modified by several extraneous factors, such as temperature, nature of drilling mud, hole diameter, and others. Consequently, correlation by electric logs actually is an indirect method of tracing zones that are lithologically similar in some respects or of following laterally continuous zones identified by their positions relative to control units or horizons (see Figure 212). Such correlation does not establish time equivalence with certainty, and its limitations are practically identical to those considered in foregoing sections. Stratigraphic identification of electrically distinctive zones requires comparison with lithologic logs and outcrops (see Figure 240, p. 617). Except for short distances, the reliability of correlations should be checked paleontologically either by foraminifera obtained from well cuttings or by fossils collected at outcrops.

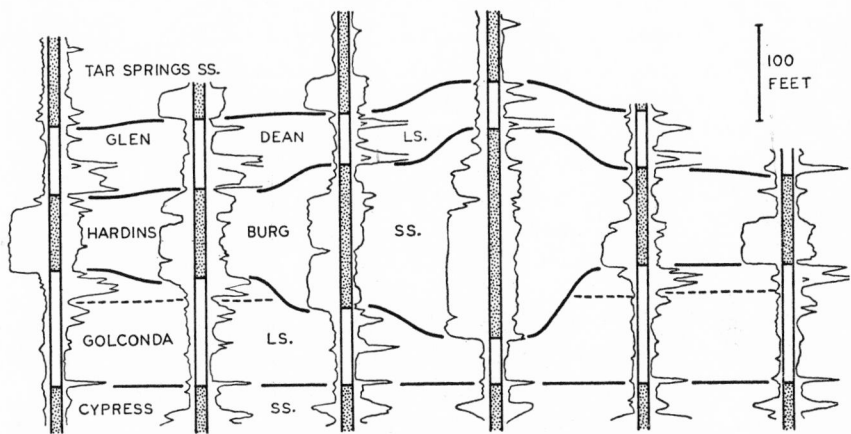

Figure 212. Diagram illustrating correlation by electric logs. The Hardinsburg Sandstone (Miss.) is identified readily from the self-potential or left-hand curve (see Figure 240, p. 617), and the principal limestone layers in the Golconda and Glen Dean formations (Miss.) are indicated by high resistivity in the right-hand curve. The occurrence of a channel cutting down into the Golconda is plainly shown by the two central logs. Rising of the upper surface of the Hardinsburg above the channel suggests that the thinner sandstone on either side contains more clayey sediment and consequently suffered more compaction under the pressure of overburden (see Figure 110, p. 293). This section in Hamilton County, Illinois, is a little less than two miles long. (After Potter and others, 1958, *Bull. Am. Assoc. Petroleum Geol.*, vol. 42, p. 1037, fig. 16.)

Unconformities

The recognition and tracing of continuous unconformities may aid in correlation because these contacts establish certain limits to the ages of adjacent strata. If two unconformities can be identified, they serve to bracket the ages of intervening beds. Erosion beneath unconformities and the possible transgressive onlap by strata above them, however, make exact correlation uncertain.

Correlation by unconformity is not common. It is mainly of interest in connection with unfossiliferous rocks and particularly the Precambrian. Probably the most reliable general correlations of this kind relate strata overlying angular unconformities observed at different places that are believed to record a single episode of structural disturbance. Because such movements were more or less localized, however, and because more than one episode of disturbance may have occurred, correlations of this type are not reliable outside of comparatively restricted areas.

Structural Development

Correlations based on the degree of structural disturbance are rather similar to those just considered because they also are related to diastrophic episodes that generally resulted in the production of angular unconformities. If, for example, two stratigraphic sections not too widely separated contain strongly deformed, moderately deformed, and undeformed strata, correlations are suggested. If the diastrophic episodes are believed to correspond, general correlations may be justified. The intensity of structural disturbances, however, is likely to decrease rapidly away from diastrophic centers, and long-range correlations of this type are unreliable.

Metamorphism

Metamorphism has resulted from diastrophism more intense than that responsible for simple structural disturbance and also from igneous activity. The degree of metamorphism, like the intensity of structural disturbance, has varied considerably from place to place in rocks of equivalent age. Therefore, different degrees of metamorphism are not reliable bases for correlation outside of comparatively restricted areas. Also some types of rock are more subject to metamorphic alteration than others. Thus, shale may have been transformed to schist, which preserves none of the original characters of the parent rock, whereas associated quartzite clearly reveals its originally sandy nature. Therefore, if differences in metamorphism are to be considered, comparisons should be made between rocks which were originally of similar types.

In the past, many correlations of rocks in different Precambrian areas have been based on the relative degrees of metamorphism exhibited. In widely separated parts of the world high-rank metamorphics, consisting principally of schists and gneisses, have been correlated and referred to the Archeozoic Era whereas lower-rank metamorphics have been considered to represent the Proterozoic. Also essentially unmetamorphosed sediments overlying rocks of Proterozoic type but lying beneath the lowest fossiliferous Cambrian strata constitute a third possible division of Precambrian rocks. Long-range correlations whose only foundation is difference of this kind are no longer taken very seriously.

Radioactivity

As explained in Chapter 1, the decay of radioactive elements furnishes means for determining the ages of certain rocks in terms of years. Before 1940 practically all such determinations were based on uranium measurements. Spectacular advances in isotopic chemistry made since that time, however, and perfection of the mass spectrometer have opened the way for age determinations based on a variety of other radioactive substances. Chief among these at the present time are carbon 14 and potassium 40.

The uranium-bearing minerals investigated in the past are contained in or are related to certain igneous intrusions. The results which they have furnished serve to date rocks and deposits of this kind. The coordination of these ages with the relative stratigraphic time scale, however, generally has not been very satisfactory. Thus, uranium dating has provided certain approximate bench marks useful in calibrating the stratigraphic time scale but it has been of only limited service in the actual dating or correlation of stratified rocks.

Unlike uranium, carbon and potassium are abundant in many sedimentary rocks and furnish means of direct age determinations. Carbon 14, with a half-life period of about 5500 years, is ideally adapted to the dating of very recent deposits such as those of the late Pleistocene. Its backward limit of usefulness is about 60,000 years. Potassium 40, with a half-life of about 1.3 billion years, is adapted to much older age determinations extending far back into Precambrian time.

All radioactive age determinations are subject to uncertainties and errors that probably are not much less than 10 percent of the indicated ages. Also, depending upon the radioactive substance investigated, a certain intermediate range of ages is likely to be most accurate, with age determinations outside this range becoming progressively less certain. Correlations based on carbon 14, in spite of any expectable errors, are much more accurate than those provided by paleontologic determinations because the decay of radioactive carbon is very rapid as compared to rates of evolution. Uranium and potassium dates are subject to comparable but much greater uncertainty. Going backward in geologic time, expectable errors in radioactive age determinations somewhere probably become equal to or exceed time intervals that are marked by observable evolutionary advancement.

Just where radioactive determinations become less accurate than conclusions based on paleontology depends upon the kinds of fossils available for study. These points probably lie somewhere late in the Paleozoic Era. Back to these points some radioactive correlations may be more accurate than paleontologic correlations, but in earlier time the situation probably is reversed and paleontologic correlations are to be preferred. In either case, however, correlations of these two kinds should be checked against each other wherever possible.

Because of the difficulties and expense involved, radioactive age determinations are not likely to be much used for local correlations, which will continue to be based on conventional stratigraphic and paleontologic observations. They are, however, sure to become increasingly important for long-range correlations and they may be expected to contribute greatly to establishing a world-wide chronology more perfect than any now known.

Paleontologic Evidence

Paleontology has been used increasingly for stratigraphic correlation since William Smith discovered that particular strata can be identified by their fossils. Before the theory of evolution was accepted, each species was believed to have been specially created and, after a definite period of time, to have become extinct. At first it was believed that cataclysmic events several times exterminated all life and that the world was then repopulated by a new creation. Later it was observed that the stratigraphic ranges of associated species are not the same. The conclusion was reached that both creation and extinction were continuous processes that resulted in gradual change and replacement of the earth's organic inhabitants.

With the acceptance of Darwin's theory, the problem of species became more complicated. This theory provides that every species gradually evolved from some ancestral species and each may have slowly evolved further into one or more descendant species. This concept holds that life is forever changing and that species do not have distinct and abrupt limits. Therefore, the differences that are observed to separate most fossil species stem from lack of knowledge and failure to discover the intermediate forms that must have existed.

Index Fossils

An index or guide fossil is a species, a genus, or perhaps some other taxonomic group that is especially noticed because it is believed to be useful in identifying strata of a certain age. Index fossils were recognized before Darwin's time and correlation by such fossils still is common practice. This is the simplest type of paleontologic correlation. It is the means employed for the distinguishing and tracing of biostratigraphic zones. The simple principle underlying this type of correlation is that the presence of a specimen of the index fossil identifies strata within the time range of this fossil. Two points should be noted: First, identification of the fossils must be accurate and consistent. Second, only the presence of the fossils is significant; their absence does not prove that the strata under consideration occupy a position outside of the range of the index fossil.

Because of evolutionary continuity, the species of paleontology, as well as every other taxonomic group, is no more than a concept. For convenience, continuous evolutionary sequences are divided into segments that are considered to be species. Many segments appear to be distinct because intermediate and connecting forms are not yet known, but new discoveries gradually fill in the gaps of the paleontologic record and distinctions between the species fade. Opinions as to the proper limits of particular species have differed from time to time and they probably always will continue to differ to some extent. In former years specific limits were much more elastic than they are today. Accordingly, there are many examples of old species that are now considered to be genera each of which has been subdivided into several more narrowly defined species. Also the present tendency for splitting in descriptive paleontology has resulted in the naming of numerous so-called species whose distinctions are uncertain if not unsound. Consequently, the application of a single name to different specimens does not prove their similarity even if the possibility of misidentification according to current standards is ruled out. In the same way, the use of different names does not guarantee that specimens actually are specifically distinct. The whole problem of species and their differentiation in paleontology is exceedingly complex. It has not received the consideration that is required to establish a sound and stable system of nomenclature. Similar problems also are posed by genera and all other higher taxonomic groups.

An ideal index fossil should be (1) easily recognized and easily distinguished from all others, (2) restricted to a narrow stratigraphic zone, (3) extensively distributed geographically, (4) adaptable to a wide range of environments so that specimens occur in many different types of rock, and (5) represented by abundant specimens. Unfortunately, fossils that meet all of these requirements are very few. Particularly, those that were unusually adaptable are likely to have been so successful that they persisted with negligible change for long intervals of time.

There are many fossils which, so far as they are known, occur only in narrow stratigraphic zones. They commonly are considered to be good index fossils which mark their zones wherever they are found. Some of the zones are so narrow, however, that there is good reason to doubt the assumption that they represent the entire stratigraphic ranges of the index fossils. Such a zone is termed a *teilzone,* which generally is equivalent to only a fraction of the corresponding *biozone* (see p. 438). The extreme limits of a biozone are rarely known because there is no certainty that another collection somewhere will not reveal the index fossil in strata older or younger than any in which it has been noted previously.

No organism can live except under certain more or less favorable environmental conditions. The geographic range of every index fossil is limited to those places where proper conditions for its existence occurred and which could be reached by migrating individuals. Likewise the vertical or stratigraphic range in any area was similarly environmentally controlled. If conditions changed and became unsuitable at any place, the local population died and was not replenished. On the other hand, if conditions elsewhere altered and became favorable, where previously they were not, the geographic range would be extended provided the new area was accessible to migrating individuals.

Thus the geographic and stratigraphic ranges of an index species or any other fossil were determined by (1) the time range of its existence, which was limited by evolutionary change or by extinction, (2) environment, and (3) the occurrence of migration routes or impassable barriers. The first and last of these limiting factors have long been realized and much discussed but the importance of environment, or ecologic control, has been badly neglected in paleontology. Many paleontologists have been satisfied to distinguish only between marine and non-marine conditions. Each of these great environmental realms, however, is subject to almost infinite subdivision on the basis of numerous variables which are of the greatest importance to organisms and have more or less strictly limited the possibilities of their existence. Probably many faunal and floral discontinuities, generally explained as resulting from physical barriers to migration or the passage of time, are actually reflections of environmental differences.

Control of the distribution of organisms in space and time exercised by environment makes all fossils indices of environmental conditions. The exact factors which permitted or inhibited the existence of particular organisms may not be understood but this conclusion is none the less important. Fossils are like the lithologic characters of rocks: Both serve to identify areas which were similar in certain important respects. Thus, paleontologic and lithologic correlations are much the same except that evolution and extinction place limits upon paleontologic correlation that do not exist in lithologic correlation. An index fossil provides no more precise correlation within the limits of its biozone, however, than does lithologic correlation.

Paleontologic Sequences

Many correlations have been made on the basis of fossil zones that do not represent the entire stratigraphic range of any so-called index fossil. Within restricted areas of uniform environment such correlations may be accurate. The possibility should not be overlooked, however, that a biologic environment like a sedimentary one may have shifted gradually with time so that a continuous zone traced for a considerable distance may be time transgressive. In separated areas there can be no assurance that local zones identified by the same species are either continuous or time equivalent. A succession of similar zones perfectly repeated at different places may seem to provide better evidence of exact correlation but such a sequence also may have shifted geographically with passing time.

Many different kinds of fossils have been used for correlation without adequate knowledge of their full stratigraphic ranges. Among the most commonly employed are foraminifera which identify subsurface zones in oil-producing regions such as the Gulf coast of the United States. Small fossils of this and other types at many places provide means of correlation where all other methods fail. Most zones of this kind are wholly empirical.

More or less gradually changing environmental conditions simultaneously affecting large areas, however, have resulted in biologic changes that may be useful and reliable in restricted correlation. Changes of this kind during the Pleistocene Period that reflect fluctuations in temperature or humidity have been most studied. For example, differences in the pollen recovered from postglacial bogs identify several zones that have been recognized in widely separated areas.

Temperature changes in the sea were not so great as on the land. Nevertheless shallow-water marine fossils in successive zones of the uplifted Pleistocene deposits near the California coast record the northward and southward migrations of differently adapted faunas that responded to cyclic fluctuations of water temperature. Accordingly these faunas can be correlated with glacial and interglacial ages. More important has been the discovery that isotopic ratios of oxygen in the calcium carbonate shells of pelagic foraminifera reflect Pleistocene temperature variations in the surface water of the sea. These cyclic differences are used to correlate zones in the sediments recovered in deep oceanic cores (see Figure 213).

Lithologic correlations in some coal fields are very difficult and uncertain because the strata are so monotonously constituted that many similar beds at different stratigraphic positions cannot be distinguished. The spores and pollen preserved in coal, however,

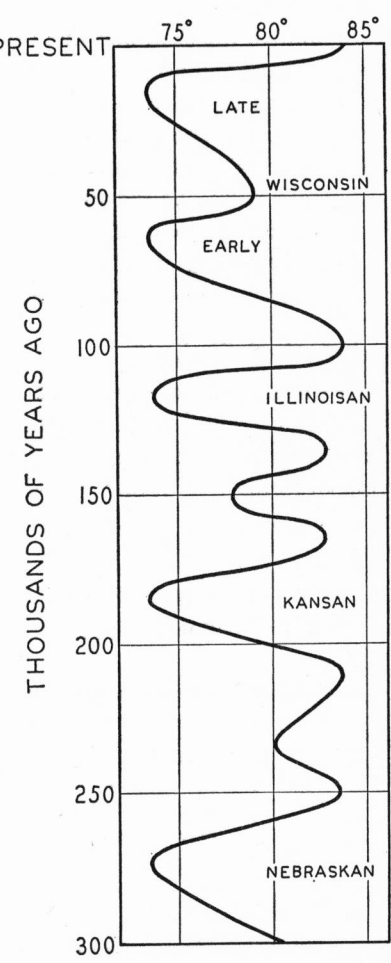

Figure 213. Curve showing temperature fluctuations in the near-surface water of tropical seas during the Pleistocene Period as determined by oxygen isotope ratios in planktonic foraminiferal shells recovered from deep-sea cores. (Generalized after Emiliani, 1958, Sci. Am., vol. 198, No. 2, p. 61.)

show some striking differences from zone to zone and they have been used for correlation. It is even possible that a characteristic succession of different spore zones within a single coal bed may aid in its identification throughout considerable areas.

In none of the examples mentioned are the fossils certainly true index species that are valid everywhere. This type of correlation generally involves the matching of strata representing intervals of time characterized by more or less widespread stages of climatic fluctuations. The fossils serve to identify environmental differences not revealed by any noteworthy features of the sediments. A unique succession of environments may be recognizable, as in some coals, but one cycle in a regular series, as in the Pleistocene deposits, may not be distinguishable from any other except by its relative stratigraphic position within the larger sequence.

Paleontologic Similarity

In the absence of recognized index fossils, many correlations have been made or suggested by comparing entire faunas or floras. Such comparisons commonly have been used to determine the relative age of a fossiliferous zone or formation in some outlying area with respect to a series of successive faunas or floras recorded from a standard or other well-known stratigraphic

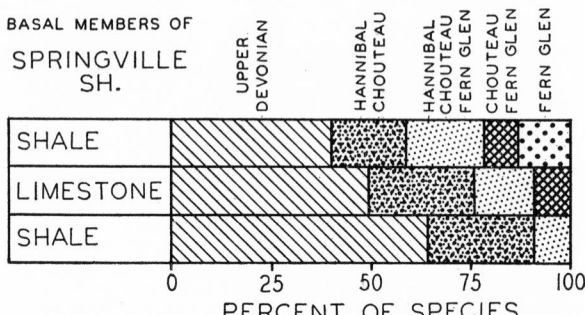

Figure 214. Bar diagram showing the proportions of conodont species identified from other formations that were collected from the basal members of the Springville Shale (Miss.) in Union County, Illinois. These proportions were used to determine the probable ages and correlation of these local members. The Upper Devonian species were disregarded under the assumption that they had been reworked from older strata. The limestone was correlated with the Chouteau Limestone, the lower shale with the Hannibal Shale (see Figure 252, p. 628), and the upper shale with the Fern Glen Formation as these are known in western Illinois and Missouri. This is an example of correlation by the precentage species method. (After Collinson and Scott, 1958, Ill. Geol. Surv., Circ. 254, p. 11, fig. 6.)

section (see Figure 214). This method, which may be termed the *percentage-species method*, is based upon the number of species common to the new fauna or flora and each of several standard faunas or floras. The greatest number of similar species or the greatest percentage similarity has generally been accepted as indication of closest similarity in age.

Because the number of species present in each fauna or flora is almost certain to be different, comparison requires that similarities be expressed as percentages. These can be calculated in different ways to give different results and suggest different conclusions. For example, the percentages of similar species in (1) the new fauna or flora, (2) the standard fauna or flora, or (3) the total combined faunas or floras can be determined as shown in Table 19. The results are different but probably the last is most significant.

TABLE 19.   Calculations to Determine Faunal or Floral Similarity by the Percentage-Species Method of Correlation

First Standard Fauna or Flora Number of Species		New Fauna or Flora Number of Species	Second Standard Fauna or Flora Number of Species	
	Number of Common Species		Number of Common Species	
B = 45	C = 10	A = 18	C′ = 12	B′ = 64
	$\dfrac{C}{A}$ = 55.5%		$\dfrac{C'}{A}$ = 66.7%	
	$\dfrac{C}{B}$ = 22.2%		$\dfrac{C'}{B'}$ = 18.8%	
	$\dfrac{C}{A + B - C}$ = 18.9%		$\dfrac{C'}{A + B' - C'}$ = 17.1%	

Some paleontologists have preferred this method to correlation by index fossils. Time relations, they have reasoned, are shown more accurately if judgment is based on entire faunas or floras instead of only a few selected species. Careful consideration of different types of species, however, shows that their time significance varies greatly. For example, the presence of long-ranging species in two faunas or floras is not good evidence of similarity in age whereas their absence from one may be much better evidence that the ages are different, as is indicated by Table 20.

This consideration suggests that species can be grouped in three classes which are different in their significance with respect to correlation:

1. Short-ranged, stratigraphically restricted species whose presence indicates approximate contemporaneity but whose absence is not necessarily significant. These are the conventional index fossils.

2. The ubiquitous species which are likely to occur in many faunas or

floras and which make up the bulk of most collections. These commonly are excellent indicators of inclusive stratigraphic zones but they are of little value for refined correlations. Their absence from collections is more likely to be significant than their presence.

3. The relatively uncommon species whose distributions are closely re-

TABLE 20.   Different Significance of Various Types of Fossils

	Presence in Both Faunas or Floras Indicates Similar Age	Absence from One Fauna or Flora Indicates Different Ages
Stratigraphic range		
Long-ranged species		More significant
Short-ranged species	More significant	
Geographic distribution		
Cosmopolitan species		More significant
Local species	No preference	
Abundance of specimens		
Common species		More significant
Rare species	No preference	
Environmental adaptability		
Adaptable species		More significant
Restricted species	No preference	

stricted environmentally. They are likely to constitute the majority of species in large and thoroughly studied faunas or floras. Their presence or absence is not particularly important as far as detailed correlation is concerned.

Advantages evidently are to be gained in correlation by considering whole faunas or floras rather than only index fossils. All species, however, are not equally significant. Consequently, species percentages do not provide the best answer to the correlation problem. If all fossils could be assigned with certainty to one of the foregoing groups, more reliable correlations might be possible. Unfortunately, classification of species in this way is not a simple matter because the qualities of all species are relative and they range continuously between wide extremes. Also this classification is not exclusive. Although it seems quite clear that certain species are more important in correlation than others, relative importance is uncertain and good judgment is an essential factor that must be relied upon.

Regardless of all other considerations, faunal or floral comparisons are meaningful only if they are made between similar biologic and lithologic facies developments. As facies become more diverse, differences in faunas or floras are less significant because greater numbers of species probably were adapted to mutually exclusive environments. Thus, within moderate stratigraphic limits, differences in faunas or floras are likely to be related more to differences in facies than to differences in age. Many examples occur in paleontology. Some of the best are provided by the thin, lithologically diverse members which succeed each other and recur repeatedly in Pennsylvanian cyclothems. Adjacent members of this kind commonly have faunas or floras with almost no species in common whereas practically identical assemblages of fossils are present in the corresponding members of other cyclothems occurring several hundred feet higher or lower in the stratigraphic section. Both the faunas or floras and the lithologic characters of these members are so similar that many miscorrelations have been made.

Evolutionary Development

The morphologic differences which distinguish more or less closely related organisms from each other are of several different types as follows:

1. Differences which serve to distinguish successive evolutionary stages in a lineage of organisms. These differences develop gradually and are characteristic of entire populations. They are responsible for the vertical discontinuities or differences between specimens in stratigraphic zones which contain successive separate segments of evolving lineages. Such discontinuities are not real but they appear to exist because of incompleteness of the known fossil record. Intermediate and connecting forms must have occurred but they have not yet been observed. As new discoveries fill these gaps, vertical discontinuities become less distinct and eventually they may disappear.

2. Inheritable differences which distinguish contemporaneous populations inhabiting different areas or environments. These are responsible for the horizontal discontinuities or differences between fossils of similar age occurring at different places. They were produced by the evolutionary divergence of different stocks descended from the same ancestral population. If only organisms belonging to a single contemporaneous stratigraphic zone or geologic time plane, such as the present, are considered, these discontinuities may or may not be real. Connecting forms must have occurred. Either they have not been found in intermediate areas or they were ancestral and are present only in older or underlying stratigraphic zones.

3. Noninheritable differences distinguishing contemporaneous populations that arose in response to different environmental influences. Such differences generally are gradational, and sharp discontinuities are not likely to occur. Among fossils, differences of this kind are very difficult to distinguish from the last type.

4. Differences between individuals or small, more or less arbitrary groups within contemporaneous populations. These differences may be inheritable but generally they are not set off by discontinuities that separate the individuals or groups from the general population. They are important mainly because they demonstrate the range of variability characteristic of every organic population.

5. Differences between different growth or developmental stages of individuals.

6. Differences resulting from sexual dimorphism.

7. Differences occurring in species characterized by alternation of generations or other similar types of polymorphism.

Most species of both fossil and recent organisms are distinguished and identified on the basis of morphologic characters. Five of the seven types of differences noted above are not significant in the differentiation of species. Only the inheritable differences (1 and 2) that have resulted from evolutionary change and characterize whole populations provide proper basis for specific or other taxonomic differentiation. If these cannot be distinguished from the others, the validity of named and described species is uncertain.

Most fossil species have been distinguished on the basis of differences whose significances are not understood. Consequently the relations of these species to each other are not known. As the number of presumed species distinguished by more and more subtle differences steadily increases, the possible evolutionary relationships may become increasingly obscure. The naming of these species, whatever their actual value or significance, gives them all the appearance of distinctive individuality and seems to place them all on an equal footing. An unknown number, however, are no more than variants of one type or another, undeserving of taxonomic recognition. Highly specialized knowledge and rare skill are becoming increasingly necessary for the specific identification of fossils. Mistakes are more and more easily made and are likely to result in erroneous positive or negative correlations by the index fossil method.

Short segments of evolutionary lines have been traced connecting some species of ammonites and a few other fossils. Generally, however, species have been little employed in attempts at evolutionary reconstruction. Although species are supposed to be the basic units of taxonomy, mostly they are so uncertain in their relations to each other that they have been passed over and phylogenies generally are based on the presumed relations of genera.

Sequences of genera exhibiting progressive evolutionary advancement are believed to have been recognized in various groups of fossils. These are very useful for long-range correlations. If the general evolutionary pattern in, for example, a family has been correctly determined, it may be possible to collate different genera occurring in different faunal or floral provinces and correlate the strata containing them on the basis of the stages of their evolutionary advancement. Because of the comparatively long stratigraphic ranges of most genera, however, such correlations are lacking in detail and they are not sufficient for the placement of minor stratigraphic units.

Careful study and comparison of precisely zoned and closely related fossils in particularly favorable areas may permit the working out of evolutionary sequences in much more detail within individual faunal or floral provinces. Such study should reveal which morphologic features gradually and progressively changed and how these changes progressed with the passage of time. Thus, a succession of sequent and transitional species populations might be recognized. For purposes of correlation their nomenclature would be unimportant. Specimens from strata of uncertain age at other places could be compared with the sequence and their positions with respect to it determined. In this way correlations could be made that would by-pass the uncertainties introduced by confusing fossil names.

Few studies of this type have been attempted but they offer great promise for the future. Possibly the most favorable fossils for them are some of the common ones that at present are of little stratigraphic value. Correlations made upon this basis are likely to be more accurate than those based upon conventional index species.

LIMITATIONS OF PALEONTOLOGIC CORRELATION

The importance of paleontologic correlation seldom has been questioned since William Smith demonstrated that rocks can be identified by their fossils. Paleontology has been employed more and more widely for this purpose and correlations have been both extended and refined as knowledge of fossils has increased. Many geologists and some paleontologists seem to believe that the process can continue almost indefinitely, with the gradual attainment of ever more detailed and perfect correlations. The basis for this belief needs to be examined critically.

The dating of rocks by their contained fossils is dependent upon the fact that life upon the earth is not static but forever changing. Some lineages of organisms have been successful in their competition with others. They adapted themselves to new environmental opportunities, extended their geographic ranges, and differentiated morphologically in a variety of ways, producing new stocks branching off from old ones. Other lineages failed in their struggle for existence. Their geographic ranges contracted and finally they became extinct. These two processes, closely related to each other, have been in constant operation since life first appeared upon the earth. The results are seen in the succession of different faunas and floras preserved as fossils.

Evolution and extinction have proceeded at variable rates in different groups of organisms and at different times. One of the principal responsibilities of paleontology is to determine the rates and reconstruct the details of evolutionary patterns. An enormous amount of work has been done with these ends in view and much exceedingly valuable information has accumulated. However, it is still fragmentary, much of it is subject to different interpretations, and a great deal more work remains to be done before the succession of life on earth is satisfactorily understood.

Present Paleontologic Knowledge

Obviously the accuracy of correlations based on paleontology cannot exceed the accuracy of paleontologic knowledge and interpretations. Most paleontologists realize the present inadequacies of paleontologic knowledge. Other geologists, however, are likely to be unaware of its deficiencies. They may not realize that there are well-known geologic formations in the most populous and easily accessible parts of the United States which have been observed and mapped for more than 100 years but whose fossils have never been carefully collected or studied. In some other large parts of the country, there is no formation whose fossils are known except in a general and superficial way. Elsewhere in the world outside of western Europe and the United States, enormous areas are almost complete blanks so far as paleontologic information is concerned.

Although great gaps remain to be filled in, many of the main features of the history of life on earth are now well known. The outlines of most episodes are blurred, but future studies may confidently be expected to sharpen some of them considerably. Nevertheless, numerous formations are essentially unfossiliferous, great volumes of rock are buried far below the surface or lie beneath the sea where presumably they are permanently inaccessible, and other great volumes have been destroyed by erosion. Also many epochs of the past, of variable duration, were nowhere represented throughout more or less extensive areas of the present land by sedimentary deposits and they are recorded only as unconformities. These deficiencies never can be made good.

Finally, the great majority of organisms of today are so constituted or live in such situations that the chance of their being preserved to become fossils of the future is exceedingly remote. Five percent of modern species certainly is an optimistic estimate for those which might be fossilized and found at some time a million or more years hence if paleontologists should survive so long. Perhaps less than 1 percent may be a more realistic estimate. There is little or no reason to suspect that a much larger proportion of ancient species will ever be discovered.

Rates of Evolution

Paleontologic correlation is possible because evolution and extinction have altered the forms of organisms and the associations in which they occur. Although change has been constant, it has proceeded slowly by stages too minute to be distinguishable in fossils present in adjacent beds. Considerable lengths of time were required for changes to proceed far enough to produce recognizably different organisms. Such lengths of time, which differed greatly in different groups of organisms and in a single group at various times, provide definite lower limits to the accuracy of paleontologic correlations.

It may be possible within a single paleontologic province to trace an evolving lineage and recognize a sequence of evolutionary stages that might be considered different species. No considerable stratigraphic section, however, has ever been zoned in such a way. Generally, adjacent zones are identified by paleontologists on the basis of fossils that are not so closely related.

The Jurassic System of England and nearby parts of continental Europe has been more closely zoned than any other system in any other region of the world. About fifty zones are recognized there in strata representing about 25 million years. This is equivalent to about 0.5 million years per zone. Most of these are teilzones, however, and many of them are significant only locally (see Figures 215 and 216). Actually there are only eleven stratigraphic divisions of the Jurassic, recognized by grades of ammonite evolution and generally considered to be stages, that are useful for correlations with other regions. These have an average time span of about 2.3 million years.

Graptolites evolved relatively rapidly and are considered to rank among the best and most reliable fossils for paleontologic zonation and correlation. In Sweden twenty-two graptolite zones have been distinguished in the 80 million years of the Ordovician Period. This averages about 3.6 million years per zone. In Great Britain there are fifteen corresponding graptolite zones averaging about 5.3 million years apiece.

The Cambrian System of North America has been subdivided into thirty zones based mostly upon trilobites. In this system, spanning about 80 million years, each zone represents about 2.7 million years. Most of these, however, are comparable to the Jurassic ammonite zones of Europe and a considerably smaller number of stratigraphic divisions can be recognized in widely separated regions.

These are examples of the most detailed paleontologic zonations that have been attempted. At present, therefore, the evolution of invertebrate fossils does not seem to provide the means for correlation within a single paleontologic province with an accuracy of much less than about 3 million years. Future studies may make somewhat closer zonation and somewhat more accurate correlation possible. There is little basis for the expectation, however, that broad paleontologic correlation can ever provide much more accurate results for the greater part of geologic time.

Correlations of strata in different paleontologic provinces and in distant parts of the world are even less certain. Except for some cosmopolitan species of ammonites, graptolites, and pelagic foraminifera, long-range correlations generally depend upon the comparison and evolutionary grades of genera rather than species. Relations are closest between North America and

Europe in one direction and Asia in the other. In some instances, for example in the Lower and Middle Cambrian, these intercontinental correlations are more satisfactory than correlations between eastern and western North America. On the other hand, many correlations between the Northern and Southern hemispheres are particularly unsatisfactory.

Buckman
in England

Bovier
in France

AMMONITE ZONES

k	
j	
i	
h	
g	
f	oxynotum
e	bifer
d	simpsoni
c	gagateum
b	lacunata

12	simpsoni
11	bifer
10	
9	
8	
7	lacunata
6	
5	gagateum
4	
3	oxynotum

Figure 215. Comparison of a succession of Jurassic ammonite zones distinguished by Buckman in England and Bovier in France, several of which are characterized by the same species. The species indicated are not necessarily confined exclusively to these zones, but the fact that they predominate at positions that do not correspond in these two areas demonstrates that the matching of local acmes does not provide sound basis for correlation. Therefore, epiboles are not time-rock stratigraphic units. The correlation of zones shown opposite each other in these two columns is not implied. Because the genera are not indicated the ammonites listed here cannot be identified by anyone who is not well versed in Jurassic paleontology. (Data from Spath, 1931, Geol. Mag., vol. 68, p. 184.)

Most genera, of course, have much longer stratigraphic ranges than do species. Evident evolution was much more rapid among mammals than in most other groups. For example, eight genera of horses which followed each other in about 45 million years persisted on the average about 5.6 million years, and carnivores averaged about 6.5 million years per genus. In contrast, one lineage of Triassic and earlier ammonites averaged about 20 million years per genus and pelecypod genera endured an average of about 78 million years each. Some genera were much shorter lived than others, however, and consequently these averages, particularly for invertebrates, do not provide a fair standard for estimating the limits of long-range paleontologic correlation. Also somewhat greater precision is possible if note is taken of the

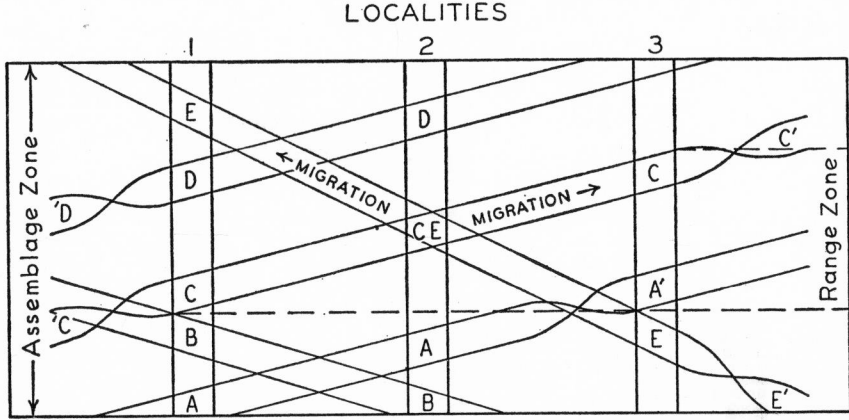

Figure 216. Diagram illustrating how zones identified by species may occur in different orders at different localities. Presumably the species migrated with shifting environmental conditions. At any locality the range of each species is strictly limited. The actual total range zone of species C is shown. In underlying and overlying strata related fossils are referred to different species that are segments of a single evolving lineage. All of the strata represented here may be considered an assemblage zone identified by the association of these five species. None of the species except C, however, is restricted to this assemblage zone. (After Arkell, 1933, *The Jurassic System in Great Britain*, p. 33, fig. 1, by permission of the Clarendon Press.)

overlapping ranges of different fossil groups. Thus consideration of whole faunas or floras is likely to provide more satisfactory results in long-range correlation than exclusive concentration on some particular group of fossils.

Conclusions

Evolution has been a slow process and its progress is imperfectly recorded by the fossils. According to various estimates, evolution is not likely to furnish reliable evidence for correlation within a single paleontologic province that, on the average, is accurate to much less than one-tenth of a geologic period. As most formations in reasonably well-known regions constitute less, and commonly much less, than one-tenth of a geologic system, paleontology alone is an insecure index to the time relationships of most formations and their limits from place to place.

For example, suppose that some system, perhaps the Mississippian, which accounts for about 30 million years of geologic time, is represented in the central United States by 3000 feet of strata. Suppose further that sedimentary deposition occurred during only one-half of the period, the other half being represented by unconformities below, within, and above the system. Thus the rocks of this region were deposited at an average rate of one foot per 5000 years; in one-tenth of the period 600 feet of strata might have accumulated. This thickness probably would be divided locally on a lithologic basis into several formations. Each of these, however, would represent such a short time span that it would not be distinguished from its neighbors by any recognizable evolutionary alteration of the fossils.

This does not mean that fossils are useless for more precise correlations. It does indicate that whatever faunal or floral differences distinguish adjacent formations are likely to be nonevolutionary. Great caution should be exercised in evaluating these differences, no matter how obvious they are or how important they appear to be, because they probably show (1) the operation of different local environmental controls, (2) the local but not necessarily general extinction of some species, or (3) the introduction of some new species as migrants from another region. All of these species may be expected to occur in other zones at other places. Thus for many detailed correlations fossils furnish evidence that is not essentially different from physical features of the sediments recording differences in sedimentary environments, source areas, and paths of transportation. Possibly some physical features of the rocks may be more conspicuous or more useful than fossils in suggesting similarities in these respects and probable equivalence in age. As previously noted, such evidence is reliable only within individual basins of deposition. Its reliability rapidly decreases as distances between localities increase.

Because of more or less effective isolation, the organic relations between different faunal or floral provinces are likely to be more remote than those connecting different parts of a single province. Consequently comparisons and correlations must be made on the basis of more general evolutionary changes and the results are less precise. Just what allowance should be made on account of these less direct relationships is uncertain. Perhaps a factor of two or three is a reasonable estimate in most cases. This might be reduced considerably if such cosmopolitan zonal fossils as ammonites or graptolites occur, but in some other instances a factor of five might not be too great. On the whole, interprovincial correlations based on paleontology are probably not accurate to much less than one-quarter of a geologic period. Here lithologic comparisons and nonevolutionary faunal or floral characters provide no prospects for achieving greater precision. Perhaps the most satisfactory correlations of the future will result from recent advances in radioactive and isotopic dating.

RELATIONS OF PALEONTOLOGY TO STRATIGRAPHY

Fossils were noted and attracted considerable attention long before rocks became objects of interest and inquiry. Before the beginning of the nineteenth century many kinds of fossils had been collected, illustrated, described, and named in various ways. Up to that time little significance was attached to them beyond their being recognized as denizens of an ancient and largely unknown world. William Smith's discovery that fossils occur in definite stratigraphic order and can be used to identify rock formations is the milestone marking the beginning of both modern stratigraphy and stratigraphic paleontology. These two studies are mutually so closely related that neither could have developed without the other. Modern paleontology, however, had to await the formulation and acceptance of evolutionary theory before it could emerge as a real science.

Stratigraphy had its origins in the German school of Wernerian geology. A local stratigraphic section based upon the principle of superposition was built up from observations in the field. The concept of universal formations then encouraged lithologic correlations that were believed applicable to the remotest regions of the earth. Smith's paleontologic method of correlation, however, won speedy acceptance and soon demonstrated the fallacy of universal formations and extensive lithologic correlations. From this point onward, stratigraphy and paleontology progressed together. An advance in one made possible a corresponding forward step in the other.

Paleontology has long been recognized as the most satisfactory means of correlation except for comparatively short distances. If fossils are to be useful for correlation, however, their positions in the stratigraphic section must be known. Therefore, the first step is necessarily the construction of a stratigraphic section. This is accomplished by observing the physical relations of as many rock units as can be recognized and traced within a fairly restricted area or district and determining their stratigraphic order.

After a section has been built up in this way, note is taken of the stratigraphic ranges of the fossils and their associations in more or less distinctive faunas or floras that are characteristic of different zones. The observation of rocks and fossils may proceed together, and paleontology may contribute importantly to the recognition and tracing of rock units even in the early stages of a stratigraphic study.

The stratigraphic section is now available for comparison with other sections that may have been or will be studied in a similar way. Comparisons are based on both lithologic and paleontologic features. It is commonly recognized, however, that paleontology becomes relatively more significant and lithology becomes less reliable as the distance between areas increases. If there appears to be conflict between lithologic and paleontologic evidence, the latter ordinarily is favored.

A stratigraphic section worked out in any area and described in general terms with respect to lithologic characters and thicknesses so that the description is applicable to the entire area rather than to a particular outcrop or locality is known as a *general section*. If a stratigraphic section is widely employed as a standard of comparison, commonly because of early thorough study, completeness, or abundance of fossils, it may be accepted and known as a *standard section.*

No previous information was available for comparison when the first general section was set up and there was no paleontologic evidence to indicate whether or not it is complete or interrupted by numerous and important stratigraphic breaks. Abrupt and conspicuous changes in the fossils occurring in adjacent beds might indicate either a stratigraphic discontinuity or a significant change in facies.

Probably no section worked out later would be exactly similar to the first. It might lack one or more fossil zones present in the first and it might include zones different from any of those previously observed. If a new zone were found to intervene between two old zones, the presumption would be made that the first section is incomplete. By combining the zones of these two sections, a composite section more complete than either of them would be constructed, and a general section applicable to a larger area would be available for further comparison. Each new section that is worked out provides information for checking, improving, and extending the composite section, which gradually becomes more perfect. This process has been going on for more than 150 years. It will continue until all strata available to observation both in outcrops and in subsurface records have been fully investigated.

Actually, the process of building up a complete and accurate stratigraphic section is not so simple because all zones are more or less local. Differently characterized zones at approximately the same stratigraphic position in different areas may be of slightly different ages, or they may be equivalent in age and only reflect differences in environment. This is a common problem. Its satisfactory solution is likely to depend more on physical than on paleontologic evidence.

If an unconformity is recognized in one section, one or more additional zones may be expected to occur at other places. Disconformities, however, are not clearly apparent everywhere and different interpretations have resulted in many disagreements. Nonevident disconformities have been presumed to occur in order to account for the absence of certain zones. Careful study may indicate that a zone in one stratigraphic section grades laterally either wholly or in part into a differently characterized zone elsewhere. As observations extend throughout larger and larger areas, changes of this kind are more and more likely to be encountered.

Some formations or zones are unfossiliferous or lacking in useful zonal fossils. Their placement and correlation with respect to a standard section pose a somewhat similar problem. Also comparisons of marine and continental strata, zoned on the basis of invertebrates and plants respectively, are particularly difficult and uncertain. In some instances, as in the Tertiary of the Atlantic and Gulf coasts on the one hand and the Great Plains and Rocky Mountain regions on the other, two different standard sections may be recognized whose mutual relations are not adequately known. Obviously, as less similar facies are compared, uncertainties increase.

Thus, fossils are zoned according to their positions in the stratigraphic section, and correlations are made upon the basis of these zones. Different incomplete stratigraphic sections and their fossils are used to supplement each other in an effort to build up a complete section and a complete succession of fossil faunas and floras. Errors introduced at any stage in the process are cumulative. Unless discovered and corrected they influence all succeeding interpretations. The equivalence of differently characterized fossil zones or differently constituted stratigraphic units may not be recognized, and these may be considered to wedge in between each other in such a way that duplication produces a composite section too thick and with too many zones. Conversely, zones or units of different ages may be mistakenly considered to be equivalent, and a composite section too thin and too simple may result. Insofar as errors of either type remain undetected, erroneous stratigraphic sections and paleontologic standards may be set up.

This circular type of evidence and reasoning involves hazards that are obvious if the mutual dependence of physical stratigraphy and stratigraphic paleontology is realized. The dangers are not easy to avoid. Both careful observation and good judgment are required to reduce them to a minimum.

SUBJECTIVE NATURE OF CORRELATION

Correlation concerns matters of fact. Strata in different areas either are or are not equivalent in age. The correlation of these strata should be based on all available pertinent evidence in accordance with the best judgment of a geologist or paleontologist. Very rarely or never is the evidence absolutely conclusive. Consequently, practically all correlations are expressions of opinion rather than established facts, and opinions may differ greatly.

Similarity of fossils commonly is considered to indicate the age equivalence of strata in different areas. It is more realistic and accurate to view such similarity in another way: to consider that it only fails to indicate a difference in age. At best, strata characterized by similar fossils are known to occupy corresponding positions in different stratigraphic sections. They are not known to be of different ages. This condition is termed *homotaxis*. The determination of actual and exact age equivalence, or *chronotaxis*, is generally an unattainable ideal. The probabilities commonly are overwhelming that correlated stratigraphic units in different areas are not exactly equivalent. Even though they largely correspond, one is likely to include parts that are somewhat older or somewhat younger than the other.

The opinion has been expressed seriously that similarity of fossils in distant areas is positive proof not of equivalence but of differences in age. The argument presented is that an appreciable time must have been required to permit organisms to migrate from one area to the other. No one can know with certainty how rapidly organisms migrated in the past. Some modern examples have been cited, however, to show that geographic ranges may have been extended with a speed so great as to have been practically instantaneous by geologic standards. For instance, a species of European marine snail was introduced at Nova Scotia and spread southward along the Atlantic coast 700 miles in less than fifty years. At this rate and moving in all directions, it could encompass the earth in less than 1000 years. An African land snail introduced in the Philippines during World War II by the Japanese spread to many parts of the islands in ten years and became so numerous that it constituted a nuisance if not a menace to certain kinds of agriculture.

These and other striking examples are unusual in that species were suddenly introduced into areas where conditions were favorable and competition was at a minimum. Somewhat similar chance introductions may have occurred in the geologic past. Most migrations of fossil species, however, involved movements in which individual species or entire faunas and floras responded to opportunities created by gradually changing local environments. Such movements may at times have been rapid, particularly if an ecologic barrier broke down. Most of them probably were much slower. Actual time rates rarely can be estimated with any degree of accuracy. Migrations that were very slow by modern standards, however, may have been accomplished in time intervals undetectable by any physical or paleontologic means.

Faunas and floras have changed on a world-wide basis as the result of evolution, which continually produced new forms of life. Older forms disappeared because either they evolved into new ones or they became extinct without leaving descendants. Faunas and floras preserved as fossils in local areas, however, commonly changed for other reasons. New species that had originated and lived for variable lengths of time in other areas shifted or extended their geographic ranges, and old forms disappeared because local conditions became unfavorable for them although they may have continued their existence elsewhere.

The appearance of new species and the disappearance of old ones are both used as evidence for the correlation of strata from place to place. Neither is decisive because it is inconceivable that any species appeared or disappeared simultaneously everywhere.

Many paleontologists have considered that the appearance of new species is more significant than the disappearance of old ones. They have reasoned that a new species must have possessed some advantages over old ones or it could not have developed. Because these advantages favored it, the new species was successful and probably it was able to extend its range rapidly. Conversely, an old species became less and less able to compete with new ones. It was crowded out first in one area and then in another. Finally it may have been restricted to a few places where for some reason it was able to maintain itself perhaps for long periods of time. Thus, it has been argued, the appearance of a new species is more likely to indicate close similarity in age than the disappearance of an old one. This reasoning may or may not be valid. Even if it is, there is small likelihood that all species of fossils present similar patterns of existence.

Various important uncertainties concerning both physical and paleontologic evidence employed in stratigraphic correlation can never be eliminated completely. Therefore, every correlation should be recognized as an approximation. It is tentative and subject to change as new evidence is obtained or as old evidence is reevaluated.

BIBLIOGRAPHY

Allan, R. S. (1948), Geological correlation and paleoecology, *Bull. Geol. Soc. Amer.*, vol. 59, pp. 1–10.
  Paleontologic correlations are insecure if facies relations are ignored.
Arkell, W. J. (1956), *Jurassic geology of the world*, Edinburgh, Oliver and Boyd.
  Chapter 1, pp. 3–14, presents the standard stages and zones of the Jurassic System.
Dunbar, C. O., and Rodgers, John (1957), *Principles of stratigraphy*, New York, Wiley.
  Chapter 16, pp. 271–288, discusses both physical and paleontologic correlation.
Erdtman, Gunner (1943), *An introduction to pollen analysis*, Waltham, Chronica Botanica, reprinted 1954.
  Main consideration is to postglacial pollen, which identifies fluctuations in temperature and humidity.
Grabau, A. W. (1913), *Principles of stratigraphy*, New York, Seiler, reprinted 1924.
  Chapter 32, pp. 1121–1144, discusses principles and methods of correlation.
Howell, B. F. (chairman) (1944), Correlation of the Cambrian formations of North America, *Bull. Geol. Soc. Amer.*, vol. 55, pp. 993–1003.
  This includes a correlation chart and list of Cambrian faunal zones.
Kosanke, R. M. (1950), Pennsylvanian spores in Illinois and their use in correlation, Ill. Geol. Surv., Bull. 74.
  The stratigraphic ranges of 130 species are discussed.
Krumbein, W. C., and Sloss, L. L. (1951), *Stratigraphy and sedimentation*, San Francisco, Freeman.
  Chapter 10, pp. 287–316, is concerned with the principles of correlation.
Neaverson, E. (1955), *Stratigraphical paleontology*, 2nd ed., Oxford, Clarendon.
  An outline description of British graptolite zones is included; see pp. 162–170.
Schuchert, Charles (1921), Methods of determining the relationships of marine invertebrate fossil faunas, *Bull. Geol. Soc. Amer.*, vol. 32, pp. 339–348.

The author discusses and presents examples of paleontologic provinces and faunas.

Simpson, G. G. (1944), *Tempo and mode in evolution*, New York, Columbia Univ. Press.

This book presents a comprehensive theoretical consideration of evolution. In several respects it is more satisfactory than the author's later work *"The major features of evolution,"* published in 1953.

Symposium (1916), General considerations of paleontologic criteria used in determining time relations, *Bull. Geol. Soc. Amer.*, vol. 27, pp. 451–530.

Papers on correlation are by E. O. Ulrich on invertebrate paleontology, Charles Schuchert on paleogeography, W. D. Matthew on vertebrate paleontology, and F. H. Knowlton on paleobotany.

Twenhofel, W. H. (1950), Correlation of stratigraphic units, *Scientia* (Rev. di Sci., Bologna), vol. 85, pp. 78–84.

Most stratigraphic correlations relate beds and fossils of similar facies rather than closely similar age.

Ulrich, E. O. (1911), Revision of the Paleozoic systems, *Bull. Geol. Soc. Amer.*, vol. 22, pp. 281–680.

Environmental differences that might affect faunal relations and correlations are ignored, see pp. 506–519.

Williams, H. S. (1903), The correlation of geological faunas, a contribution to Devonian paleontology, U.S. Geol. Surv., Bull. 210.

Chapters 1 and 2, pp. 10–41, consider the relations of fossil faunas to environments and the record of migration and evolution in geographic and stratigraphic faunal variations.

Wilson, L. R. (1946), The correlation of sedimentary rocks by fossil spores and pollen, *J. Sediment. Petrol.*, vol. 16, pp. 110–120.

A method of correlating coal beds by vertical variation in the relative abundance of spores is explained.

CORRELATION CHARTS

Committee on Stratigraphy of the National Research Council
(published in *Bull. Geol. Soc. Amer.*)

Cambrian. Correlation of the Cambrian formations of North America, B. F. Howell (chairman) (1944), vol. 55, pp. 993–1004.

Ordovician. Correlation of the Ordovician formations of North America, W. H. Twenhofel (chairman) (1954), vol. 65, pp. 247–298.

Silurian. Correlation of the Silurian formations of North America, C. K. Swartz (chairman) (1942), vol. 53, pp. 533–538.

Devonian. Correlation of the Devonian sedimentary formations of North America, G. A. Cooper (chairman) (1942), vol. 53, pp. 1729–1794.

Mississippian. Correlation of the Mississippian formations of North America, J. M. Weller (chairman) (1948), vol. 59, pp. 91–196.

Pennsylvanian. Correlation of Pennsylvanian formations of North America, R. C. Moore (chairman) (1944), vol. 55, pp. 657–706.

Permian. C. O. Dunbar (chairman), in preparation.

Triassic. Correlation of the Triassic formations of North America exclusive of Canada, J. B. Reeside, Jr. (chairman) (1957), vol. 68, pp. 1451–1513.

Correlation of the Triassic formations of Canada, F. H. McLearn (1953), vol. 64, pp. 1205–1228.

Jurassic. Correlation of the Jurassic formations of North America exclusive of Canada, R. W. Imlay (1952), vol. 63, pp. 953–992.

Correlation of the Jurassic formations of Canada, Hans Frebold (1953), vol. 64, pp. 1229–1246.

Cretaceous. Correlation of the Cretaceous formations of Greenland and Alaska, R. W. Imlay and J. B. Reeside (1954), vol. 65, pp. 223–246.

Correlation of the outcropping Cretaceous formations of the Atlantic and Gulf coastal plain and Trans-Pecos Texas, L. W. Stephenson and others (1942), vol. 53, pp. 435–448.

Correlation of the Cretaceous formations of the Greater Antilles, Central America and Mexico, R. W. Imlay (1944), vol. 55, pp. 1005–1045.

Correlation of the Cretaceous formations of the Western Interior of the United States, W. A. Cobban and J. B. Reeside (1952), vol. 63, pp. 1011–1044.

Correlation of the Cretaceous formations of the Pacific border, Willis Popenoe and others, in preparation.

Correlation of the Cretaceous formations of Canada, F. H. McLearn, in preparation.

Cenozoic. Correlation of the Cenozoic formations of the Atlantic and Gulf coastal plain and the Caribbean region, C. W. Cooke and others (1943), vol. 54, pp. 1713–1723.

Correlation of the marine Cenozoic formations of western North America, C. E. Weaver (chairman) (1944), vol. 55, pp. 569–598.

Nomenclature and correlation of the North American continental Tertiary, H. E. Wood (chairman) (1941), vol. 52, pp. 1–48.

16

Historical Geology

SCIENCE AND HISTORY

At first thought science and history seem to be two distinct disciplines so diverse in their objectives and their methods that no comparison is possible. True, the strictly physical sciences, physics and chemistry, are concerned with the investigation of timeless principles and laws and therefore might appear to possess no historical qualities. Even though these principles and laws presumably are unchanging and eternal, the materials with which they deal are not. Spectacular advances in the understanding of atomic structure have demonstrated the reciprocality of matter and energy, and the evolution of the chemical elements is a subject of investigation and speculation that is historical in nature.

All other sciences find their ultimate basis in physics, whose principles, when they are understood, can be expressed in beautifully simple mathematical terms. Each other science introduces its own complexities as it reaches out beyond the fundamental laws of physics to encompass a more or less specialized field dealing with some restricted aspect of the universe. For this reason, other sciences are less readily analyzed mathematically and so appear at present to be less exacting. Actually, the farther a science is removed from physics, the more complex it becomes because it is concerned primarily with more intricate relations and reactions. These in a very real sense are conditioned by environments, and a complicated and interwoven chain of cause and effect operates in nature in which every reaction alters an environment and no later reaction can ever produce exactly the same effect. Thus evolution in some form is in progress with respect to every aspect of the universe.

Each great conventional division of the natural sciences has been split into smaller and smaller segments until its distinctiveness has seemed to disappear. The development of borderline fields also has bridged the gaps between divisions, and the unity of all science becomes progressively more evident. With increased specialization, however, the interests and viewpoints of many scientists have tended to narrow more and more. Each investigator pursues his own particular specialty with such intensive concentration that its relations to science as a whole may be overlooked or seem to be of small concern. However satisfying his discoveries and conclusions may be to the scientist himself, their real importance can be measured best by their applications in broader fields. The accumulation of detailed knowledge is essential but it is no more than the initial step in scientific progress. Synthesis of details into a united whole is the grand objective. This becomes increasingly difficult, however, and demands a rare breadth of vision and imagination.

Geology in its entirety probably is the most varied and complex of all the natural sciences because it is founded upon and combines the principles of the other more basic sciences and draws increasingly upon them for its accomplishments. Geology is a synthesis of the physical and biologic sciences as these are applied to an understanding of the only part of the universe with which man has direct contact, that is, the earth. Each of these sciences has its evolutionary aspects, which become more evident and more important as science reaches out farther and farther from its fundamental base in physics. The evolutionary aspects meet in geology and are reinforced by the fact that the present condition of the earth cannot be understood except through comparison with its past. Thus consideration of the evolution of the earth focuses attention upon its history.

Some history is no more than a narrative account of a series of events arranged in the order of their occurrence. The narrative may be true and detailed, but it is unsatisfying and largely meaningless if the relations of these events and the reasons why one followed upon another are not understood. Much of historical geology as it is now known and as it is commonly presented is merely a narrative of this type and a rather poorly integrated one at that. It consists mainly of an account of shifting shallow seas, rising mountains, and sinking basins. The main events that have altered the surface of the earth during perhaps the last 12 percent of its existence are fairly well established, but most details are hazy and earlier happenings are very inadequately known. Thus at present much historical geology can hardly be considered scientific. From time to time new theories drawn from physical and chemical concepts are presented in attempts to explain to some extent the sequence of events. Such theories generally arise as speculations and they require continued and most critical testing in the light of new information supplied by both field and laboratory studies. It is obvious that an enormous amount of work remains to be done before a satisfactory account of the history of the earth can be compiled.

GEOLOGIC SYNTHESIS

Because of its multiple foundations, geology unites an unusual diversity of interests extending from the very small to the very large—for example, the structures of molecules and of continents—and these range widely throughout the realms of both physical and biologic science. Many of the subjects investigated by geologists might be classified with one of the other natural sciences were it not for the factor of motivation. Experience has shown that numerous studies apparently remote from the central and orthodox geologic field, but of definite interest to geologists, are not likely to be undertaken soon by other scientists. Consequently, geologists have of necessity applied the principles and techniques of other sciences to a variety of problems in certain borderline areas in order to obtain the information they desired. The diversity of these areas is so great that the concepts and vocabularies familiar to workers in one field may be unintelligible to workers in another. For example, there are no obvious relations connecting the X-ray diffraction pattern of a mineral, the isotopic composition of carbon dioxide, the evolutionary development of trilobites, and the distribution of earthquakes. If these were representative examples of geologic research there would be little reason for contending that geology is a science in its own right.

The central area of geology is the study of rocks as they occur in nature, and the traditional arena of its operations is the field. Nature in general and geology in particular are not static, but, so far as the practical possibilities of observation are concerned, rocks are very nearly so. Although rocks have been subjected to the influences of heat and pressure for long intervals of time and thereby altered, these forces cannot be observed at work, nor can the laboratory reproduce and maintain natural conditions. Thus the character of these forces and the duration of their action must be inferred, mainly from the structure and composition of the rocks and their relations as they now occur. Field observations are restricted to the grosser relations and characters of rocks and their constituents. More detailed studies, however, can be made in the laboratory by a variety of methods and thereby a fuller knowledge of the qualities and probable reactions of geologic materials can be gained. Such laboratory studies, leading off in all directions, largely account for the centrifugal expansion of geologic interests and investigations.

Most geologic processes are so slow that their progressions cannot be observed or measured well enough for them to be evaluated. As one consequence, little interest has developed in predicting long-term changes in the condition of the earth because they are not likely to affect man's welfare within foreseeable future time. As another, practically all considerations of the dynamics of geology are related to the past and find expression in the narration and explanation of geologic history. This is a unique feature of geology that is not duplicated in other sciences, which are more concerned with the present or the future. Geology as an academic science is backward-looking and finds its satisfaction in an understanding of what has happened. As a practical science, however, it is immensely important because it provides the only effective guide to the exploitation of the earth's mineral resources, upon which man's present and future welfare depends to an ever increasing degree.

All geologic studies fall more or less clearly into one or the other of two classes. Studies of the first class are devoted to the investigation of the *materials* of geology; they seek to *determine* the characters, properties, and spatial relations of all rocks, their constituents, and their derivatives. This is *descriptive geology* and here belong most conventional geologic studies. A vast body of descriptive information has been amassed and studies of this type continue to be pressed in ever greater detail. Although much remains to be learned, descriptive geology is well advanced and provides the data upon which a narrative type of geologic history has been built.

Geologic studies of the second class are devoted to investigation of the *forces* that have acted on geologic materials and the *processes* that have controlled or influenced the formation and alteration of all rocks; they seek to *explain* the characters, properties, and relations of the rocks. This is *dynamic* geology. It has been less extensively and less successfully pursued than descriptive geology and its present status is far from satisfactory in spite of much recent progress. Some of the simpler processes are adequately understood but many geologic processes and interactions are exceedingly complex and the effects of forces acting under extreme conditions of pressure and temperature and for extended periods of time are very incompletely comprehended. Consequently most interpretations of the dynamic aspects of geology are based more on speculation than on a modicum of knowledge. A much better understanding of this subject must be gained before geologic history can become a comprehensive and coherent exposition of terrestrial development.

Geologic history is essentially an organized synthesis of all geologic knowledge. Every advance in geologic research contributes directly or indirectly to its perfection and it is only in this way that all geology is unified. Geologic data are so voluminous, however, and so diverse that they must be systematized to make them comprehensible. This is accomplished largely in three steps. First, specialized data contribute to the understanding of materials and processes and to the formulation of principles and generalizations pertinent to one or another of the major subdivisions of geology. Most of these then are applied to the interpretation of stratigraphy. Stratigraphy in turn provides the organization that permits broad historical presentation and explanation.

Complete geologic synthesis requires organization with respect to both space and time. Spatial relations find expression in geography, which is static. Time relations are revealed by tectonic developments, which are dynamic. Historical geology, therefore, is compounded of these contrasting elements. Its narrative is most clearly expressed by the alternate consideration of paleogeographic conditions and paleotectonic changes.

PALEOGEOGRAPHY

Paleogeographic reconstructions are intended to present the features of the earth's surface as these existed in the past. All geographic features are transitory. The success of paleogeographic interpretation depends upon (1) identification of past geographic features and their regional relations, (2) accurate correlation of conditions and events throughout wide areas, and (3) reduction of the time element to the greatest possible extent.

Paleogeographic Evidence

Various kinds of geologic evidence contribute more or less directly to paleogeographic interpretation. The most important are (1) stratigraphic, (2) paleontologic, (3) sedimentologic, and (4) tectonic. Each kind is significant in a different way. Together they provide the basis for reconstruction.

Stratigraphic Evidence

Stratigraphic evidence is the most direct and positive. For example, the presence of marine strata in any area is proof that this area was occupied by the sea. In contrast, the absence of such strata is inconclusive evidence that marine submergence did not occur because formerly existing marine strata may have been eroded. In the same way, if distinction can certainly be made, the presence of non-marine beds precludes the existence of marine conditions and establishes the presence of a basin of non-marine deposition. Concordance in the present distribution of marine deposits with the patterns of ancient epicontinental seas is likely to be less and less close as progressively older strata are considered because of greater opportunities for the destruction and removal of rocks by erosion or their metamorphic alteration at more numerous intervals throughout a longer expanse of time.

Stratigraphic correlation provides the time control that determines the accuracy and degree of contemporaneity of regionally related paleogeographic features and conditions. This is extremely important because inaccurate correlations are likely to result in misinterpretations. Likewise the time limits within which correlation is possible are critical because, if the limits are wide, interpretations are certain to be generalized and they may fail to reveal not only relationships as they actually existed at any time but also the significance of relationships.

Paleontologic Evidence

Paleontology plays a prominent part in stratigraphic correlation and environmental interpretation but these require no further consideration here. Of much more immediate importance is the reliance that has been placed on fossils as indicators of the connection or lack of connection between areas of sea and areas of land. In general the similarity of fossils in different regions has been accepted as proof of more or less direct connection whereas differences of fossils in strata believed to be equivalent in age has been regarded as indicating the intervention of physical barriers. In this way the existence of land bridges across oceans and the connection of continents have been postulated, and epicontinental seas have been visualized as joined to the oceans in various directions. Also different parts of epicontinental seas have been considered to be unconnected embayments originating from different sources.

Many interpretations of this kind were made before paleontologists recognized the importance of ecology in controlling the distribution of animals and plants now preserved as fossils. Some of these interpretations are presently known to be incorrect and all supposed evidence of this kind should be most critically reappraised. Physical evidence substantiating the connection or separation of areas of land or areas of sea generally is lacking or has not been sought. For example, most of the Paleozoic epicontinental seas of North America have been shown on maps as joined at one time or another with the oceans in all four directions. The only positive physical evidence for these postulations is the extension of some Paleozoic formations northward up the Mackenzie River valley to the Arctic Ocean. Environmental differences rather than physical barriers certainly account for the differences of fossils in some nearby areas. Environmental similarities also might result in the occurrence of similar fossils in some areas that were not in close communication with each other.

Some fossil occurrences provide evidence of temperature and other climatic conditions in the past that are paleogeographically important (see Figure 217). For example, the existence of coral-bearing reefs and coal beds north of the Arctic Circle indicate mild if not warm temperatures. From this the conclusion has been drawn either that world climate was at times much more uniform and warm than it is today or that the continents or poles have shifted notably during the course of geologic time. Coral studies based on the

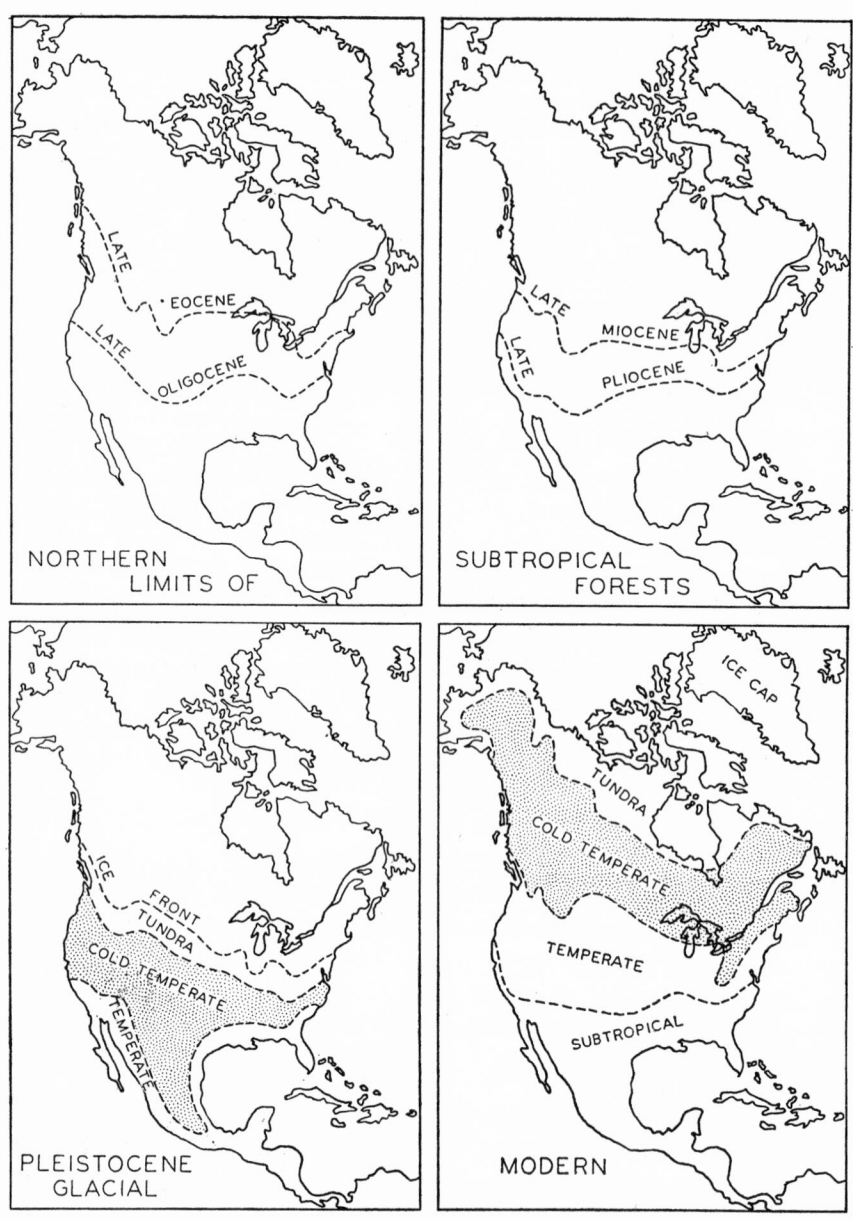

Figure 217. Maps of North America showing the shifting of climatic zones during Cenozoic time as revealed by the distribution of fossil plants. (After Dorf, 1957, *Weatherwise*, vol. 10, p. 58, fig. 2.) See also Figure 218.

assumption that maximum growth indicates locations near the equator have led to the suggestion that the continents have shifted with respect to the equatorial zone.

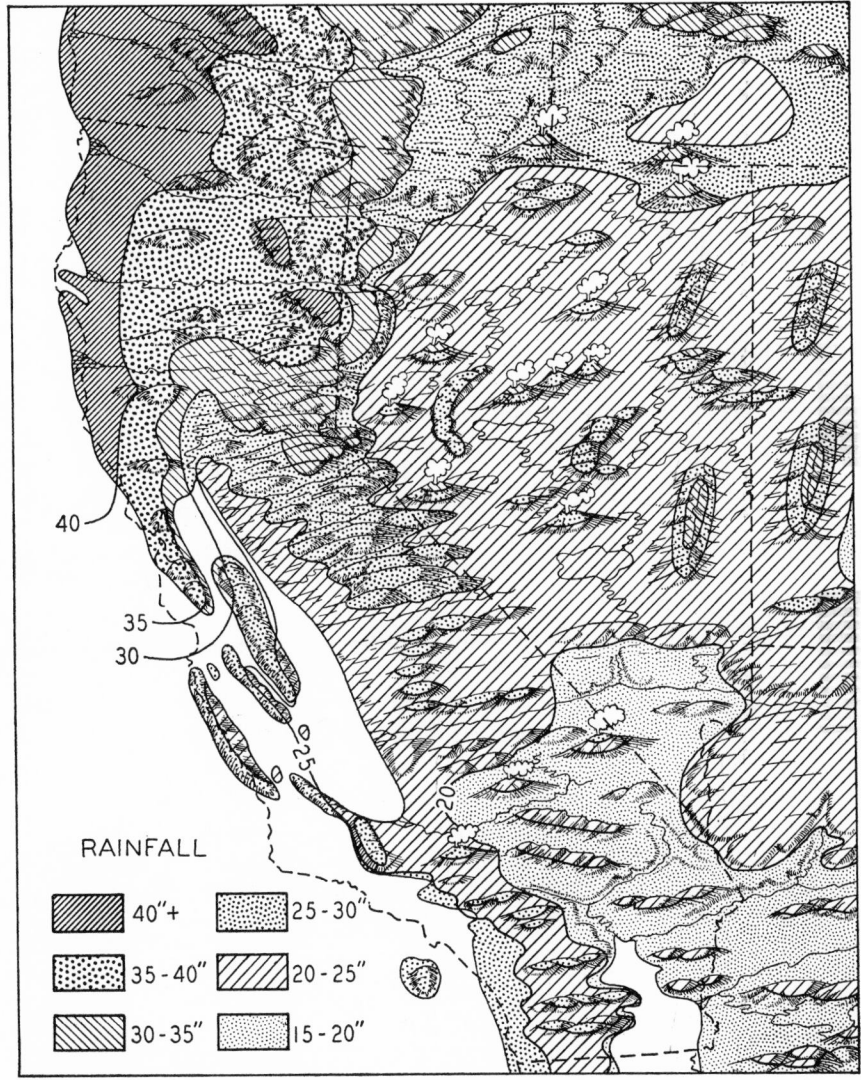

Figure 218. Map of California and adjacent states during Mio-Pliocene time showing the diagrammatic reconstruction of generalized topography and rainfall zones as indicated mainly by variations in the fossil floras. (After Axelrod, 1957, *Bull. Geol. Soc. Amer.*, vol. 68, p. 19, pl. 1, and p. 36, fig. 5.)

Some conclusions of this kind have been generalized to an unwarranted extent. As an example, Carboniferous coal swamp forests commonly have been regarded as recording a warm and humid climate and the general climate of all Carboniferous time has been interpreted accordingly. Vegetable material that constitutes the coal beds accumulated, however, only at intervals that all together make up a relatively small fraction of the Carboniferous. The coal beds certainly are not sufficient evidence for the conclusion that the climate was continuously either warm or humid. Some geologists believe that this was exactly the time of the great late Paleozoic glacial period when ice covered large regions in the Southern Hemisphere.

Fossils furnish evidence that may be used in the interpretation of some aspects of paleogeography although such approaches generally have been neglected. For example, marine fossils may give some indication of depth of water (see Figure 133, p. 325) and other hydrographic conditions—currents, salinity, turbulence, clarity, and so forth. Terrestrial vertebrates likewise provide evidence of the environments they inhabited. The teeth of Tertiary herbivores were adapted to types of plants that suggest certain climatic and topographic conditions, and their limbs reflect ways of life related to the terrain in which they lived. The reptiles and amphibians of the Texas Permian red beds seem to provide good evidence that this region was not such a barren and arid desert as is commonly supposed. Finally, many plants are excellent indices to climates of the past (see Figure 218).

Sedimentologic Evidence

Evidence furnished by the sediments rarely has been utilized fully in attempted reconstructions of paleogeography. Sediments provide direct information regarding environments of deposition, and some conclusions also can be drawn concerning the location and the topographic and climatic conditions of source areas. For example, the coarseness and degree of sorting of detrital material are related to the dynamics of transportation. Distinction between fluvial and marine or lacustrine deposits ordinarily can be made. Relative depth of water and distance from shore or source are indicated to some extent (see Figure 219). Calcareous sediments are somewhat less revealing but they suggest shallow depth in addition to generally mild temperature and clear water.

The direction of sedimentary transportation is recorded by regional coarsening and such structures as cross-bedding, current ripple marks, and sediment grain orientation. The mineralogic characters of detrital material reveal the kinds of rock from which sediments were derived and may aid in the identification of source areas. Also the minerals present and their degree of alteration furnish evidence concerning rapidity of erosion and transportation and may contribute to conclusions regarding topography and climate of the parent terrain.

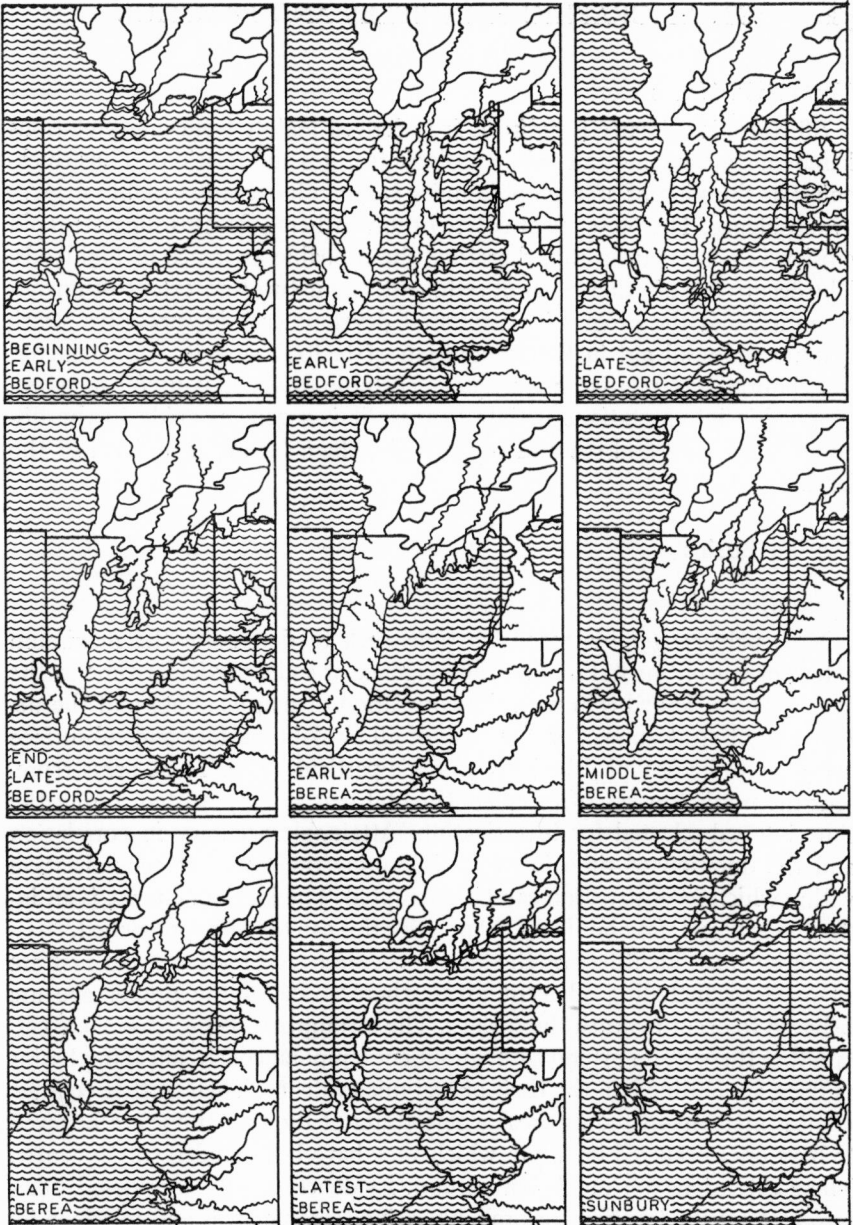

Figure 219. Series of paleogeographic maps of Ohio and neighboring regions showing changes in the relations of land and sea and the location and growth of deltas. These relations are inferred to have existed at relatively closely spaced intervals of time during the early part of the Mississippian Period. The interpretations are based on very detailed stratigraphic and sedimentologic studies mainly of subsurface data. The time intervals are too short for paleontologic correlations to be serviceable in subdividing this part of the stratigraphic section. (After Pepper and others, 1954, U.S. Geol. Surv., Prof. Paper 259, pls. 13 A to 13 I.)

Tectonic Evidence

All tectonic evidence is indirect. It is derived mainly from interpretations based on stratigraphic and sedimentologic features and relations. Thus thickening or thinning of stratigraphic units commonly records variable degrees of subsidence. The presence of coarse or unweathered detritus suggests rapid erosion in nearby areas and, therefore, the probable existence of highlands. The occurrence of other types of sediment, the nature and extent of unconformities, and the progressive structural developments in successive stratigraphic zones all aid in the recognition of tectonic activity, its character, distribution, and relative importance. Tectonic evidence is useful in paleogeographic interpretations mainly because it is a general guide to the distribution of land and sea and suggests the character and condition of the land.

Marine Basins

Epicontinental Seas

Most paleogeographic reconstructions seek to determine the maximum extent of epicontinental marine submergence at some particular time in the geologic past. They begin with the correlation of marine strata and the delineation of areas known, on the basis of all available surface and subsurface evidence, to be occupied by beds of some particular age. These areas represent the minimum extent of epicontinental seas as they existed during the time interval selected for investigation. Attainable accuracy in correlation and the duration of time intervals determine the limits of generalization within which reconstruction can be attempted. The ideal, of course, is an instant in geologic time but in actual practice this can only be approached.

Marine areas identified by the known occurrence of marine strata first are enlarged by including adjacent areas where strata of the proper age are believed to occur beneath the surface. The assumption seems reasonably certain that these strata extend throughout contemporaneously subsiding basins as these are outlined on the basis of tectonic evidence. Then further enlargement is made by including areas where strata of the proper age are believed to have once occurred but from which they have been eroded subsequently. These extensions are much less certain. Evidence usually considered takes into account the locations of probably rising tectonic areas and relations indicated by the fossils with respect to probably connected marine basins.

Contrasting paleogeographic reconstructions—which have been attempted rarely if at all—would seek to determine the minima of epicontinental submergence at times of greatest continental elevation or lowest relative sea level. Evidence most useful for this purpose is provided by unconformities whose extent limits the areas of possible flooding by the sea. In either type of

reconstruction hydrographic interpretations should be made on the basis of
evidence provided by the sediments and fossils.

Shorelines

If ancient shorelines can be located, the accurate outlining of epicontinental seas constitutes a relatively minor problem (see Figure 220). Comparatively little decline in the level of strand lines, however, undoubtedly resulted in the emergence of large areas of shallow sea whose deposits at once
became subject to erosion and may have been completely stripped away.

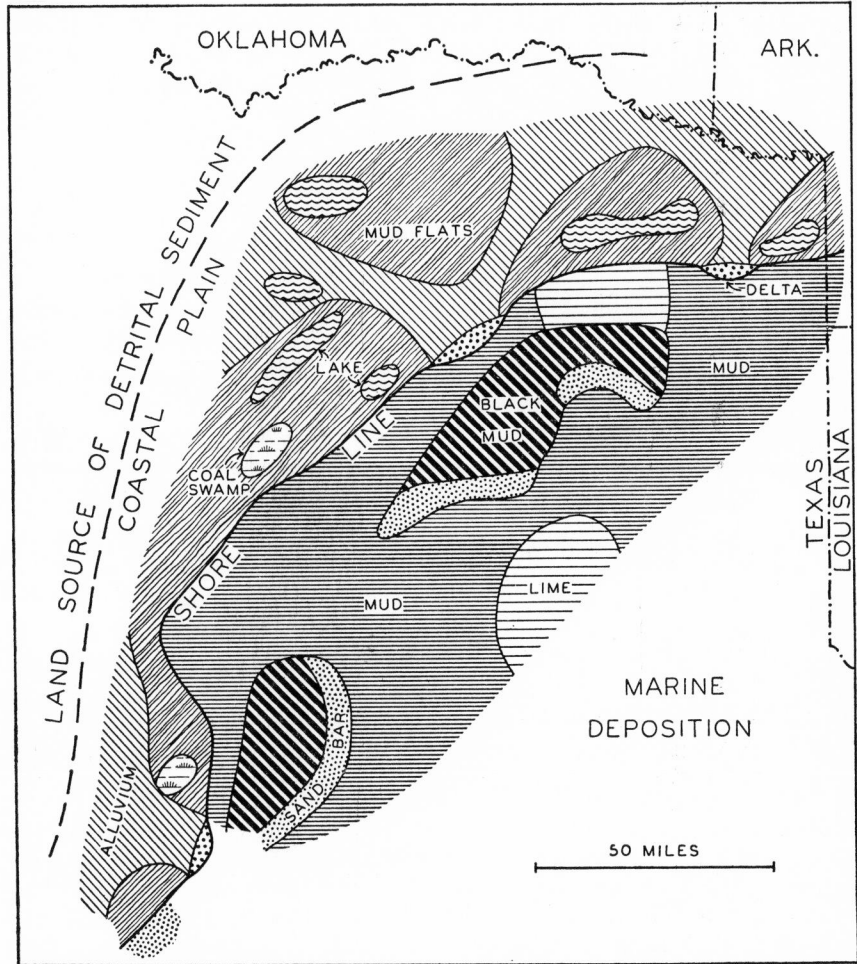

Figure 220.   Paleogeographic and lithotope map of part of northeastern Texas near
the end of the Jurassic Period based on detailed subsurface studies. (After McKee and
others, 1956, U.S. Geol. Surv., Misc. Geol. Invest., Map I-175, pl. 9, fig. 2.)

Many geologists seem to have overlooked this rather obvious possibility; the conclusion has been common that shorelines lay not far beyond the present outcrops. This is clearly shown by paleogeographic maps indicating postulated persistent island areas at the sites of such structures as the Ozark and Nashville domes.

Certainly established examples of extensive stripping and the migration of outcrop zones far from the original limits of deposition are few. The former existence of Middle Mississippian limestone across the Ozark dome, however, is indicated by the occurrence of fossiliferous residual chert throughout that area. An even better example is provided by the presence of Pennsylvanian marine fossils in the Michigan basin. These are evidence of the former marine connection of this area with one or more of the other now isolated Pennsylvanian basins. There can be no doubt about the original continuity of strata that have been removed without a trace from an up-arched zone at least 200 miles wide. Similar or even more extensive downdip outcrop migrations of other ages probably occurred at numerous other places. A few marine fossils observed in the Dunkard Group (Perm.) of southeastern Ohio are separated by nearly 1000 miles from the nearest strata of similar age in Kansas with which they almost certainly were once connected. Also the entire Canadian shield may have been covered formerly by thin Middle Ordovician and Middle Silurian strata.

Local shallow-water, cross-bedded, and sandy strata in dominantly limestone sequences on the east flank of the Ozarks probably indicate temporary near-shore deposition during parts of Middle Devonian and late Middle Mississippian time and suggest the nearby occurrence of a temporary Ozark island. Sedimentary structures and lateral lithologic changes in beds of other ages and at other places may furnish hints of the nearness of other shores. Obscure evidence of this kind, however, rarely has been utilized in connection with paleogeographic interpretations. During some geologic epochs shorelines may have shifted so rapidly, so far, and so often that the patterns of land and sea were too unstable for detailed paleogeographic reconstruction. This apparently was true during much of the Pennsylvanian Period in the interior of North America, where marine waters ebbed and flowed repeatedly across a zone hundreds of miles wide within spans of time too brief to be distinguished by any change in fossils.

Oceanic Connections

Presumptions regarding the patterns made by epicontinental seas and the connections of these seas with surrounding oceans have been powerfully influenced by various divergent concepts respecting the existence and relations of faunal and floral provinces and tectonism. Many of these concepts are more or less equivocal. Consequently the inferences drawn from them are likely to be highly speculative.

As mentioned previously, similarities or differences in fossils have guided the postulation of migration routes and barriers. In considerations of this type environmental controls are exceedingly important but they have commonly been neglected or misinterpreted. For example, Middle Silurian fossils of the area extending along the Great Lakes formerly were believed to represent two faunas, one of northern and the other of southern origin. These were supposed to have been separated generally but not continuously by a land barrier. It is now known that these fossils constitute two closely associated faunas characteristic of different environments, the so-called northern one being adapted to the shallow turbulent water habitat of reefs and the other to interreef areas of deeper quiet water. Correlations also are of prime importance, and the fossils of animals adapted to different environments have been interpreted as identifying beds of different ages. Slight differences of opinion about correlations may result in diametrically opposed conclusions regarding the sites of origin and directions of dispersal of organisms whose fossils are considered to be significant.

Epicontinental seas began as embayments of the oceans that variously expanded, connected, and contracted. Many features of their extent are known but evidence of their origins and the communications that they developed or maintained with the oceans and each other commonly is lacking. Those paleogeographers who have subscribed to the existence of borderlands generally visualized long narrow embayments that followed geosynclines and then spread laterally across the continent. To explain faunal relations in strata of similar ages, they conceived it necessary to postulate portals or breaks in the borderlands for which no stratigraphic or structural evidence exists. To other paleogeographers, these portals have seemed troublesome or dubious. The difficulties at least partially disappear, however, if the borderlands are replaced by island arcs. One of the most persistent uncertainties with respect to the paleogeographic form of North America concerns the possible connection of the interior Paleozoic seas with the Gulf of Mexico along the course of the present Mississippi Valley.

Reconstruction of world paleogeography and particularly the relations of the continents and ocean basins have been characterized by great inconsistency. Actually there is very little evidence that can be relied upon to guide accurate interpretation. Many long-range correlations are insecure, and all conclusions have been greatly influenced by theoretical considerations and speculations including such doubtful processes as floating of the continents, wandering of the poles, and elevation or subsidence of great regions that now lie beneath the sea.

Terrestrial Paleogeography

Attempts to reconstruct paleogeography of the land encounters difficulties different from those arising in connection with consideration of the sea. Land areas are much less clearly indicated than areas of the sea. Most ancient land areas are (1) no longer in existence because they were destroyed by later erosion, (2) buried more or less deeply by more recent sediments, or (3) submerged beneath the present seas and oceans. The most direct remaining evidence of them consists of unconformities and deposits of non-marine sediments that accumulated and have been preserved in terrestrial basins.

Extent of Land

Methods by which the patterns of ancient seas are reconstructed have been explained. They emphasize the known and presumed extent of marine submergences and the remainder is supposed to have been land. If this method were reversed and reconstructions of the extent of known and presumed land were made, these probably would be much smaller, at least at times of maximum submergence. The differences between these two kinds of estimates would indicate large, very doubtful areas. Probably many reconstructions have considerably underestimated the extent of marine submergence.

Distributions of land fossils, mostly vertebrates and plants, provide some evidence concerning the connection or isolation of land areas. Except in post-Mesozoic time these fossils are less significant than those of marine animals, however, because (1) the record of land life is much more incomplete and terrestrial fossils are much less common and much less widely distributed, (2) terrestrial environments are considerably more varied than marine, and (3) ancient land environments are less well understood and more difficult to differentiate and identify. Terrestrial fossils are so rare in rocks older than the Carboniferous that they are practically of no service. From Carboniferous time onward they become increasingly useful as indicators of some aspects of environments but they have been little employed in the reconstruction of paleogeographic relations before the Tertiary epochs.

Terrestrial Basins

Erosion of land areas produces sediments most of which eventually are delivered to the sea. Transportation is likely to be interrupted, however, and much sediment finds temporary resting places upon alluvial surfaces along the way. If differential subsidence occurs, alluvial basins may develop in which considerable quantities of sediment accumulate under non-marine conditions. Such deposition is most likely to occur in or adjacent to upland areas but the strata may be destroyed by later erosion stimulated by regional elevation that commonly characterizes such areas. Consequently non-marine sedimentary deposits of the later geologic epochs are more abundant and more widely distributed than older ones. They also are better known because they are more likely to occur at or near the present surface of the land.

Deposits preserved in terrestrial basins provide the most reliable records of the characters of ancient land areas. The stratigraphic records of similar areas have been destroyed and other larger regions where sediments did not accumulate are indicated only by gaps in the stratigraphic record. The deposits of terrestrial basins, therefore, are uniquely important in the reconstruction of terrestrial paleogeography.

Unconformities

Unconformities that resulted from emergence and possible attendant subaerial erosion also are records of terrestrial conditions. Many disconformities probably indicate relatively low-lying and featureless coastal areas. Large quantities of detritus derived from other regions may have been swept across them while only minor local erosion was accomplished. Angular unconformities, on the other hand, may indicate former areas of considerable topographic relief but, because the balance maintained between local uplift and erosion rarely can be determined, the actual nature of the land surface is somewhat doubtful. Unconformities, therefore, surely indicate only the final nature of a land surface as it existed before burial by younger sediments. In general, the greater the stratigraphic gap occurring at an unconformity, the less can be determined concerning the nature of the land surface that it represents.

Sedimentary Interpretations

Conclusions concerning locations of the more prominent uplifted areas, whose erosion produced large quantities of sediment in the geologic past, are largely dependent, and inferences concerning the topography and climate are almost entirely dependent, upon the characters of the sediments derived from them. The more obvious types of evidence that are useful in the reconstruction of terrestrial paleogeographic conditions include (1) areal distribution of non-marine sedimentary rocks, (2) their general lithologic characters and lateral variations, (3) their thicknesses, and (4) gross structural features of older rocks. More obscure evidence is provided by (5) minor structures indicating direction of sediment transportation, (6) size and sorting of sedimentary particles, and (7) mineralogy. Few paleogeographic interpretations have utilized all the evidence of this kind that is fairly readily available.

Upland areas that produced large quantities of sediment obviously could not have been located where deposition was in progress. Many such regions suffered important structural disturbances associated with their elevation. Therefore, areas whose older rocks are structurally complex are more promising source sites than areas of nearly horizontal strata.

The direction of sediment transportation leads away from source areas and this, if it can be determined, suggests the quarter in which the sources lay (see Figure 137, p. 338). Evidence may be provided by cross-bedding, current ripple marks, orientation of sedimentary particles, progressive decrease in coarseness of material, better sorting, and perhaps decreasing thickness, although the last is by no means certain. Most evidence of these kinds, however, actually indicates only the direction of depositing currents. Because transportation was not necessarily direct, it is not reliable in detail and may be inconsistent.

The mineralogic characters of sediments suggest more or less clearly the types of parent rock that were subject to erosion, and corresponding sources can be sought. Certain peculiarities, particularly in the heavy mineral fraction, may point to some restricted source. Mineralogy, in the case of first-cycle sediments, also provides much information concerning the type and rapidity of weathering and erosion and thereby gives some indication of the topography and climate in source areas.

In general, terrestrial sediments provide more reliable information regarding the locations of and conditions in source areas than do marine sediments. Terrestrial sediments are more likely to have been transported directly and deposited closer to their sources. They also are less likely to have been mixed or subjected to prolonged reworking that would have altered the original characters of the sediment significantly.

Foundered Land

The sedimentary record provides ample evidence that movements of elevation and depression have been in almost constant operation and have repeatedly altered the topographic aspects of the continents. The mechanism responsible for these movements is quite unknown. Opinions regarding its nature and action in the geologic past have differed widely. Some of the most important disagreements have been concerned with the periodicity of movements and the permanence of the continents.

Most geologists agree that the stratigraphic record in North America furnishes no evidence that any part of this great region ever was submerged to depths comparable to those now prevailing in the surrounding oceans. Most strata and their fossils are accepted as indication of shallow seas whose bottoms rarely lay much below the limit of light penetration although the geosynclines and some of the more important basins may at times have been occupied by deeper water. The deepest submergence that seems to be reasonably well substantiated appears to have occurred in the Permian basin of west Texas, where the surrounding reefs are believed to have risen about 2000 feet above the nearby bottom. Some European geologists, however, have concluded that portions of the Mesozoic seas of the present Alpine region may have been much deeper.

If it is true that regions roughly corresponding to the present continents have stood consistently higher than the ocean basins since long before the beginning of the Paleozoic Era, the possibility of important continental enlargement by marginal accretion during that time seems to be ruled out. This, however, does not eliminate the possibility that marginal portions of the continents or other regions that once stood high may have sunk deeply beneath the sea. Nevertheless, seismic interpretations of density distribution in layers of the earth's crust beneath the oceans generally are considered to be opposed to the latter possibility.

Uncertainties regarding the location and character of continental margins in past ages introduce serious problems in paleogeographic reconstruction. Interpretations are certain to differ greatly depending upon the views that are accepted regarding such tectonic features as borderlands and island arcs. The possibility also must be entertained that interarc basins such as those of the East and West Indies were formerly elevated and constituted parts of the continental regions.

The evidence is reasonably good that at least some portions of both the eastern and western coasts of North America have sunk deeply beneath the sea since Mesozoic times. Thus the area of this continent, as it commonly is measured to the edge of the continental shelf, has been reduced by this amount and there is no evidence that the loss has been compensated by comparable elevation and additions along other continental margins. Other portions of the world suggest somewhat similar relations. The continents, including their shallowly submerged portions, perhaps were larger in the past than they are now. If foundering of other important portions of former continental regions has occurred, the most likely areas appear to be the basins enclosed by modern island arcs and the basin now occupied by the Mediterranean Sea. Much more extensive foundering has been postulated by some theoretical geologists.

Paleogeographic Maps

The foregoing discussion indicates rather clearly that paleogeographic reconstruction is beset at present by many difficulties and much uncertainty. This also is apparent when similar paleogeographic maps made by different persons, or by the same person at different times, are compared (see Figures 221 and 222). Certain broad likenesses may be noticed but in many cases these are overshadowed by great differences in detail. Striking lack of correspondence is not uncommon. It has led some critics to conclude that these maps are not worth the paper they are printed on.

Each paleogeographic map actually is a generalized presentation of geographic relations as they are supposed to have existed within the time span of some restricted stratigraphic sequence that is believed to be equivalent throughout an extensive area. The strata and the intervals of time that have been considered and treated as units in this way have varied greatly. In

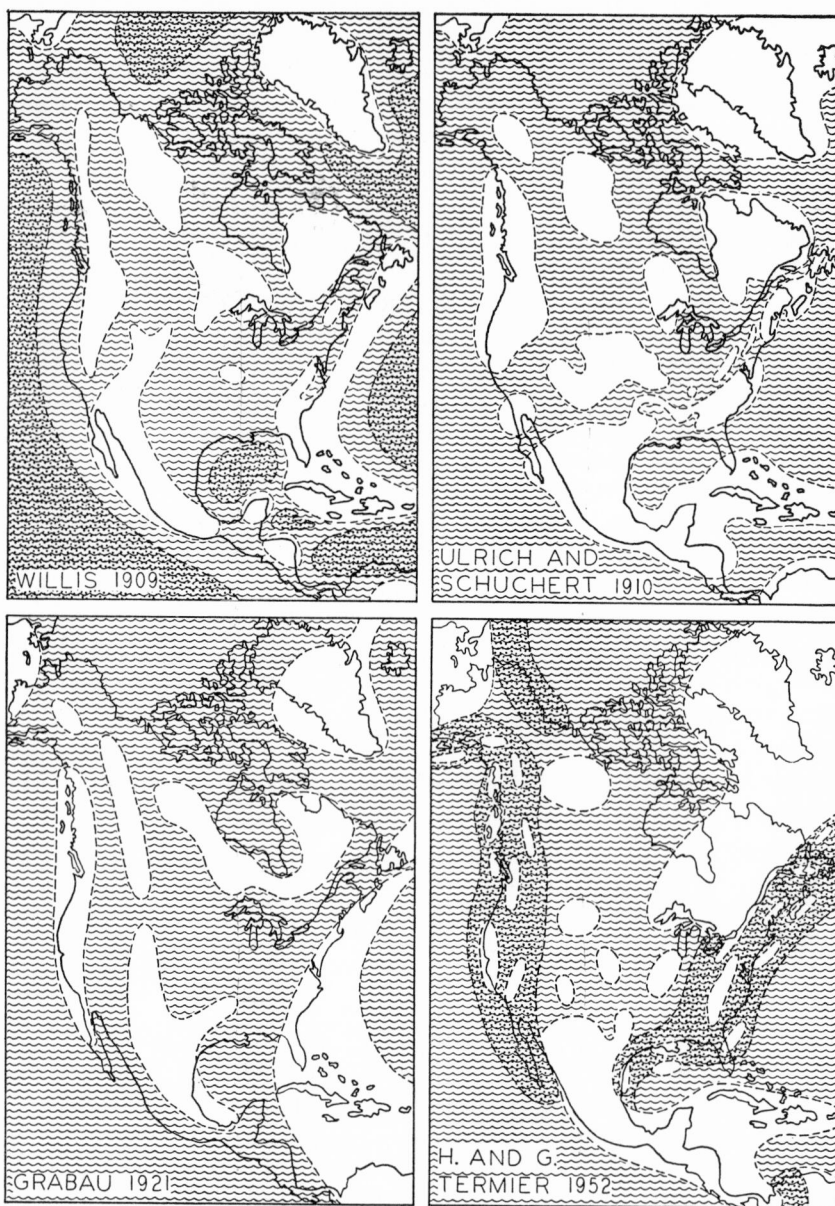

Figure 221. Four paleogeographic maps representing North America during Middle Ordovician time. These illustrate clearly the differences in interpretation based upon essentially identical data that are possible. The first three maps accord with the formerly widely held continental borderland theory. The last is constructed to conform to the latterly popular island arc theory. Willis made a distinction between epicontinental seas and ocean basins. The Termiers indicated geosynclines. (After Willis (Middle Ordovician), 1909, *J. Geol.*, vol. 17, p. 254; Schuchert (Lowest Trenton), 1910, *Bull. Geol. Soc. Amer.*, vol. 20, p. 606, pl. 54; Grabau (Trenton), 1921, *Textbook of geology*, vol. 2, p. 278, fig. 1090, by permission of D. C. Heath and Co.; and H. and G. Termier (Middle Ordovician), 1952, *Histoire géologique de la biosphère*, p. 282, map 6, by permission of Masson et Cie.)

the most elaborate paleogeographic studies, a minimum of about 3 to a maximum of more than 10 million years is represented by a single map. The possibility of attaining much greater refinement with any reasonable degree of accuracy throughout large regions is very doubtful. Other well-known series of paleogeographic maps are much more generalized.

In addition to unavoidable generalizations, paleogeographic maps possess other defects and disadvantages that should be clearly recognized. The chief of these is that the source and reliability of data used in their construction cannot be indicated adequately except in elaborate explanations which, even if they were presented, would be consulted and evaluated by few viewers of the maps. Thus the merits or shortcomings of a paleogeographic map are almost impossible to assess. On the whole, these maps have an appearance of definiteness and precision that is quite misleading (see Figure 223). Only a person who has attempted to make them can realize fully to what a great extent the features they show are conjectural rather than presentations of reasonably well-established facts.

It should be obvious to anyone

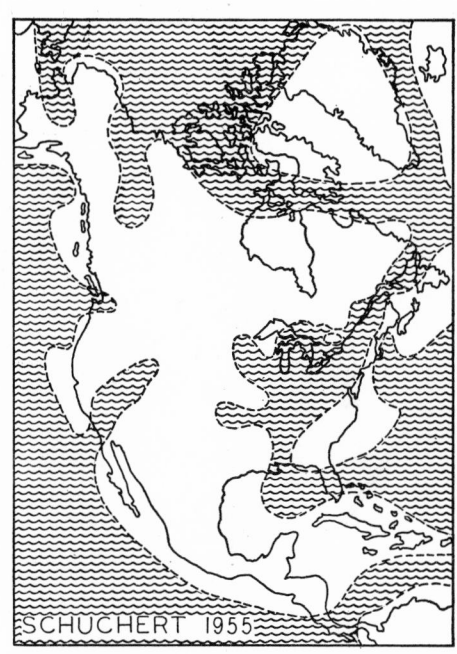

Figure 222. Paleogeographic map of North America during Middle Ordovician time (Lower and Middle Trenton). This was Schuchert's latest interpretation, published posthumously. Compare it with the Ulrich and Schuchert map of Figure 221. (After Schuchert, 1955, *Atlas of paleogeographic maps of North America*, pl. 15, by permission of John Wiley and Sons.)

that the quantity as well as the quality of stratigraphic information is important in paleogeographic reconstruction. For example, in many parts of the United States the zones in which formations outcrop are known with great accuracy, and abundant well records provide much data on subsurface stratigraphic conditions and distributions. In contrast, many outcrop details are doubtful in relatively inaccessible or undeveloped regions, such as arctic Canada and Alaska and large parts of Mexico and Central America, and no subsurface data are available. Consequently, even if correlations and other interpretations are correct, paleogeographic maps are much more reliable in some areas than in others. Some evaluation of the degree of reliability can be made if the areas of actual outcrop are shown and the presumed subsurface extension of the strata under consideration is indicated separately on the maps.

The conclusion is not unreasonable that the value of paleogeographic maps is rather small because their construction involves too much guesswork and they are based on too scanty data that are too likely to have been

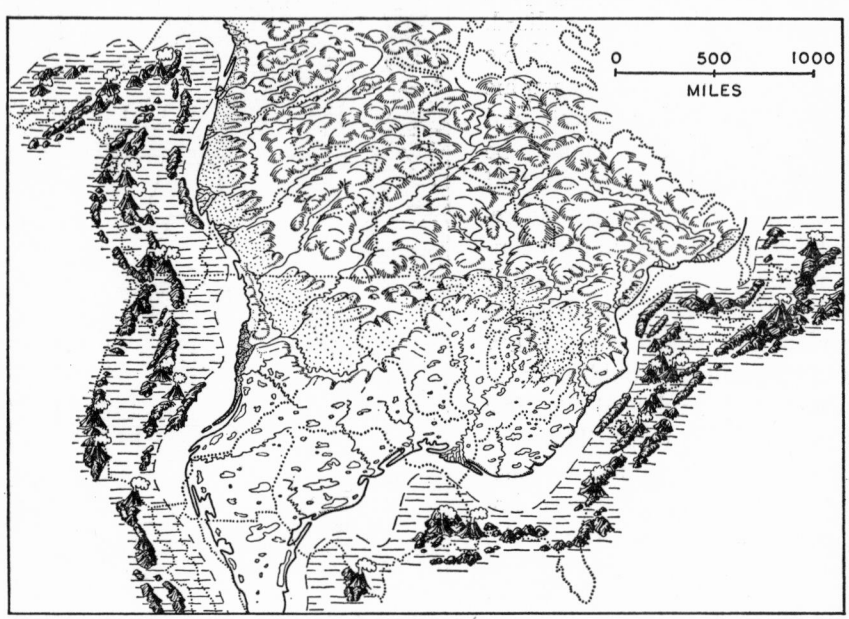

Figure 223. Paleogeographic map of the United States and Canada during early Middle Ordovician time (early Chazyan). The topographic features, although highly imaginative, add greatly to the paleogeographic interpretation. Shown in successive concentric order are (1) eugeosynclines with volcanic islands, (2) miogeosynclinal zones lapping upon the continental borders, (3) limy coastal plain consisting of emergent early Ordovician sediments, (4) sandy plains underlain by Cambrian sediments, and (5) the Precambrian shield. The base is palinspastic, and the map is drawn out laterally to compensate for later thrust faulting. (After Kay, 1951, Geol. Soc. Amer., Mem. 48, p. 1, pl. 1.)

misinterpreted. This undoubtedly is true if the maps are accepted at their face value. If, however, the present limitations of paleogeographic reconstruction are understood clearly, these maps serve a very useful purpose. Stratigraphic, paleontologic, and structural features are varied and complex. So much scattered information requires consideration that no single person can hope to keep it all in mind. By presenting as much of this information as possible on a map, a certain type of organization is attained, spatial relations are indicated, and there is less likelihood that significant information will be overlooked. In spite of the recognized inadequacy of the information and the uncertainty of its interpretation, a paleogeographic map provides some indication of conditions as they existed at a definite stage in the geologic evolution of a region. The map should be recognized as being only one of several possible interpretations, and alternatives can be visualized readily by anyone who is reasonably well acquainted with the regional geology and

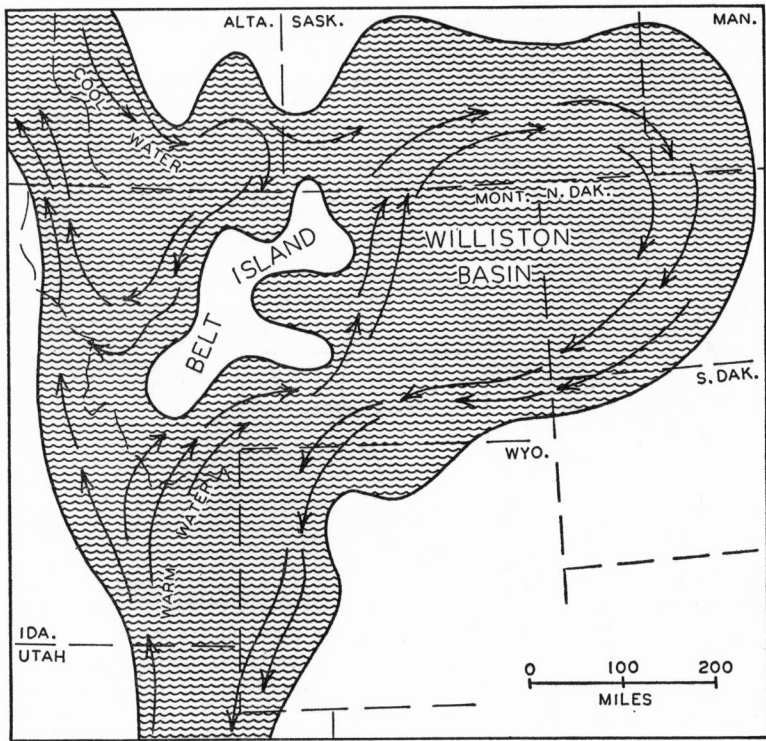

Figure 224. Paleogeographic map of the Williston basin region during the deposition of the Piper B stratigraphic unit (Jur.). The reconstruction of currents in the restricted epicontinental sea is based mainly on the distribution of limy sediments, which are interpreted as identifying areas of warmer water. (After Peterson, 1957, *Bull. Am. Assoc. Petroleum Geol.*, vol. 41, p. 423, fig. 12.)

paleontology of the epoch represented. Considerations of this kind direct attention to critical areas where additional information would be particularly valuable, to the special type of information that would be most useful, and to needed reevaluations of already existing information. Thus, in a way, each map is a guidepost pointing toward a desired objective and, if the suggested investigations are pursued, progressively more satisfactory and reliable paleogeographic maps will be made possible.

Most paleogeographers have been so preoccupied with considering the relations of land and sea that their maps show little else. The possibilities and opportunities for further reconstructions should not be overlooked. These have to do with depth and nature of the sea bottom, direction of ocean currents (see Figure 224), height of tides, topography of the land (see Figure 225), including location of mountains and other uplifted areas and courses of the rivers, sites of volcanic action, and all the factors that combine

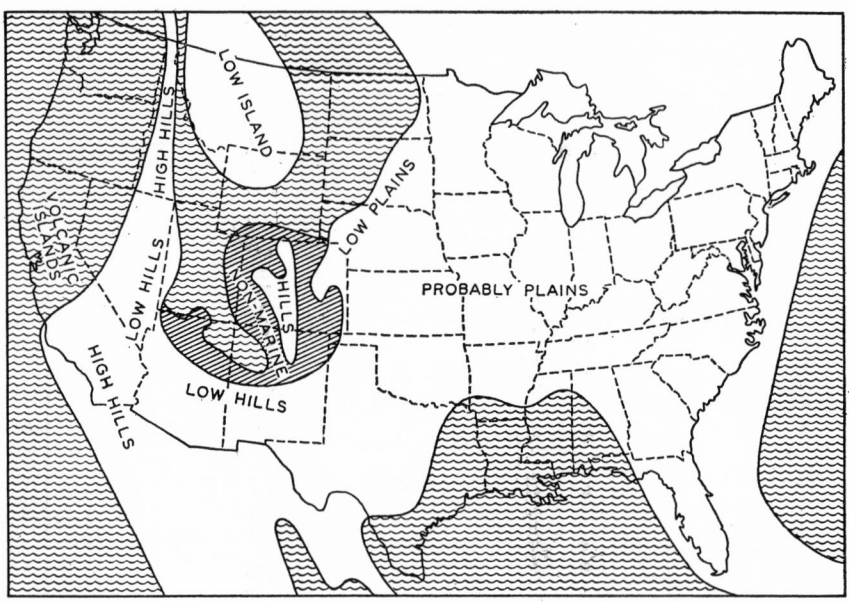

Figure 225. Paleogeographic map of the United States during the early part of late Jurassic time (latter half of Callovian time). In addition to the usual shorelines this map shows an area of non-marine deposition, the occurrence of volcanic islands, and notations regarding topography of the land based mainly upon structural history and the amounts and kinds of sediments derived from them. (After Imlay, 1956, U.S. Geol. Surv., Misc. Geol. Invest., Map I-175, pl. 8, fig. 5.)

to determine climate (see Figure 218, p. 577). These are all features of geography that should, if possible, be represented on paleogeographic maps. Conclusions drawn from stratigraphic and paleontologic data mostly are very indirect and at present more or less uncertain, but with proper attention something can be learned about many paleogeographic features. Any advances made in this direction will add importantly to understanding, and fill in some significant details of geologic history.

Some of the vagueness of paleogeographic maps, inherent in their generalized nature, also could be dissipated if each epoch chosen for interpretation were represented by two maps. One would show the maximum extent of marine submergence and the other would indicate the minimum. Between them, these maps would provide a much better picture of actual geographic relations even if advances and retreats of the epicontinental seas were not synchronous everywhere and neither map presented the instantaneous snapshot that is desired.

TECTONIC DEVELOPMENT

Tectonic action generally has been slighted in connection with paleogeography, probably because the primary objective was to prepare maps showing conditions as they existed at selected instants in the geologic past and movement was considered unimportant. Obviously conditions changed, but the changes commonly were viewed mainly as alterations in the patterns of land and sea. Geosynclines have recieved attention because they were believed to provide the primary seaways where submergence of the continents began. Some consideration also has been given to adjacent uplands that produced the thick sediments deposited in the geosynclines. Connections between epicontinental embayments and connections between these embayments and the oceans, however, mostly have been located without regard to structure of the rocks. Some of the postulated connections cut directly across well-established structural trends and probably are misinterpreted.

The most accurate paleogeographic maps at best are no more than static records of past conditions. They fail to indicate the dynamic relations of the features they show. The development and the importance of these features cannot be understood unless they are considered in relation to tectonic activity that was in more or less constant operation and accounts for most of the changes in the surface appearance of the earth throughout all geologic time.

Tectonic Evidence

Much of the evidence that is useful in deciphering tectonic history and development is the same as that employed in the reconstruction of paleogeography. It is mainly stratigraphic and is derived from knowledge of the distribution and characters of sediments. Data on thicknesses of stratigraphic units, however, are much more significant than in paleogeography, but paleontologic relations are less noteworthy. Structural features including dynamic metamorphism and igneous activity also are important. Such evidence reveals the relative stability of different areas, indicates whether they were depressed or elevated, and gauges the movements that affected them.

Variations in the thickness of equivalent strata are only an approximate measure of the amount of subsidence because sedimentation probably did not begin upon a perfectly horizontal surface and probably did not maintain a horizontal upper surface of deposition. Compaction was not uniform; fine-grained rocks like shales represent greater original thicknesses than coarser ones like sandstones. These discrepancies, however, become less important as larger areas and thicker stratigraphic sections are considered. Subsidence in basins generally varied from time to time. It may have been interrupted by uplift that resulted in erosion. Thickness of strata does not record reversals of this kind but indicates only the total relative movement that occurred during a particular interval of time.

Structural trends are revealed by thickening and thinning of strata, and isopach maps are useful in their recognition. If isopach data show marked elongation of the basins, nearby uplifted areas probably were somewhat similarly shaped and roughly parallel. The occurrence of very coarse and thick detrital sediments is indication of closely adjacent uplands that were being eroded rapidly.

Estimates of uplift are much less certain. They can be attempted, however, by calculating the volume of sediment deposited in nearby basins and allocating it to the area that was subject to erosion.

Structural relations at unconformities and paleogeologic maps record the results of tectonic movements, resulting erosion, and subsequent overlapping deposition that can be dated in the geologic past (see Figure 259, p. 635). Such data derived from subsurface records are particularly valuable because relations have remained unchanged and they preserve evidence of former structural trends along which subsequent movement may not have occurred. A succession of unconformities does not necessarily indicate a corresponding succession of disturbances, however. These may have been produced by intermittently active erosion during a time of continuing uplift of a nearby area.

Metamorphism and large igneous intrusions identify deeply eroded areas that must have been greatly uplifted. Volcanic activity generally accompanied structural disturbance but not necessarily the uplifting of tectonic mountains.

Positive and Negative Areas

The study of paleotectonics seeks to reconstruct the development of all geologic structures occurring in the earth's crust and to determine the relations of the movements that produced them. The deep ocean basins and the continental regions are contrasting structures of the first order, but so little is known about the geology of the ocean basins that attention must be devoted almost exclusively to the continents.

The tectonic aspects of continental regions serve to subdivide the latter into areas of three types: (1) stable or neutral areas that have fluctuated little in elevation, (2) rising or positive areas, and (3) subsiding or negative ones. Probably the ocean basins consist of three similar types of areas but these cannot be well differentiated because they are not accessible to detailed geologic observation.

The neutral portions of the continents stand or have stood close to sea level for long periods of time. Alternate shallow submergences and low emergences perhaps have resulted from eustatic variations in sea level, as during the Pleistocene glacial and interglacial ages, as much as from slight changes in absolute elevation. The positive areas were more or less constantly worn down by erosion so that they did not necessarily stand high. The negative areas formed basins in which sediments accumulated. They did not, therefore, necessarily become deeper topographic features.

The pattern of positive, neutral, and negative areas has not remained the same. At times the movement in certain areas has ceased or been reversed. The geosynclinal cycle is an example of subsidence changing to uplift and being followed by relative stability. This seems to have been characteristic of certain particularly mobile belts. Elsewhere such a cycle may not have progressed to completion. Subsidence may only have slowed down and finally stopped. Uplift also may begin in an area that has not passed through a previous pronounced subsiding stage.

Geologic structure of the older rocks has grown constantly more complex because these rocks have been affected by all later tectonic movements. Such movements have continued slowly or they have been repeated in particular areas throughout very long periods of time. The centers of similar movements have gradually shifted laterally. The ultimate causes of these movements and their changes are unknown but probably most of them have been related to physical processes operating deep within the earth. Surface processes also have been important although they may have produced only secondary results. Thus the shifting of surface loads as one area was eroded and lightened while another was weighted by accumulating sediment probably accentuated movements that would not otherwise have proceeded so far or for so long a time.

Movements of the positive and negative areas of the continents have determined and progressively altered the structural framework of great regions. Although it is possible that movement in some areas may have developed solely in response to internal forces, probably many areas of movement owe their locations and their forms to features of the continental framework and areas or zones of weakness related to previous tectonic movements and more ancient structural developments and trends. Geologic structure as seen today tends to present a somewhat distorted picture of tectonic movements as they were in operation at any time in the geologic past. So far as can be determined, most modern rising or subsiding areas are fairly extensive and have fairly simple patterns. It seems unlikely that ancient patterns, related to what probably was a less complicated underlying structural framework, were more complex. They may have been much more simple.

Paleotectonic Maps

The distribution of rising and sinking areas has controlled the patterns shown by both paleogeographic and paleotectonic maps. As commonly presented, therefore, such maps may be expected to exhibit certain general similarities. Most paleogeographic maps do little more than emphasize the presumed positions of ancient shorelines whereas paleotectonic maps indicate the amount of subsidence in basins, as measured by the thicknesses of sedimentary deposits, and the locations of mountain ranges or other kinds of uplands (see Figure 226). Theoretically these maps should differ importantly because the former aim at representing conditions as they existed at some particular instant in the past whereas the latter show the results of processes that operated during some definite interval of time. Commonly these differences are not apparent because it has been the practice to add paleotectonic data to generalized paleogeographic maps (see Figure 88, p. 253).

Stratigraphic correlation is important as a control of paleotectonic maps because the thicknesses of strata of equivalent age must be determined throughout extensive regions. The stringency of this control, however, is not so great as in paleogeographic studies. If a series of maps is prepared, an error in one of them resulting from miscorrelation is compensated in the next. Also thicknesses of strata can be measured or closely estimated whereas the positions of shorelines are matters of interpretation and are subject to much uncertainty. Therefore, so far as subsiding basins are concerned, paleotectonic maps generally are much more objective and reliable than are paleogeographic maps.

Estimation of the amount of uplift in eroded areas is much less certain. Mountains already in existence may have been deeply eroded without further elevation. Rapid uplift may not have been accompanied by comparable erosion. The existence of lofty mountain chains today is proof that erosion at many places has not kept pace with uplift. Consequently the rising portions of any region might not correspond with either the most prominent uplands or the areas that were the source of the greatest quantities of sediment. The correct interpretation of such relations on paleotectonic maps is very difficult.

The accurate location of rising areas is another problem. Some evidence as to where the most important of these areas occurred is provided by the distribution of coarse sediment and possibly by the structure of older rocks beneath an unconformity. Although subsidence in basins can be approximated with contours similar to isopachs, data are insufficient for the similar representation of uplifted areas. Ordinarily no more precise indication of them is warranted than that which can be shown by highly generalized hachure patterns.

Paleotectonic maps, like paleographic ones, are seriously distorted in areas of strong folding and particularly of overthrusting, where compression has resulted in important horizontal shortening. In order that relations may be shown correctly, data should be plotted on a palinspastic base (see Figure 223, p. 590).

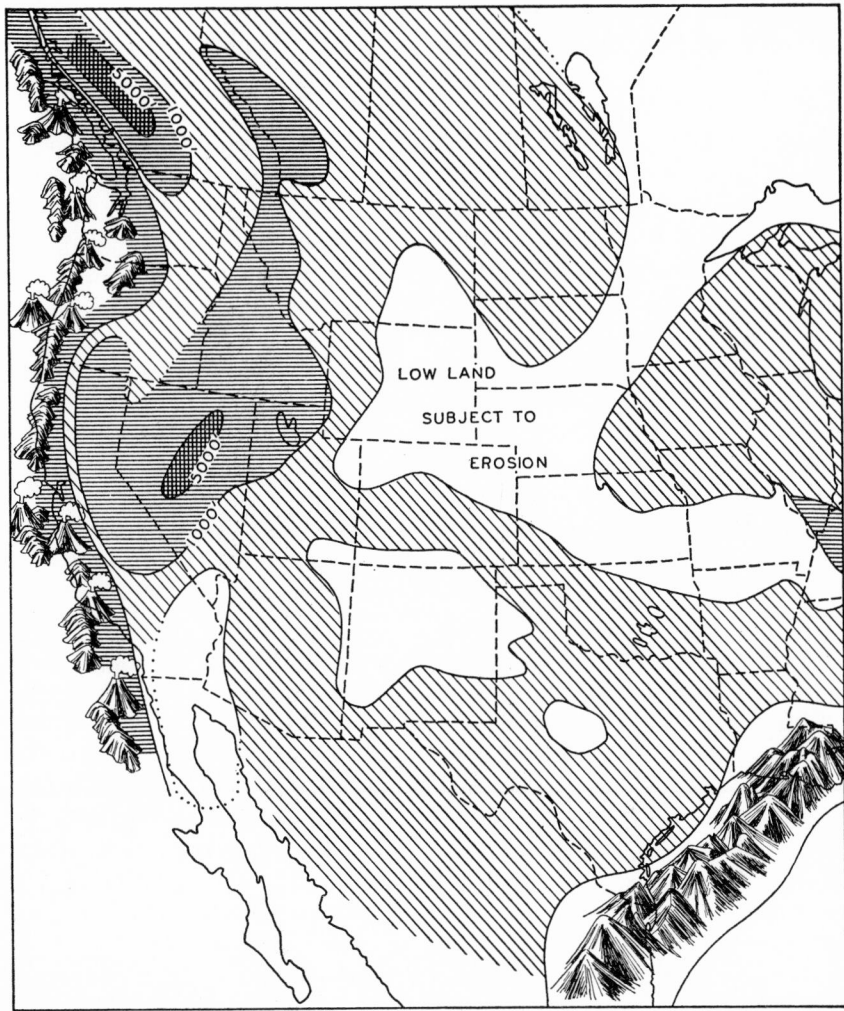

LOW LAND

SUBJECT TO

EROSION

Figure 226. Paleogeographic map of the western United States during the Devonian Period. In addition to the usual features this map shows in a very general way the thickness of Devonian sedimentary rocks and distinguishes between epirogenic and orogenic land. These are important because they indicate degrees of subsidence and uplift. The original is titled "Paleotectonic Map." (After Eardley, 1949, *Bull. Am. Assoc. Petroleum Geol.*, vol. 33, p. 662, fig. 2.)

HISTORICAL GEOLOGY

All geologic studies, if they are undertaken with an objective extending beyond the collection of some particular kind of specialized data and its classification and interpretation or the solution of some restricted problem, are aimed more or less directly in one or the other of two directions. These are (1) practical or economic geology in its broadest sense or (2) historical geology. Many studies, of course, contribute to both. Practical investigations commonly yield some by-products of scientific interest, and the results of most academic studies sooner or later find some kind of practical application.

As previously explained, historical geology is the product of the coordination and systematization of all geologic knowledge. It is concerned with the nature and orderly relations of all the materials that make up the earth and with all the forces and processes that have controlled its development and shaped it as it now exists. The geologic elements that are synthesized in historical geology are grounded in physics, chemistry, and biology. Most of them are related in a preliminary way with respect to both space and time in the general field of stratigraphy. The historical applications of many geologic studies may not be apparent immediately, but there can be no doubt regarding the logical progression that leads from stratigraphy to historical geology.

Both stratigraphy and historical geology are concerned with space and time. Stratigraphy deals primarily with rock masses as related to these frames, and space is its first consideration. Many of its elements are objective facts and its horizons are more or less restricted geographically. In contrast, historical geology is mostly concerned with conditions, happenings, and change, and time is of first importance. Its elements are mainly interpretations derived from stratigraphy and its horizons commonly embrace the whole earth.

Many of the factual details that play very important parts in the development of knowledge in subsidiary geologic fields shrink to insignificance in comparison with the broad sweep of historical geologic interests. For example, the manner in which a stratigraphic section is subdivided into parts, the exact thickness of a formation or its variations in thickness, the features that serve to distinguish it from others including minor structures, the nature of fossil preservation, the physical relations at a stratigraphic contact, and many others are of small concern. They have served a most useful purpose in laying the foundation and in cementing the varied elements upon which historical geology is erected and they now can be ignored. Indeed, historical geology is so expansive in its outlook that it cannot afford to be concerned greatly with details of this sort.

At the same time that details are passed over, larger problems come in view. It becomes apparent that explanations are needed to account for the relations of geologic features as they occur in space and of geologic events as they progressed in time. These fundamental problems cannot be attacked directly and solutions have been sought mainly within the realm of theory. They are concerned with highly complex physical, chemical, and mechanical relations and reactions to ever changing conditions that are very little understood. Perhaps satisfactory solutions to some of these problems never will be found but the search for them continues. Each problem that is recognized suggests new information that is needed. These requirements direct attention backward first to stratigraphy and then to other subdivisions of geology in a ramifying fashion. This is the process that accounts for much of the expansion of geologic interests and explains the necessity for increased specialization in restricted geologic fields.

Historical geology requires the integration of all geologic observations, interpretations, theories, and inferences. The relations that are indicated are numerous, complex, and difficult to grasp in their entirety. They can be made most understandable by compilation and presentation in the form of maps although sections, diagrams, and verbal explanations may be needed to clarify the details. Those maps that are indispensable for this purpose are (1) paleogeographic maps, showing both hydrographic and topographic features, (2) paleogeologic maps, illustrating in a different way stages in the geologic evolution of the earth, and (3) paleotectonic maps, showing the surficial results of processes operating deep within the earth's interior. Paleogeographic and paleogeologic maps provide control with respect to spatial relations, and paleotectonic maps serve to connect them and indicate relations with respect to time.

The fact that all three kinds of maps rely most heavily upon stratigraphic data for their construction emphasizes the importance of stratigraphy to geologic science as a whole. Stratigraphy clearly occupies a central position where various types of synthesis are accomplished. It also provides a unique vantage point from which attention can be directed most advantageously either to specialized studies of many kinds or to the broadest aspects and most fundamental problems of geology.

BIBLIOGRAPHY

Moore, R. C. (1933), *Historical geology*, New York, McGraw-Hill.
>This is a comprehensive and well-balanced textbook.

Moore, R. C. (1958), *Introduction to historical geology*, 2nd ed., New York, McGraw-Hill.
>This competent conventional elementary textbook is mainly devoted to presentation of commonly accepted explanations and generalizations.

Pirsson, L. V., and Schuchert, Charles (1924), A *text-book of geology*, 2nd ed., vol. 2, *Historical geology*, by Schuchert; New York, Wiley.
>This old and well-known work still ranks high among more recent American texts.

Schuchert, Charles (1910), Paleogeography of North America, *Bull. Geol. Soc. Amer.*, vol. 20, pp. 427–606.
>Fifty maps extend from the Lower Cambrian to the Pleistocene and the text explains methods of paleogeography and features of the maps.

Schuchert, Charles (1955), *Atlas of paleogeographic maps of North America,* with introduction by C. O. Dunbar, New York, Wiley.

Eighty-four maps extend from the earliest Cambrian to the Pleistocene as these stood at the time of Schuchert's death in 1942.

Simpson, G. G. (1940), Mammals and land bridges, *J. Wash. Acad. Sci.,* vol. 30, pp. 137–163.

General consideration is given to intercontinental migrations of Tertiary mammals. The principles developed can be applied to the migrations of other organisms, both terrestrial and marine.

Simpson, G. G. (1947), Holarctic mammalian faunas and continental relationships during the Cenozoic, *Bull. Geol. Soc. Amer.,* vol. 58, pp. 613–688.

The principles of the former article are applied to Cenozoic connections of North America and Eurasia across the Bering Strait.

Snider, L. C. (1932), *Earth history,* New York, Century.

This unconventional textbook presents generally accepted material in a more than ordinarily interesting manner.

Termier, Henri, and Termier, Geneviève (1952), *Histoire géologique de la biosphère, la vie et les sédiments dans les géographies successives,* Paris, Masson.

Thirty-five paleogeographic maps of the world extend from the Lower Cambrian to the Pleistocene and a companion map of the modern world is included. See pp. 264–265 and 274–344.

Part IV

APPENDIX

The importance of the graphic presentation of geologic information and the conduct of geologic field work extend far beyond stratigraphic studies. The complexities of stratigraphic data and their relations, however, make illustration a matter of more than ordinary interest to stratigraphers. Many obvious advantages are to be gained by the use of abundant figures to supplement descriptions if they are thoughtfully clear and simple. Ingenuity can devise many ways to present stratigraphic data visually and make them readily understandable.

Stratigraphy is much more dependent upon field work than are several other major branches of geology. Field work, therefore, is of particular importance to stratigraphers. As in the past, much of the future progress of stratigraphy will be a direct product of studies in the field. Much future field work is likely to require increasing skills and to involve investigations in difficult and remote regions where field procedures may be the determining factor of success or failure.

17

Graphic Representation

THE GRAPHIC presentation of stratigraphic data is extremely useful because (1) the details of many stratigraphic features and their relations can be expressed more clearly in visual than in verbal form and (2) the interrelations of some stratigraphic features can be investigated most easily by graphic methods. Illustrations do not eliminate the necessity for description because no diagram can show more than a very small part of all the data that require attention. Carefully chosen and executed illustrations, however, can simplify descriptions and make them more readily understandable.

Stratigraphy is concerned with the qualities, forms, structures, distributions, and relations of sediments and sedimentary rocks within a three-dimensional framework. Two of the dimensions are the familiar ones of length and breadth. The third or vertical dimension can be expressed in accordance with either one or the other of two unrelated scales, thickness and time. Most stratigraphic diagrams are highly selective, and those that are dimensional present data with respect to some particular attribute of rocks in reference to one, two, or more rarely three directions. Some representations combine two diagrams, as, for example, an areal geologic and a structural contour map. These may add an extra dimension or show other important relations that are not revealed by either diagram alone. Further combinations, however, are likely to be confusing because the individual diagrams become difficult to differentiate and understand.

Many stratigraphic diagrams are more or less pictorial because they present data with reference to (1) location and direction in the two-dimensional horizontal framework of a map or (2) a vertical scale of thickness or of time either with or without one horizontal dimension. Some employ conventionalized patterns identifying different kinds of rocks that are easily recognized and add to their pictorial quality. Diagrams of this kind are largely qualitative. A great variety of diagrams constitute another class that is predominantly quantitative and generally lacks pictorial characters. These distinctions are not sharp. Many diagrams combine some features of the different classes. In general, non-pictorial diagrams are simplest, but not necessarily the easiest to understand, and complexity increases as one, two, or three spatial dimensions are represented.

DIMENSIONLESS DIAGRAMS

Most dimensionless diagrams are non-pictorial. They record numerical data and are particularly serviceable in illustrating the textural and structural characters and composition of sediments and sedimentary rocks such as (1) quantitative comparisons, (2) statistical distributions, (3) relations of two or three variable factors, and (4) orientation in two or three dimensions. They rarely are useful in revealing stratigraphic features except in an indirect manner. These diagrams are of many different types.

Bar Diagrams

Bar diagrams consist of bars or lines whose lengths are plotted against a constant scale showing the numerical values of whatever property is under consideration. The values may be simple measurements or counts, percent-

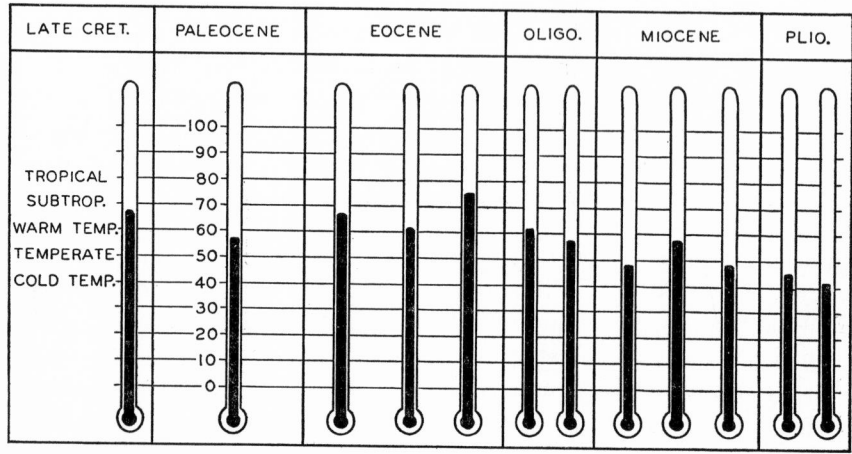

Figure 227. Modified bar diagram showing in a generalized way successive climatic fluctuations in the northwestern part of the United States during late Cretaceous and Tertiary time based on the occurrence of fossil plants. The imaginative addition of simple pictorial quality to a bar diagram makes it attractive and more readily understandable. (After Dorf, 1955, Geol. Soc. Amer., Spec. Paper 62, p. 587, fig. 3.)

ages or more rarely other ratios. They are particularly effective in the comparison of a single property measured for different materials, at different places or at different times (see Figure 227). Examples are drilling time of different strata successively penetrated in a well (which is a direct measurement reflecting hardness), number of foraminifera present in comparable quantities of sediment samples (which is a count), and amount of insoluble residue in different beds (which generally is expressed as a percentage).

More elaborate bar diagrams show data for several related properties simultaneously. In them the bars are divided into segments or multiple bars may be used, each representing a property distinguished by an identifying pattern (see Figures 228 and 229). Segment lengths may be determined by measure-

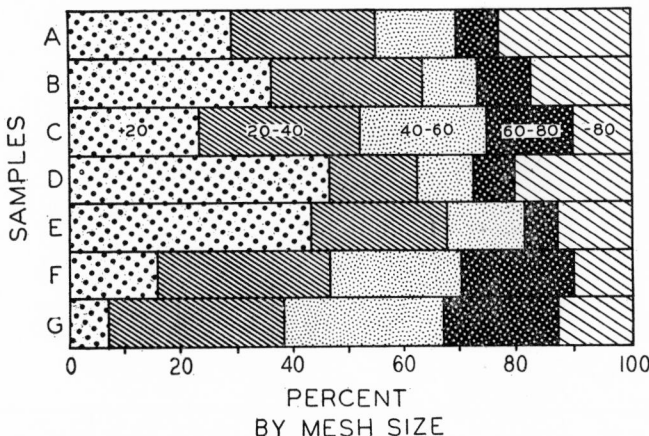

Figure 228. Bar diagram showing the size analyses of several sedimentary samples. This emphasizes the comparison of proportions rather than quantities although of course the data are quantitative and in each of these samples the fractions must add up to 100 percent. (After LeRoy, 1950, *Subsurface geologic methods*, p. 192, fig. 81, by permission of the Colorado School of Mines.)

ment, count, or on a percentage basis. If percentages are indicated, these may be calculated, as in the case of insoluble residues, on the basis of the actual amount of each constituent, and the total lengths of bars show the same relations as in a simple diagram, or on the basis of the proportions of constituents, and each bar totals 100 percent and all are of equal length. Diagrams of this type can show, for example, the compositions of such things as rocks, fossil faunas, brines, and so forth to any desired degree of detail.

Pie Diagrams

Pie diagrams are circles divided into sectors and are adapted to showing any relations that can be expressed as percentages but little else (see Figure

230). They are much less generally useful than bar diagrams and less suited to making direct comparisons between different sets of observations except relatively simple ones. They have an advantage over bar diagrams, however, if comparisons with respect to relative location are desired because they can be placed at proper positions on a map or other diagram where angles can be compared more accurately than lengths of bars (see Figures 50, p. 139; 82, p. 242; and 131, p. 321).

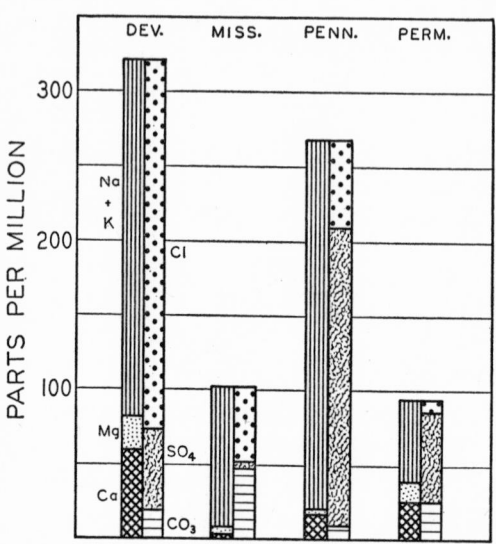

Figure 229. Bar diagram indicating the chemical composition of oil field brines from four localities in the Rocky Mountains. These double bars show quantities and proportions very effectively. (After Crawford, 1950, *Subsurface geologic methods*, p. 288, fig. 121, by permission of the Colorado School of Mines.)

Histograms

A histogram is a special type of bar diagram in which the bars show the proportionate relations or frequency distribution in a sample or in a set of observations that is separated into a series of classes generally bearing a regular mathematical relation to each other (see Figure 231). The classes may be related arithmetically, geometrically, logarithmically, or in some other way. The bars are scaled regularly against a common measure, such as a numerical count or by weight or volume, which may be expressed as a percentage. The number of possible measures and the variety of class arrangements and consequently the number of types of histograms is very great. Diagrams of this kind have been used most commonly in geology to illustrate the size composition of sediments. In this case the classes generally are separated at a series of geometrically decreasing grain sizes and the bars are scaled against percentage by weight. Many other applications are possible. For example, thickness of strata might be shown by count in a series of arithmetic classes, cross-bedding might be shown in classes by angle of dip, or joints might be shown in classes determined by direction. Commonly a class relationship is chosen that will produce a distribution pattern resembling a "normal" distribution. Related histograms identically scaled are very easily compared visually, and similarities or differences are readily perceived (see Figs. 24, 25, pp. 88–89).

Star Diagrams

A star diagram is a type of histogram in which quantities are shown radiating from a common center (see Figure 232). The similar orientation of comparable bars makes their identification in different diagrams much easier than in an ordinary histogram, whose bars are all parallel to each other.

Frequency Distribution Curves

Histograms are imperfect representations of frequency distributions if the properties upon which class separations are based are continuously variable and cannot be indicated by a series of discontinuous whole numbers. Classes of this kind are arbitrary. A different selection would produce somewhat different bar patterns (see Figure 233). Also the step-like bars of all histograms suggest discontinuous distribution even though this may not be the case, as, for example, if classification is based on the sizes of objects, angles, or compass directions.

The same distribution can be rep-

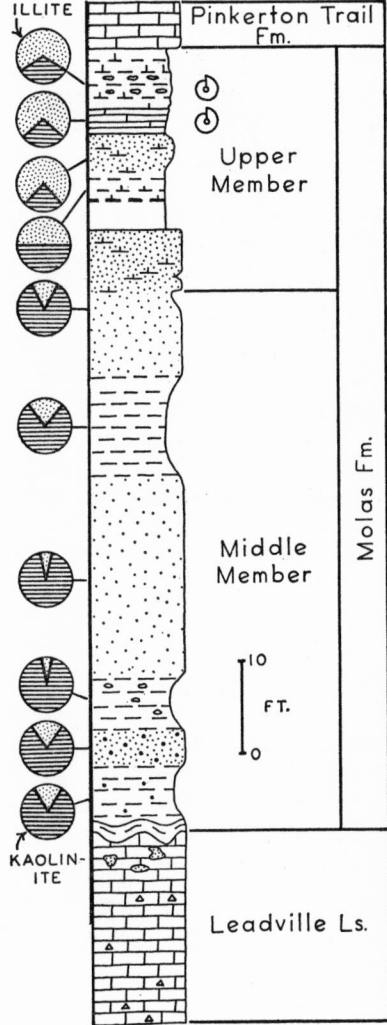

Figure 230. Detailed Columnar section with pie diagrams showing the proportions of kaolinite and illite present in different stratigraphic members. The Molas Formation (Penn.) consists of material produced by the prolonged weathering of a nearby land area. The lower member, not present here, is a relatively undisturbed residual soil. The material of the middle member is similar but it was transported, more or less sorted, and deposited under non-marine conditions. The upper member is marine, and fossiliferous zones are indicated by the shell symbols. Great increase in the illite content of the upper member may have resulted from alteration of kaolinite in a marine environment (see also Figure 130, p. 319). (After Merrill and Winar, 1958, *Bull. Am. Assoc. Petroleum Geol.*, vol. 42, p. 2115, fig. 4C.)

resented by a curve drawn so that it passes through the mid-point at the summit of each bar. By decreasing class intervals and increasing the number of bars, the curve may be made more accurate. A perfect curve, however, cannot be constructed directly from the analysis of a continuous distribution no matter in what detail the observations are made.

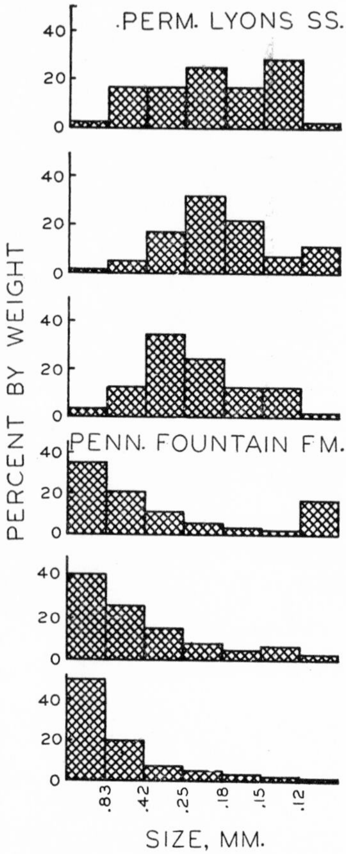

Figure 231. Histograms showing the size distributions of sedimentary grains in several samples from two sandstone formations in Colorado. Visual comparison clearly shows characteristic differences. (After Le-Roy, 1950, *Subsurface geologic methods*, p. 186, fig. 77, by permission of the Colorado School of Mines.)

Many distribution curves resemble normal probability curves if the class relations are selected properly (see Figure 23, p. 86). Consideration of the kinds of classes employed and the types of deviation from the normal curve may lead to the formulation of generalizations or "laws" that seem to control the distribution of related properties.

Cumulative Distribution Curves

A different type of curve can be obtained by converting the measure of each class to a percentage of the total measures, adding the percentages consecutively, and plotting each total above the end point of the last class whose percentage has been added (see Figures 23, p. 86, and 233, p. 610). The curve drawn through these points generally is S-shaped. It is relatively accurate even though a large number of classes is not distinguished. Certain values useful for statistical comparison can be read directly from such a curve. Also several curves plotted on the same graph can be compared visually more easily than similarly plotted ordinary distribution curves.

Like histograms, cumulative curves can be plotted against a variety of horizontal scales which influence their shapes.

The most important value read from cumulative curves is the so-called mean or average, which is marked by the point where a curve crosses the 50 percentage coordinate. It should be noted that this value is not a true average unless the measures are numerical counts. In the case of sedimentary analyses, for example, this mean indicates a grain size so located that half of the bulk sediment consists of larger grains and half of smaller ones. The number of smaller grains is, of course, much greater than the number of larger ones and the actual average grain size is much smaller than this value.

Two-Coordinate Diagrams

The relations of two variables, either counts, measurements, or ratios, can be indicated as points located with reference to two coordinates. Values of the variables do not have to be expressed in the same units, and a great variety of coordinate scales can be employed in any convenient combination.

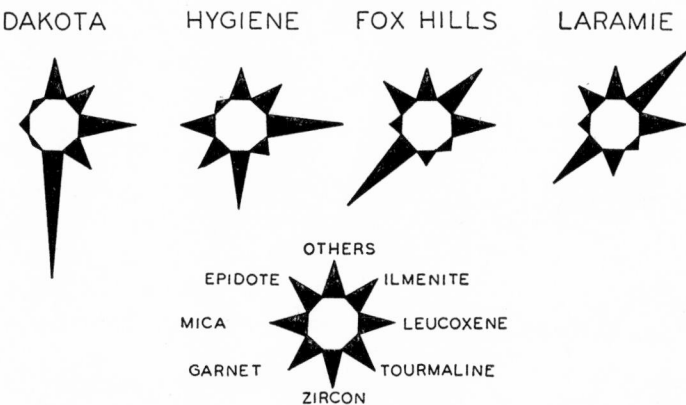

Figure 232. Star diagrams showing the relative abundances of several heavy minerals in Upper Cretaceous sandstones of the Colorado Front Range. (After Goldstein, 1950, *J. Sediment. Petrol.*, vol. 20, p. 89, fig. 3.)

Consequently these diagrams are of many types. They provide means of investigating the possible relationships of any pair of measurable properties of sediments or rocks. For examples see Figures 14, p. 62, and 115, p. 300.

A series of points representing similar measurements plotted with reference to the same coordinates produces a *scatter diagram* that can be analyzed statistically. Close grouping shows close relationship. Points scattered along a trend outline a mean curve indicating general progressive relationships. If scattering is not too great, a curve of this type permits prediction (see Figure 112, p. 297).

Several different series of similar measurements can be plotted on the same diagram and easily compared. They may reveal significant similarities or differences as shown in Figure 114, p. 299.

Triangular Diagrams

Triangular diagrams are particularly adapted to showing relations in three component systems. They have served extensively in the arbitrary classifica-

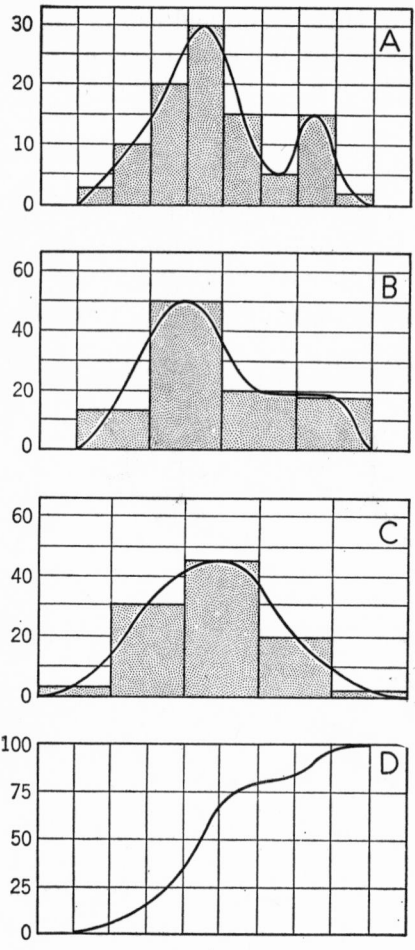

Figure 233. Histograms, frequency curves, and cumulative curve of size distribution in a hypothetical sediment. The three upper graphs show how the selection of class intervals may affect the patterns provided by diagrams of this kind.

tion of sediments and rocks and they also are useful for some other purposes (see Figure 234).

The three components or properties that are compared must be of similar type and be measured in the same units. For purposes of sedimentary classification, they must predominate to such an extent that other similar components are relatively unimportant but if comparison only is the objective, this is not necessary. Measures of the three components are added, converted to percentages, and plotted as points within the triangle according to the three-component grid. A series of points representing similar measurements produces a scatter diagram, and close grouping demonstrates close relationship. Different scatter diagrams of this type can be compared visually and significant similarities or differences are clearly apparent (see Figure 56, p. 164). Triangular diagrams are rarely used for statistical comparisons although such use is possible.

Actually a triangular diagram shows nothing that is not equally evident in a plot of the same data on a two-coordinate grid because, if any two percentages are determined, the third is thereby fixed, as shown in Figure 235. Triangular diagrams

Figure 234 (opposite). Triangular diagrams showing ways in which sediments may be classified with respect to the relative amounts of sand, silt, and clay. Innumerable other classifications also are possible. The areal pattern shown by any sediment or facies map will be determined by the classification that is adopted. The classification shown at the lower right was used in the study of modern Gulf of Mexico sediments sponsored by the American Petroleum Institute. This differs from the so-called standard subdivision of the triangle advocated by others (see Figure 202, p. 530). (After Shepard, 1954, J. Sediment. Petrol., vol. 24, pp. 152–157, figs. 1 to 7.)

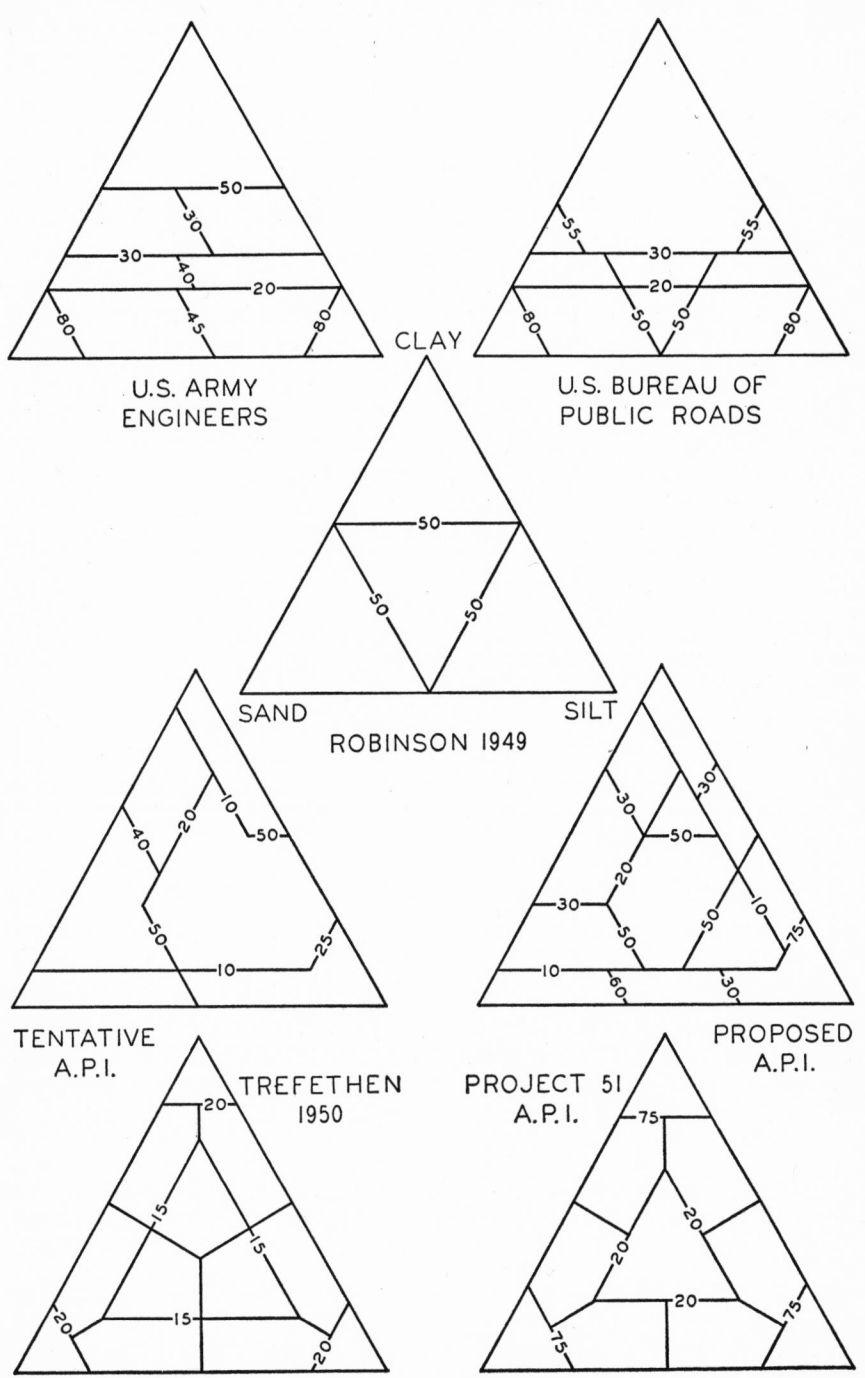

U.S. ARMY
ENGINEERS

U.S. BUREAU OF
PUBLIC ROADS

CLAY

SAND   SILT

ROBINSON 1949

TENTATIVE
A.P.I.

PROPOSED
A.P.I.

TREFETHEN
1950

PROJECT 51
A.P.I.

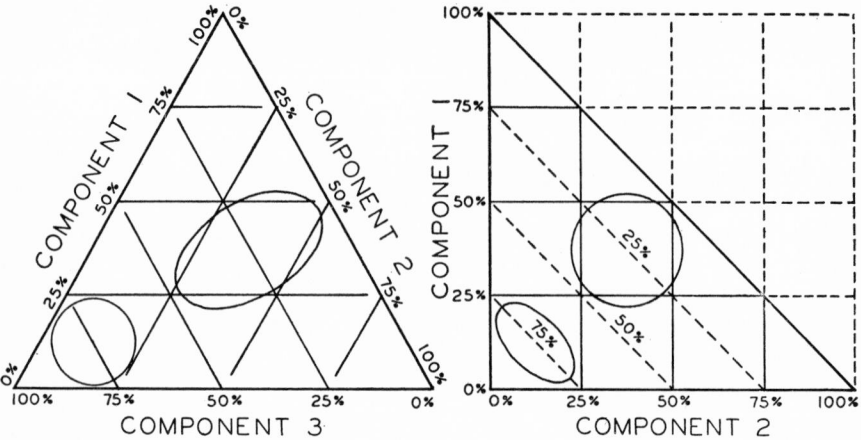

Figure 235. Diagram to show that the plotting of proportionate data in a three-component triangle is not essentially different from their plotting in a two-coordinate rectangle. If two of the percentage values are determined, the third is fixed and it can be ignored.

seem to be preferred, however, because equilateral triangles possess a pleasing symmetry that is lacking in right triangles. There is even less reason to choose a triangular diagram for plotting two variables, although this has been done (see Figure 236).

Sediments and sedimentary rocks generally are such complex mixtures of constituents that a three-component system is not adequate to distinguish all of their important variations. A four-component system can be based on a

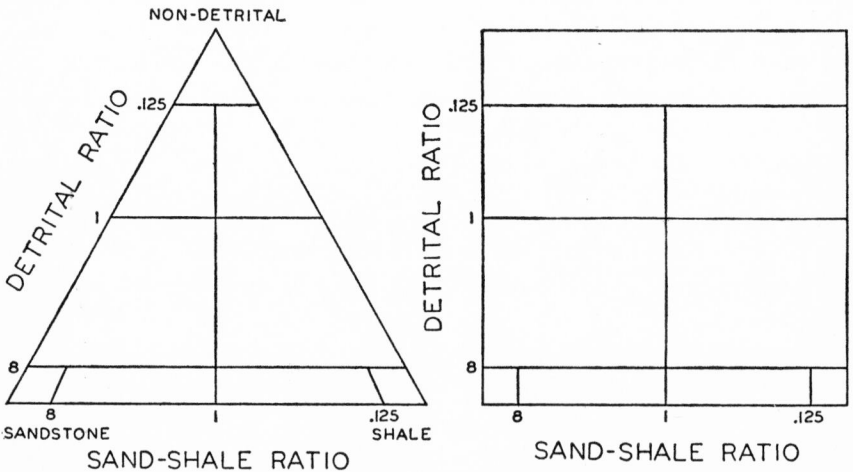

Figure 236. Diagram to show that subdivision of a three-component triangle according to detrital and sand-shale ratios is not essentially different from the subdivision of a two-coordinate rectangle.

tetrahedron (see Figure 203, p. 531), but a corresponding diagram is difficult to construct and relations are not so clearly indicated.

REPRESENTATIONS IN ONE DIMENSION

A limited number of different kinds of diagrams show stratigraphic relations in one dimension, the vertical, which can be scaled either as a linear
measure of thickness or of depth or in an inexact approximation of relative
time.

Columnar Sections

A columnar section generally is a pictorial representation of a succession
of strata whose lithologic characters are indicated by conventionalized patterns. All columnar sections are fundamentally similar and all are plotted
against measured or estimated thickness. They differ chiefly in the scale at
which they are drawn and the details they show.

Three types of columnar sections can be recognized: (1) outcrop sections,
(2) lithologic well logs, and (3) composite sections. Outcrop sections show
in more or less detail the actual succession of strata observed at an outcrop.
In their simplest form, lithologic patterns are enclosed between parallel
vertical lines (see Figure 187, p. 497). One of these lines, however, may be
drawn irregularly so that the more resistant strata are made to project beyond
the weaker ones and thus a profile somewhat similar to that which occurs at
an outcrop is suggested, as shown in Figure 230, p. 607. Commonly any dip
at the outcrop is ignored and the strata are drawn horizontally although a
section may be shown inclined as it actually occurs.

Well logs generally are represented by narrow columns between straight
vertical lines. They may reproduce a driller's log, be based on studies of well
cuttings or cores, or be interpretations of electric logs (see Figure 240, p.
617). Graphic well logs should be accompanied by notations regarding the
kind of data upon which they are based because different types of logs vary
considerably in their accuracy and details. Most well logs are based on samples collected at more or less regular intervals that came from several different strata and consequently the logs are somewhat generalized. Some driller's logs are misleading because different kinds of rock were not carefully
identified.

Composite columns are based on data drawn from various sources. They
may record observations made at several to many outcrops, the logs of wells,
or both (see Figure 237). Many columns of this type are generalized sections
intended to represent the stratigraphic succession of an area or an extended
region. In them, details that vary from place to place are ignored and at best
an effort is made to show only the most characteristic features of formations
or other stratigraphic units. Because thicknesses vary somewhat at different

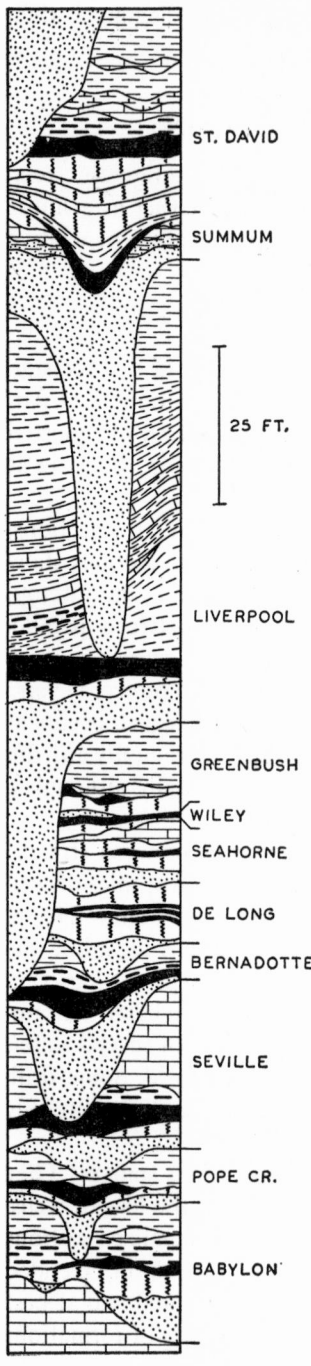

ST. DAVID

SUMMUM

25 FT.

LIVERPOOL

GREENBUSH

WILEY

SEAHORNE

DE LONG

BERNADOTTE

SEVILLE

POPE CR.

BABYLON

places, average thicknesses generally are indicated (see Figure 238).

A variety of symbols or abbreviations may be used in addition to lithologic patterns to record noteworthy features of particular strata or zones such as color, the occurrence of fossils, oolites, pyrite, and so forth. These generally are placed close beside the column at appropriate positions (see Figure 239). Drilling time of wells or other properties that can be measured may be represented by a bar diagram extending parallel to the columnar section.

Electric Logs

Electric logs consist of curves that are continuous records of self-potential and resistivity measured in wells and plotted against depth, as shown in Figure 240. These curves are influenced by many different factors, and familiarity with local conditions is required for their accurate interpretation. In a general way, however, they indicate differences in the lithologic characters of strata and many lithologic changes are shown with great precision.

The self-potential curve customarily is located to the left and one or more resistivity curves are present to the right. Curve deviations to the left are negative and to the right positive. Shales ordinarily show high self-potential and low resistivity. They are recorded by narrow intervals between the curves which are relatively flat and featureless.

Figure 237. Columnar section representing part of the Pennsylvanian System as developed in western Illinois. Although this section is much generalized it attempts to show many of the stratigraphic variations occurring in the area. The strata are grouped in cyclothems as these were recognized originally. (After Wanless, 1931, Ill. Geol. Surv., Bull. 60, p. 192, fig. 46.)

Limestones commonly are indicated by moderate negative self-potential and strong positive resistivity. Most sandstones show strong negative self-

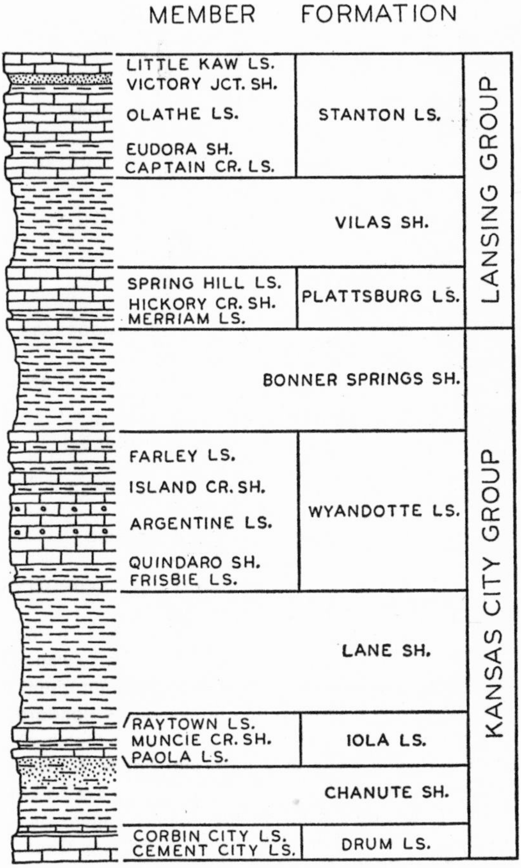

MEMBER   FORMATION

Figure 238. Generalized columnar section of part of the Pennsylvanian System as developed in eastern Kansas. The irregular outline to the left indicates harder and softer layers and serves to emphasize the lithologic differences of formations and members. The strata here are cyclically arranged but for practical purposes they are grouped in contrasting lithologic units recognized as formations. See also Figure 172, p. 470. (After Moore, 1936, Kan. Geol. Surv., Bull. 22, p. 45, fig. 8.)

potential and positive resistivity somewhat less than that recorded for limestone. The fluid content of sandstones, however, may influence the resistivity

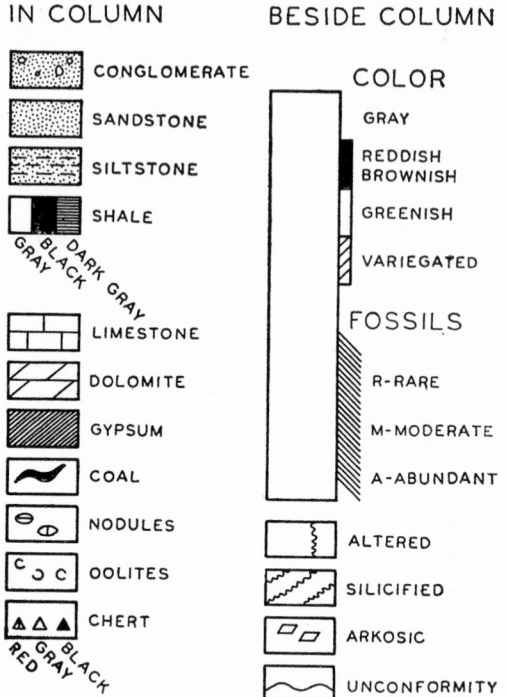

Figure 239. A system of symbols used in the graphic presentation of lithologic details in columnar stratigraphic sections. Some, such as those representing sandstone, limestone, and dolomite, are standard in most illustrations. Others are adapted to the needs of a particular study or a particular figure. A great variety of other symbols and conventions are to be found in geologic publications. (After Wengerd and Matheny, 1958, *Bull. Am. Assoc. Petroleum Geol.*, vol. 42, p. 2059, fig. 4.)

curves greatly. If salt water occurs, resistivity is likely to be reduced, and oil may increase resistivity so that it exceeds that of limestone.

Checking electric logs against well cuttings or cores at critical points is required for accurate interpretation, and a lithologic log may be plotted between the curves for purposes of comparison. With experience, however, pinching and swelling of the interval between curves can be translated mentally into lithologic characters. Stratigraphic identifications and correlations commonly are made directly from electric logs.

A few other kinds of well logs are recorded as curves somewhat similar to those of the standard electric logs. They furnish useful stratigraphic information if they are properly interpreted. These include other types of self-potential and resistivity logs, induction logs, radioactivity logs, temperature logs, caliper logs, and so forth.

Range Charts

Most range charts are non-pictorial representations of the occurrences of such things as fossils or heavy minerals in a stratigraphic section. Plotting ordinarily is against a stratigraphic section or relative time, and the scale is indefinite and may be quite irregular. A few range charts consist of pictures of fossils placed opposite the strata of a columnar section in which they have been found.

Non-pictorial range charts are of two types (see Figure 241). One is simply a tabulation, in which occurrence is indicated by symbols or letters placed in compartments in stratigraphic order. The other is a bar diagram plotted against time or stratigraphic units. The first is more useful for the presentation of detailed data. The bar charts, however, are more striking and they can be compared and interpreted much more rapidly. They are better representations of more or less generalized data and particularly the overall ranges of occurrence. Relative frequencies can be shown by variations in the symbols or letters or by the width of bars.

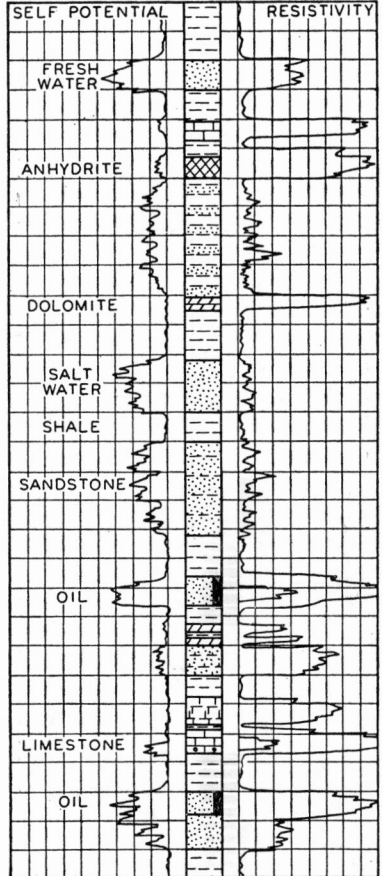

Figure 240. Diagram showing part of an electric well log and the lithologic characters of the corresponding stratigraphic section. Variations in the self potential and resistivity curves reflect the physical nature of the rocks and their contained fluids and serve to identify different kinds of strata. (After Stratton and Ford, 1950, *Subsurface geologic methods*, p. 365, fig. 152, by permission of the Colorado School of Mines.)

REPRESENTATIONS IN TWO DIMENSIONS

Vertical Diagrams and Sections

Diagrams showing relations in two dimensions are vertical if one of the dimensions is thickness, depth, or time. Many of them are closely linked to unidimensional diagrams.

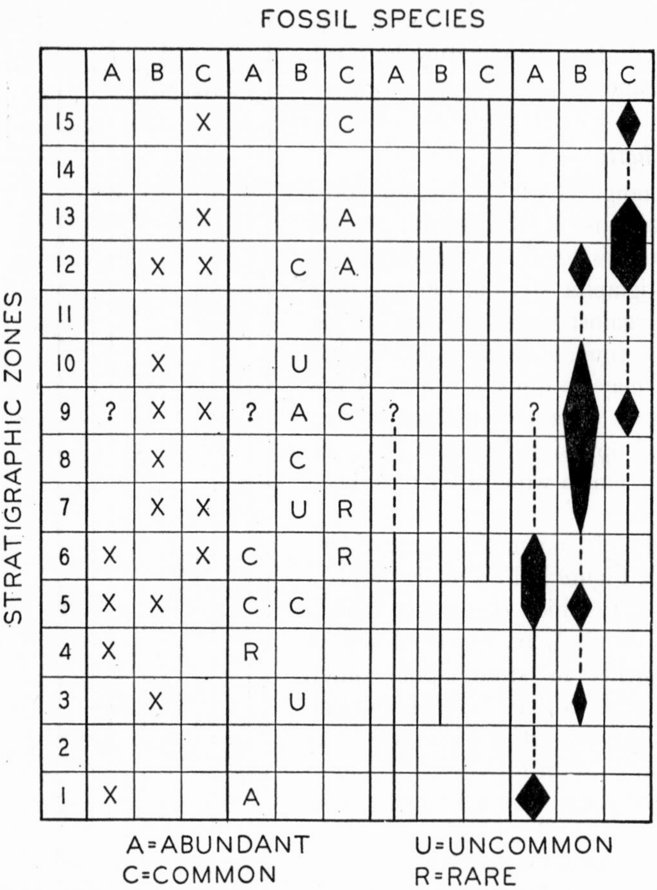

FOSSIL SPECIES

STRATIGRAPHIC ZONES	A	B	C	A	B	C	A	B	C	A	B	C
15			X			C						◆
14												⋮
13			X			A						◆
12		X	X		C	A					◆	◆
11											⋮	⋮
10		X			U					◆		⋮
9	?	X	X	?	A	C	?			?	◆	◆
8		X			C		⋮			⋮		⋮
7		X	X		U	R	⋮			⋮		
6	X		X	C		R				◆	⋮	
5	X	X		C	C						◆	
4	X			R							⋮	
3		X			U						◆	
2											⋮	
1	X			A						◆		

A = ABUNDANT   U = UNCOMMON
C = COMMON   R = RARE

Figure 241. Hypothetical range chart showing several ways in which the occurrence of fossils in a stratigraphic section can be indicated. The first three columns record by X the presence of species. The second three also show relative abundance. The lines in the next three indicate the total known ranges. The patterns in the last three columns show all of the information provided by the others and are more effective for easy comprehension (see Figure 65, p. 191).

Correlation Diagrams

Correlation diagrams show interpretations of the lateral relations between strata occurring at different places by connecting correlation lines. These lines may represent either uniform time or lithologic boundaries. Stratigraphic sections being correlated are generally indicated by columnar sections drawn to a uniform scale although electric logs may be used instead (see Figure 212, p. 545). The columns may be spaced evenly, as in Figure

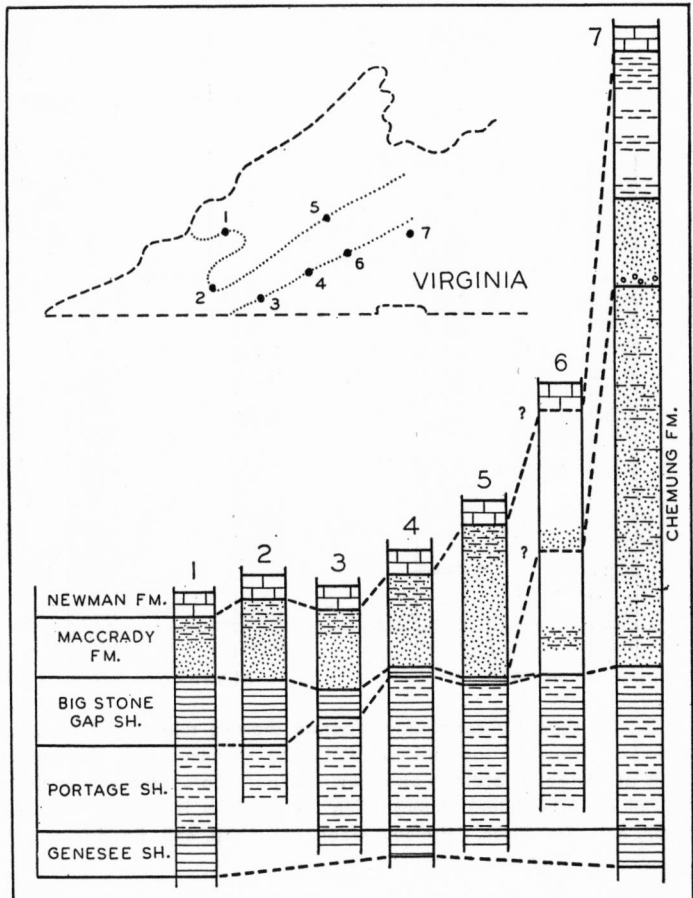

Figure 242. Stratigraphic correlation diagram of Upper Devonian and Lower Mississippian formations in western Virginia. The columnar sections here are much generalized. No scale is provided. The spacing of columns is uniform and does not correspond to the distances between localities. The correlation lines suggest time lines, and there is no indication of lithologic intertonguing or lateral gradation. (After Stose, 1924, *J. Geol.*, vol. 32, p. 313, fig. 1.)

242, or according to some scale representing horizontal distance, as in Figure 243. Some well-characterized or convenient horizon commonly is selected as a horizontal base line above and below which all stratigraphic thicknesses are measured. The columns may be arranged, however, according to actual elevations or, if they are well logs, they may be plotted downward from a horizontal surface. Every correlation diagram should either be accompanied

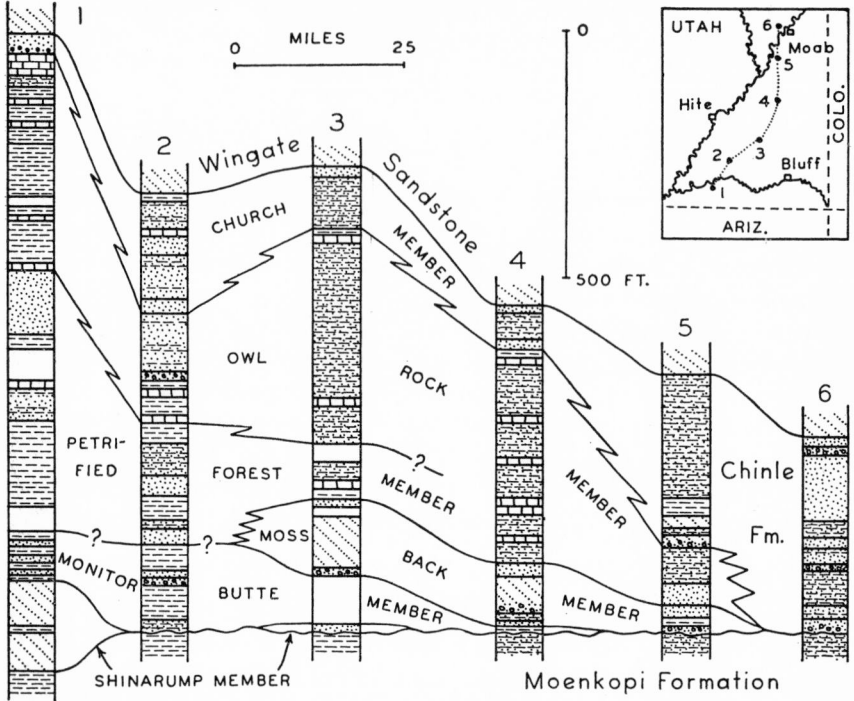

Figure 243. Stratigraphic correlation diagram showing relations of members of the Chinle Formation (Trias.) in southeastern Utah. The columnar sections record detailed measurements at particular localities and they are spaced proportionally to distances between these places. The lateral intergrading of members is plainly indicated. (After Stewart, 1957, *Bull. Am. Assoc. Petroleum Geol.*, vol. 41, p. 448, fig. 4.)

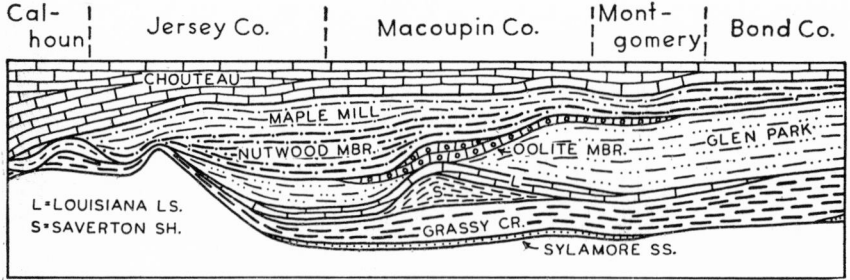

Figure 244. West-east stratigraphic section showing the relations of Kinderhookian formations (L. Miss.) in the subsurface of Illinois. This section ignores all structure. The strata are plotted downward from the top of the Chouteau Limestone. Outcrop studies indicate that considerable lateral gradation as well as variations in the thicknesses of the

by an index map showing the geographic locations of the columns or have these adequately located in some other way.

Stratigraphic Sections

Stratigraphic sections are similar to correlation diagrams except that (1) horizontal distances correspond to a uniform scale, (2) sections at control points are not emphasized, (3) formation boundaries or lithologic patterns are extended across the whole diagram, and (4) abrupt changes in thicknesses or in the inclinations of boundaries commonly are rounded out. Examples are presented in Figures 244 to 248.

Sections of this type may extend in an irregular zigzag manner between control points or they may follow a uniform direction or change direction slightly at only a few widely separated places. In the latter cases the section may actually pass through few control points and stratigraphic thicknesses and other data are carried laterally to the line of section from nearby places of observation or measurement. Thus these sections are more complete stratigraphic representations than are correlation diagrams but they commonly are more generalized.

Structural Sections

These are the most perfect cross sections. Ordinarily they show formation boundaries or general lithologic characters in nearly as much detail as stratigraphic sections drawn to similar scales and in addition the true or inferred structural relations of the strata from place to place. All formation or other stratigraphic boundaries occur at positions determined by actual elevations measured or estimated at outcrops or in well records. Where data of this kind are lacking, boundaries are extended in accordance with known or inferred stratigraphic intervals although these may vary at different places.

Structural sections are best suited to illustrate structure and stratigraphic

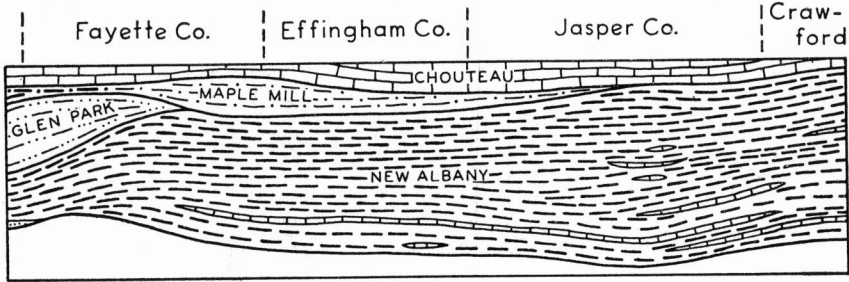

lithologic units occurs in the Kinderhook. This is not shown in the section. No scale is provided but the vertical dimension is much exaggerated. (After Workman and Gillette, 1956, Ill. Geol. Surv., Rept. of Invest. 189, pl. 1, sections H-I.)

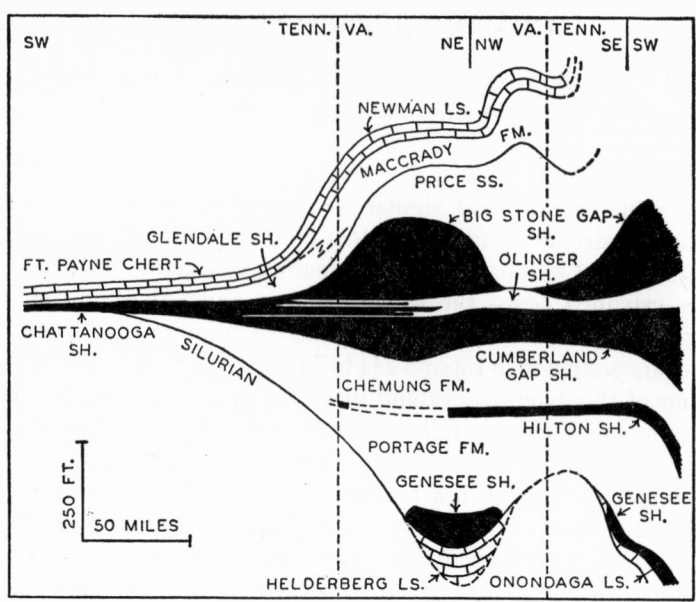

Figure 245. Stratigraphic section showing the relations of Upper Devonian and lower Mississippian formations in parts of eastern Tennessee and western Virginia. This section extends in an irregular line that would be better understood if an outline map were provided. Structure is ignored, and thicknesses are plotted upward and downward from the middle part of the Chattanooga Shale. This diagram illustrates extreme distortion resulting from exaggeration of the vertical scale, which here is about 500 times. (After Swartz, 1929, *Am. J. Sci.*, ser. 5, vol. 17, p. 444, fig. 3.)

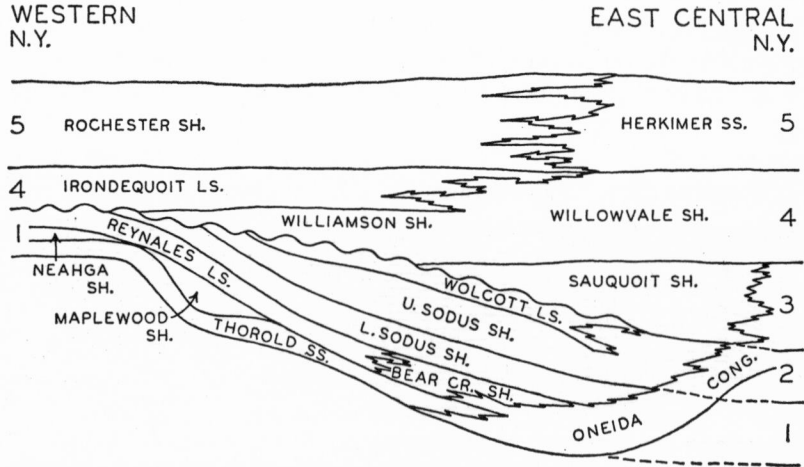

Figure 246. Correlation diagram indicating the relations in New York of lower Silurian formations corresponding to five ostracod zones. It shows lateral lithologic gradations and the existence of an unconformity. (Data from Gillette, 1947, after Fisher, 1956, *J. Geol.*, vol. 64, p. 623, fig. 4.)

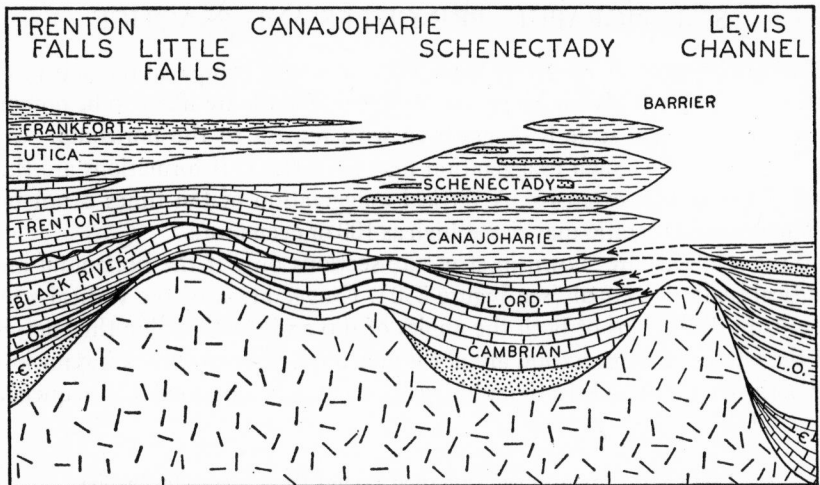

Figure 247. Stratigraphic section of Cambrian and Ordovician strata in part of New York. This diagram attempts to show in a generalized way the lithologic characters, thicknesses, and distributions of a large number of formations. These are not distinguished or named on this reproduction of the original diagram. For the sake of clarity only the major stratigraphic divisions are indicated. (After Ulrich and Ruedemann in Ruedemann, 1932, 16th Intern. Geol. Congr., Guidebook 4, p. 126.)

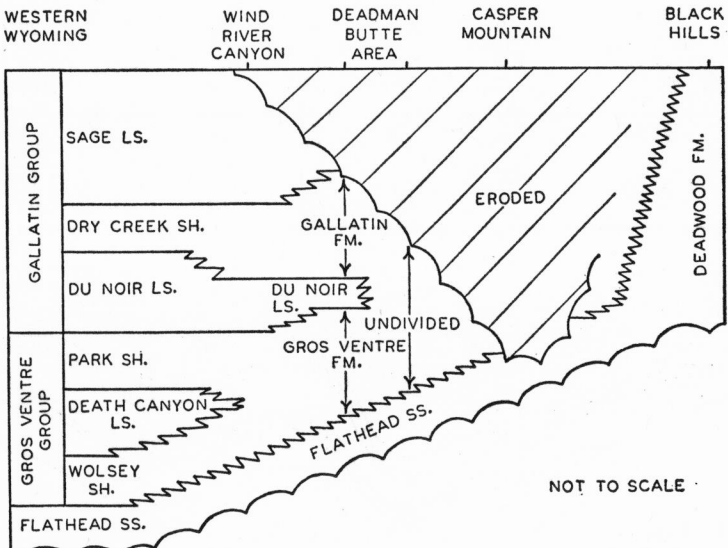

Figure 248. Highly schematic correlation diagram showing the relations of recognized Cambrian stratigraphic units in Wyoming and the Black Hills. A diagram of this kind clearly shows the relations of names, but all details are lacking. It has more the features of a correlation chart than any kind of stratigraphic section. (After Woodward, 1957, Bull. Am. Assoc. Petroleum Geol., vol. 41, p. 220, fig. 3.)

relations in areas of relatively steep dips or where complications are introduced by faulting. If dips are gentle, structural details are likely to be obscure unless the vertical scale is exaggerated with respect to the horizontal scale (see Figure 249). Such exaggeration may be extreme if formations are thin and the section is extensive. A vertical exaggeration of ten times is not uncommon and this ratio may rise as high as 100 or even more.

True relations are shown in structure sections only if the horizontal and vertical scales are equal (see Figure 250). Exaggeration of the vertical scale results in distortions of both the angles of dip and stratigraphic thicknesses. If the effects of exaggeration are not understood, very erroneous impressions of both structural and stratigraphic relations may be obtained. Consequently

TABLE 21.   Approximate Distortion Factors for Angles of Inclination
(Upper Figures) and Stratigraphic Thicknesses (Lower Figures)
Shown in Structural Sections Resulting from Relative
Exaggerations of the Vertical Scale

Vertical Exaggeration	Actual Dip of Strata					
	5°	10°	20°	45°	60°	80°
X 2	1.9	1.9	1.8	1.4	1.2	1.1
	.99	.96	.86	.63	.55	.50
X 5	4.7	4.1	3.1	1.7	1.4	1.1
	.91	.75	.51	.28	.23	.20
X 10	8.2	6.0	3.8	1.9	1.4	1.1
	.76	.50	.27	.14	.11	.10
X 50	15.4	8.4	4.3	2.0	1.5	1.1
	.22	.11	.06	.03	.02	.02
X 100	16.7	8.7	4.4	2.0	1.5	1.1
	.11	.06	.03	.01	.01	.01

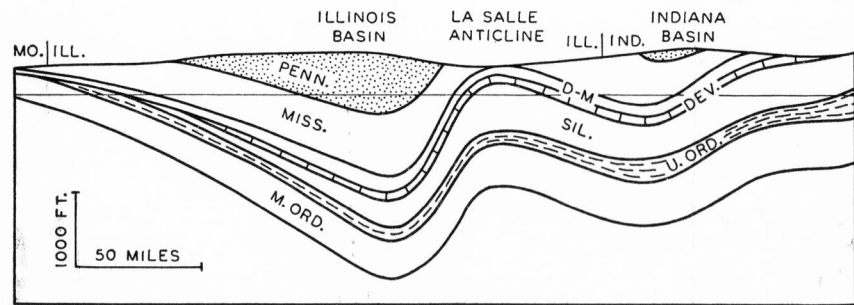

Figure 249.   Generalized stratigraphic and structural cross section extending from the Mississippi River to the Appalachian basin. Although the vertical scale of this section is exaggerated 150 times, the structures are so gentle that little obvious distortion is ap-

excessive vertical exaggeration should be avoided and the relative scales of all sections should be plainly indicated.

Vertical exaggeration results in showing dips steeper than they actually are but their distortion is progressively less pronounced in more steeply dipping strata. Also this distortion increases with increasing vertical exaggeration but at a relatively declining rate.

Vertical exaggeration causes stratigraphic thicknesses to appear to be less than they actually are (see Figure 251). This distortion increases with both greater exaggeration and steeper dips. Table 21 shows the approximate magnitudes of these discrepancies for selected combinations of vertical exaggeration and stratigraphic inclination.

Stratigraphic thicknesses are plotted to scale in ordinary stratigraphic sections, whatever their vertical exaggeration, and comparable discrepancies in thickness may not result unless there is considerable thickening or thinning of stratigraphic units.

Correlation Charts

In vertical representations, thickness and time are alternative dimensions. One cannot be indicated by equal intervals at different places without distortion of the other. Correlation diagrams generally are based on comparisons of equal thicknesses, but correlation charts attempt to show comparisons by equal time (see Figures 252 to 254). The first commonly emphasizes lateral variations in lithologic characters and thickness. The second emphasizes the correlation of recognized and generally named stratigraphic units. In neither is the horizontal scale or direction particularly important, but both have a horizontal dimension because strata at different localities are compared.

Most correlation charts are non-pictorial because lithologic characters are

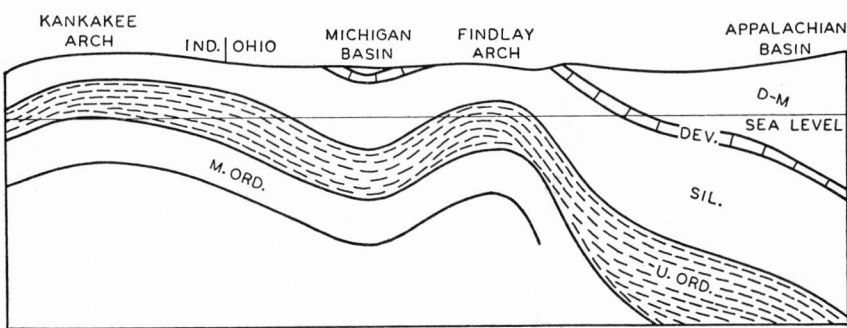

parent. Without great exaggeration the stratigraphic section and structure along this line could not be shown. (Data from Ballard, 1938, *Bull. Am. Assoc. Petroleum Geol.*, vol. 22, pp. 1536–1537, fig. 1.)

rarely indicated except in formation names. Geologic time intervals cannot be estimated accurately enough to be plotted against any uniform scale, so the vertical dimension is only relative and is likely to be very irregular. Al-

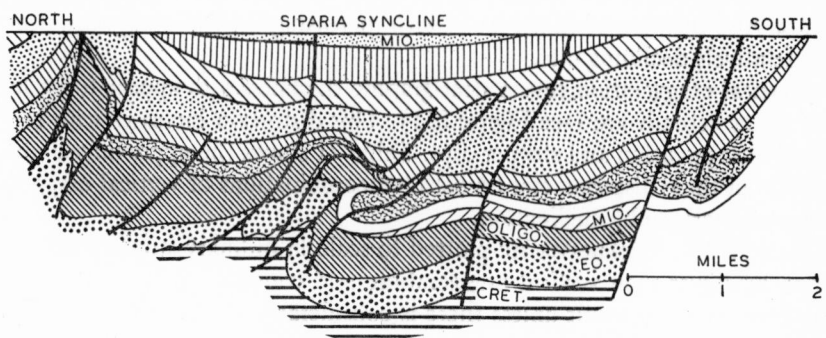

Figure 250. Structure section of Tertiary strata in the southern part of Trinidad Island, West Indies. This section is drawn to true scale and there is no vertical exaggeration. Structure of this intensity and complexity cannot be shown adequately by structural contours. (After Bitterli, 1958, Bull. Am. Assoc. Petroleum Geol., vol. 42, p. 151, fig. 3A.)

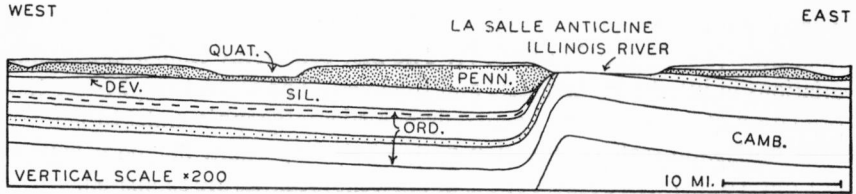

Figure 251. Stratigraphic and structural section across the La Salle anticline in northern Illinois. The vertical exaggeration is so great that the stratigraphic units appear to be thinned on the steep flank of the anticline. The section crosses the axis of this structure at an angle of about 25 degrees. If the intersection were at right angles the apparent thinning would be much greater. (After Weller, 1945, Ill. Geol. Surv., Geologic map of Illinois, section A-A'.)

though these charts consist of stratigraphic columns comparable to columnar sections, correlation charts are more tabulations of stratigraphic data than actual diagrams.

Horizontal Diagrams and Maps

Horizontal representations may be concerned (1) only with relative directions or (2) with locations or distributions in a horizontal plane. Those of the first type are non-pictorial. Those of the second type are maps of one kind or another and present data in a more or less pictorial manner.

Rose Diagrams

The simplest indication of direction is a properly oriented arrow as shown in Figure 255. Arrows can represent single observations or the averages of several observations. Frequencies can be indicated by the size or strength of arrows (see Figure 137, p. 338).

A whole series of directional observations can be recorded most effectively by a rose diagram, of which there are several types. It may be a circle in which each observation of direction is represented by a correspondingly oriented line extending either outward from the center or inward from the circumference. The number of similar observations can be indicated by the length of lines. The spaces between lines may be filled in to produce solid figures (see Figure 256C). A generalized type of rose diagram may show only the outer ranges of a series of directions as a sector of the circle, as in Figures 256A and 257. Diagrams based on the center may omit the circle, or the size of the circle may be proportional to the number of observations. Diagrams based on the circumference are like inwardly projecting bar diagrams (see Figure 256B).

Rose diagrams are easily compared visually and they are commonly employed to record the orientation of cross-bedding, joints, and other directional features of the rocks as shown in Figure 258.

Geographic Maps

Geographic maps are essential as bases for the presentation of much geologic data. Depending on their scale and purpose, they range from simple outlines to very detailed maps showing many of the physical, cultural, and political features of an area. Geologic information can be added by (1) properly located symbols such as dips and strikes or simple diagrams such as histograms, rose diagrams, and so forth, (2) boundary lines with or without contained distinctive areal patterns or colors, or (3) contours if the geologic data can be quantified.

Areal Geologic Maps

The commonest geologic maps show the areal distributions of formations or other stratigraphic units as they occur at the surface of the earth. The outcrop areas of different units may be indicated only by boundary lines but such maps are likely to be difficult to read unless the geology is very simple. Generally the outcrop areas are identified by distinctive patterns or colors keyed to an explanatory legend. More complete information is provided if the map also is accompanied by a generalized columnar section and one or more cross sections.

A properly constructed areal geologic map with an adequate but simple explanation provides a great amount of information. It shows the stratigraphic succession of mapped units, suggests their relative thicknesses, and indicates structural features. From it subsurface conditions and distributions can be inferred. If scattered dips and strikes are provided, the map can be read even more accurately.

As the scale of an areal geologic map increases and the geology is shown in greater detail, the interpretative element in mapping becomes more important. Consequently, on detailed maps the degree of actual control should be indicated so that the viewer can judge the reliability of different features and make alternative interpretations if he considers them to be more likely. This can be done by showing the actual areas of rock exposures and indicating, by solid or variously broken lines, the degree of certainty with which formation boundaries and faults are shown. Many geologic maps appear to be more detailed and more accurate than they really are. Thus they are not as objective presentations of geologic facts as they should be.

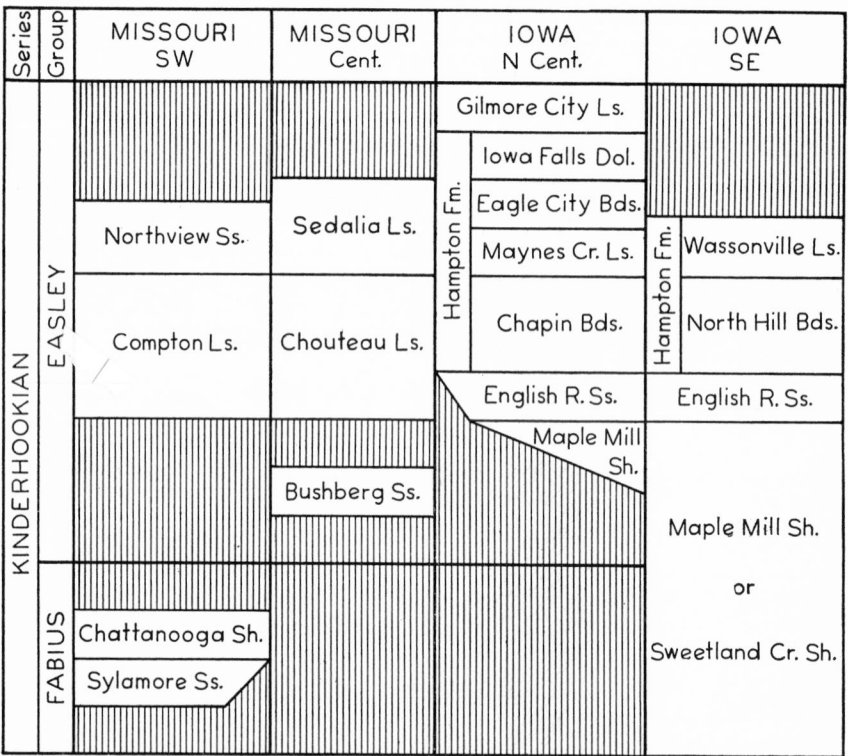

Figure 252. Correlation table showing relations of the Kinderhookian formations (L. Miss.) in the upper Mississippi Valley region. This is the standard type of correlation table that attempts to show nothing but the time relations of named units. An important hiatus in the stratigraphic section is indicated by vertical ruling. Minor breaks in the sequence probably occur but generally they are ignored. The correlations are more or less generalized. They are based on paleontologic evidence, lateral continuity of strata, similarity of lithologic features, and apparent similarity in stratigraphic position. In some areas forma-

Paleogeologic Maps

These are maps that show the areal geology of the surface as it was at some time in the geologic past or as it would now appear if all the strata were stripped off above some particular horizon (see Figure 259). A varied areal pattern occurs only at a buried surface of unconformity, where erosion cut down to different strata that previously had been more or less warped, folded, or otherwise disturbed. Paleogeologic maps are based principally on subsurface data, mainly well logs, and their detail is dependent upon the abundance and distribution of the data. Control also is provided by the stratigraphic relations observed along the outcrop of an unconformity. These maps cannot be extended with much assurance beyond such outcrops.

Unconformable relations and their reflections in paleogeologic maps are

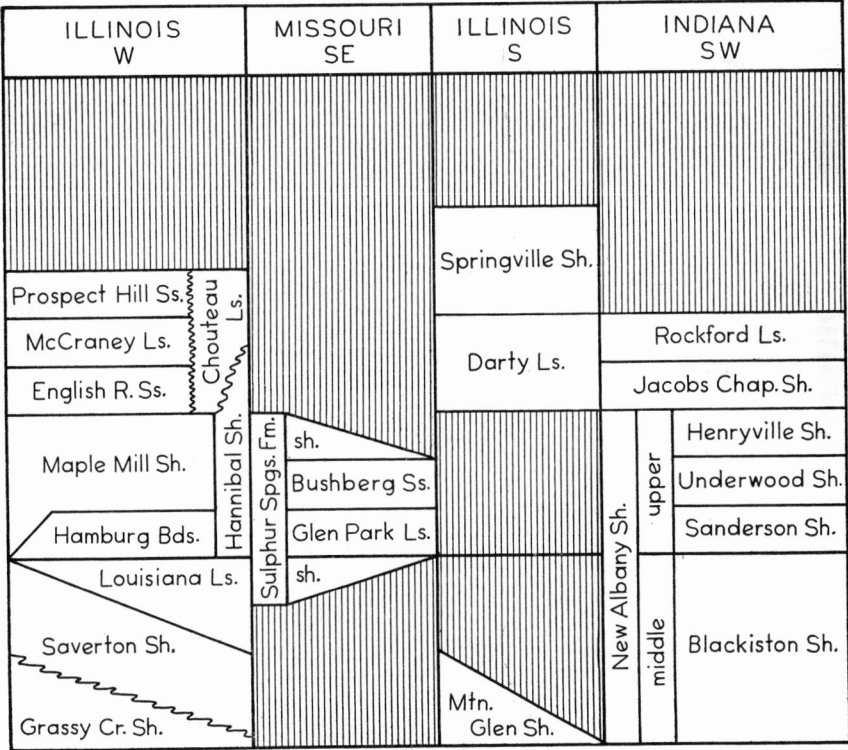

tions have been subdivided into members. Lateral lithologic gradation may be indicated where it is considered to be important. The Kinderhookian rocks of this region provide the basis for a good example of this kind of chart because numerous more or less equivalent lithologic units have been recognized and named in nearby areas. The lower part of the New Albany Shale of Indiana generally is assigned to the Devonian. There is disagreement as to whether the formations of the Fabius Group are Devonian or Mississippian. (After Weller and others, 1948, *Bull. Geol. Soc. Amer.*, Vol. 59, chart after p. 196.)

particularly useful in indicating the nature and amount of tectonic activity that marked different episodes in the development of depositional basins. These maps also provide a guide to the varied stratigraphic sections that are to be encountered by drilling operations at different localities.

Subgeologic Maps

A subgeologic map shows the areal relations of strata that immediately overlie an unconformable surface (see Figure 260). Its pattern may indicate

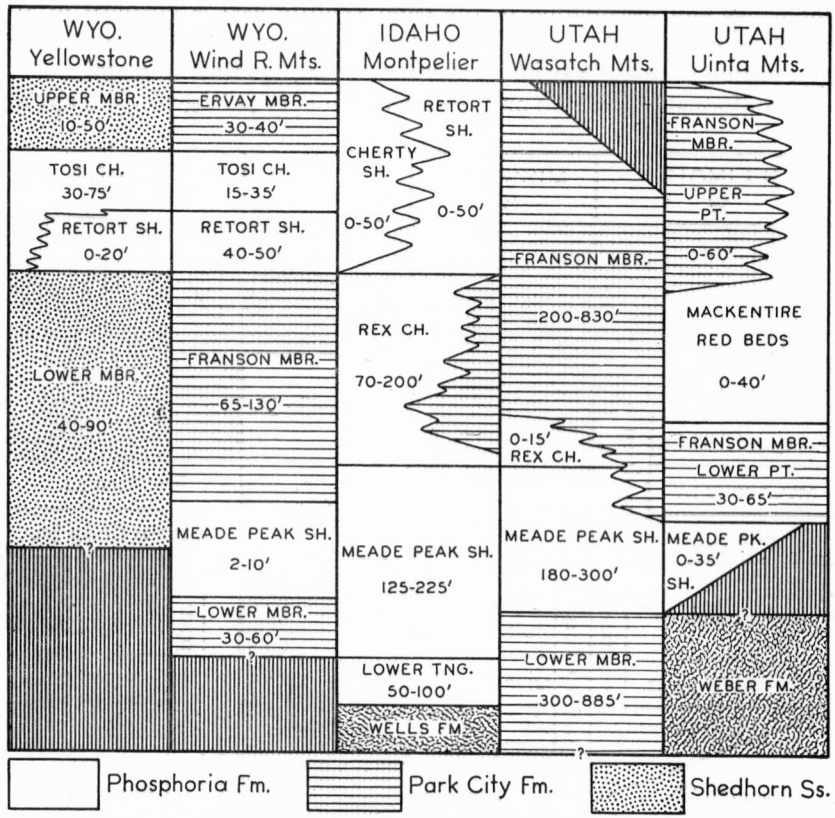

Figure 253. Correlation chart showing the lateral relations of three intertonguing Permian formations of approximately equivalent age and their subdivisions in the central Rocky Mountains. The general conventions used in this chart are the same as those of Figure 252. The relations appear to be more complex because members and tongues are recognized throughout considerable areas, where they carry the same names but vary more or less in age. Notice that the lower strata of this time interval are assigned in some areas to the Wells and Weber formations that are mainly of Pennsylvanian age. (After McKelvey and others, 1956, *Bull. Am. Assoc. Petroleum Geol.*, vol. 40, p. 2836–2837, fig. 4.)

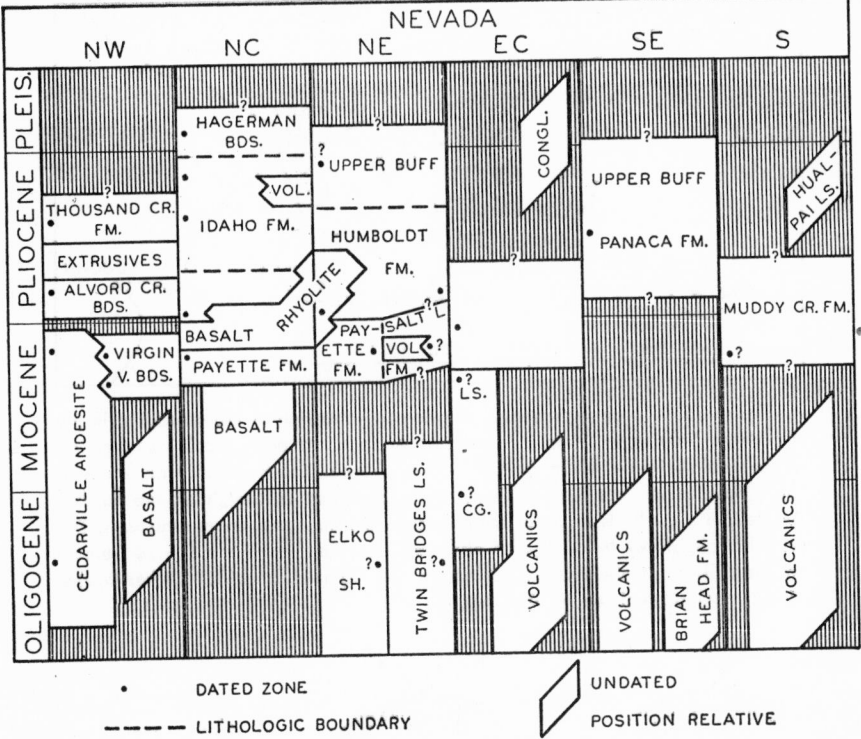

Figure 254. Correlation chart showing the time relations of post-Eocene rocks in several parts of Nevada. Many of the units recognized are lake beds, tuffs, or extrusive volcanics known in limited areas where stratigraphic succession and lateral equivalence are obscure. Consequently if ages cannot be determined paleontologically the positions, other than relative ones, are more or less uncertain. Stratigraphic hiatuses were not indicated by vertical ruling in the original of this chart and the occurrence of units without names like that in the east central column might be overlooked. (After Van Houten, 1956, *Bull. Am. Assoc. Petroleum Geol.,* vol. 40, p. 2816, fig. 6.)

overstepping formations or other units deposited in a gradually transgressing sea. More commonly, however, the stratigraphic relations record irregular transgression interrupted by one or more regressions that may be indicated by corresponding younger unconformities. Such maps are relatively rare but they can show some features of composite unconformities more satisfactorily than in any other way. Like paleogeologic maps, these are based largely on data furnished by well records.

Paleogeographic Maps

Unlike the previously noted geologic maps, which are predominantly factual, paleogeographic maps are mainly interpretations. Most simply they

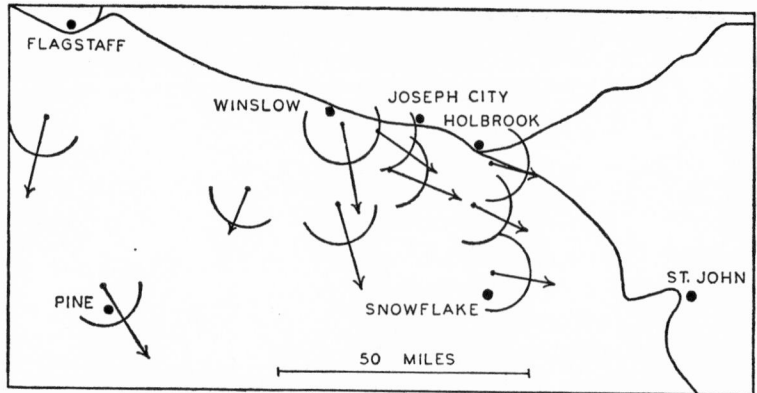

Figure 255. Map with arrows showing the direction of cross-bedding in the Coconino Sandstone (Perm.) in part of Arizona. At each locality studied an arrow points in the mean direction of measured cross-bedding. The length is an indication of "consistency" which was calculated by weighting the number of steeper cross-beds in order to emphasize the most prominent structures. The circular arc shows the range of observed directions in all but the 10 percent of most aberrant observations. Compare with Figure 136, p. 337. (After Reiche, 1938, *J. Geol.*, vol. 46, p. 921, fig. 4.)

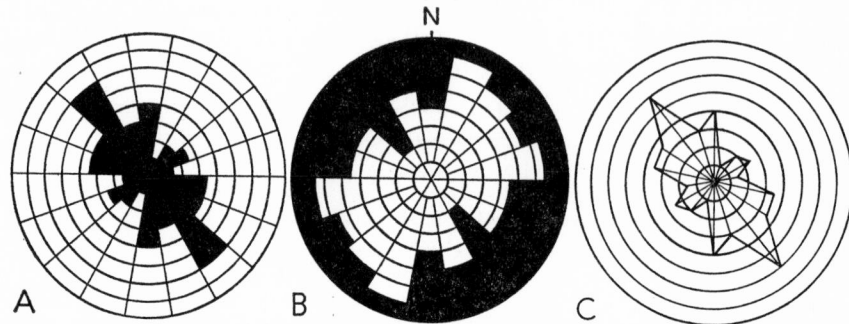

Figure 256. Varieties of rose diagrams. Those of type A greatly exaggerate what appears to be a preferred orientation because of the expansion of segments outward from the center. A chi-square test indicates that the probability of this distribution's being nonrandom is only 84 percent. B shows the same data plotted inward from the circumference instead of outward from the center. Orientation here is not so strongly emphasized. C shows the same data plotted by connecting the ends of lines whose lengths are proportional to the number of observations. This lessens somewhat the exaggeration of the type A diagram. A (after Martinez, 1958, *Bull. Am. Assoc. Petroleum Geol.*, vol. 42, p. 602, fig. 13) records fifty-four optical measurements indicating the predominant c-axis orientation of quartz grains in twelve thin sections of sandstone from the Bell Canyon Formation (Perm.) from Culberson County, Texas. Many quartz grains have been observed to be elongated parallel to the c-axis. The orientation indicated by these measurements corresponds approximately to the orientation of fusulinids and is about at right angles to ripple marks in this formation.

attempt to show the distribution of land and sea as these existed at some moment in the geologic past (see Figures 221 and 222, pp. 588, 589). They may be elaborated, however, in various ways by indication of areas of non-marine deposition, evaporitic basins, volcanism, continental ice sheets, highlands subject to severe erosion, and so forth (see Figure 218, p. 577). The ideal, rarely approached even remotely, is a complete geographic and hydrographic map showing the extent and physiographic nature of the land and the depth and bottom conditions of the sea (see Figure 220, p. 581).

Paleogeographic maps are based on geologic and paleontologic data supplemented by considerable imagination. They actually indicate conditions and relations as these are supposed to have existed for some appreciable interval of time and consequently they are generalized. Recognition of the nature, distribution, and correlation of all strata of some particular age is of primary importance in their construction. The paleogeography of any region whose geology and paleontology are not known in great detail is bound to be more or less uncertain. In fact the doubts inherent in paleogeographic interpretation are such at present that no two persons would be likely to produce nearly similar maps of any large region even though the maps were based on identical information.

Figure 257. Rose diagram recording the results of 123 measurements of cross-bedding direction in the Aux Vases, Renault, and Yankeetown formations (Miss.), mostly in southwestern Illinois. Unlike sand grains and similar objects, whose orientation is bipolar (see Figure 256), cross-bedding and current ripple marks are oriented unidirectionally. Therefore, rose diagrams that represent their measurements are unsymmetrical. (After Potter and others, 1958, *Bull. Am. Assoc. Petroleum Geol.*, vol. 42, p. 1026, fig. 7.)

Palinspastic Maps

Folding and overthrusting, chiefly in geosynclinal zones, has resulted in compression of the rocks and shortening of segments of the earth's surface that may be measured in many miles. Consequently points that are now close together may originally have been far apart. Such displacements have produced what appear to be unnatural relations, as, for example, the telescoping of sedimentary facies of some Paleozoic formations in the Appalachian region. If it is desired to return geographic localities or geologic features to their former relative positions, expansion of the present map is necessary (see Figure 261). Such an expanded map is a palinspastic map, which may be used as a base for the presentation of either paleogeographic or paleogeologic interpretations. Because the amount of shortening rarely can be determined accurately in much disturbed areas, palinspastic maps are no more than approximations, and attempts at such reconstruction have not been common.

Facies Maps

Facies maps are designed to show differences within strata of equivalent age and thus to provide means for comparing the results of contemporaneous

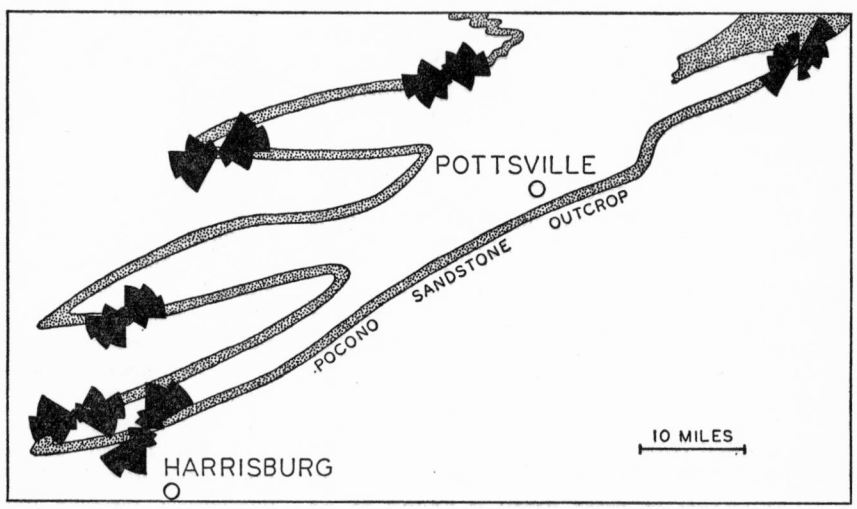

Figure 258.   Map showing by rose diagrams the orientation of plant stem fragments in the Pocono Sandstone (Miss.) at six localities in Pennsylvania. These fragments are generally oriented parallel to ripple marks and at right angles to cross-bedding observed at the same localities. All of these features are indications of current direction. (After Pelletier, 1958, *Bull. Geol. Soc. Amer.*, vol. 69, p. 1052, fig. 13.)

but laterally variable processes and conditions. The differences may be of any kind that is distinguishable in sediments or sedimentary rocks. Those that have been emphasized are (1) lithologic, (2) biologic, and (3) tectonic, but the first have received by far the most attention. Facies maps do not necessarily deal with strata corresponding to conventional stratigraphic units. Ideally they should show differences within the strata of units representing very restricted intervals of geologic time and extend throughout a large area. Because of the limitations of correlation, this ideal generally can only be approached. In actual practice, a unit that is closely restricted in time also is restricted areally and a unit that can be traced satisfactorily throughout a large region is likely to represent so long a time interval that its facies are much generalized.

Facies can be distinguished and mapped qualitatively or quantitatively.

Qualitative maps commonly employ patterns to identify more or less indefinite facies (see Figures 195 and 196, pp. 510–511). These maps are not likely to be either detailed or accurate unless facies contrast strongly and their gradations are abrupt. If quantitative differences can be expressed in a simple way numerically, as in the measure of a single property or by the comparison of two related properties as a ratio, a contoured map can be prepared and arbitrarily differentiated facies indicated, or these can be left to the imagination or needs of any viewer of the map (see Figures 200 and 201, pp. 528, 529). Facies based on more complex relations involving two, three, or more variables are indicated on a map by patterns keyed to the arbitrary divisions of a diagram, most commonly a triangular diagram (see Figures 197, p. 512, and 206, p. 533).

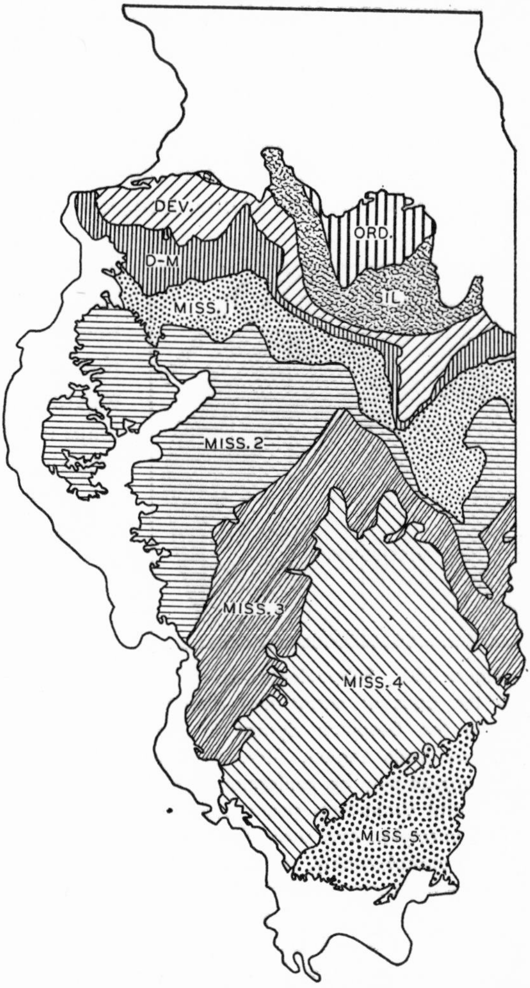

Lithofacies Maps

As the name indicates, these are maps of facies differentiated on the basis

Figure 259. Pre-Pennsylvanian geologic map of Illinois showing the northward overlap of basal Pennsylvanian strata from high Upper Mississippian to Middle Ordovician. The stratigraphic section thus overlapped is about 5000 feet thick. This is not necessarily evidence, however, of 5000 feet of erosion subsequent to late Mississippian time and before the deposition of earliest Pennsylvanian. (Modified from Wanless, 1955, *Bull. Am. Assoc. Petroleum Geol.*, vol. 39, pp. 1760–1761, fig. 2.)

of lithologic characters. Although these characters are related mainly to physical and chemical processes and conditions, they also include those of biologic origin that affect the composition and appearance of sediments and rocks.

Most lithofacies maps show the areal extent of facies within some kind of stratigraphic unit as determined by subsurface records. The commonest ones make arbitrary distinctions within a continuously variable complex based upon either (1) proportions of the three most abundant types of rock in a stratigraphic unit such as limestone, sandstone, and shale or (2) relations of detrital and sand-shale ratios. Many other kinds of lithologic characters can be used in the differentiation of facies, however, and more complex combinations of characters may be utilized. Altogether a great variety of lithofacies maps can be prepared for a single stratigraphic unit. Because of the arbitrary limits and the different characters considered in relation to each other, the facies patterns of several maps devoted to the same area are likely to be very different.

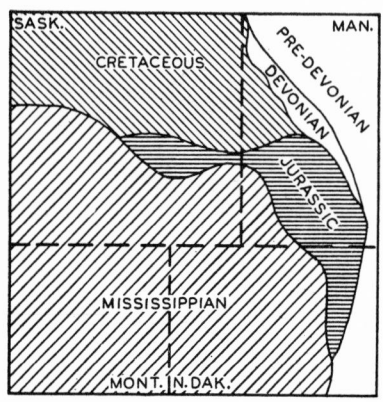

Figure 260. Subgeologic map showing the ages of strata that directly overlie the Devonian System in the Williston basin region. Although the Mississippian may be conformable, Jurassic and Cretaceous strata overstep the Mississippian and succeed the Devonian unconformably. Maps of this kind are not common but they provide useful information regarding stratigraphic relations and the areal distribution of formations at important unconformities. (After Baillie, 1955, Bull. Am. Assoc. Petroleum Geol., vol. 39, p. 612, fig. 13.)

Isolith Maps

Isolith maps are concerned with a single kind of rock occurring within a stratigraphic unit rather than with a complete stratigraphic section. They are closely related to lithofacies maps and might be regarded as specialized maps of this kind. There are many possible types of isolith maps. For each kind there might be as many maps prepared as there are different kinds of rock in the stratigraphic unit being studied. They may be patterned maps, like common lithofacies maps, but generally they are contoured on the basis of some measurable property, relation, or ratio.

The most obvious isolith map is one that shows the total thickness (Figure 198, p. 525) or percentage (Figure 180B, p. 486) of one kind of rock present in a stratigraphic unit without regard to its disposition within the unit. Other maps may show the number of beds that exceed a certain thickness (Figure 199, p. 526) or the average thickness of the beds. Also they may show more detailed lithologic features, such as the average grain size or degree of sorting in sandstones, the amount of insoluble residues in limestones,

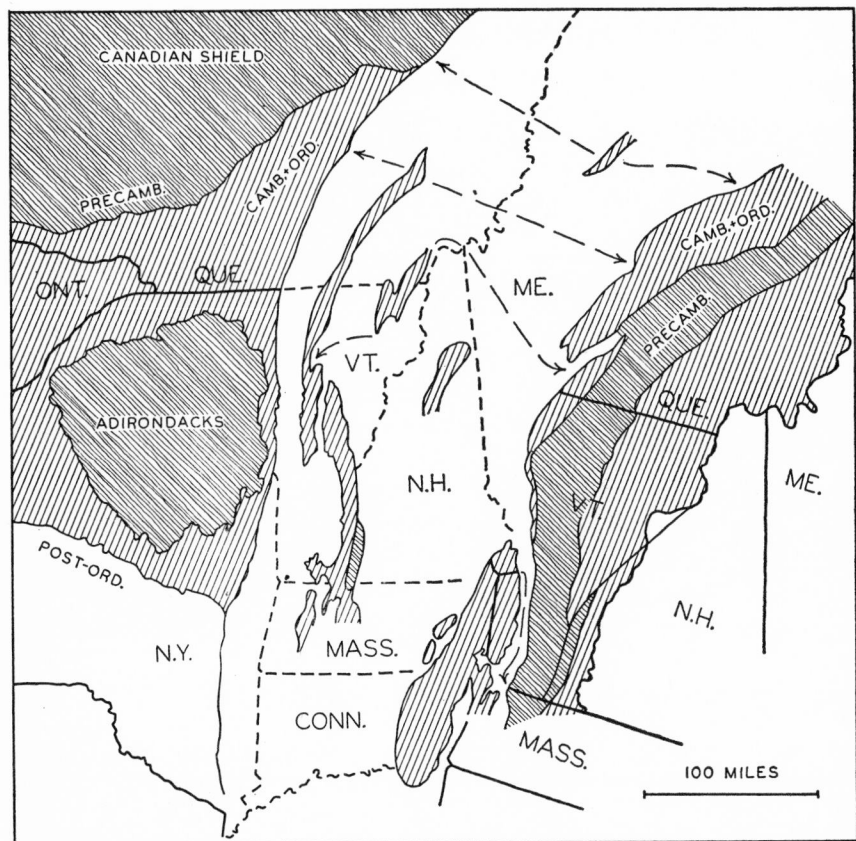

Figure 261. Palinspastic map showing the relations of early Paleozoic rocks in western New England. According to this interpretation, westward overthrusting has brought rocks that originally occurred in areas 100 to 150 miles apart into close association. The map attempts to return them to their former geographic positions. The displaced state boundaries provide a frame of reference. (After Kay, 1937, *Bull. Geol. Soc. Amer.,* vol. 48, p. 286, pl. 5.)

or the amount of silt or lime in shales. These and other features of the rock can be compared in the upper and lower halves or other fractions of stratigraphic units. Patterned isolith maps reflecting more complex relations, such as mineralogic or other details of composition, are possible but not many are likely to be made because of the labor required for their preparation.

Lithologic Maps

Lithologic maps are similar to areal geologic maps in that they show the distribution of outcropping rocks at the surface of the earth. They are different, however, because they are not concerned with conventional successive stratigraphic units but only with the occurrence of strata of different lithologic types (see Figure 262). The strata that they show are variously related both vertically and laterally. Some may split, intertongue, or wedge out between each other more or less irregularly. These maps commonly illustrate stratigraphic sequences that are equivalent but differently constituted from place to place.

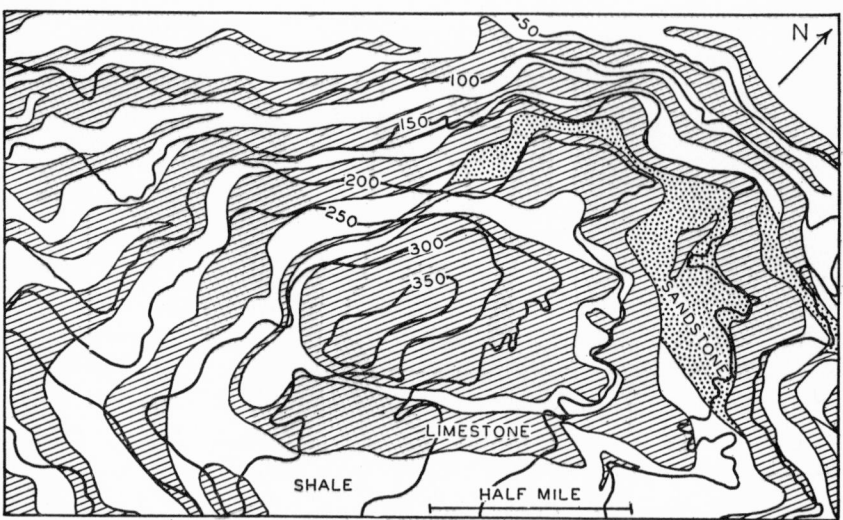

Figure 262. Lithologic map showing outcropping zones of limestone, shale, and sandstone on Mt. Vizcaya, Batan Island, Albay Province, Philippines. The strata here are part of a very thick middle to upper Tertiary stratigraphic section. Individual units are discontinuous, and subdivision into useful lithologically different formations is not possible. Topographic contours are drawn at 50-meter intervals. (After Crispin and others, 1955, Phil. Bur. Mines, Spec. Proj. Ser., Publ. 3, pl. 1, sheet 2.)

Lithologic maps also are closely related to lithofacies maps because they show the relations of strata that might be classed as lithosomes whose variable development could be utilized to distinguish lithofacies. These maps are most useful in indicating the stratigraphic details within thick heterogeneous formations whose strata are so irregular that satisfactory subdivision into reasonably consistent members is not possible.

Biofacies Maps

Lithofacies and other related maps are diagramatic presentations of factual lithologic data, and biologic data may seem to be amenable to somewhat similar treatment by somewhat similar methods. Actually, however, biologic data present a much more complicated problem because they are less easy to classify or express in quantitative terms and their meanings are much less certain. The measurements to be employed in biofacies differentiation are a particular source of difficulty. Those that have been suggested and used to some extent are (1) geographic distribution of species, genera, or other taxonomic groups (see Figure 133, p. 325), (2) number of species representing selected taxonomic groups, (3) number of specimens representing selected taxonomic groups, and (4) weight of specimens belonging to such groups. The first makes no distinctions between very rare and very common fossils. Counts of individuals may be satisfactory for gastropods, horn corals, and other fossils that commonly occur whole, but not for bryozoans and crinoids, rarely found entire, for trilobites and ostracods that moulted, or for colonial corals that might be counted as one or many individuals. Finally, little or no importance can be attached to the relative weights of such disparate fossils as, for example, brachiopods or pelecypods and foraminifera.

The mapping of areas large enough to show much in the way of facies differences depends mainly upon subsurface records. Even the best cuttings and cores from wells cannot be expected to provide representative faunas or floras except of microfossils. Consequently the actual basis for biofacies is severely limited. Also the variable occurrence of fossils in the different zones that constitute most stratigraphic units is almost sure to obscure interpretations. These are serious difficulties but the situation is not entirely hopeless. As the environmental relations of fossils are more fully determined, a better basis will be provided for the differentiation of biofacies that are likely to have some meaning at least in zones of outcrop where reasonably complete collections of fossils can be obtained.

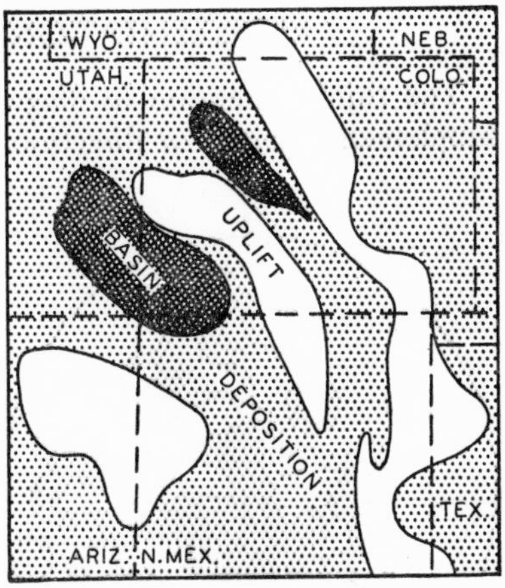

Figure 263. A much-generalized and simplified paleotectonic map showing areas of pronounced uplift and depressions in which evaporites accumulated during Pennsylvanian and Permian time in Colorado and neighboring states. Much of the Pennsylvanian and Permian sediments deposited outside of the evaporite basins consist of marginal marine, deltaic, and coarse non-marine material (see Figure 267, p. 647). (After Litsey, 1958, *Bull. Geol. Soc. Amer.,* vol. 69, p. 1159, fig. 11.)

Paleotectonic Maps

Paleotectonic maps present interpretations rather than factual data. They are closely related to paleogeographic maps but, instead of showing geographic relations as these are supposed to have existed in the geologic past, they attempt to indicate movements of subsidence and uplift that altered geographic relations (see Figure 263, also Figure 226, p. 597). Most paleotectonic maps are crude and much generalized representations based on stratigraphic data that have not been carefully analyzed. Perhaps greater precision could be attained if lithofacies and isopach maps were first constructed and used as guides in their preparation.

So-called *tectofacies maps* generally are only incomplete paleotectonic maps. They are not comparable to other facies maps because differentiation of facies is almost wholly interpretative and is based on little more than regional variations in thickness of the stratigraphic section. They are incomplete because they are concerned only with areas of subsidence where sediments accumulated and have been preserved. Interpretations of uplifted regions are more uncertain, but some evidence of conditions and happenings in them is provided by the sediments. More complete paleotectonic maps require a broader as well as more detailed consideration of stratigraphic data.

REPRESENTATIONS IN THREE DIMENSIONS

The third dimension in diagrams and maps useful in stratigraphy that supplements spatial or directional relations in a horizontal plane may be measurements of (1) angular inclination in a vertical plane, (2) surface relief or elevation, (3) depth, or (4) thickness.

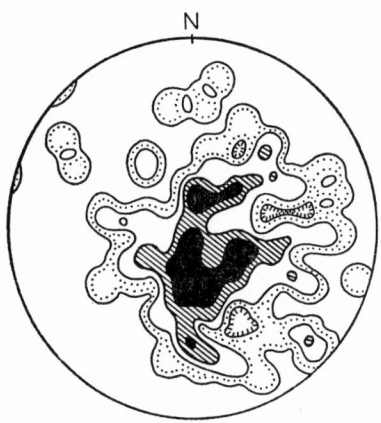

Figure 264. Contoured equal-area polar-coordinate diagram showing the orientation of the short c-axis of 100 pebbles in glacial outwash observed in eastern Wisconsin. Slight imbrication in a southeastern direction is indicated. Similar plotting of the long a-axis shows orientation in the opposite direction. This conforms with studies of delta gravels and seems to establish a southeastern direction of flow of the stream that transported these pebbles. (After Krumbein, 1939, J. Geol., vol. 47, p. 700, fig. 14.)

Polar-Coordinate Diagrams

Polar-coordinate diagrams are particularly well adapted to showing the orientation of lines, planes, and unsymmetrical bodies in three-dimensional space (see Figure 61, p. 180). Such orientation also can be indicated crudely in ordinary two-coordinate diagrams but these do not reveal relations clearly. Various standard spherical projections might be used, but an equal-area polar diagram is most convenient because a scattering of points can be converted easily to numerical data. Diagrams produced by contouring these data show relations very plainly and make visual comparison easy, as shown by Figure 264.

Diagrams of this type add a third dimension to data that might be presented in rose diagrams. They have been used extensively in structural geology to indicate such things as the direction and dip of joints and various kinds of lineation and in petrography to show petrofabric relations. The latter application particularly may be useful in stratigraphic interpretation to determine, for example, the direction of sediment-depositing currents as shown by the orientation of sand grains and fossils.

Maps

All geologic maps are based on geographic maps that indicate various relations either as they exist today or as they are supposed to have existed at some time in the geologic past. Areal geologic maps are essentially two dimensional because they are concerned primarily with the relations of surface geologic features to the horizontal dimensions of modern geography. A third dimension is suggested, however, by the structural relations which are more or less apparent. Structural features and the third dimension in geology are more clearly expressed in areal geologic maps if these features can be related to topography, which is the third dimension indicated by some geographic maps. Other kinds of geologic maps, of which structure contour and isopach maps are the principal examples, are designed to show three-dimensional features. They are much less closely related to geography except for the location and orientation of these features.

Relief Maps

Many geographic maps, particularly small-scale ones devoted to large regions such as whole continents or countries, provide some generalized indication of topography. Specialized relief maps, however, are designed to show the form of surface features in much greater detail. The most perfect kind indicates topography by means of contour lines and makes the best base for a detailed areal geologic map. In a similar way, the depth of water can be shown by contours on a hydrographic map. Relief features of both land and submarine surfaces also can be shown by shading or hachuring but these are more generalized conventions than are contours. Shaded or hachured maps are less satisfactory as geologic base maps because patterns or colors representing geologic features are likely to be obscured. Hachuring, however, may be useful to indicate topography on reconnaissance geologic maps if the scale is small, or better topographic data are not available. Also hachuring can be employed advantageously to show generalized features of relief on paleogeographic maps.

Structural Contour Maps

These maps show by means of contours the position of some particular stratigraphic horizon with respect to a selected horizontal plane, most commonly sea level (see Figures 107, p. 280, and 180C, p. 486). The assumption generally is made that differences in elevation of the contoured horizon record tectonic movements and that warping or folding has displaced the horizon from an originally horizontal position. Although this is true in a general way, it is not exactly so because the contoured horizon probably never was perfectly horizontal and differential compaction of underlying strata probably accounts for part of the inequalities of elevation that now occur.

A stratigraphic horizon well adapted for structural contouring generally (1) is marked by abrupt and conspicuous lithologic contrast, (2) is believed to approximate a time plane closely, and (3) is present in the subsurface throughout the area to be mapped. The advantages provided by a sharp and clear contact are obvious because recognition in well records is relatively easy and certain. Such a contact, however, is not everywhere available. If it is necessary to utilize a more obscure horizon, exact correlations are likely to be correspondingly less sure and the structure may not be interpreted accurately. In either case the contoured horizon may transgress time planes and, therefore, present a somewhat distorted guide to tectonic movements. Even though the horizon marks a contemporaneous depositional surface, this almost certainly varied in elevation from place to place. Also if the horizon is an unconformity, its structure may not be exactly parallel with the structure of either underlying or overlying strata. If the horizon is well chosen and carefully traced, however, discrepancies of these types ordinarily are not serious.

Contoured maps are better suited to show gentle structures than are structural cross sections because the latter require vertical exaggeration to make gentle structural relations clear. A contoured map also indicates the structure of an area completely and it is better than a series of any number of cross sections. On the other hand, a map of this kind presents the structure of only the single contoured horizon whereas sections show the relative structures of all strata. More than one set of structural contours can be superimposed on a single map but such a combination is almost certain to be confusing and difficult to read.

The accuracy of structural contour maps depends upon the adequate number and proper distribution of controls in the form of well records and outcrops. In some areas the contoured horizon may not be reached by wells at critical places. At other places it may have risen above what is now the surface and have been eroded. Where the position of the horizon is not known from direct evidence, it must be estimated on the basis of the observed positions of higher or lower horizons and the thicknesses of the intervals that separate them. Thus structural contours can indicate estimations of elevations far below the reach of the deepest wells and above the surface of the earth. If estimations of this kind are made, the possibility must not be overlooked that intervals between horizons may vary in thickness from place to place. If the estimations involve much uncertainty, it may be preferable to show the structure of different parts of an area by contours drawn on different horizons whose elevations can be determined with greater accuracy.

Basic procedures in the construction of structural contour maps are very simple but the actual practice is an art. First the contour interval is chosen. Then short segments of the proper number of contours are located between adjacent control points as indicated by elevations of the horizon at those points. Finally segments representing equivalent elevations are connected. The spacing of contours between control points and the courses of contours between the segments so spaced may be done almost mechanically, as shown in Figure 265, or they may be governed by the judgment and experience of the one who makes the map. Maps produced by different persons may differ greatly but all are technically correct insofar as the actual direct evidence is concerned. Nevertheless, one map may be superior to another because it indicates more natural or more probable structural relations or conforms to structural trends that are known to be characteristic of the region (see Figure 266). Except for small-scale or obviously generalized structural contour maps, all control points should be indicated so that the viewer can see what features of the map are definitely fixed and what details might be interpreted differently.

Table 22 shows relations between differences of elevation in the distance

TABLE 22.   Relations Between Stratigraphic Dips Measured in Feet per Mile and in Angles

Dip in Feet per Mile	Angle of Inclination	Angle of Inclination	Dip in Feet per Mile
10	6′	10′	15
50	32′	30′	46
100	1° 05′	1°	92
250	2° 40′	2° 30′	231
500	5° 24′	5°	462
750	8° 03′	7° 30′	695
1000	10° 43′	10°	931
2500	24° 59′	30°	3048
5000	43° 25′	45°	5280

of one mile, as indicated by structural contours, and the angular dips of strata.

Isopach Maps

Isopach maps show the thicknesses of stratigraphic units by means of contours (see Figure 267, also Figure 180D, p. 486). Measurements are made vertically. If strata are not horizontal, this results in some exaggeration. Table 23 indicates the discrepancies introduced by increasing dips.

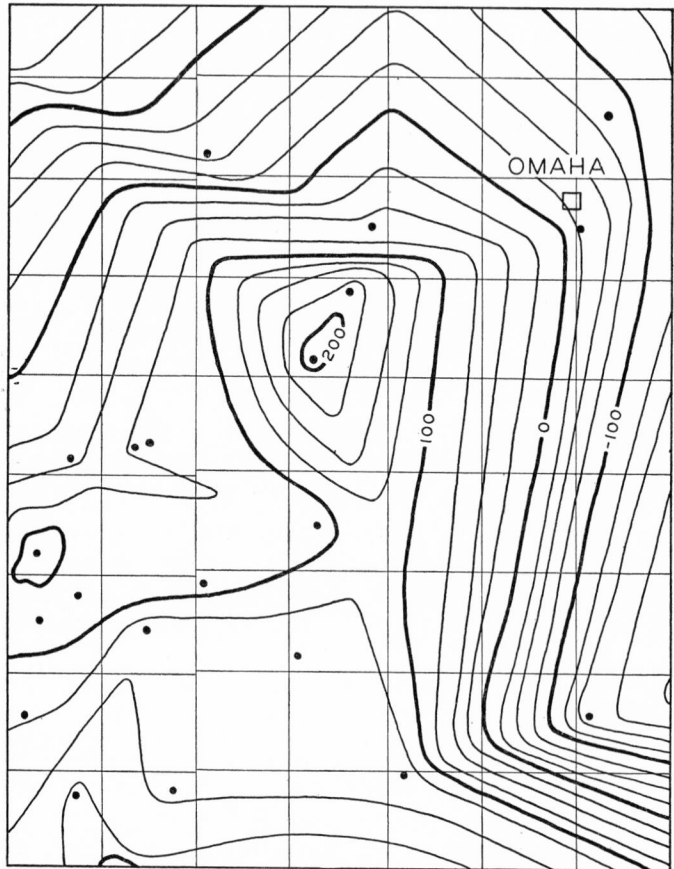

Figure 265.   Structural contour map based on Coal No. 6 (Penn.) in parts of Saline and Gallatin counties of southern Illinois drawn on a one-mile-section line grid. This is an example of mechanical contouring in which little or no consideration was given to anything except known elevations at scattered localities. It is correct insofar as this information is concerned. This map, however, has a very artificial appearance and almost certainly provides an inaccurate representation of the actual structure. (After Cady, 1938, Ill. Geol. Surv., Circ. 42, map 1.)

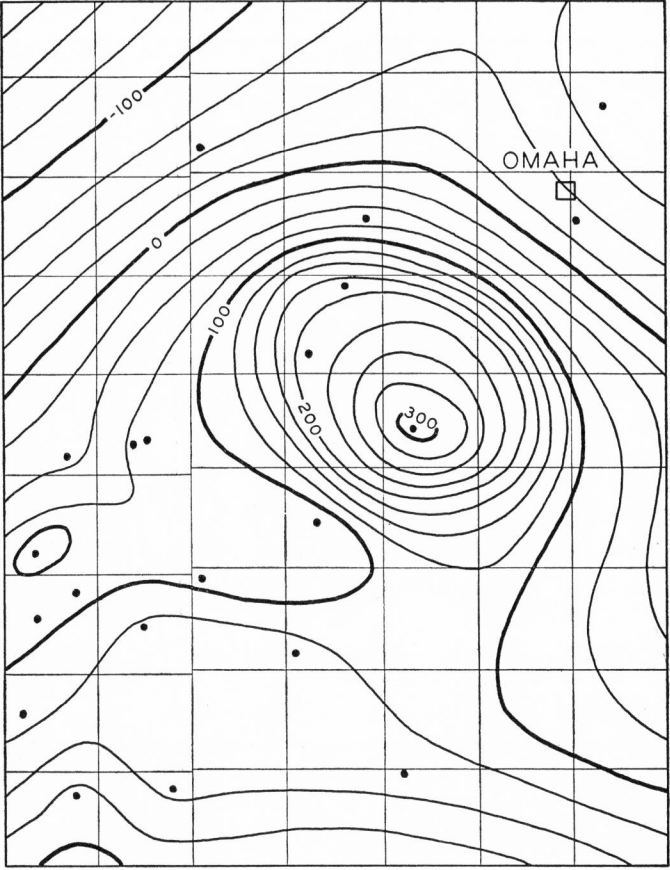

Figure 266. Structural contour map based on Coal No. 6 (Penn.) of the same area shown in Figure 265. This map is based on identical data except for the addition of one elevation on top of the Omaha dome furnished by later drilling and the elimination of one datum point in the southeastern part of the map that seems to have been misinterpreted. This map, however, has been drawn to conform with structural trends and relations as they are known in this part of Illinois. It involves interpretations and may be erroneous in details, but probably it indicates actual structure more accurately than the other map. (Based on data from English and Grogan, 1948, *Structure of typical American oil fields,* vol. 3, p. 202, fig. 3, and Swann, 1951, *Bull. Am. Assoc. Petroleum Geol.,* vol. 35, p. 2566, fig. 4.)

Maps showing the true thicknesses of stratigraphic units would be useful in some studies but their preparation would require considerable calculation. Dips generally are so gentle in areas where strata are mapped by isopachs that most discrepancies are unimportant. Although the suggestion has been made that a different name be applied to maps showing exaggerated thicknesses of dipping beds, almost all so-called isopach maps are of this type.

TABLE 23.   Increase in Apparent Thickness of Strata
Resulting from Inclination

Dip	Thickening	Thickening	Dip
5°	0.4%	1%	7° 42′
10°	1.5%	2%	11° 22′
15°	3.5%	3%	13° 52′
20°	6.4%	5%	17° 45′
25°	10.4%	10%	24° 38′
30°	15.5%	20%	33° 33′

Isopach maps showing vertical thicknesses are more useful than true thickness maps because of the way in which they are related to structural contour maps. Thus, subtraction of the elevations provided by one structural contour map from those provided by another produces thicknesses that allow the construction of an isopach map of intervening strata. By reversing this process and adding thicknesses shown by an isopach map to, or subtracting them from, structural elevations, data are provided for the construction of another structural contour map of a higher or lower horizon. Thicknesses indicated by isopach maps generally are considered to be approximate measures of subsidence within a depositional basin during the time required for accumulation of the strata. This is not necessarily true because depositional surfaces probably were not exactly horizontal, thicknesses may have been reduced by erosion at an unconformity, and compaction of sediments certainly occurred and may have resulted in irregular thickness reductions.

The contouring of an isopach map commonly is more simple than the contouring of a structural map because variations in thickness are likely to be gradual and fairly regular. The control points where the thicknesses of strata are accurately known should be indicated on all detailed isopach maps.

Rates of stratigraphic thickening or thinning are shown by the contour interval and the spacing of the contours of isopach maps. Relative rates are not indicated and this fact may be overlooked. Isopach maps of two formations ranging respectively in thickness from 10 to 50 feet and from 1010 to 1050 feet would show the same amount of variability. Obviously, however, variability of the thinner formation is relatively much greater. Differences in thickness can be calculated easily as percentages and contoured to produce maps closely related to isopach maps (see Figure 180D, p. 486). Both

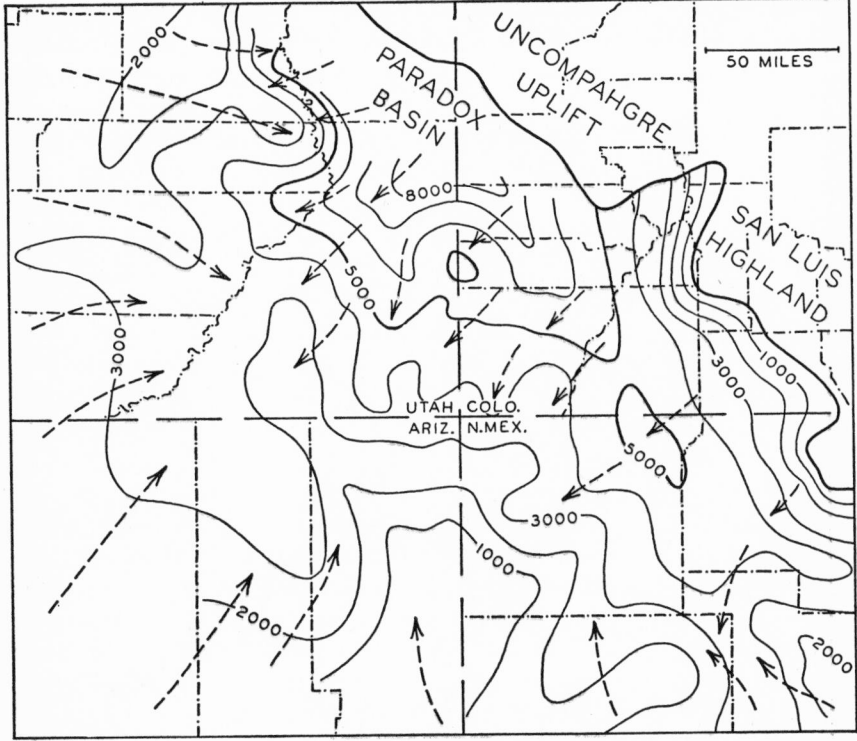

Figure 267. Isopach map showing the thickness of Pennsylvanian and Permian strata in the Four Corners region. Irregularities in thickness here are related mainly to tectonic downwarping in the Paradox basin. Arrows show the directions of movement of sediment consisting of arkosic materials derived from the northeast and quartz sands derived from the west and southwest. Interfingering of these sediments occurs in the central part of the region. (After Wengerd and Matheny, 1958, *Bull. Am. Assoc. Petroleum Geol.*, vol. 42, pp. 2094–2095, fig. 18.)

kinds of maps show the same trends but *rate-of-thickening maps* are contoured in a more significant measure of variability.

Perspective Diagrams

The pictorial quality of a diagram is improved greatly by the introduction of perspective. At the same time, some corresponding sacrifice may be involved making the diagram less suited to the presentation of detailed information. This sacrifice commonly is related to the matter of scale, and most perspective diagrams are much generalized. They are best adapted, therefore, to the illustration of geologic relations in such a way that they are quickly and easily understood particularly by persons who are not accustomed to the conventions of other types of geologic diagrams.

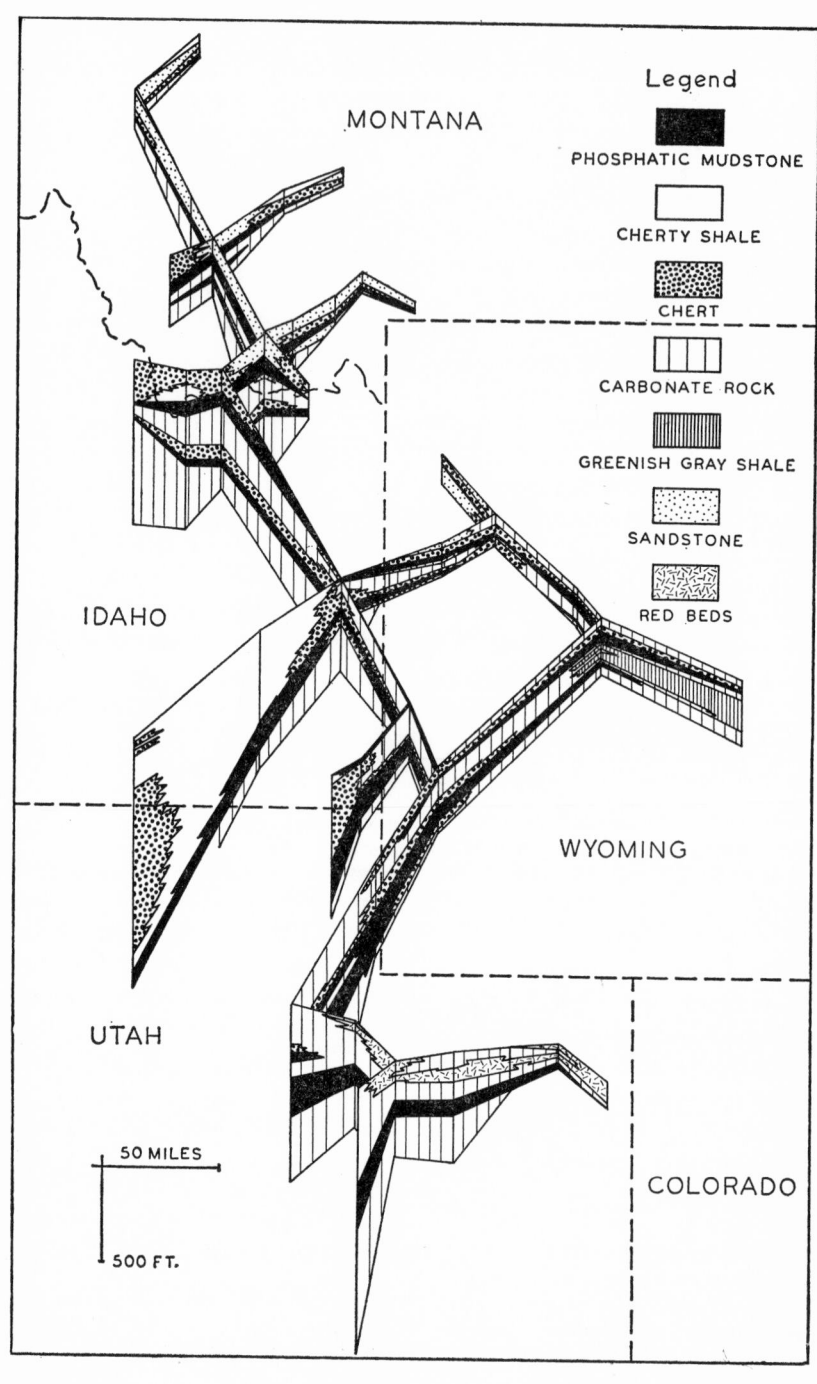

Legend

PHOSPHATIC MUDSTONE

CHERTY SHALE

CHERT

CARBONATE ROCK

GREENISH GRAY SHALE

SANDSTONE

RED BEDS

MONTANA

IDAHO

UTAH

WYOMING

COLORADO

50 MILES

500 FT.

Normal Panel Diagrams

Panel or fence diagrams are combinations of a map and geologic cross sections. In normal panel diagrams, the map is a true plan providing undistorted horizontal dimensions. The third dimension is furnished by sections that are located on the map in their true positions. They may extend in any direction, intersect, and branch. Depending upon controls, they may make almost any kind of pattern (see Figure 268).

Control is provided by stratigraphic columns commonly derived from well records. These are drawn vertically on the diagram so that they extend either upward or downward from the points marking their locations. It is most natural to extend the columns downward from the map but, whichever way they may be drawn, they appear to most persons to rise above it. The stratigraphic units of adjacent columns are then connected and distinguished by appropriate patterns. The sections thus formed are true to scale, both horizontal and vertical, although the latter generally requires exaggeration.

Sections that extend from left to right laterally across the diagram are undistorted. Foreshortening, however, results in distortion of other sections. This increases with the angle at which the sections lie, and those that extend vertically on the diagram are reduced to lines. Consequently the map should be oriented in such a way that most of the sections extend as nearly laterally as possible. Directions should be clearly indicated on the map.

Isometric Panel Diagrams

These diagrams differ from the last in the treatment of the base map. It is redrawn in such a way that regularly arranged grid lines, intersecting at right angles on the plan, meet at angles of about 60 and 120 degrees. This produces foreshortening and makes the map appear to lie at an angle to the plane of the drawing (see Figure 269). The perspective effect is proportional to the difference between adjacent grid angles. In such a map all horizontal angles are distorted and horizontal scales vary. Before the map is redrawn it should be oriented so that most of the sections extend laterally across the diagram because they become progressively foreshortened as they approach the vertical.

An isometric panel diagram may be superior to a normal one in pictorial quality because perspective is accentuated. The vertical scale of all sections is uniform, but these diagrams have the disadvantage of a variable horizontal scale.

Figure 268 (*opposite*). Panel or fence diagram showing the lateral intertonguing relations of Permian strata of different lithologic characters in part of the Rocky Mountain region. This diagram is based upon a geographic map presented in true proportions. The top of each stratigraphic column is correctly located on this map so that the geologic sections lie below it. (After McKelvey and others, 1956, *Bull. Am. Assoc. Petroleum Geol.*, vol. 40, pp. 2830–2831, fig. 2.)

Stereographic Panel Diagrams

If isometric diagrams represent rectangular areas, they seem unnatural because there is no foreshortening in depth or apparent distance from the observer. This can be overcome by stereographic projection, which gives the
effect of more perfect perspective. In stereographic diagrams, parallel lines

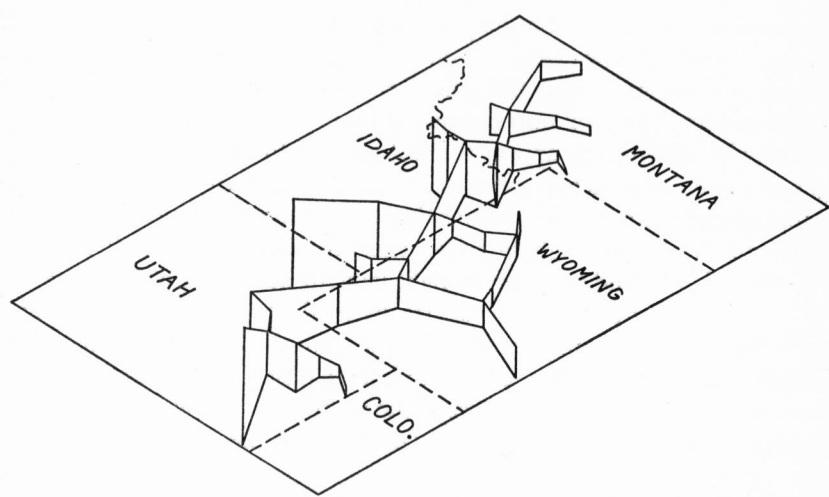

Figure 269. Panel diagram showing in outline the same pattern of stratigraphic
sections illustrated in Figure 268 based on a diagonal isometrically projected map.
Because of their different orientation with respect to the viewer some of these sections
are less and others are more foreshortened than in the other figure. These sections
appear to rise above the map but actually they lie below it.

lying in any plane converge and meet at points upon an imaginary distant
horizon, as shown in Figure 270. All angles are distorted and neither horizontal nor vertical scales are constant. This type of diagram is rarely used for
panel diagrams because of difficulties of construction that generally are not
compensated by any noteworthy advantages.

Ribbon Diagrams

Panel diagrams show geologic sections zigzagging from control point to
control point in an irregular angular manner. In a ribbon diagram branching
and intersecting sections are omitted and the angles between others are
rounded out so that a single continuous section is presented that flows in
graceful curves across the map (see Figure 271). Ribbon diagrams can be
constructed in conformity with plane, orthographic, or stereographic map
projections.

Block Diagrams

Block diagrams are perspective drawings of solid bodies that represent portions of the earth (see Figure 20, p. 73). They are the most realistic of all geologic diagrams. They are excellently adapted to showing the generalized

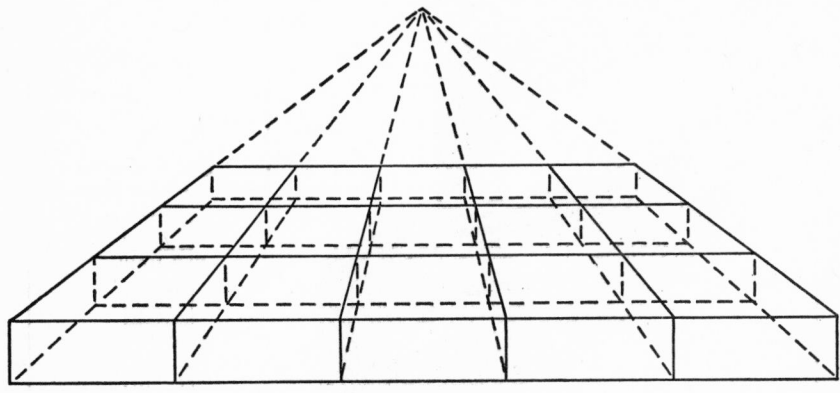

ONE POINT PROJECTION

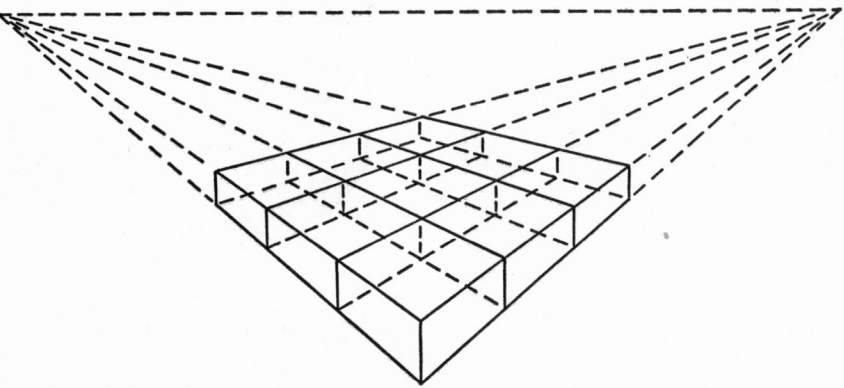

TWO POINT PROJECTION

Figure 270. Diagrams showing methods of construction of blocks in one-point and in two-point perspective. Blocks of the latter type possess upper surfaces that appear to curve downward toward the viewer. If true perspective is to be attained, all vertical lines should converge toward distant lower points.

relations of surface geology and topographic relief to stratigraphy and structure. An ordinary block diagram shows a surface area and two geologic cross sections on the forward vertical faces of the block. It is possible to produce many variations, however, by altering the shape of the block so that other

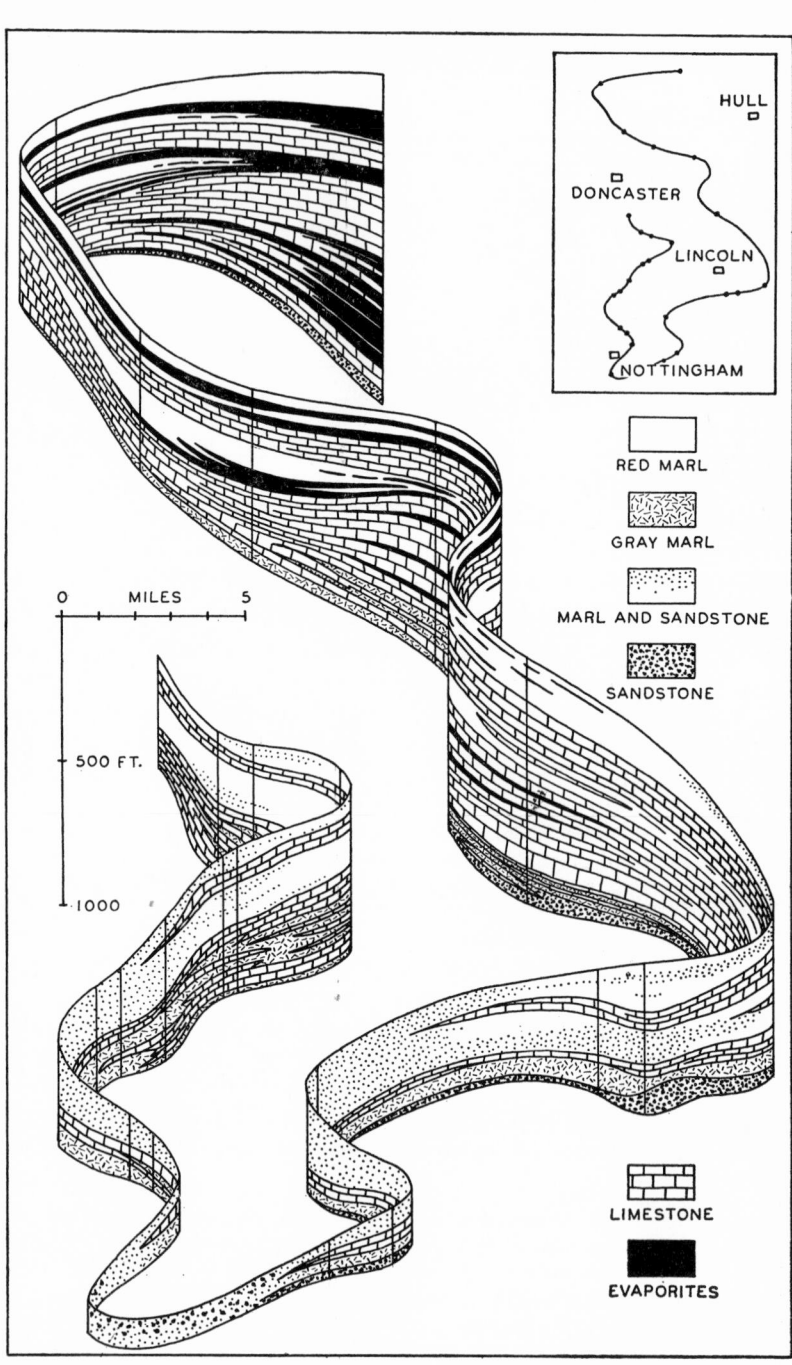

HULL

DONCASTER

LINCOLN

NOTTINGHAM

RED MARL

GRAY MARL

MARL AND SANDSTONE

SANDSTONE

0   MILES   5

500 FT.

1000

LIMESTONE

EVAPORITES

sections are presented or by dividing the block into parts and offsetting them (see Figure 272).

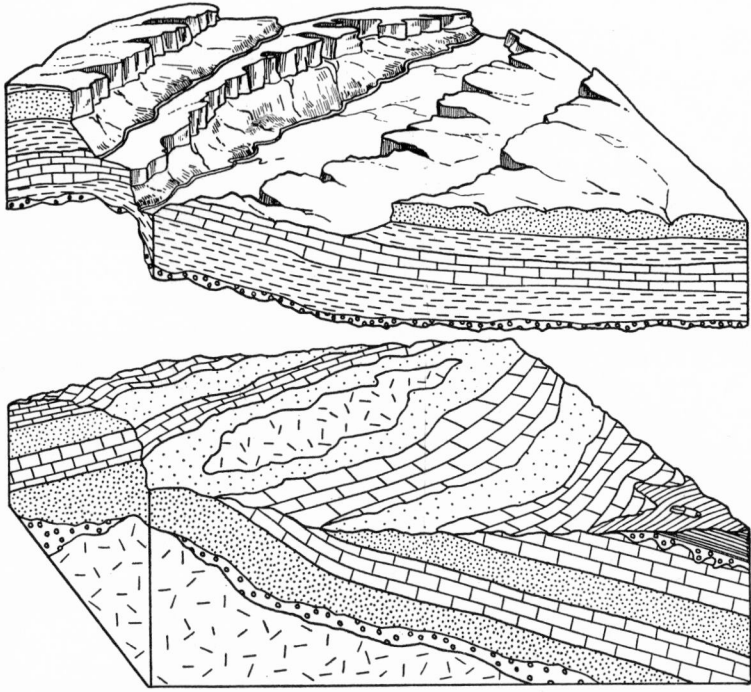

Figure 272. Block diagram showing surface topography and subsurface geology. This block has been separated at an unconformity and the parts have been displaced to reveal more of the geology than could be indicated otherwise. The projection here is isometric, but because the block has an irregular shape it does not appear to be distorted. (After Low, 1950, *Subsurface geologic methods,* p. 899, fig. 472, by permission of the Colorado School of Mines.)

Block diagrams may be constructed by either isometric or stereographic projection. The latter method is more complex and the blocks are more difficult to draw, but the better perspective that stereographic blocks provide makes them superior and more effective (see Figure 273).

Figure 271 (*opposite*). Ribbon diagram showing the stratigraphic relations and lateral variations in the Permian rocks of Yorkshire and the East Midlands, England. A diagram of this type serves much the same purpose as a panel diagram. This one is based on a geographic map in true proportions as indicated in the inset. (After Edwards and Trotter, 1954, *British Regional Geology, The Pennines and adjacent areas,* 3rd ed., p. 60, fig. 23, by permission of the Controller of Her Britannic Majesty's Stationery Office.)

PHOTOGRAPHS VERSUS SKETCHES

Good photographs are the most perfect of all illustrations. They are not, however, the best illustrations for many purposes because they are nonselective and show all features in as much detail as scale, distance, and conditions of light and shade permit. If attention is to be directed to certain aspects of

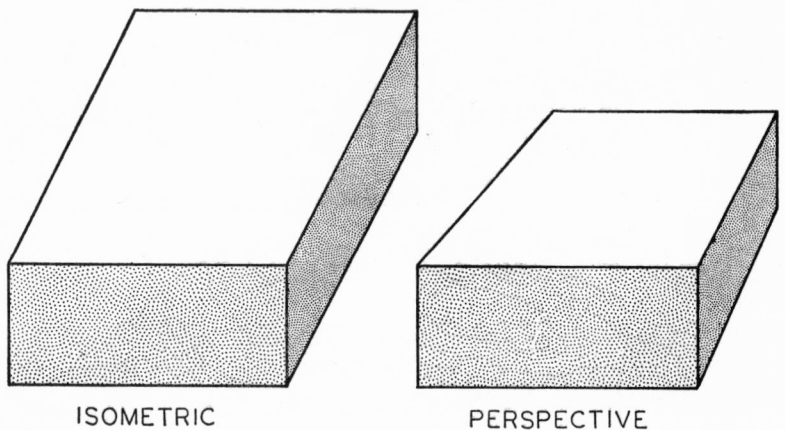

ISOMETRIC   PERSPECTIVE

Figure 273. Blocks drawn in isometric and in one-point perspective. The former presents an optical illusion of distortion although the dimensions of the block actually are uniform. This can be avoided by construction of a block that does not have a regular rectangular upper surface.

a photograph, it may be necessary to identify them in some way or to accentuate them by retouching so that greater contrast is achieved or sharper contacts are provided. Poor photographs generally are worse than useless.

Aerial Photographs

Many aerial photographs made in areas of moderate to high relief show topographic and physiographic features with great clarity and detail. Even in such areas, however, single photographs may reveal little if they were made at midday when the surface of the earth was evenly lighted and shadows were not well developed. In areas of low relief aerial photographs show little besides vegetation patterns, drainage lines, and cultural developments. These are likely to obscure features of more significance. If details other than topography are of interest, sketch maps generally are much superior to photographs as illustrations.

Landscapes

Although few landscapes can be described briefly and one good illustration is worth many words, the best photograph or sketch is inadequate because nothing can substitute for the sweeping view that is obtained by an observer on the spot. Except for panoramas, any illustration represents only a more or less narrow angular fraction of a view and it may be disappointing because the relations of the features that it shows to others on either side are not revealed. Even panoramas generally fail to provide the sense of direction that is necessary for relating the varied features of a landscape.

The effectiveness of any photograph is heightened by contrast and good composition. Contrasting features of outdoor views, however, may have little geologic significance and artistic composition must be sacrificed, perhaps, in order to bring points of geologic interest into prominence. Photographs rapidly decline in effectiveness with lessened topographic relief and distance. The geologic characteristics of many landscapes are less satisfactorily shown by photographs than by accurate sketches which emphasize some features and omit confusing details. In general, simple sketches are more effective than elaborate ones.

Outcrops

Most ordinary outcrop photographs are of little interest because they do not show much more than bedding or weathering characteristics and these can be duplicated closely at many outcrops of many ages. Outcrop illustrations generally are superfluous unless they reveal such details as unconformable relations, noteworthy irregularities of stratification, organic or concretionary structures, or other distinctive features. These commonly can be indicated more effectively in sketches than in photographs.

Specimens

Specimens or details of sediments or rocks that are to be illustrated natural size or at only moderate reductions or enlargements are best shown by photographs. The features of interest generally are minutiae of configuration or relations that may be lost or distorted in drawings. Where complete accuracy is desirable, no drawing can be relied upon because its fidelity cannot be evaluated and some features are almost certain to be accentuated at the expense of others.

Microphotographs

Photographs of many thin sections are confusing because of indistinctness. Numerous features are visible through a microscope where the eye can distinguish slight differences of shade or color that are lost in reproduction. This is particularly true of slides viewed in polarized light with crossed nicols. Many photomicrographs require labeling or an explanatory sketch to make them understandable. If this is so, the actual photograph serves little purpose except as an inconclusive check on an interpretation.

The photographing of small objects such as sand grains or foraminifera under a microscope poses problems that can be overcome only with special equipment and the development of skill. Good photographs are much superior to drawings. If sharp focus in depth is not attainable, however, carefully made drawings generally are preferable to hazy photographs.

BIBLIOGRAPHY

Donn, W. L., and Shimer, J. A. (1958), *Graphic methods in structural geology*, New York, Appleton-Century-Crofts.
   This book is mainly devoted to the solution of geologic problems by graphic methods.
Lahee, F. H. (1952), *Field geology*, 5th ed., New York, McGraw-Hill.
   Chapter 19, pp. 615–690, describes the construction and use of many kinds of geologic illustrations.
LeRoy, L. W. (1950), Graphic representations, in L. W. LeRoy (ed.), *Subsurface geologic methods*, 2nd ed., Golden, Colo. School Mines.
   Well logs, correlation charts, and geologic cross sections are briefly considered.
Lobeck, A. K. (1958), *Block diagrams and other graphic methods used in geology and geography*, 2nd ed., Amherst, Emerson-Trussell.
   The problems of perspective, the construction of diagrams, and landscape sketching are explained in detail.
Low, J. W. (1950), Subsurface maps and illustrations, in L. W. LeRoy (ed.), *Subsurface geologic methods*, 2nd ed., Golden, Colo. School Mines.
   The author discusses structural contour, isopach, paleogeographic, and facies maps, cross sections and block diagrams.
Low, J. W. (1957), *Geologic field methods*, New York, Harper.
   Chapter 10, pp. 414–437, describes illustrations of greatest use to the field geologist and explains field photography and sketching.
Royal Dutch Shell Companies (1958), *Standard legend*, The Hague, N. V. de Bataafsche Petroleum Maatschappij.
   This is a very complete compilation of conventional signs, symbols, colors, and abbreviations for use on geologic maps, stratigraphic sections, well logs, etc.
Sebring, Louie, Jr. (1958), Chief tool of the petroleum geologist: The subsurface structural map, *Bull. Am. Assoc. Petroleum Geol.*, vol. 42, pp. 561–587.
   The preparation and use of structural contour maps is described.
Willis, Bailey, and Willis, Robin (1934), *Geologic structures*, 3rd ed., New York, McGraw-Hill.
   Chapter 14, pp. 326–357, describes graphic methods for the solution of structural problems.

18

Field Work and Geologic Mapping

Most systematic field work is undertaken for the immediate purpose of constructing a geologic map. This may or may not involve the preliminary steps of discriminating the stratigraphic units that are to be recognized and determining their stratigraphic order.

All geologic maps are fundamentally similar in that they show the surface distribution of a succession of chosen rock units. They differ principally in the scale at which areal geology is reproduced and the detail which contributes to their accuracy and completeness. The field work necessary to produce a geologic map varies greatly depending upon (1) purpose of the map, (2) time available for mapping, (3) type and scale of existing base maps, (4) character and climate of the country, (5) transportation and living conditions, and (6) constitution of the field party.

FIELD WORK

Much geologic field work has been motivated by scientific curiosity and a desire to learn more about the composition, structure, and history of the earth. The knowledge so obtained has had great and increasing economic value and all government surveys have emphasized the economic importance of their activities. Before the beginning of the present century, non-governmental economic geology contributed little to the advancement of geologic science.

The spectacular rise of the petroleum industry has completely altered this situation. At the present time a majority of all geologists are connected in one way or another with this industry. Prior to the Second World War much petroleum geology was descriptive and empirical. At first it consisted largely of field surveys and geologic mapping—that is, it was essentially two-dimensional geology. As anticlines discovered at the surface were drilled, however, and new oil fields became more difficult to find, greater and greater attention was devoted to subsurface stratigraphy—that is, three-dimensional geology. This was successively aided importantly by gravitational, seismic, and other kinds of instrumental surveys and by electric and other types of geophysical well logging. The success of these methods has been such that many petroleum geologists in the United States now are not greatly concerned with field work.

Since the Second World War, several of the larger oil companies have established geologic research laboratories. These are engaged in investigating many types of scientific problems. It is hoped that the results when they are made known will benefit their sponsors, but they are certain to be important in other geologic applications. The sequence of development in the geologic activities of the petroleum industry in much of the United States has passed the field-work stage but has not progressed so far in less developed regions and particularly in many foreign countries. There the most direct and by far the least costly method of acquiring information is geologic field mapping.

Mining geology has made somewhat less progress in both the scientific discovery of new mineral deposits and the continued development of old ones. Most mines being worked today were located on the basis of surface outcrops and prospecting. At present most mining geology is in a position comparable to the pre-World War II stage of petroleum geology. As known deposits are worked out, however, and new supplies of ores and other minerals are required, geological field surveys augmented by geophysical and geochemical methods of prospecting are being called upon increasingly.

Few areas in the world today are totally unknown geologically. Only a very small proportion of the world outside of the more industrialized nations, however, has been explored geologically in any detail. Even in the United States large areas remote from the more populous communities and the established oil- and mineral-producing districts are inadequately known geologically. An enormous amount of geologic work remains to be done and almost everywhere it must begin with field work. More and more attention will be devoted particularly to the less developed parts of the world as mineral resources are depleted elsewhere.

Geology in its broader aspects is not an exact science. It is too complex, and too few of its details are available to direct observation and study. Every additional outcrop that may develop and each new well that is drilled provides some fresh information to substantiate previous knowledge or to suggest a different interpretation. Restudy of every area brings new facts to light. The time may never come when the geology of any area will be completely and perfectly understood.

The law of diminishing returns does not necessarily apply to geologic field work. The acquisition of some new information, attention to some neglected detail, or the application of some new idea may at any time result in a significantly better understanding of the geology of any area, large or small. There is little prospect that field geology will decline in importance in the foreseeable future even though less is being done now than in some former years.

The Field Geologist

A number of special qualities are required of a successful field geologist. Among the most important are:

1. A strong physique. Field geology is a strenuous occupation. It commonly requires much walking and climbing in difficult terrain and other forms of sustained physical exertion. Ability to withstand fatigue and rapid recuperation are essential. Without them a geologist's enthusiasm for his work is sure to diminish and his observational abilities are quickly dulled. Efficiency requires continuous activity without flagging effort, interest, or attention to details.

2. Knowledge and love of nature and an outdoor life. The great attraction of field work for many geologists is its outdoor nature and its freedom from the confinement and routine of an office or a laboratory. To one who is interested in nature, field work is never dull. Every situation provides something new and stimulating whether it is directly related to geology or not. Field work in most populated regions entails few inconveniences or dangers but in wild or remote country self-reliance in every respect is of the greatest importance. Depending upon local circumstances, proficiency in woodcraft, horsemanship, the handling of canoes or other small boats, and the care of motors may be essential to successful work. Also knowledge of firearms, first aid, and simple medicine may be required to insure personal safety.

3. Adaptability. Living and working conditions in all kinds of country and among all kinds of people demand adaptability in a high degree. The field geologist must make the best of all circumstances and be willing to accept in good spirit inconveniences and discomforts where these cannot be avoided. Particularly in foreign lands, standards of living are less high than those to which he is accustomed and climate may be less pleasant than at his home in a temperate region. A sustained and sympathetic interest in the people among or with whom he must work and in their country can do much to lessen the effects of trying or unfamiliar conditions.

4. Basic training and experience. A field geologist's enthusiastic interest in

his work is taken for granted because without this his accomplishments are not likely to be satisfactory. His training should be broad and include a reasonably good foundation in all of the major branches of geology. A library is rarely within his reach and consultation with specialists generally is not possible during the course of field work. Consequently a field geologist should be able to recognize and evaluate all kinds of geologic evidence or he is likely to overlook features of great significance to the problems under investigation. Experience also is important but this can be acquired only in actual practice. Good field procedures cannot be taught in the classroom nor can they be gained by reading books.

5. Planning and executive ability. All geologic field work requires careful planning, both advance planning for an entire project and procedural planning of day-to-day activities. The efficiency of field work depends upon using the available time to the best advantage and conserving effort. This is particularly important if the field party consists of several persons whose activities must be coordinated. Assistants' lack of experience can be compensated only by the party chief's ability to direct them competently. Preliminary planning for work in remote or difficult country which involves the selection of equipment and supplies requires especially sound judgment based on experience because the efficiency, comfort, and even safety of the party depend upon it. Adventures, which do not always turn out happily, generally are the result of inadequate planning or poor judgment.

6. Diplomacy and tact. Much geologic field work involves contacts with strange people and trespassing on private property. Diplomacy and tact are often required to establish and maintain good relations with landowners and other local people. This may be especially important in distant regions where outsiders or foreigners are regarded with suspicion or dislike. Patience and tolerance as well as diplomacy and tact also contribute to the smooth and efficient operation of a field party where several persons are closely associated and live and work together for considerable periods of time. In camp life particularly, personal idiosyncrasies may become major sources of irritation. An even temperament and sense of humor are required to avoid tensions that might result in friction and unpleasantness.

The Field Party

Field work in many parts of the United States presents few problems. A conveniently located town generally is selected as headquarters and the area being studied is reached by daily automobile travel. Under most circumstances an individual geologist can work successfully alone. Commonly, however, parties consist of two whose cooperation can effect considerable economy of time and effort. Separate daily or half-day foot traverses can be planned so that backtracking to the place where the car was left can be avoided. Companionship and the opportunity to discuss problems and compare ideas add to the pleasure and success of field work. Also apprenticeship in the field is the best way for inexperienced geologists to acquire necessary skills. Parties may consist of three or more geologists, but larger numbers working together generally are less advantageous than several two-man teams operating more or less independently.

In populous regions two geologists rarely need to be together in the field except upon occasions when observations are being compared or especially significant outcrops are being studied. In wild or rugged regions, however, a minor accident may result in a major catastrophe unless assistance is close at hand. Under these conditions prudence and safety demand that two men work together in such a way that they are never far apart and each knows at all times exactly where the other is. Little is gained by the presence of a third geologist except under unusual circumstances. Two or rarely more teams, however, may work advantageously out of the same headquarters.

Camp life and travel in difficult or sparsely inhabited country involves much work that is not related to geology. The geologists' efficiency is much increased if a cook and general handy man is provided to take over routine camp duties. In reconnaissance surveys, camp may be moved almost every day, and packers, boatmen, or other help can free geologists for their special work.

Wage scales are relatively low in many foreign countries. Local men generally are employed for all but the actual geologic work. Local personnel including camp staff, if necessary, laborers to carry equipment and specimens, cut brush, manage transport animals, man boats, and so forth, and perhaps interpreters and guides are commonly available. Trustworthy local companions may make it unnecessary for geologists to work together. In some very wild or disturbed areas an armed guard may be needed for protection.

Living Conditions

Living quarters available for a geologic field party vary greatly according to local circumstances. They constitute no problem in most parts of the United States or other well-developed countries, where accommodations can be obtained in some conveniently situated town. Elsewhere, and particularly in some countries where local living conditions are much lower than in the United States, camping may be necessary. In some ways camping complicates geologic activities because it requires the maintenance and transportation of considerable equipment. Unless an adequate camp staff is provided, it may absorb an appreciable amount of the geologists' time and energy that otherwise could be devoted to field work. On the other hand, camping may contribute greatly to efficiency by permitting a party to locate in or near its area of operations and thus save much daily to-and-fro travel.

Camp equipment needs to be carefully selected to provide the greatest amount of comfort and convenience and at the same time constitute the least impediment consistent with local circumstances. Thus it may be possible to maintain a more elaborate camp if it is more or less permanently settled than if a party is constantly on the move. Also the type of transportation and labor force available places limitations on the total amount and the weight and size of items that are included. Finally, climate is an important factor because different and generally more equipment is needed under severe than under mild conditions.

The problem of food closely parallels that of living quarters. In settled regions inhabited by people of European stock, adequate meals generally can be obtained. The diets of other peoples, however, may not be suited to American tastes and needs. Although certain staple foods can be obtained almost everywhere that people live, these may require supplementing to insure a well-balanced and palatable diet. If camping is necessary, food must be transported in addition to camp gear. If provisions can be replenished easily and often, the problem of supply is a minor one. Otherwise careful selection and planning are essential in order to insure an adequate but not overabundant supply without adding unnecessarily to transportation problems.

Transportation

A field geologist must go to the outcrops wherever they occur. Much of his time and energy are expended in moving from place to place and transportation is a matter of great importance. Motor vehicles are, of course, relied upon in settled regions where roads exist. In recent years the jeep has proved extremely serviceable in many off-road areas in open and relatively unfenced country. Although motor transport has speeded field work in many regions, it has its drawbacks. Motor vehicles rarely will carry a geologist directly to an outcrop unless it is located by the roadside, and speedy travel may make him overlook inconspicuous exposures. Also too great reliance on mechanical transportation tempts a geologist to neglect areas that are not readily accessible. Walking cannot be eliminated if field work is to be conducted conscientiously and thoroughly.

In rough, remote, trackless, or forested regions, transportation is much more difficult and travel is much slower. Riding and pack animals are serviceable in many kinds of country inaccessible to motor vehicles. Regions of navigable streams and small lakes may be traversed best with canoes. Field work adjacent to large lakes and the seacoast may be accomplished most easily by using small motorboats. None of these types of transport, however, eliminate the necessity for walking. A geologist's legs will always be his most essential, reliable, and often most convenient means of travel for short distances.

In recent years, small airplanes and helicopters have performed important service in transporting field parties to and from relatively inaccessible areas and in supplying them. Air transport, however, is rarely useful in the actual conduct of field work.

OUTCROPS

Rock outcrops provide by far the most important source of geologic information in many regions, and most geologic field work is devoted primarily to their study. Also most geologic maps are based upon the observation of outcrops although this may be supplemented by well records and the interpretation of physiography, soils, and other features. Consequently the occurrence and distribution of outcrops determines to a very great extent the accuracy, speed, and general success of field work and geologic mapping. The nature and abundance of outcrops largely depend in turn upon (1) resistance of rocks to weathering and erosion, (2) amount of residual soil or other overburden, (3) topography, and (4) climate.

Nature and Abundance of Outcrops

Factors controlling the nature and abundance of rock outcrops are all relative. Several of them are closely interrelated. They interact in complex combinations to produce quite varied results. Table 24 summarizes the optimum conditions favoring opposite extremes.

TABLE 24. Main Factors Controlling the Abundance and Nature of Rock Outcrops

Many Outcrops	Few Outcrops
Steep slopes	Gentle slopes
Few but heavy rains	Moderate rainfall, well distributed
Hard rocks	Soft rocks
Cool climate	Warm climate
Mechanical erosion	Chemical weathering and solution
Thin overburden	Thick overburden
High altitude	Low altitude
Deep erosion	Shallow erosion
Little vegetation	Dense vegetative cover

The first three or four factors generally are the most important and several of the others are their more or less direct consequences. The control exercised by these factors varies considerably. For example, temperature is much less important in arid than in humid regions whereas the importance of rock hardness is the reverse.

Knowledge of the topography and climate of a region that is to be investigated geologically permits predictions to be made regarding the nature, abundance, and location of rock outcrops. If in addition something is known about the general geology and the types of rock to be expected, these predictions are very useful in formulating plans for field work.

Locations of Outcrops

As a general rule, the best rock outcrops occur in the beds and banks of streams where mechanical erosion is most active. If hard strata are present and overburden is not excessive, outcrops also are likely to occur intermittently upon the steeper slopes and hilltops. In many regions of abundant but not excessive rainfall, sandstone is the most resistant kind of rock and commonly caps the hills and ridges. Limestone is more resistant and may form the topographic prominences in regions of very heavy rainfall, where mechanical erosion is accentuated, and in dry regions, where solution is not an important process of destruction.

In regions of topographic maturity with deep residual soil, natural outcrops are likely to be few. They are confined mainly to the larger and deeper valleys where they consist mostly of the more resistant strata. In many regions of this type the best exposures occur in road and railway cuts, quarries, and other excavations. Erosion of newly cleared or cultivated land may result in the development of new outcrops in active gullies and, at the same time, the burying of former outcrops along lower stream courses that are being filled with silt.

Thick loess deposits blanket uplands and obscure most outcrops in some areas adjacent to rivers that drain glaciated regions. Also sand dunes in arid country and near some beaches have covered large areas and obscured all outcrops. In low flat areas such as coastal plains and undrained intermontane basins no outcrops occur. All bedrock is hidden by unconsolidated deposits of very recent origin.

A special situation is provided by the glaciated till plains of the northern and northeastern United States. Some areas are so heavily drift covered that the deepest valleys do not reach bedrock. Elsewhere excellent outcrops may occur where streams have cut new valleys into fresh rock that is not obscured by thick accumulations of residuum. At a few places very large erratic blocks are included in the glacial drift; where exposed, these may be mistaken for true outcrops. In contrast, almost all soil was removed from large areas in parts of Canada by glacial action and extensive exposures occur without the benefit of much topographic relief.

BASE MAPS

Maps are pictorial representations of some portion of the earth's surface that, depending upon their purpose, emphasize some features of the area and ignore others. Almost all maps utilized in geology are constructed as though the area were viewed vertically from above. The distances between all points are represented at a uniform scale. The accuracy of maps varies greatly with their detail and the care with which they have been made. Maps of very large areas necessarily are distorted to some extent because it is impossible to reproduce all parts of a spherically curved surface accurately upon a flat plane.

Maps serve two purposes in geology. First, they aid a geologist in finding his way from place to place and in locating more or less precisely any spot where geologic observations may be made. Second, they serve as a base upon which geologic data are plotted, and show the mutual relations of various geologic features by their respective locations. Certain kinds of stratigraphic work can be accomplished without the aid of maps. Strata can be studied, measured, and described and stratigraphic sections can be pieced together and correlated. The three-dimensional relations of stratigraphic units, however, cannot be determined accurately without knowledge of their areal extent. This requires that they be mapped, and geologic mapping is one of the steps essential to stratigraphy.

Topographic Maps

Topographic contour maps, where available, generally are preferred as the base for geologic mapping. Without the representation of surface relief that these maps provide, many features of a geologic map cannot be understood.

The pattern of a geologic map is determined by the intersections of two sets of planes: (1) those of variously steep surface slopes and (2) those of variously inclined formation boundaries and faults. If the topographic planes are indicated on the map, the other set can be more or less accurately inferred from the geologic pattern. Thus a geologic map presented on a topographic base has a third-dimensional quality that permits the visualization or construction of geologic cross sections. These relations are less important as the scale of maps decreases, the pattern becomes more generalized, and the relative influence of surface inequalities declines.

Much of the United States has been mapped topographically by the United States Geological Survey. Many of the earlier maps were surveyed at a scale of 1 to 125,000 or roughly two miles to an inch. Later the scale was increased to 1 to 62,500 or approximately one mile to an inch. The resulting 15-minute quadrangles are the topographic maps familiar to all American geologists. More recently areas of special interest have been mapped at a scale of 1 to 24,000 or about two and one-half inches to the mile. Topographic contour intervals vary depending upon map scales and relative relief.

Topographic surveying is a highly skilled profession. The quality of maps produced has varied considerably with the competence and care exercised by the surveyor. In general, quality has steadily improved, particularly for the maps produced since the late 1920's, when aerial photographs began to be used for topographic control. Before that time, many minor features, especially of the drainage patterns, were inaccurate because the surveyor filled in by guess small areas that were not reached by his plane-table traverses. For example, at some places the heads and mouths of small tributaries to the larger streams were incorrectly connected. Errors of this kind are now rare.

All topographic maps are generalized because the steepness of slopes and elevations are estimated by the surveyor and shown by contours sketched in between the points that were actually located instrumentally. The contours commonly do not reveal minor topographic features that are geologically significant. Therefore the field geologist must locate many outcrops by estimating their positions with respect to cultural and more prominent topographic features that are represented on the map. Any inaccuracies in the base are automatically carried over to the geologic map. Most outcrops can be located fairly satisfactorily, but in low or featureless country and in densely wooded areas location may be very difficult. If important errors or discrepancies are recognized in the topographic map, the geology must be fitted to them and, therefore, it is distorted. No geologic map can be more accurate than its base.

The estimation of outcrop elevations on topographic maps is commonly less satisfactory than estimates of geographic locations. Unless the points are situated along roads, in the bottoms of valleys, or on the crests of ridges that have been traversed by the topographic survey, elevations rarely can be determined within a limit of error less than the contour interval and uncertainty may be much greater. If more accuracy is required, instrumental surveys or measurements by hand level or aneroid barometer must be made. If more precise geographic location of outcrops is nesessary, pace-compass or plane-table traverses must be run.

Most well-developed or industrialized foreign countries are provided with topographic maps equal to or better than those of the United States. Other countries and particularly those regions where American geologists may be employed are likely to be almost entirely unsurveyed.

Other Maps

Many other kinds of maps exist but most of them have been made without accurate and comprehensive surveys, are too small in scale, or lack details necessary for a good geologic base. Road maps of settled regions may be useful for superficial or reconnaissance studies if their scales are suitable. In large parts of the central United States where surveys of the public lands were made and many roads extend east and west or north and south along the section lines, fairly accurate locations of outcrops can be made on small-scale road maps. This is not true, however, of the region included in the original American colonies where the land was not systematically surveyed, in parts of the Mississippi Valley and southwest including much of Texas where landownership dates back to French and Spanish grants, or in areas where the road pattern has been controlled by topographic features. Almost all road maps are deficient because they do not show the minor drainage patterns, differential topographic relief, or elevations. With them, detailed field work cannot be planned or executed efficiently.

In unmapped or inadequately mapped territory, plane-table surveys can be made concurrently with geologic field work to determine the locations and elevations of outcrops. In open country with fairly abundant outcrops, most rapid progress can be made if the geologist acts as rodman and selects the most important stations to be surveyed as he examines outcrops while the instrument work is done by a topographic engineer. Similar surveys in brushy or wooded areas are much more difficult. Generally a survey party works separately but in close contact with the geologist. In mapping of this kind, a geologist does not need to be a skilled surveyor but he should thoroughly understand instrumental operation in order to plan and direct the work to best advantage.

Aerial Photographs

Since the 1920's aerial photographs have been used increasingly in both topographic and geologic mapping. These photographs are of two types: (1) verticals, and (2) obliques. Vertical photographs show the land surface from directly overhead. They can be used as the base for geologic field work. Oblique photographs are directed laterally as well as downward. They show the landscape from a point below the photo plane toward or to the horizon. Because of foreshortening, oblique photographs are less serviceable as a mapping base. They present a lateral view comparable to what one is accustomed to see from a high hill, and both topographic and geologic features are more easily recognized by one unskilled in photo interpretation than in verticals. Because adjacent pairs of both types of photographs overlap, they can be observed with a stereoscopic viewer. This brings out topographic relief and distance in exaggerated form because the exposures were made at a distance from each other far exceeding distance between the eyes.

Instruments and methods have been devised for constructing excellent maps from aerial photographs. With a small amount of surface control consisting of measured base lines and a few instrumentally determined elevations at high and low points, remarkably accurate contoured topographic maps can be made from verticals. Without any control, contoured form maps can be drawn that are very useful, but the exact scale is not known and the contour interval is uncertain. Obliques reveal the features of much larger areas than verticals and points can be accurately located, but these photographs are not well suited to the construction of reliably contoured topographic maps.

Aerial photographs, if they were not taken from too high an altitude, generally are superior to maps for planning geologic field work in unfamiliar territory. When viewed stereoscopically they reveal the topography in great detail, vegetative cover, and possibly the larger outcrops. Geologic features are clearest in arid regions where vegetation is sparse and soil is thin or above timber line in mountainous areas. Structure is most plainly shown where stratified rocks of alternating hardness are inclined at moderate angles. The major structural features of a region may be apparent, however, even where residual soil is thick and forests are dense. Very commonly certain areas can be recognized as having more probable geologic interest than others. Experience in photo interpretation is important because surficial patterns of cultivation, woodlands, and so forth may be confusing.

Vertical photographs are ideal for locating rock outcrops in the field in most regions that are not largely forest covered. Lone trees, the corners of fields, junctions or changes in the courses of small streams, or roads can be identified on the ground and serve as precise reference points. Some local features such as cultivated areas, however, may change greatly with passing time and care must be exercised if the photographs are not recent ones. Accurate location beneath a heavy growth of trees is almost impossible.

In much unforested country geology can be sketched with precision quickly, easily, and without the use of instruments directly on individual vertical photographs. Stereoscopic pairs of prints can be carried in the field and studied with a pocket viewer. Formations in many areas can be traced between outcrops on the basis of minor topographic features—small gullies, changes in slope, and so forth—or of differences in vegetation which are not shown on any map. By being provided at all times with a three-dimensional bird's-eye view of his surroundings, a geologist commonly can gain a speedy understanding of geologic relations better than that which he might obtain by hours or even days of painstaking field work without this aid.

Although geology can be sketched directly on vertical aerial photographs, these ordinarily do not provide a satisfactory base for a finished geologic map. The photographs are not all uniform in scale nor are directions constant because a photoplane cannot be flown at exactly the same elevation or on an undeviating course. Most photographs are slightly tipped because the plane cannot be held in an exactly horizontal position. Also the photographs are somewhat distorted, most noticeably in their marginal parts if the surface relief is great. Finally, the photographic detail is confusing and patterns or colors identifying different formations do not show up and contrast against it with desirable distinctness.

If a base map has been constructed from photographs, the transfer of geology from individual photographs is not difficult. Special projectors have been perfected to make direct comparison easy and exact. If, however, the base is a topographic map made by conventional surface surveying, imperfections and discrepancies are certain to occur. These must be compensated by skillful adjustments or the final geologic map may show what appear to be unnatural and improbable relations.

After field work has progressed so far that the expression of different formations in the aerial photographs has been determined, considerable mapping can be done in many regions by study of the photographs alone. Thus areas between field traverses can be filled in and it may be possible to extend the map far beyond the traversed area. If the accumulation of information that can be obtained only by the actual observation of outcrops, such as detailed measured sections or the collection of fossils or lithologic specimens, is not necessary, an enormous amount of laborious field work may be obviated and mapping can be speeded up accordingly. The success of such procedures depends to a very great extent upon the clarity with which the photographs reveal geology.

Under favorable conditions study of photographs provides much valuable information concerning wholly unknown territory. Thus a great deal may be learned about an area before field work is undertaken or about a region in which field work is not possible. Different kinds of rocks can be distinguished on photographs by their reactions to weathering and erosion even though their exact lithologic nature cannot be determined. Stratified sedimentary rocks and massive igneous bodies generally appear quite different. Shaly strata are weak and commonly they are more deeply eroded than resistant sandstone or limestone beds. Without any field work it may be possible to build up an empirical stratigraphic section, estimate thicknesses of units, identify and trace some beds for long distances, and work out the structure in considerable detail. Ages of the rocks and most details of their lithologic character, however, remain unknown.

Most natural features discernible on aerial photographs have some geologic or physiographic meaning. The criteria for their interpretation are the same as those used in field work but some of the familiar field criteria are not available to the photogeologist. In compensation, some features and their regional relations are revealed with a clarity and to an extent that is never realized in field work. Alterations of the landscape resulting from the works of man, such as changes in the vegetative patterns, modifications of topography, and diversions of drainage systems must be recognized and not confused with natural features. In many regions, however, the distribution of cultivated areas is significant because it emphasizes differences in topography and soil conditions.

Evidence that aids in stratigraphic interpretation includes (1) drainage patterns, (2) topographic expression, (3) vegetative zones, and (4) surface color.

Drainage patterns commonly are the most conspicuous and first-noticed features of aerial photographs. At many places they are accentuated by the occurrence of steep slopes and variations in vegetation. Depending upon whether they show dendritic, trellis, or other forms, conclusions can be drawn rapidly regarding the structure of stratified rocks.

Topographic expression primarily demonstrates variability of rock hardness. Hard and soft beds can be distinguished and traced singly or in groups. Dip slopes and the orientation of ridges indicate strike and dip.

Vegetative zones show differences in soil development, fertility, and moisture which generally are related to underlying rocks. Cultivation may accentuate or obscure natural patterns.

Difference in surface shades commonly indicate corresponding color differences in either rocks or soil. Confusion is possible, however, because of variable shadows, moist and dry areas, bare or vegetated earth, and other differences.

Geologic interpretation is relatively more difficult and pertinent features may be obscure or lacking in areas of (1) very low relief, (2) thick cover of soil, glacial drift, or other overburden, (3) forest growth except possibly when hardwoods have shed their leaves, (4) extensive cultivation, (5) urban development, and (6) winter snow cover.

GEOLOGIC MAPPING

The making of a geologic map is the immediate objective of much stratigraphic field work. Before actual mapping can begin, however, two preliminary steps are necessary. First, the stratigraphic units that are to be mapped must be decided upon and their boundaries must be set. The units may be either those that have been distinguished previously and possibly mapped in nearby areas or new units that are better suited to mapping in the area of the survey. Second, the natural sequence of the units to be mapped must be determined. If the units are familiar ones, the sequence is already known from previous studies elsewhere. During the course of field work it may be advantageous or become necessary to differentiate new stratigraphic units that either consist of strata intervening between old units or beds constituting subordinate parts of old units. Likewise it may be desirable to recognize somewhat altered boundaries between old units. Neither of these possibilities complicates geologic mapping particularly although revision may be required in those portions of a map that have been completed before a decision necessitating change was made. If, however, the stratigraphic section is unfamiliar and it has not been subdivided previously, the differentiation of units and the determination of their sequence may be accomplished while the first two processes involved in geologic mapping noted below are in progress.

Geologic mapping is accomplished in four steps: (1) the discovery of outcrops or other kinds of pertinent information, (2) the location of outcrops geographically, (3) the identification of outcrops with reference to units of the stratigraphic section, and (4) the relation of outcrops to each other which reveals the local structural conditions. Each step is a separate process and requires a different type of observation and reasoning. The steps follow each other in natural order for each outcrop independently. Generally each is consequent upon its predecessor although the second and third steps may be reversed. The sequence of steps does not need to be completed for one outcrop before it is started for another. The sequence must begin with the discovery of an outcrop. This must be located and identified, but identification may be delayed until after other outcrops have been discovered and related. Finally the outcrop is coordinated with other outcrops previously or subsequently discovered, located, and identified. Thus this sequence of steps progresses at variable rates for several to many outcrops at the same time.

In addition to this sequence, a fifth step, interpretation, should not be neglected. Interpretation does not fall into order with the other steps although it cannot attain its full potential until the foregoing sequence has been completed. Progressive and tentative interpretation is important because it serves to direct attention to features and relations that otherwise might be overlooked. Thus it insures a better understanding of many geologic conditions at all stages of a field investigation and it may contribute greatly to efficient field procedure. For example, interpretation of the relations of outcrops to topography and geographic location may aid in the discovery of other outcrops. Also interpretation of lateral lithologic changes may help to resolve uncertainties of identification, local correlation, and stratigraphic relations. All experienced field geologists make interpretations of these and other kinds more or less unconsciously. If the desirability of constantly revised interpretation is kept clearly in mind, field work is almost certain to proceed more rapidly and its results are sure to be more satisfactory.

Finding Outcrops

The task of finding outcrops varies, depending upon the nature of the area being mapped, the kind of map desired, and the time available for mapping. In areas of hard rocks, steep slopes, thin overburden, and sparse vegetation outcrops are likely to be abundant and conspicuous. Here the discovery of outcrops is no problem and the field geologist may be concerned chiefly with how many and what distribution of outcrops should be located and carefully observed. This situation is reversed, of course, in areas of soft rocks, gentle slopes, low relief, thick overburden, and dense growth of vegetation. Here outcrops must be sought assiduously. Experience and knowledge regarding places where they are most likely to occur are important. Also a geologist must decide whether it is better to search carefully for obscure outcrops or move on to another place where outcrops might be found more easily and quickly. In areas of this kind, fragments of float rock in the beds of streams commonly lead to outcrops. Such evidence of their occurrence should be looked for at all convenient places. In some areas the best exhibits of bedrock are provided by artificial exposures, and first attention should be given to cuts along roads and railways and to quarries and other excavations.

The thoroughness with which exposures are searched out is determined by the degree of detail that is desired in geologic mapping and interpretation. The time available for field work may be devoted to finding and studying every outcrop. Such work is comparatively slow. It involves much footwork and requires the geologist actually to go everywhere that an outcrop might occur. It is the most desirable type of field work from a scientific standpoint, but greater speed may be demanded by practical considerations. Somewhat more rapid progress may be possible if attention is directed mainly to tracing out formation contacts. In areas where formations are relatively thick, this may eliminate the necessity of examining considerable areas. Generally the resulting map is nearly or quite as accurate as one produced by more thorough and detailed field work. Less information, however, would be obtained concerning the characters of formations; therefore, less complete and reliable interpretations would be possible.

In reconnaissance studies emphasis is placed upon obtaining the greatest amount of information concerning the largest area in the least possible time. There are various kinds of reconnaissance investigations. For example, an area may be reconnoitered in preparation for more detailed work, or the sole objective may be to obtain general information without thought to any further study. In either case, results are best shown upon a map, but a map is especially important and generally is necessary for the latter kind of survey.

Reconnaissance geologic mapping requires experience, careful planning, and special skills if it is to yield the most satisfactory results. It demands the sacrifice of detail and complete coverage to speed. Generally little time is devoted to the search for outcrops. Observations are made along lines of traverse that are laid out with the purpose of visiting the most promising localities with the greatest ease. Traverses are most advantageous if they extend at right angles to the strike of dipping beds, thus permitting determination of stratigraphic sections and structure at the same time, but nature of the terrain may necessitate less direct routing. Depending upon the amount of information needed, observations may be made almost as fast as it is possible to travel. Reconnaissance mapping is most effective in open country with abundant outcrops and enough relief to permit remote inspection of a wide zone on both sides of the line of traverse. Observations are more restricted in mountainous or wooded country, and the map cannot be expanded laterally with much assurance. If good topographic maps or, better still, aerial photographs exist, it may be possible to fill in the main features of geology between the lines of traverse.

Many features other than actual outcrops are revealing and useful in all types of geologic mapping. They are most important in areas of poor out-crops, in reconnaissance investigations, and in very detailed mapping. For example, residual soil gives some indication of the nature of underlying rock, and some limestones can be identified by their types of chert. Resistant strata or formations produce topographic benches, dip slopes, and ridges. Seeps or springs may mark contacts between impervious shale and overlying sand-stone or limestone strata.

Locating Outcrops

No geologic map can be more accurate than the location of its outcrops. All locations should be made as precisely as possible, but it is particularly im-portant that greater care be devoted to locations as mapping is done in greater detail. Likewise the need for accurate location increases with the scale of mapping and greater complexity of structure.

Outcrops and other features of geologic interest are located with reference to points that can be recognized on whatever base is used in mapping. A topographic map generally is considered a good base, but actually the num-ber of points that are precisely located on it is rather small. Aerial photo-graphs generally furnish much more detail and make more accurate location possible. If estimation of distance and direction from known points does not provide sufficiently exact locations, short traverses should be run to outcrops by pace and compass, with hand level or aneroid, or by plane table. In very detailed or large-scale mapping, it may be necessary to survey in all outcrops by plane table regardless of the kind of base used.

In reconnaissance mapping, the very accurate location of outcrops and other points is not important. Ordinarily aerial photographs or most maps that show topographic and cultural features are sufficient for estimation of position. If no base exists, however, a rough survey of some kind must be made. It may be possible in open country to establish approximate locations by hand compass triangulation and intersection from several prominent land-marks. Otherwise it may be necessary to determine traverse direction by compass and to estimate distance by odometer or travel time.

Field maps should show not only the location but also the extent of out-crops. Areas of outcropping rocks can be indicated on a map by color or by enclosing lines. These should be recorded directly in the field. Knowledge of the distribution and abundance of outcrops and other features upon which a geologic map is based is desirable particularly in areas of scanty control. Without it the reliability of a map cannot be judged. Most final maps do not present such information and a viewer cannot determine which parts are based on adequate evidence and which are not. Consequently many geo-logic maps give the appearance of being more definite and accurate than they really are.

Identifying Outcrops

Strata observed in outcrops are identified as constituting part of some particular formation on the basis of (1) lithologic features, (2) characteristic fossils, or (3) relative stratigraphic position. These singly or in combination generally are distinctive.

Lithologic characters provide the most common and useful means of identification. Some formations are so uniformly different from all others within a region that almost any part of one of them can be recognized with little chance of error. Examples are the sugary-textured St. Peter Sandstone (Ord.) of the upper Mississippi Valley and the red argillaceous Bainbridge Limestone (Sil.) of southeastern Missouri and the neighboring part of Illinois. Many formations of heterogeneous composition contain some strata that are characteristic and others that are not. A formation of this kind is the St. Louis Limestone (Miss.) of the upper Mississippi and lower Ohio valleys. Much of it consists of more or less crystalline limestone that might belong to any one of half a dozen other formations in this region. It also includes very fine-grained, almost lithographic, and commonly bituminous limestone that is distinctive. If strata of the latter type are present in an outcrop the formation can be readily identified. If not, other evidence must be sought. Finally, some formations have no unique features. No matter how well they are exposed they cannot be recognized except by their positions in the stratigraphic section. For example, several Upper Mississippian sandstones in southern Illinois and western Kentucky are so similar that they cannot be distinguished surely without the identification of intervening limestone and shale formations. An observant field geologist notices and remembers many features of formations, useful in their local identification, that are too subtle to be described clearly enough to be of much benefit to others.

Fossils may be more diagnostic of some formations than lithologic features. Lithologic appearance and composition may be duplicated in rocks of almost any age, but fossils are certain to be different unless formations occupy approximately similar positions in the stratigraphic section. More time generally is required to search for characteristic fossils than to make lithologic observations, and few stratigraphers are sufficiently skilled in paleontology to make full use of fossils. Also many strata are almost if not entirely unfossiliferous. Consequently most geologic mapping is based primarily on lithologic characters.

Every field geologist should be familiar with the principal index fossils of the formations that he maps. The number generally is not great and with instruction from a paleontologist he can learn to recognize them fairly easily. More complete knowledge of fossils also is very useful. Many species that are not of index value occur locally in some kind of zonal arrangement that may aid in distinguishing one part of a formation from another. As an example, a certain association of species may occur commonly near the top of a formation. If this association is recognized in an outcrop, occurrence of the formation boundary close above can be inferred. The progressive gradual change of a fauna from place to place may anticipate a change in lithologic development that, if encountered unexpectedly, might provide a stratigraphic puzzle. A good knowledge of paleontology becomes more important as the stratigraphic section is less well known. In reconnaissance mapping of an unfamiliar region, determination of stratigraphic succession may depend upon the relative dating of formations by their fossils.

Formations are most easily identified if they are exhibited in large and continuous exposures where the range of lithologic characters in different strata can be observed and a good opportunity is afforded for finding fossils. As outcrops become smaller and more widely separated, identification is more uncertain. Many outcrops consist of undiagnostic strata without characteristic fossils. Their identity commonly can be established only by their stratigraphic relations to other beds. The careful observation of especially good outcrops and the measurement of well-exposed stratigraphic sections provide information of great value for comparison with and identification of other outcrops. The best fossils do not necessarily occur at the larger and more conspicuous exposures. Wherever good fossils are discovered, and particularly where they are collected for laboratory study, every effort should be made to locate the zone from which they come accurately within a formation. Constant comparison and checking of lithologic characters and fossils against stratigraphic position is required to insure against the misidentification of many outcrops.

Relating Outcrops

Strata exposed at outcrops are related to each other both vertically and horizontally and the determination of their relations is essential to accurate geologic mapping. Conditions are simplest and relations are most obvious in structurally uncomplicated areas where strata are horizontally disposed. There, vertical relations are revealed by outcrop elevations. It may be possible to construct a complete stratigraphic section by compiling data obtained at a series of outcrops whose ranges in elevation overlap. Strata exposed at different places but at equal elevations are laterally related and equivalent. In such areas, formation boundaries commonly extend essentially parallel to the topographic contours.

Dipping strata that diverge farther and farther from the horizontal become more difficult to relate at separate outcrops because elevation no longer is a guide to stratigraphic sequence. A complete stratigraphic section can be pieced together with much less certainty, and the local detailed correlation of as many conspicuous and distinctive beds as possible is required. Formation boundaries at the surface are the intersections of dipping stratigraphic planes with topographic slopes. If dips vary from place to place, the accurate mapping of boundaries becomes a complex geometric problem and clear visualization of three-dimensional relations is essential. As dips approach the vertical, relations again become more simple because differences in elevation have no effect on outcrop pattern in an area of vertical strata. There, a stratigraphic section and stratigraphic intervals can be measured horizontally at right angles to the strike. Strike direction also determines lateral continuity, but accurate tracing is required because strike direction is not likely to be constant. The direction of stratigraphic sequence, as indicated by evidence of top or bottom by cross-bedding or other structures, must be determined in areas of nearly vertical beds. As dips become more gentle, however, there is less likelihood of overturning even in areas of complex structure although nearly horizontal, completely upside-down strata do occur.

Folding of strata results in dip reversal as well as variation. Determination of the stratigraphic relations of beds at separate outcrops becomes more difficult where folding is close and structural details may not be adequately exposed. In areas of isoclinal dips, folds may be so closely compressed that their axes are obscure. Close attention to top and bottom observations is necessary to understand the structural relations.

Faulting of sedimentary rocks is common and has produced important displacements of strata at many places. Fault movement consists of vertical and horizontal components. In high-angle faults the vertical component generally is more conspicuous although it is not necessarily more important. Horizontal movement, approaching gliding along bedding planes, commonly has dominated in low-angle faults, but vertical movement also was necessary to produce overthrusting. Faults rarely are actually exposed except in areas of extraordinarily good outcrops. Generally their presence is inferred on the basis of the relations of intermittently exposed strata, shearing, silicification, and brecciation in and adjacent to fault zones, and of topographic expression.

Vertical discordance of adjacent outcrops in areas of gentle dips and horizontal discordance of outcrops along the line of strike in steeply dipping strata are the most common indications of fault displacement. In beds inclined at intermediate angles, both vertical and horizontal relations are affected. Faults emerging parallel to bedding planes are most plainly revealed by repetition or elimination of some portion of the normal stratigraphic section, but somewhat similar relations also may occur at high-angle faults that cut sharply across the bedding. Relations of these types are most likely to be recognized in connection with faults of large displacement. Many minor faults undoubtedly escape detection. In all geologic mapping, however, great discretion should be exercised in the postulation of faults that cannot be observed directly. As a general rule, faulting should not be inferred in the absence of conclusive evidence unless no other reasonable explanation for the discordant outcrops can be suggested.

Interpreting Outcrops

Most geologic knowledge has had its origin in the observation and interpretation of outcrops. Observations furnish the basic information, which invites explanation and, when interpreted, generalizations and theories result. These then are tested by additional observations, which support or contradict previous conclusions, and modifications or alternatives may be suggested, to be tested in their turn. This is the scientific method as it is applied in field geology.

All outcrops, even the smallest and simplest, possess so many features that an observer is unlikely to note them all. His attention is directed naturally to those in which he is most interested. Others commonly are neglected or overlooked entirely. Because interests and experience vary widely, a single outcrop may appear quite different to different persons. Also because an individual's interests change somewhat as his experience expands, an outcrop may not appear exactly the same on successive visits and new features are almost certain to be noticed.

Every feature of an outcrop is a subject for examination and explanation and can raise a variety of questions in the mind of an alert observer. Some questions yield to rather obvious answers but many more do not. Experience has shown that observation is stimulated and made more thorough and effective if every outcrop is viewed in the light of more or less well-formulated questions. If problems are recognized and answers are sought, some information bearing upon their solution is very likely to be obtained. On the other hand, if a field geologist regards an outcrop as no more than a spot to be located on a map for the purpose of controlling the drawing of formation boundaries or structure contours, he gains little besides mechanical experience for himself and fails to make more than a fraction of the contribution to geologic science that he might.

The place to raise questions about outcrops and the strata that they reveal is in the field. Perhaps some of the questions can be answered on the spot. Some direct attention to more or less obscure features or relations that had not been noted previously or had not been considered interesting or important. Questions are likely to indicate the necessity for similar observations at other outcrops. Other questions suggest the desirability of laboratory studies concerning lithologic features or fossils, and specimens can be collected for this purpose. The questions raised and the problems that they bring to light may range through the entire spectrum of geologic interests and include such diverse topics as the physiographic response of different strata to weathering and erosion, the relations of jointing to lithologic characters or structural trends, the genesis of bedding features in different kinds of rock, the comparative textures of thin and thick strata, the relative compactibility of calcareous and carbonaceous shales, the orientation of fossils in different types of sediment, the relations between size variability and abundance of fossils, and many others. In a way, the answers to a great variety of questions, and contributions to the solution of a great variety of problems may be regarded as by-products of field work, whose primary purpose is geologic mapping, but in the end many of them may prove to be much more interesting and important than a geologic map.

BIBLIOGRAPHY

Brouwer, A. H. (ed.) (1922–29), *Practical hints to scientific travellers*, vol. 1, Leyden, Brill; vols. 2–6, The Hague, Nijhoff.
>   This work consists of a series of articles by different authors devoted to out-of-the-way countries in tropical, desert, and arctic regions.

Desjardins, Louis (1950), Techniques in photogeology, *Bull. Am. Assoc. Petroleum Geol.*, vol. 34, pp. 2284–2317.
>   Discussion is devoted to methods and results of the geologic interpretation of aerial photographs.

Eardley, A. J. (1942), *Aerial photographs: Their use and interpretation*, New York, Harper.
>   An explanation of aerial photographs is given, with particular attention to their use in geology.

Forrester, J. D. (1946), *Principles of field and mining geology*, New York, Wiley.
>   This book is devoted mainly to economic geology but contains material useful in more general but detailed geology.

Greenly, Edward, and Williams, Howel (1930), *Methods in geological surveying*, London, Murby.
>   A history of cartography is given and a description of methods useful in detailed geologic mapping.

Lahee, F. H. (1952), *Field geology*, 5th ed., New York, McGraw-Hill.
>   This comprehensive handbook is devoted to elements of geology, field methods, and interpretation.

Low, J. W. (1957), *Geologic field methods*, New York, Harper.
>   All phases of geologic field work are discussed in this practical manual.

Raisz, Erwin (1948), *General cartography*, 2nd ed., New York, McGraw-Hill.
>   Simple but comprehensive, this account of maps and mapping has sections on aerophotography, diagrams, geologic maps, etc.

Smith, H. T. U. (1943), *Aerial photographs and their applications*, New York, Appleton-Century.
>   Aerial photographic mapping and interpretation are explained, with special consideration to topographic and geologic aspects.

Smith, H. T. U. (1950), Progress and problems in photogeology, *Photogram. Eng.*, vol. 16, pp. 111–118.

  This article presents photogeology as applied geomorphology and lists factors limiting interpretation and the means of overcoming them.

Thurrell, R. F., Jr. (1953), Procedures and problems of photogeologic evaluation, *Photogram. Eng.*, vol. 19, pp. 434–449.

  Brief consideration is given to the main factors influencing the geologic interpretation of aerial photographs.

Willis, Bailey, and Willis, Robin (1934), *Geologic Structures*, 3rd ed., New York, McGraw-Hill.

  Chapter 13, pp. 292–325, discusses geologic field methods and equipment.

INDEX

Page numbers in italics identify illustrations.

Abrasion, by sediment, 148–149
 glacial, 161
 of limestone, 61
 of sand grains, 92
Abrolhos Islands, southernmost reefs, 169
Abyssal red clay, 173, 174, 271
Abyssal zone, 164
Acadian disturbance, 387
Acid test for carbonates, 63
Acme of fossil, 438, 449
Adams, F. D., *21*, 30
Adams, J. A. S., 346
Adams, J. E., *167*, 189
Adams, L. H., *342*
Adirondack dome, 281
Adirondack sandstone facies, 515
Age, 416, 418, 449, 450
Agnotozoic Era, 44
Ahrens, L. H., 15
Alabama, Clinton iron ore, 76
 Lithostrotion zone, 426
 Mississippian System, 478
Alberta, Devonian basin, 171
 Devonian reefs, 494
Alberti, F. A. von, 37
Aleutian Islands, extension of Alaskan
 Mountains, 264
Algae, calcareous, 196, 490
 in oolites, 127
 Precambrian, 99, 147
Algonkian System, 43
Allan, R. S., 567
Allee, W. C., 233
Allegheny division, upgrading of, 434
Allegheny flora in Illinois, 477
Allegheny Formation, correlation with,
 477
Allegheny plateau, Devonian-Mississippian
 relations, 399, *399*, 400
Alling, H. L., *102*
Alluvial fans, 175, 481
Alluvium, color, 133
 surface markings, 111
 The, 40
Alpine region, Mesozoic seas, 586
Alpine revolution, 386
Alps, different from Appalachians, 254
American Commission on Stratigraphic
 Nomenclature, capitalization of
 names, 455–456
 formations, 422
 horizon, 439
 notes, 453–454
 reports, 452–453

American Stratigraphic Code, formations,
 421–422
 glacial stage, 450
 horizon, 439
Ammonites, cosmopolitan, 559, 562
 depth zonation of, *218*
 evolution of, 559, 560
 evolutionary lines, 556
 zonation by, 444, 559
 zones, *560*
Amphibians, 203
Amsden Formation, age of, 430
 restriction of, *431*
 time boundary in, 441–442
Anderson, K. C., *489*
Andrichuk, J. M., 228, *314*
Anhydrite, 70–75
 primary or secondary, 74
 shrinking of, 75
Animals, environmental distribution, 205
 tracks and trails, 111, 323
Anthracolithic System, 39
Antilles (Lesser), volcanic island arc, 246
Appalachia, 253
Appalachian geosyncline, features of, 250–
 251
 history of, 273, 285
Appalachian Mountains, as inner miogeo-
 syncline, 262
 as secondary arcs, 267
 as typical geosyncline, 249
Appalachian region, Allegheny Formation,
 477
 Big Lime, 461
 carbon ratios in, 66
 Catoctin Formation, 69
 Catskill delta, 503
 Chattanooga Shale, 431
 Clinton iron ore, 128
 drillers' terms, 461
 Mississippian-Pennsylvanian boundary,
 440
 Paleozoic misinterpretations, 481
 Pencil Cave, 461
 Pennsylvanian cyclothems, 372, 373,
 373
 Pennsylvanian subdivisions, 426, 434
 Pennsylvanian System, 440
 pre-Pennsylvanian unconformity, 440
 sediment thickening in, 339
 stratigraphic section of, 622
 tectonic arcs, 267
 Unicoi Formation, 69
Appalachian revolution, 381, 386, 387
Arab philosophers, 19

683

DATE DUE